HUMAN BEHAVIOR

AND

THE PRINCIPLE OF LEAST EFFORT

HUMAN BEHAVIOR

AND

THE PRINCIPLE OF LEAST EFFORT

An Introduction to Human Ecology

by

GEORGE KINGSLEY ZIPF, Ph.D.
Harvard University

ADDISON-WESLEY PRESS, INC.
CAMBRIDGE 42, MASSACHUSETTS
1949

Printed in the United States of America

PREFACE

Nearly twenty-five years ago it occurred to me that we might gain considerable insight into the mainsprings of human behavior if we viewed it purely as a natural phenomenon like everything else in the universe, and if we studied it with the same dispassionate objectivity with which one is wont to study, say, the social behavior of bees, or the nestbuilding habits of birds. The present book reports the results of the extended inquiry that ensued in the course of those years, and which led to the disclosure of some fundamental principles that seem to govern important aspects of our behavior, both as individuals and as members of social groups.

1. The Question of Practical Application.

It is inescapable that the attitude of the natural scientist towards human behavior will differ from that of the man or woman of affairs who is faced with the practical need of solving urgent human problems, even though the two attitudes are by no means irreconcilable. Thus the scientist hopes that from an objective study of the actual ways that we human beings do in fact behave, he may disclose the nature of the underlying principles that govern our conduct. But though the scientist's interests are said to stop at that point, he must nevertheless admit that a knowledge of these underlying principles will inevitably help others to live *more efficiently,* whether as individuals, or as members of teams that co-operate and compete—and whether in the roles of those who primarily do the leading, or in the roles of those who primarily do the following.

After all, the basic natural principles that govern man's responses to the incentives of prospective rewards, or that govern the proportion of executive leaders to followers (in corporation, labor union, army, political party, or social club), or that govern the rise and decline of fashions, or that govern the distribution of relative power and control in any dominance system, from the family unit to the nation, or that govern the circulation of persons, goods, services, ideas, and information over the earth's surface in the exchange of the products of our labor—just to enumerate a few of the principles that we shall treat—are not likely to remain idle curiosities, so long as each man must daily co-operate and compete with others in order to live. Nor are these principles particularly out of place at the present time, when we seem to be faced with an impending planned economy in which a few persons will tell many others how they *should behave*—often perhaps without regard to how people *do* behave.

On the other hand, just because we treat objectively and dispassionately of the mainsprings of human behavior, without any particular reference to how people "should" behave, that does not necessarily mean that I for one feel personally obliged to deprecate the almost universal belief that all mankind "should" co-operate and get along together like one happy team that is bent upon "social progress." Nevertheless I do note that, in spite of this universal belief, there is virtually no agreement as to the particular ways and means whereby the worthwhile objective of universal human co-operation is to be achieved.

It is obvious that some persons and groups have personal and group *preconceptions* as to precisely how the world "should" co-operate. These preconceptions are sometimes so deeply rooted that the individuals in question can barely talk with others whose similarly profound preconceptions happen not to agree with their own. In so doing they seem to block *communication,* and thereby to impede the better world understanding and co-operation they so fervently desire. It is further obvious that many of these persons and groups are so rigid and inflexible in their preconceptions that they are not to be budged from them either by incentive rewards of any amount or by threats of direst harm.

Neither the natural scientist nor the practical social engineer can afford to ignore the power of these preconceptions, to which even the best intended incentives are often subordinate and from which, only too often, the gravest individual and group misery can result.

Nevertheless, to the natural scientist, man's preconceptions do not belong to some other world, but instead are merely further natural phenomena. As such they are a part of the total natural phenomenon of human behavior and merit an investigation into their mainsprings quite as much as the rest of human behavior. Indeed, in many situations, the preconceptions involved are largely determinative of the rest of the behavior.

Our emphasis upon the effect of man's preconceptions is by no means new to present-day thinking, even though, in actual practice, a given person's attitude towards a particular *vocabulary* of individual or group preconceptions that confront him may depend upon what his particular problem is.

Thus, for example, the personnel man in a sizable factory, store, labor union, or armed group, who is obliged to deal daily with a large number of persons of diverse cultural and socio-economic backgrounds, has the continual task of understanding and of reconciling his group's conflicting preconceptions, so that the group can effectively *communicate* in reference to its common tasks, incentives, and risks. The personnel man does not need to be told that it is efficient for his group to have a common *language,* in the broad sense of having like responses and evaluations to like stimuli within the functioning of the group. His task is essentially that of understanding the existing diverse preconceptions, so that he can restructure them into a more harmonious whole.

The case is somewhat different, however, with the politician who wants votes, or with the marketer who invents styles or has something to sell. For here the game may be simply the most effective manipulation of the existing preconceptions, without any thought of altering them. A politician, though meritorious, who casually ignores his constituents' preconceptions, or else tries to superimpose his own logic upon them, is only too likely to fall before another and even far less capable politician who knows the preconceptions of his constituents, and who says, in substance, "My friends, I understand your feelings perfectly, and am heartily in accord with them."

Yet just because one man's preconceptions often flaunt another man's logic in what seems to him to be a highly capricious manner, we may by no means suppose that man's preconceptions are random and haphazard, and without a certain logic of their own. On the contrary, in our study of the dynamics of language and the structure of the personality, we shall find that a vocabulary of preconceptions is quite orderly and is governed by quite definite underlying principles. Nor are we in any way disposed to argue that the deliberate use of these underlying principles by the personnel man, politician, and marketer will not help him to alter or to manipulate more effectively the particular vocabulary of preconceptions with which he happens to be confronted.

It is perhaps well at this point to elucidate our more general terms *language* and a *vocabulary of preconceptions,* lest they be confused with the more familiar terms, *words* and *speech,* with which, incidentally, they are intimately related.

To this end, since we have just spoken of the marketer's problem, let us by way of illustration begin with a "brand name" of goods (for example, G.E., Frigidaire, Chesterfield). A given brand name may be so favorably known that many persons will prefer, and even pay more for, the brand goods than for unnamed goods, although even a connoisseur could not tell the difference. In short, *a specific brand name tends to evoke a specific response in reference to human wants,* and in so doing may be said to represent a sort of preconception.

Let us note, however, that a brand name is also a *word,* and nothing but a *word.* Whatever the principles may be that govern the behavior of words in their favorable and unfavorable connotations, and in their fashionableness and obsolescence, will also govern to a considerable extent the ups and downs and competition of brand names. (Hence our later study of *words* and *speech* is germane to a study of fashions and preconceptions.)

But let us go further. Instead of a brand name, let us consider a trademark which identifies a particular product or service quite as effectively as a brand name, but which contains not a single word. This trademark is a *sign* or a *signal* which, like a brand name, evokes a more or less stereotyped response. Although a trademark is not a word, and therefore not an element of speech, we shall later see that it is in fact an element of what we may call the group's language. (And we shall attempt to demonstrate that things like trademarks will behave in a manner quite similar to that of words.)

But we do not need to stop with the trademark. There are many stereotyped things, such as kinds and qualities of clothes, ways of doing one's hair, manners of gesticulating and of talking, places and times where one is seen or not seen, which convey information about the person in question. Although these things are neither words, brand names, .nor trademarks, they tend to evoke more or less stereotyped responses and, in so doing, they belong to the *language* of the group in question—quite as much as the group's words, and phrases, and sentences.

To illustrate the import of this broader concept of language, let us paint a picture. It is evening; a costly automobile with liveried chauffeur drives up before the opera house; and out steps milady elegantly gowned and jeweled. She fumbles in her purse and conspicuously gives the beggar a coin, and then skips up the stairs. That is the picture.

All the parts of this picture relate to the problem of the production and distribution of goods and services and of rewards. Yet, as we shall note in detail, all parts of the picture—the car, chauffeur, opera, woman, gown, jewels, coin, and beggar—are *also* problems in *language* (and in *preconceptions*).

And so if at times in the opening chapters of our demonstration, we seem to be almost pedantically concerned with the phonetic and semantic minutiae of human speech which are apparently of little importance in the robustness of everyday life, may the reader of imagination reflect that we may thereby be gaining insight into the total *language* of the group, whose minutiae may at times be extremely important in everyday life, in politics, in marketing, or in just plain getting along together.

In thus placing a study of the principles of language before that of the economy of geography, or of the distribution of economic power and social status, or of the waxing and waning of prestige symbols and cultural vogues, we perhaps confess to a certain personal preconception as to what is likely to be most important in the difficulties of actual everyday practical human problems, from which confusion, heartache, and misery arise.

2. The Question of Natural Science.

Although we have not evaded the question of the possible practical value of scientific principles in the solution of actual problems in human behavior, we nevertheless must point out that the present study is offered purely as a work of science.

More specifically, it is the expressed purpose of this book to establish The Principle of Least Effort as the primary principle that governs our entire individual and collective behavior of all sorts, including the behavior of our language and preconceptions.

An investigator who undertakes to propound any such primary scientific principle of human behavior must discharge three major obligations towards his reader. First, his argument must be supported by a large number and variety of verifiable observations of relevant phenomena. Second, his theory must be logically self-consistent throughout, with all terms and operations relating to his observations explicitly defined. Third, his entire demonstration should be presented in such a way that it will be readily understandable to the reader who, in the present case, is assumed to have a genuine interest in the underlying principles of human behavior, without necessarily having any specialized or technical training in the fields in question.

As to the first point—the number and variety of observations—we may claim in all modesty to have increased the number of our observations to such a point that they may be viewed as empiric natural laws, regardless of the correctness of any of our theoretical interpretations. In other words, by means of the accepted methods of the exact sciences, we have established an orderliness, or natural law, that governs human behavior. Moreover, the variety of our observations, which extend from the minutiae of phonetic and semantic behavior to the gross distributions of human populations, goods, services, and wealth, is sufficient, I believe, to give pause to the superficial opinion that the observed orderliness on these fundamental matters has nothing to do with the practical affairs of everyday life. We stress this fact in the hope that any person who may sincerely wish to apply these findings to the solution of his own problems may do so with a feeling of confidence, even though some of the findings may not be entirely in line with current preconceptions about how people "should" behave.

As to the second point—the theoretical aspect of the study—that is, the theoretical demonstration of the Principle of Least Effort—we submit that our theory, *like all other theories in natural science,* does *not* claim either that no other theory can be found that will also rationalize our data, or that no other data will ever be found that do not controvert our theory. On the contrary, the reader is invited not only to weigh our own theory, but to find a more cogent theory and more instructive data. To this end, we have tendered suggestions for further elaborational research, and have tried to open further theoretical vistas for the possible use of others, whether these others be professional students who are interested in original research of their own, or nonprofessional laymen who simply like to adventure with new ideas.

As to the third point—the manner of presentation of the material—we have prepared the manuscript in such a way that it will be entirely understandable to anyone interested in the topic, regardless of his previous training. In short, every step in observation, analysis, and statistical description has been explained simply and in detail for the reader's complete comprehension if he has only a modicum of patience. Nor is this simplified presentation entirely amiss for the specialized reader, not every one of whom may be supposed to be familiar with all the fields upon which the present study touches (e.g., economics, sociology, cultural anthropology, psychology—both general and Freudian—linguistics, and semantics). In this connection it might be remarked that we have restricted our bibliographical references to those publications germane to the discussion at hand and which will serve to orient the reader further in the bibliography of any of the special fields.* We have not tried to present exhaustive

* Because the preparation of our manuscript was essentially complete at the time, we were unable to include a discussion of the recently appeared "Kinsey Report" in connection with our own discussion of an individual's homosexual-heterosexual balance, in which we have arrived at conclusions—on the basis of entirely different kinds of data—that undeniably support the "Kinsey" findings. Hence reference is here made: A. C. Kinsey, W. B. Pomeroy, and C. E. Martin, *Sexual Behavior in the Human Male,* Philadelphia: Saunders, 1948.

bibliographies of the fields in question, nor exhaustive discussions of the materials in the fields.

In the course of the many years of research that is reported in the present study, I have been deeply indebted to many persons for their wise counsel and their much needed encouragement. Chief among these have been Dr. J. L. Walsh, the Perkins Professor of Mathematics and former Chairman of the Division of Mathematics at Harvard University; Dr. M. H. Stone, now Andrew MacLeish Distinguished Professor of Mathematics and Chairman of the Department of Mathematics at the University of Chicago; Dr. John C. Whitehorn, Professor of Psychiatry at the Johns Hopkins Medical School and Director of the Henry Phipps Psychiatric Clinic; Dr. George H. Chase, Dean of the University, now Emeritus, at Harvard University; Dr. Abbott Payson Usher, Professor of Economics at Harvard University; and Dr. George A. Lundberg, Professor of Sociology and Chairman of the Department of Sociology at the University of Washington.

Thanks to the cheerfulness and managerial skill of my good wife, who effected drastic domestic economies, it was possible for me to engage some clerical help for the investigation of types of problems for which research grants are by no means plentiful.

Many of the observations reported I owe to the generous and enthusiastic help of my undergraduate and graduate students at Harvard University and Radcliffe College, as more particularly mentioned in the text. I am grateful to the Clark and Milton Funds at Harvard University for a much appreciated grant that aided in the preparation of the manuscript of this book.

This book, which has been nearly six years in the writing, has been read in its entirety by Professor J. L. Walsh, who has discussed with me all important aspects of the theory and who has gone over all the data carefully. Without his constructive help and continuing encouragement, I doubt that I could have seen this book to an end.

I am also grateful to several friends, who prefer to remain anonymous, for helping to make this book understandable to the general reader by reading substantial portions of it in their capacities as "intelligent laymen."

To all these is dedicated with gratitude and affection whatever may be found of value in the following pages. The errors therein, however, remain in all cases my own.

George Kingsley Zipf

Newton, Massachusetts
April 19, 1948.

CONTENTS

Part One

Language and the Structure of the Personality

CHAPTER ONE

INTRODUCTION AND ORIENTATION

Everyone in the course of his daily living must to some extent move about in his environment. And in so moving he may be said to take paths. Yet these paths that he takes in his environment do not constitute his entire activity. For even when a person is comparatively at rest, there is still a continual movement of matter-energy into his system, through his system, and out of his system if only in the accomplishment of his metabolistic processes. This movement of matter-energy also proceeds over paths. Indeed, a person's entire body may be viewed as an aggregate of matter that is in transit at differing speeds over different paths within his system. His system in turn moves about as a unit whole over paths in his external environment.

We stress this concept of movement over paths because we shall attempt to demonstrate in the course of our following chapters that every individual's movement, of whatever sort, will always be over paths and will always tend to be governed by one single primary principle which, for the want of a better term, we shall call the *Principle of Least Effort*. Moreover, we shall attempt to demonstrate that the structure and organization of an individual's entire being will tend always to be such that his entire behavior will be governed by this Principle.

And yet what is this Principle? In simple terms, the Principle of Least Effort means, for example, that a person in solving his immediate problems will view these against the background of his probable future problems, *as estimated by himself*. Moreover he will strive to solve his problems in such a way as to minimize the *total work* that he must expend in solving *both* his immediate problems *and* his probable future problems. That in turn means that the person will strive to minimize the *probable average rate of his work-expenditure* (over time). And in so doing he will be minimizing his *effort*, by our definition of effort. Least effort, therefore, is a variant of least work.

In the interest of defining and of elucidating the Principle of Least Effort, and of orienting ourselves in the problem of its demonstration, we can profitably devote this opening chapter to a preliminary disclosure of the Principle, if only on the basis of commonplace cases of human behavior that are admittedly oversimplified for the sake of a more convenient initial exposition.

I. THE SELECTION OF A PATH

Sometimes it is not difficult to select a path to one's objective. Thus if there are two cities, *A* and *B*, that are connected by a straight level highway with a surface of little friction, then this highway represents simultaneously the *shortest,* the *quickest,* and the *easiest* path between the two cities—or, as we might say, the highway is at once a path of *least distance* and of *least time* and of *least work.* A traveller from one city to the other would take the same path regardless of whether he was *minimizing* distance, time, or work.

On the other hand, if the two cities happen to be separated by an intervening mountain range, then the respective paths of least distance, and of least time, and of least work will by no means necessarily be the same. Thus if a person wanted to go by foot from one city to another by least distance, he would be obliged to tunnel through the base of the mountain chain at a very great expense of work. His quickest course might be over the tops of the mountains at a great cost of labor and at great risk. His easiest path, however, might be a tortuous winding back and forth through the mountain range over a very considerable distance and during a quite long interval of time.

These three paths are obviously not the same. The foot-traveller between the two cities cannot, therefore, simultaneously minimize distance, time, and work in a single path between the two cities as the problem now stands. Which path, therefore, will he take? Or, since the above case is fairly typical of life's daily problems, in which impediments of various sorts obstruct our way, which path do we actually take? Clearly our selection of a path will be determined by the particular *dynamic minimum* in operation.

II. THE "SINGLENESS OF THE SUPERLATIVE"

The preceding discussion of the selection of paths not only illustrates the meaning of a *minimum* in a problem in dynamics but also prepares the ground for a consideration of the concept of the *"singleness of the superlative"* [1] which, incidentally, will provide an intellectual tool of considerable value for our entire inquiry.

The concept of the "singleness of the superlative" is simple: no problem in dynamics can be properly formulated in terms of more than one superlative, whether the superlative in question is stated as a *minimum* or as a *maximum* (e.g., a *minimum* expenditure of work can also be stated as a *maximum* economy of work). If the problem has more than one superlative, the problem itself becomes completely meaningless and indeterminate.

We do not mean that a particular situation will never arise in which the minimizing of one factor will not *incidentally* entail the minimizing of another or other factors. Indeed, in our preceding section we noted a situation in which the easiest path between two cities might be a straight level highway that also represented the shortest and quickest path. Instead we mean that a general statement in dynamics cannot contain more than one superlative if it is to be sensible and determinate, since a situation may arise in which the plural superlatives are in conflict.

Perhaps the simplest way to emphasize the singleness of the superlative is to present as an example a statement with a single superlative that is meaningful and determinate. Then we shall note how meaningless and indeterminate the statement immediately becomes when a second superlative is added.

As a suitable example we might take the imaginary case of a prize offered to the submarine commander who sinks the *greatest number* of ships in a given interval of time; in this case, *maximum number* is the single superlative in the problem. Or we might alter the terms of the problem and offer a prize to the submarine commander who sinks a given number of ships in the *shortest possible* time; in this second case, *time* is the *minimum;* and, since it is the only superlative in the statement, the problem is quite meaningful and determinate. In either of the above examples the submarine commander can understand what the precise terms of the prize are.

Yet when we offer a prize to the submarine commander who sinks the *greatest number* of ships in the *shortest possible time,* we have a double superlative—a *maximum* number and a *minimum* time—which renders the problem completely meaningless and indeterminate, as becomes apparent upon reflection.

Double superlatives of this sort, which are by no means uncommon in present-day statements, can lead to a mental confusion with disastrous results.*

In the present study we are contending that the entire behavior of an individual is at all times motivated by the urge to minimize effort.

The sheer idea that there may be only one dynamic minimum in the entire behavior of all living individuals need not by itself dismay us. The physicists are certainly not dismayed at the thought that all physical process throughout the entire time-space continuum is governed by the one single superlative, *least action.*† Indeed, the presence of only one single superlative for all physical process throughout the entire time-space continuum can even be derived logically from the basic postulate of science that there is a unity of nature and a continuity of natural law (in the sense that the same laws of nature govern all events in time-space). For, according to this postulate, the entirety of time-space, with all its happenings, may be viewed as constituting a single problem in dynamics which in turn can have only one single superlative—a superlative which in the opinion of physicists is that of *least action.*[4]

By the same token, the sheer idea of there being one single superlative for all living process is not in and for itself an *a priori* incredibility.

On the other hand, there is also admittedly no *a priori* necessity for our believing that all living process does in fact behave at all times according

* As pointed out years ago, the frequent statement, "in a democracy we believe in the *greatest* good for the *greatest* number," contains a double superlative and therefore is meaningless and indeterminate. (In Part Two we shall see that the distribution of goods and services are in fact governed by a single superlative.) Intimately connected with the "singleness of the superlative" is what might be called the *singleness of the objective* whose implications are often overlooked (i.e., the pursuit of one objective may preclude or frustrate the pursuit of the second objective). These two concepts apply to all studies in ecology.[2]

† The principle of least action was first propounded by Maupertuis in the eighteenth century, and has been subsequently conceptually sharpened by others.[3]

to one single invariable superlative, such as that of least effort. That, after all, must first be established empirically, as was done with the principle of least action. We can even now note how bizarre the effect would be if a person behaved at one moment according to one dynamic minimum, and at the next moment according to an entirely different dynamic minimum. Nor would the effect be any less bizarre if one person's life were governed throughout by one superlative while his neighbor's life followed a totally different superlative.

In order to emphasize the ludicrousness of a variety of different superlatives, let us assume that each person consists of two parts, and that each part has a different dynamic superlative of its own. For example, let us assume that one part of the person is governed by least work while the other is governed by least time. In that case the person will represent two distinct problems in dynamics, with the result that he will be, effectively, two distinctly different individuals with two distinct sets of dynamical principles. One part of him, in its eagerness to save work, might conceivably even "get lost" from the other part of him, in its eagerness to save time.

Nor would the situation be different if we assume that a person now minimizes one factor and now another without any single governing principle behind the total phenomenon. For if the person's entire metabolistic and procreational system is organized, say, for the purpose of minimizing work in all its action, then there would have to be a simply staggering alteration of structure and of operation if the person in question were suddenly to minimize time. Since sudden alterations of such proportions are unknown, we are perhaps not overbold in suspecting *a fortiori* that an individual's entire activity from birth to death is governed throughout by the same one single superlative which, in our opinion, is least effort.

But that is not all. If we remember the extent to which offspring inherit the forms and functions of their parents, we may suspect that this inheritance is possible only if the offspring also inherit the parental dynamic drive that governs the parental forms and functions that are inherited.

Furthermore, if we view the present-day variety of living process as the result of slow evolutionary changes from an initial similarity of form and function, then we can understand *a fortiori* how the one initial single common dynamic superlative might well remain unchanged from generation to generation, regardless of how enormous the changes in forms and functions might become; and that, in turn, will mean that all individuals, regardless of their differences in form and function, will still be governed by the same single superlative.

But though we may argue at length as to the plausibility of one single superlative for all living process, yet, even if this were the case, we should still need to disclose what, in fact, the particular superlative in question is.

An actual disclosure of the single hypothetical superlative in question may be difficult for quite obvious reasons. If we take our previous example of the two cities with an intervening mountain chain, in which the paths of least distance, least time, and least work are three different paths, we are obliged in all candor to admit that sometimes one of these paths is taken and sometimes another. For that matter, a tunnel may be dug through the base of the mountain to save distance, while airplanes are flown over the same mountain to save time, while pack horses continue to take the easier and more leisurely winding route. Or, to take another case, sometimes the reader will dart through traffic at considerable risk in order to save time in crossing a street; and sometimes he will take the longer and safer path to the corner, where he will wait for the traffic light. Even if we assume that we are all governed by the same one single dynamic superlative, which superlative is it?

But although the superlatives in the foregoing examples seem to be different, are they nevertheless irreconcilable? Before answering this question, let us remember the physicists' claim that according to their law of falling bodies, all free-standing bodies will fall (by least action) to the earth. Yet, despite this claim, we have all observed how leaves sometimes rise in the air, or how birds take off from the ground and fly out of sight, much as if they were exceptions to the law of falling bodies. Of course we know from a more careful inspection of the problem that these leaves and birds are by no means exceptions to the law of falling bodies; on the contrary, if all the factors in the problem are taken into consideration, they are behaving quite in accordance to the physical law in question.

May not the same be true of the three different paths to the other side of the mountain? Even though each of these paths may be taken simultaneously by someone, and even though a given person may now take one path and now another, there remains the possibility that the adoption of one or another by an individual under varying sets of circumstances is governed by the operation of some further single dynamic minimum that forever remains invariant. In any event, we shall argue that such is the case.

More specifically, we shall argue that if we view the above types of situations against the broad background of the individual's present and future problems, we shall find that an extraordinary expenditure of work at one moment, or an extraordinary haste in one situation, may simply be temporary devices for reducing the probable rate of the individual's work expenditure over subsequent periods of his life.

In short, we shall argue that the invariable minimum that governs all varying conduct of an individual is least effort.

III. THE PRINCIPLE OF LEAST EFFORT

Perhaps the easiest way to comprehend the meaning and implications of the Principle of Least Effort is to show the inadequacies of sheer *least work,* to which *least effort* is closely related. This is all the more worth doing because some persons (see below) apparently believe that least work is the basic minimum of living process, as often seems to be the case in particular situations that are considered out of context.

If we remember, however, that an individual's life continues over a longer or shorter length of time, then we can readily understand how the least work solution to one of his problems may lead to results that will inevitably increase the amount of work that he must expend in solving his subsequent problems. In other words, the minimizing of work in solving today's problems may lead to results that will increase tomorrow's work beyond what would have been necessary if today's work had not been completely minimized. Conversely, by expending more work than necessary today, one may thereby save still more work tomorrow.

And, as we have argued about the functional relatedness of today and tomorrow, we may argue about the functional relatedness of the entire succession of events throughout the individual's whole life, in which the rate of his expenditure of work at one moment may affect the minimizing of his work at subsequent moment(s).

In view of the implications of the above quite obvious considerations, we feel justified in taking the stand that it is the person's *average rate of work-expenditure over time* that is minimized in his behavior, and not just his work-expenditure at any moment or in any one isolated problem, without any reference to his future problems.

Yet a sheer *average rate of work-expenditure over time* is not an entirely meaningful concept, since no mortal can know for certain what his future problems are going to be. The most that any individual can do is to estimate what his future problems are *likely to be,* and then to govern his conduct accordingly. In other words, before an individual can minimize his average rate of work-expenditure over time, he must first estimate the probable eventualities of his future, and then select a path of least average rate of work through these.

Yet in so doing the individual is no longer minimizing an average rate of work, but *a probable average rate of work;* or he is governed by the principle of the *least average rate of probable work.**

For convenience, we shall use the term *least effort* to describe the preceding least average rate of probable work. We shall argue that an individual's entire behavior is subject to the minimizing of effort. Or, differently stated, every individual's entire behavior is governed by the Principle of Least Effort.

Now that we have described what the Principle of Least Effort is, let us briefly illustrate it.

At the risk of being tedious, let the first example be our previous case of the two towns, *A* and *B,* that are separated by an intervening mountain range. Here we can see the enormous amount of work that could be saved in travel and trade if the two towns were connected by a tunnel of least distance through the base of the mountain; we can also see the enormous amount of work that it would take to construct such a tunnel. We are simply arguing that when the probable cost in work of digging the tunnel is estimated to be less than the probable work of not having the tunnel, then, if the necessary work for construction is available, the tunnel will be dug. The problem relates, therefore, to the probable amounts of work involved, as

* To avoid a possible verbal confusion, let us note that we are not discussing *least probable* average rate of work, but a *probably least* average rate of work.

estimated by one or more persons. Naturally, these persons can have been mistaken in their estimates, with the result that the tunnel can either succeed beyond their wildest hopes, or dismally fail. For we do not deny that "a person's hindsight is generally better than his foresight." We merely claim that a person acts on the basis of his "foresight"—with all that that will later be found to imply—according to the Principle of Least Effort.

The above type of argument will also apply to a path of least time over the mountain. Thus the enormous cost of flying munitions over the mountain to save time in supplying an army in combat on the other side may be more than justified by the future probable work that is thereby saved.

These cases of the different paths to the other side of the mountain represent instances of collective action and of collective economies, since, for example, a tunnel through a mountain is obviously not constructed by a single person but by the collective effort of a great many persons.

And yet we are not restricted to examples of collective effort in illustrating our Principle of Least Effort, which we contend also applies to an individual's own behavior. We might take the case of a student whose particular path of least effort out of his classroom would seem offhand to be the path that leads from his seat to the nearest aisle, and thence out of the door, through the hall, to the nearest stairway. On the other hand, in the event of a fire, the student might conceivably prefer to run with least time to the nearest window and adopt a path that is simultaneously a path of least work and of least time and of least distance to the ground. This path will also be a path of least effort, as estimated by himself, even at the risk of months in the hospital with a broken back. Other students may prefer to take paths through the smoke-filled corridors. These paths are also paths of least effort, as estimated by the students in question. Afterwards, when, as, and if all the students foregather, they can decide which of them, in the light of subsequent events, actually were the shrewdest gamblers in the sense of having both most correctly comprehended the nature and estimated the probabilities of the problem in their lives that was caused by the unexpected fire.

From this second example we note that the operation of the Principle of Least Effort is contingent upon the *mentation* of the individual, which in turn includes the operations of *"comprehending"* the "relevant" elements of a problem, of *"assessing their probabilities,"* and of "solving the problem in terms of least effort." We mention this vital consideration of *mentation* right here and now, so that we may prepare ourselves for the task of defining mentation, and of showing that the structure and operation of mentation are also governed throughout by the Principle of Least Effort. since an individual's mentation is clearly a part of his total behavior, and hence subject to our Principle of Least Effort.

The foregoing examples suffice to illustrate what the Principle of Least Effort is, and what its implications may be for everyday problems. By and large, our explanations of the above commonplace examples are pretty much in line with the way the reader himself would have explained them. We mention this consideration in order to suggest that our chief task may not be that of persuading the reader to adopt a totally new way of thinking, but rather of formally describing and of scientifically establishing the basic principle of our habitual way of thinking.

IV. THE SCOPE OF THE PRINCIPLE: "TOOLS–AND–JOBS"

Our previous examples have illustrated the theoretical operation of the Principle of Least Effort in particular situations that involved either individual or collective behavior. They did not illustrate, however, our contention that the Principle governs the *totality* of a person's behavior at all times. Since we shall find it necessary to devote considerable space to a demonstration of the economy of mentation, which is only a part of a person's total behavior, we obviously cannot hope in the course of a few paragraphs to illustrate the economy of the *totality* of a person's behavior by means of one single telling example.

Nevertheless it may be useful for the sake of preliminary orientation to suggest how a great deal of a person's total behavior can be expressed in the form of a simple problem of tools-and-jobs whose elements are quite familiar in everyday life. The problem of *tools-and-jobs* is the same as the problem of *means* and *ends,* or of *instruments* (or agents) and *objectives.* We shall adopt the homelier term, *tools-and-jobs,* to emphasize the commonplace nature of the problem under discussion.

Regardless of the terms employed, it is evident upon reflection that according to the Principle of Least Effort there are two aspects to the economy of the *tools-and-jobs* in question. In the first place, there is the economy of *tools.* In the second place, there is the economy of *jobs.*

To clarify the significance of these two economies, let us briefly illustrate them in terms of carpentry *tools* and carpentry *jobs.*

We all know from experience that when a person has a carpentry *job* to be performed, he directly or indirectly seeks a set of carpentry *tools* to perform the job. And, in general, we may say that *jobs seek tools.*

But what is often overlooked is the equally obvious fact that when a person owns a set of carpentry *tools,* then, roughly speaking, he directly or indirectly seeks a carpentry *job* for his tools to perform. Thus we may say that *tools seek jobs.*

This reciprocal matching of tools to jobs and of jobs to tools may conveniently be described by the phrase, *tools-seek-jobs-and-jobs-seek-tools.*

Upon further reflection, we note that the concept of this italicized phrase is ultimately unsatisfactory because it defines tools in reference to jobs and jobs in reference to tools. Hence, unless either the tools or the jobs are fixed, the companion term remains undefined. In subsequent chapters, we shall find a third frame of reference that will serve to define both *tools* and *jobs* in conditions where neither is fixed.

For the purpose of a preliminary orientation, however, we can illustrate superficially some of the more obvious implications of the reciprocal economy of matching tools and jobs under the assumption that either the tools or the jobs are fixed. We shall begin with the example of an automobile manufacturer, and then turn to the case of an imaginary person called John.

If the owner of a manufacturing plant has the *job* of making pleasure automobiles, then, theoretically, he will seek to use those tools that will manufacture the automobiles with a maximum economy, as is observably the case with all automobile manufacturers. The same urge of economy presumably activates the manufacturers of other kinds of goods. In short, the kinds of jobs (or objectives) that a person has to perform will determine the kinds of tools (or means) that he employs for their performance.

Nevertheless, the above situation might well be immediately changed with the sudden outbreak of war that introduces a whole new set of national jobs—or objectives—while suppressing a great many of the erstwhile peacetime ones. During the war the automobile manufacturer may no longer be permitted to manufacture his peacetime pleasure cars; and the same will doubtless be true of many other kinds of manufactures. That will not mean, however, that the manufacturing plants in question will remain idle for the duration of the war. On the contrary the plants will be "converted to war work." That is, they will perform the new kinds of war jobs.

What, more precisely, takes place under this "conversion to war work"? Theoretically, each plant will seek to perform that particular kind of war job most nearly adapted to its present peacetime toolage; that is, it will seek to perform the particular job for which it can re-tool with least work (effort). Thus the automobile factory may make tanks, or jeeps, or gun carriages of some sort. Generalizing upon this case, we may say that tools-seek-jobs-and-jobs-seek-tools throughout the entire nation at war.*

After the war is over, the manufacturers again face the need of "conversion." This does not mean that the manufacturers will necessarily revert to production of their prewar lines of goods, although they may. They may find it easier to convert their wartime toolage to the production of some entirely different kind of peacetime goods. In this conversion to peacetime activity, we may again say that *tools-seek-jobs-and-jobs-seek-tools.*

The foregoing example of the manufacturing plant is instructive for two reasons. *First,* it shows what might be called the complete *relativism* of the problem, with little that is permanently stable over any extended period of time; for by just such successive steps of "adaptive evolution" a plant that begins with the manufacture of microscopes may find itself manufacturing perfumes a century later, without a single one of the original kinds of tools and processes still employed. *Secondly,* the example of conversion of tools to war and then to peace indicates that our problem of economy is twofold, since it involves not only the more familiar important problem of the selection of economical means (tools) but also the somewhat less familiar but no less important problem of the selection of economical objectives (jobs), in the *reciprocal economy* of matching tools to jobs and jobs to tools.

The above example is tendered only to illustrate the general relativism

---

* The case of the automobile manufacturer is oversimplified, since we have deliberately ignored problems of labor, management, and raw materials, which will be treated in detail in Chapters 9 and 11. Theoretically, the total supply of war jobs will be distributed to the total supply of manufacturers in such a way that the total work of re-tooling and of manufacture of the desired items will be least (cf. Chap. 5).

of the fundamental problem of tools-and-jobs as well as the twofold economy of their reciprocal matching. Since these two considerations are obviously important in our theory, it is not unreasonable for the reader to ask even now just how we may hope to study them *quantitatively*.

Curiously enough, we shall find in the forms and functions of the entities of human speech an almost perfect example of the general relativism of tools and jobs and of the twofold economy of selection. For, as we shall later see more specifically, the forms and meanings of words represent merely a special case of tools that perform jobs. We shall find that the forms and functions of words are quite capable of being studied quantitatively by means of the objective methods of empiric science, with results that will be applicable to the general economy of all tools and jobs.

Indeed, it will be the precise information that we gain from a study of the case of speech that will suggest how every individual may be viewed in his *entirety* as a single set of integrated tools-and-jobs; and that the *total* behavior of the individual can be viewed as a case in which tools-seek-jobs-and-jobs-seek-tools with a maximum economy of effort. This view of an individual as a set of tools-jobs does no violence to our commonsense feelings about the matter, as we shall now see as we turn from the case of the automobile manufacturer to that of an imaginary person called John who, we shall suppose, is in love with Mary.

John, after work, tidies himself before going to see Mary, who is similarly tidying herself to see John. In these two persons we have, theoretically, a case where jobs-seek-tools-and-tools-seek-jobs. Each may be viewed as both a set of tools and as a set of jobs for the other person. Together they face a period of reciprocal adjustment, during which each side alters its tools and jobs to effect a more economical "match." In this respect John (or Mary) is quite similar to our previously discussed automobile manufacturer, who also had to alter his tools and jobs to match them more economically to the jobs and tools of others.

Yet in saying that John (or Mary) is a set of tools-and-jobs that is seeking a complementary set of jobs-and-tools, we are obviously dealing with two different economic problems in each person. Thus, in the case of John, there is the *first* problem of organizing John's own individual set of tools in such a way that they will operate with maximum economy in performing their jobs of self-support, self-defense, and procreation. Then there is the *second* problem of economically moving John as a unit system of tools over the earth's surface in the quest of jobs for his tools and of tools for his jobs (e.g., John seeks Mary). Clearly, these two economies to which John is continually subject are not the same. Yet they have one salient feature in common: in either case there is always the problem of moving matter-energy over paths of least effort, whether the matter-energy thus moved represents John's individual tools in operation, or whether it represents John as a total whole.

In other words, we may say two things about John in reference to our theoretical paths of least effort. First, we may say that John *is a set of paths* over which matter-energy proceeds into his system of toolage, through his system of toolage, and out of his system of toolage. Secondly, John, as a unit, *takes paths.* According to our Principle, all these paths, of whatever sort, will be paths of least effort, even though John's *intrasystematic set* of paths may seem to be rigidly stereotyped and determinate, whereas John's *extra-systematic* unit action may seem to be comparatively optional and indeterminate.

Paths of least effort are only probable paths, regardless of the comparative degrees of probabilities that the paths in question will be taken. If we now inspect more closely the manner in which John selects his *extra-systematic* path to his rendezvous with Mary, we shall gain further insight into the degree of precision to which any path of least effort is calculated, and also into the general economy of a perseveration, or a repetition, of activity that accounts for the apparently stereotyped rigidity of John's *intra-systematic* paths.

To begin, let us ask whether John, in selecting a path of least effort to Mary, will perchance take a slide rule and surveyor's transit, and calculate his path to Mary with the precision of a civil engineer who is surveying a roadbed for a railway that is to wind through a mountain range where every inch counts. Obviously not, and for a very good economic reason: *the work of calculating a path of least effort must be included in the total work of taking the path of least effort.* Nothing is gained by calculating a particular path of least effort to a greater degree of precision, when the added work of so calculating it is not more than offset by the work that is saved by using the more precisely calculated path. John, therefore, in selecting an easiest probable path to his objective, will minimize the total effort of calculating and of taking the path in question. The same will theoretically be the case of every other path of least effort.

This consideration leads to a second one. If John expects to take the same path repeatedly, then he can afford to calculate it more precisely, since the additional work of calculation can be distributed over the repeated trips. From this we see that there is an inherent economy of effort in repeatedly taking the same paths, since one saves thereby the work of repeated calculations. In short, there is an economy in the repetitiveness of one's acts of behavior. Thence the growth of "habits."

We mention this consideration in order to suggest that the *intrasystematic* paths over which John's individual tools behave *within* his own system will still be paths of least effort, even though they may seem to be stereotyped to the point of complete rigidity because of the relatively high frequency of recurrence of the action in question. The sheer fact that our physiological behavior is highly predictable does not preclude the possibility that it takes place over paths of least effort; on the contrary, as we shall later argue in detail, intrasystematic paths are stereotyped because they are frequent, *and the reverse.*

This view of John as simultaneously both *taking* paths and *being* paths leads ultimately to a profound question in dynamics that will occupy our attention in the course of our demonstration.

If we restrict our attention to John as a set of paths in reference to which matter-energy moves into John's system, through John's system, and out of John's system, we note that there is nothing in this transient matter-energy that can be called permanently "John." And since the matter-energy is not John—or, if one will, since the actual physical tools of his system are not John—what then is John?

All that is left, according to our theory, is the *system* of paths itself, over which the matter-energy moves while acting in the capacity of being John's tools in operation. Yet does even this system of paths represent what is permanently John? Obviously not, since these paths are only probable paths and by no means fixed. Indeed, we know that the particular system of paths of an aged man are far from being the same as his system of paths when he was an embryo. Even as matter-energy is continually moving over paths, so too paths are continually changing.

And yet if all the matter-energy in John's system of tools in operation is transient and ephemeral to the system, and if the paths, or processes, are also variable, what, then, is left over in the total phenomenon to represent that apparently enduring entity called John?

This is clearly a primary question that is inherent in our concept of tools-and-jobs and one which will confront every other investigator into the field of biosocial dynamics. The question is simple: What is John?

At present we merely point to the existence of this question, which we shall candidly face in the course of our demonstration, when we shall attempt to answer it. If we mention it now, it is only in order to suggest what is attached to the view that an individual is a set of tools-and-jobs which in turn seeks jobs-and-tools.

We shall later define more precisely what we mean by *tools* and by *jobs* and by the reciprocal economy of *matching* the two. Our present discussion of the topic is intended merely to indicate the scope of the Principle of Least Effort, and to suggest a possibly fruitful manner of studying the problem of the economy of a person's *total* behavior.

This *total* behavior, as we have seen, consists of two economies. John is not only subject to the economy of organizing his own *individual* self; he is also subject to the economy of a *collective* organization with what lies outside his system. For the convenience of exposition, we shall divide our demonstration into two parts, the first devoted primarily to a discussion of the economy of the organization of the individual, and the second to the economy of the organization of the *collective* group of individuals in reference to each other and to the rest of nature.

We can see from the very nature of the case that the one economy of the individual will influence the other economy of the collective group, and the reverse.

V. PREVIOUS STUDIES

Now that we have discussed the meaning of the Principle of Least Effort and have indicated its general scope, let us review earlier studies of the topic before presenting a prospectus of the chief steps of our own ensuing demonstration. We shall begin (*A*) with the earlier studies of *collective* human economy, as represented by the economists; then (*B*) we shall consider studies of *individual* economy as conducted by psychologists. This summary review will also serve to let us take a position towards these earlier studies.

A. Collective Economy

It is questionable whether our analysis of the particular case of the economy of digging a tunnel through the mountain added one single consideration that would not have been completely covered by the older schools of "classical" or "orthodox" economics. These schools have never been in any doubt that the factor that is minimized in such collective enterprises is "labor," or work. Nor do they view their topics so narrowly that they fail to take into account the concept of risk which, in turn, is intimately connected with the concept of probable work. A great deal of economic theory, therefore, belongs to the history of the topic we are considering.

Closely related to the field of economics are the fields of sociology and of cultural anthropology, to whose thinking we are also indebted. Earlier quantitative observations in these fields, as well as in the field of general biological ecology, will often be referred to in the course of our demonstration.

B. Individual Economy

Less widely known than the above studies, yet surely no less important, are the studies of the factor of work in the motivation of human behavior as conducted with painstaking care by experimental psychologists. The results of these studies have led to the theoretical formulations of Drs. N. E. Miller and J. Dollard,[5] and to those of Dr. C. L. Hull[6] (see below), who is himself an experimentalist. Although the actual experimentation in the field of motivation has been too extensive to be discussed in detail here, we shall at least give a short account of some of the main steps of the theoretical development of the concept of economy.

Among the very earliest experimentalists to be concerned with the topic of work were three persons: (1) Dr. J. A. Gengerelli in his "The Principle of Maxima and Minima in Learning,"[7] (2) Dr. L. S. Tsai in his "The Laws of Minimum Effort and Maximum Satisfaction in Animal Behavior,"[8] and (3) Dr. R. H. Waters in his "The Principle of Least Effort in Learning."[9] By the term *effort* in these titles, the authors without exception mean *work*. In addition, there is also the "principle of least action" that was borrowed wholesale from the physicists by Dr. R. H. Wheeler, who advanced it as a primary psychological principle without any supporting proof; * we mention Dr. Wheeler's "principle of least action in psychology"[10] lest we other-

* In the original simple terms of Maupertuis, the principle of least action states that when a mass, *M*, moves from a given point at a given moment of time to another point at another moment of time, it will proceed along a course in which the sum of all products of all masses when multiplied by their respective distances moved and by their respective velocities will be a minimum.

wise seem to be unaware of it; and we discard it for the reason pointed out by Dr. Waters: Dr. Wheeler has in fact done nothing scientifically except, at best, to enunciate a postulate which he saw fit to make, yet for the validity of which there is not the slightest bit of evidence.

As to the other three persons, Dr. Gengerelli states his *Principle of Maxima and Minima* as follows:

> "The behavior of an organism elicited by a given stimulating situation which affords relief to an internal need of that organism tends, with repetition, to approach, in terms of time, space, and effort involved, the minimal limit compatible with the relief of that need; the nature of the limit being defined by the structure of the organism and of the external situation."

Dr. Tsai in turn states his *Law of Minimum Effort* as follows:

> "Among several alternatives of behavior leading to equivalent satisfaction of some potent organic need, the animal, within the limits of its discriminative ability, tends finally to select that which involves the least expenditure of energy."

Of these two principles, the one by Tsai is preferable because, as Dr. Waters pointed out (see below), Tsai frankly recognizes the limiting effect of the discriminative capacity of an animal; in short, an animal's "choices" are limited to those of whose existence the animal is aware. We should like to point out that both of the above propositions contain terms that need to be defined objectively.

Dr. Waters, after criticizing the above, showed the need of devising experimental situations that will separate the respective paths of least work, of least distance, and of least time, so that the preferred minimum can be observed. Dr. Waters' own experimental setup to this end did not disclose the unambiguous minimum he had expected. The rats in Dr. Waters' experimental labyrinth showed a marked preference for paths along a wall —a preference that has itself been studied quantitatively with great insight by the physiologist, Dr. W. J. Crozier [11] and G. Pincus.

Dr. Waters presented quite cautiously a rationalization of his observations in terms of least work, to which he added many qualifications that merit careful study. In closing his argument, Dr. Waters made the following statement (p. 17):

> "Thus Theseus, after slaying the minotaur, found his way out of the labyrinth and to his loved one by following the string which he had carried with him into the labyrinth. Perhaps this was not the most direct route in terms of distance, time, or effort, but it was the only sure way he had of escaping. Likewise our rats found that by sticking to the outside pathways they more readily achieved the goal." *

This simple statement represents one of those anomalies in the history of science that always merits mention, though in mentioning it we most certainly do not mean to discredit Dr. Waters' excellent experimentation,

* Perhaps rats running along a wall are less likely to be hit.

much less Dr. Waters' admirable cautiousness about the principle of least work. We merely call attention to the fact that the case of Theseus suffices to disprove the Gengerelli-Tsai principle of *least work* that Dr. Waters was trying to establish, and inadvertently provides instead an excellent example of *least average probable rate of work* (or our Least Effort) which we believe is the correct minimum.

But to continue, in 1943 Dr. C. L. Hull[12] in his *Principles of Behavior* set forth three postulates that relate to reactive inhibitions, on the basis of which he developed a corollary law of *less work* (p. 294) as follows:

> "If two or more behavior sequences, each involving a different amount of work (W), have been equally well reinforced an equal number of times, the organism will gradually learn to choose the less laborious behavior sequence leading to the attainment of the reinforcing state of affairs."

Hull's principle of *less work* was based upon the research of those whom we have already discussed above, and upon that of Dr. R. S. Crutchfield's study of "Psychological Distance as a Function of Psychological Need."[13] In 1944, a year after Hull's publication, Dr. M. E. Thompson in "An Experimental Investigation of the Gradient of Reinforcement in Maze Learning"[14] provided a further excellent set of observations in support of Hull's corollary principle of less work.[15]

Hull's corollary principle, as stated by him, seems, like that of Tsai's, to be also a corollary of our Principle of Least Effort, as will be apparent from our demonstration. Thus, for example, when there are two or more possible courses of activity from one given point-moment to another given point-moment, for which the prerequisites are the same and of which the consequences are the same, then theoretically the course of least work will be adopted, since this course is also the course of Least Effort. We mention this consideration because many of the phenomena of speech, if viewed in isolation over a short period of time, will be found to conform to Hull's corollary of less work. The same would seem to apply to many other restricted experimental situations.*

In addition to the above approach by experimental psychologists, of which the foregoing account is only a barest outline, there was the general theoretical study of "vectorial analysis" by Kurt Lewin in his *Principles of Topological Psychology*.[16] This study, though stimulating to read, suffered both from a paucity of supporting data and from the lack of a satisfactory theory to account "vectorially" for the progression of a person from one situation to the other. On the other hand, the gifted experimentalists, Drs. J. F. Brown and A. C. Voth, have observed instances of "topological vectors" in the field of vision.[17] Nor should we fail to mention, if only in passing, the extremely interesting observations of the social behavior of ants as made by the topological psychologist and biologist, Dr. T. C. Schneirla.[18]

---

* See, for example, O. H. Mowrer and H. M. Jones, "Extinction and Behavior Variability as Function of Effortfulness of Task";[20] J. E. De Camp, "Relative distance as a factor in the white rat's selection of a path,"[21] etc.

The writer's publications in the field of the dynamics of behavior began in 1929, in which cases of least work were found in the speech process.[19]

The foregoing outline is by no means complete. In the following chapters we shall discuss in detail the observations of other investigators, including those of sociologists, which for that reason are not included above. The above outline serves to suggest both the increasing interest on the part of objective scientists in the topic of biosocial dynamics, and a growing feeling of the urgent need for a single unifying biosocial principle.

Only by venturing to set up general unifying principles for others to criticize and to prune and to restructure, even as those persons we have just mentioned have ventured and are venturing to do—and as we shall also attempt to do—may we hope, I believe, ultimately to disclose the desired principle.

VI. PROSPECTUS

In the foregoing pages we have presented a preliminary orientation into the nature and scope of the Principle of Least Effort, as well as a short summary of the earlier studies of the principle of least work in animal behavior. Let us now present a brief outline of the main steps of our own ensuing demonstration.

Some pages back we pointed out that the Principle of Least Effort will theoretically govern the behavior both of the individual and of the collective group. For convenience we shall divide our demonstration, therefore, into two parts, with Part One devoted to a study of the least effort of individual behavior, and Part Two to that of collective behavior.

We also mentioned that the organization and behavior of speech offered an excellent example of the general economy of tools-and-jobs. For that reason, our demonstration in Part One will begin with a study of speech.

The eight chapters of Part One fall in general into three rough groups: Chapters 2–4; Chapters 5–6; and Chapters 7–8.

The first group begins in Chapter 2 with a study of words and their meanings from the viewpoint of the speaker. Here we shall attempt to show both the presence of an economy of work and the even distribution of that work over time. In short, we shall approach the problem of Least Effort from the angle of *the even distribution of minimized work over time.*

In Chapter 3 we shall consider the case of formal semantic balance in which tools and jobs become altered in order to effect a more economical reciprocal balance, as previously suggested. Our discussion in this chapter will be conducted largely in terms of a mechanical analogue, called the Tool Analogy, which will serve both to objectify the problem of formal semantic balance in speech, and to facilitate a definition of terms. As we disclose the principles that govern the forms and functions of speech entities by means of our Tool Analogy, it will become evident that these principles will also apply to any set of mechanical tools that meet the terms of the Analogy.

In Chapter 4 we shall study the verbalizations of children in order to show that the principles disclosed empirically will also apply to the development, or evolution, of a person's speech. Chapter 4 closes the first group of chapters that are devoted to least work.

The second group begins with Chapter 5, where we view speech as a sensory impression upon the auditor instead of as an expression of a speaker. In this chapter we shall leave the concept of least work, and turn to a theoretical proof of the Principle of Least Effort itself from the accumulated data on speech up to that point. We also shall extend our argument about the Least Effort economy of the special case of speech to the Least Effort of economy of the entire sensory field. In so doing, we shall attempt to show that our Tool Analogy may be accurately descriptive of all biological forms and functions—a consideration that will lead to Chapter 6.

In Chapter 6 we face the problem of an individual's ego that serves as a frame of reference to the person's "psychosomatic" system of "tools-jobs." For, as we remember from our discussion of John as a system of matter in transit over paths that may themselves change, we came upon the ultimate question: "What is John?" Hence in Chapter 6 we shall essay a definition of an organism, including John. We shall also examine more precisely the terms *tools* and *jobs,* as we inquire into the economy of organic evolution. In order to show that the Principle of Least Effort applies to the forms-functions of all living organisms and not just to man, we shall construct a hypothesis on the basis of the Principle of Least Effort that relates to the distribution of biological species, genera, and families over the earth's surface; and we shall find from the observations of Dr. J. C. Willis that these are distributed as we have predicted from our Principle. Apart from showing that the Principle of Least Effort provides a sufficient explanation of all biological evolution (as an alternative to the more familiar Darwinian principle of "the survival of the fittest") the demonstration of Chapter 6 is also to be noted because it contains our only attempt to show inductively-deductively that the Principle of Least Effort applies to the entire biosocial continuum. In the closing parts of this chapter we shall attempt to provide a dynamic basis for the drives of the Freudian death wish, and "life wish" as defined by ourselves. This will pave the way for Chapter 7, with which our third rough grouping of chapters begins.

Chapter 7 defines what we mean by *mind as a system of mentation,* as we turn to the problem of demonstrating the dynamics of symbolic process (i.e., semantic dynamics). We shall begin with an inspection of certain aspects of sexual behavior, with special emphasis upon man's sexual bipolarity (i.e., his heterosexual-homosexual balance) which will provide the necessary key for an understanding of *symbolic process,* under which we shall include semantics, syntax-semiotics, and *semantic dynamics.* Thence we shall turn to the problem of *culture* and of a cultural *language* of which speech is only one small part; in short, we shall extend our earlier analysis of speech to all modes of social communication, regardless of whether they are verbal or nonverbal. Here we shall arrive at certain problems of semantic dynamics that refer to the economy of generic and specific classifications, which we shall study by appealing to certain features of the mental disease known as schizophrenia. By the end of this chapter we shall be able to define objectively what we mean by the term *personality* and also by the phrase *language and the structure of the personality.**

The inductive-deductive demonstration of the foregoing chapters will be used as the basis for a somewhat more relaxed discussion of the economy of the language of dreams and of art, with which we shall close Part One.

In Part Two we shall turn to the economy of human social behavior, for which we have laid the groundwork in Part One. Our treatment of the economy of human social behavior will be grouped around three main topics.

The first topic is the economy of geography, which we shall discuss in two chapters (Chapters 9 and 10). Chapter 9 will discuss inductively-deductively what is essentially a case of stable national equilibrium. Chapter 10 will discuss the problem of unstable intranational equilibrium, as well as the problem of stable and unstable international equilibrium.

Our second topic will be the distribution of economic power and social status, to which we shall devote Chapter 11. We shall begin with a consideration of nations as dominance-systems, and proceed thence to the question of relative dominance in the interactions of small groups.

Our third topic will be that of prestige symbols and vogues, which we shall consider in our closing Chapter 12, where we shall also seek to integrate Part Two with Part One. Indeed the end of Chapter 12 of Part Two will lead immediately to the very considerations with which we shall open our inductive-deductive demonstration in Chapter 2, to which we now turn.

---

* We may also have suggested to the professional mathematician that sufficient data are now available for a field that might conceivably be called *applied topology*.

CHAPTER TWO

ON THE ECONOMY OF WORDS

As we turn now for the remainder of our study to a demonstration of the Principle of Least Effort, we should keep in mind certain general considerations that will be helpful in guiding our steps. For example we should remember that if Least Effort is indeed fundamental in all human action, we may expect to find it in operation in any human action we might choose to study. In short, any human action will be a manifestation of the Principle of Least Effort in operation, if this Principle is true; therefore all human action is potentially grist for our mill.

In the interest of economy we shall select for our own demonstration first those particular kinds of human action which will most readily admit of the disclosure of the underlying Principle. That is, we shall strive constantly to approach and study our hypothetical Principle from what seems to us to be its most accessible side. For a scientific demonstration can be likened to mountain-climbing—a task in which the mountaineer may either select a path of easiest ascent if he is eager to reach the top, or where he may choose a path of pronounced obstacles if he desires primarily to impress others with his skill. In this study we shall select what seems to be the path of easiest ascent.

Our path is the one that begins with a study of human speech as a set of tools. More specifically, it begins with a study of a vocabulary of words as a set of tools.[1] The reason for selecting this as a beginning is, as we shall see, that the study of words offers a key to an understanding of the entire speech process, while the study of the entire speech process offers a key to an understanding of the personality and of the entire field of biosocial dynamics. Hence the contents of the present chapter will be of crucial importance for our entire study because in this chapter we shall untie a knot that we shall find duplicated again and again in other biosocial phenomena. The care and completeness with which we untie this first knot will render all future knots so much the easier to untie.*

I. IN MEDIAS RES: VOCABULARY USAGE, AND THE FORCES OF UNIFICATION AND DIVERSIFICATION

Man talks in order to get something. Hence man's speech may be likened to a set of tools that are engaged in achieving objectives. True, we do not yet know that whenever man talks, his speech is invariably directed to the

* For the sake of simplification we shall use the term *least effort* in the present chapter to apply not only to situations of least probable work, but also to situations in which the argument is restricted to immediate behavior, which is technically one of least work.

attainment of objectives. Nevertheless it is thus directed sufficiently often to justify our viewing speech as a likely example of a set of tools, which we shall assume to be the case.

Human speech is traditionally viewed as a succession of words to which "meanings" (or "usages") are attached. We have no quarrel with this traditional view which, in fact, we here adopt. Nevertheless in adopting this view of "words with meanings" we might profitably combine it with our previous view of speech as a set of tools, and state: *words are tools that are used to convey meanings in order to achieve objectives.*

Yet once we say that words are tools, we broach thereby the question of the possible economies of speech; and as soon as we inquire into the possible economies of speech we remember that the sheer ability to speak at all represents an enormous convenience in present-day human social activity, whereas the inability to speak is a signal handicap. Since both the conveniences of being able to speak, and the handicap of being unable to do so, refer admittedly to the saving of effort, we may say that there is a *potential general economy in the sheer existence of speech,* in the sense that some human objectives are more easily obtained with speech than without it. The case is similar to that of a set of carpenter's tools whose sheer existence may be said to have a potential general economy for the carpenter.

But beyond this potential general economy of speech there are further possibilities for economy in the manner in which speech is used. For if speech consists of words that are tools which convey meanings, there is the possibility both of a more economical way, and of a less economical way, to use word-tools for the purpose of conveying meanings. Hence in addition to the general economy of speech *there exists also the possibility of an internal economy of speech.*

Now if we concentrate our attention upon the possible internal economies of speech, we may hope to catch a glimpse of their inherent nature. Since it is usually felt that words are "combined with meanings" we may suspect that there is latent in speech both a more and a less economical way of "combining words with meanings," both from the viewpoint of the speaker and from that of the auditor.*

From the viewpoint of the speaker (the *speaker's economy*) who has the job of selecting not only the meanings to be conveyed but also the words that will convey them, there would doubtless exist an important latent economy in a vocabulary that consisted exclusively of one single word—a single word that would mean whatever the speaker wanted it to mean. Thus if there were m different meanings to be verbalized, this word would have m different meanings. For by having a single-word vocabulary the speaker would be spared the effort that is necessary to acquire and maintain a large vocabulary and to select particular words with particular meanings from this vocabulary. The single-word vocabulary, which reflects the *speaker's economy,* may be likened to an imaginary carpentry kit that consists of a single

* Later we shall define *a meaning* of a word as a *kind of response* that is invoked by the word.[2]

tool of such art that it can be used exclusively for all the *m* different tasks of sawing, hammering, drilling, and the like, thereby saving the labor of otherwise devising, maintaining, and using a more elaborate toolage.

But from the viewpoint of the auditor (the *auditor's economy*), a single-word vocabulary would represent the acme of verbal labor, since he would be faced by the impossible task of determining the particular meaning to which the single word in a given situation might refer. Indeed from the viewpoint of the auditor, who has the job of deciphering the speaker's meanings, the important internal economy of speech would be found rather in a vocabulary of such size that it possessed a distinctly different word for each different meaning to be verbalized. Thus if there were *m* different meanings, there would be *m* different words, with one meaning per word. This one-to-one correspondence between different words and different meanings, which represents the *auditor's economy,* would save effort for the auditor in his attempt to determine the particular meaning to which a given spoken word referred.*

As far as the problem of words and meanings is concerned, we note the presence of two farreaching contradictory economies that relate in each case to the number of different meanings that a word may have. Thus if there are an *m* number of different distinctive meanings to be verbalized, there will be (1) a *speaker's economy* in possessing a vocabulary of one word which will refer to all the *m* distinctive meanings; and there will also be (2) an opposing *auditor's economy* in possessing a vocabulary of *m* different words with *one* distinctive meaning for each word. Obviously the two opposing economies are in extreme conflict.

We may even visualize a given stream of speech as being subject to *two "opposing forces."* The one "force" (*the speaker's economy*) will tend to reduce the size of the vocabulary to a single word by unifying all meanings behind a single word; for that reason we may appropriately call it the *Force of Unification.* Opposed to this Force of Unification is a second "force" (*the auditor's economy*) that will tend to increase the size of a vocabulary to a point where there will be a distinctly different word for each different meaning. Since this second "force" will tend to increase the diversity of a vocabulary, we shall henceforth call it the *Force of Diversification.* In the language of these two terms we may say that the vocabulary of a given stream of speech is constantly subject to the opposing *Forces of Unification* and *Diversification* which will determine both the *n* number of actual words in the vocabulary, and also the meanings of those words.

In adopting the term *force* to describe the two opposite economies that

* Nor does the word need to be spoken; it may also be written. The situation of the writer-reader is analogous to that of the speaker-auditor in respect of internal economies of usage of words, even though a reader is not so immediately present to a writer as an auditor is to a speaker, and even though the word-usage of written speech may differ somewhat from that of spoken speech for reasons that we shall scout in a later chapter. If we continue for the time being to discuss words without dichotomizing between written and spoken verbalizations, we do so in the interest of a legitimate simplification which seems to be justified at the beginning of our analysis of words and their usage, as we think the reader will agree upon reflection.

are hypothetically latent in speech, we must remember that the term refers to what people will in fact do and not to what they are at liberty to do if they wish. For we are arguing that people do in fact always act with a maximum economy of effort, and that therefore in the process of speaking-listening they will automatically minimize the expenditure of effort. Our Forces of Unification and Diversification merely describe two opposite courses of action which from one point of view or the other are alike economical and permissible and which therefore from the combined viewpoints will alike be adopted in compromise. From this it follows that whenever a person uses words to convey meanings he will automatically try to get his ideas across most efficiently by seeking a balance between the economy of a small wieldy vocabulary of more general reference on the one hand, and the economy of a larger one of more precise reference on the other, with the result that the vocabulary of n different words in his resulting flow of speech will represent a *vocabulary balance* between our theoretical Forces of Unification and Diversification.*

II. THE QUESTION OF VOCABULARY BALANCE

We obviously do not yet know that there is in fact such a thing as *vocabulary balance* between our hypothetical Forces of Unification and Diversification, since we do not yet know that man invariably economizes with the expenditure of his effort; for that, after all, is what we are trying to prove. Nevertheless—and we shall enumerate for the sake of clarity—if (1) we assume explicitly that man does invariably economize with his effort, and if (2) the logic of our preceding analysis of a vocabulary balance between the two Forces is sound, then (3) we can test the validity of our explicit assumption of an economy of effort by appealing directly to the objective facts of some samples of actual speech that have served satisfactorily in communication. Insofar as (4) we may find therein evidence of a vocabulary balance of some sort in respect of our two Forces, then (5) we shall find *ipso facto* a confirmation of our assumption of (1) an economy of effort. Therefore much depends upon our ability to disclose some demonstrable cases of vocabulary balance in some actual samples of speech that have served satisfactorily in communication.

Fortunately, if a condition of vocabulary balance does exist in a given sample of speech, we shall have little difficulty in detecting it because of the very nature and direction of the two Forces involved. On the one hand, the Force of Unification will act in the direction of *decreasing* the *number* of different words to 1, while *increasing* the frequency of that 1 word to 100%. Conversely, the Force of Diversification will act in the opposite direction of *increasing* the *number* of different words, while *decreasing* their

* We shall consistently capitalize the terms, Force of Unification and Force of Diversification, in order to remind ourselves that these Forces do not represent forces as physicists traditionally understand the term, but only the natural consequences of our assumed underlying economy of effort. Moreover our term *balance* will include what are technically known as *steady states* and the *equilibria* of the physicist and of the economist.

average *frequency* of occurrence towards 1. Therefore *number* and *frequency* will be the parameters of vocabulary balance.

Since the number of different words in a sample of speech together with their respective frequencies of occurrences can be determined empirically, it is clear that our next step is to seek relevant empiric information about the number and frequency of occurrences of words in some actual samples of speech.

A. Empiric Evidence of Vocabulary Balance

James Joyce's novel *Ulysses,* with its 260,430 running words, represents a sizable sample of running speech that may fairly be said to have served successfully in the communication of ideas. An index to the number of different words therein, together with the actual frequencies of their respective occurrences, has already been made with exemplary methods by Dr. Miles L. Hanley and associates who have quite properly argued that all words are different which differ in any way "phonetically" in the fully inflected form in which they occur (thus the forms, *give, gives, gave, given, giving, giver, gift* represent seven different words and not one word in seven different forms).[3]

To the above published index has been added an appendix from the careful hands of Dr. M. Joos, in which is set forth all the quantitative information that is necessary for our present purposes. For Dr. Joos not only tells us that there are 29,899 different words in the 260,430 running words; he also ranks those words in the decreasing order of their frequency of occurrence and tells us the actual frequency, f, with which the different ranks, r, occur. By consulting this appendix we find, for example, that the 10th most frequent word ($r = 10$) occurs 2,653 times ($f = 2{,}653$); or that the 100th word ($r = 100$) occurs 265 times ($f = 265$). In fact, the appendix tells us the actual frequency of occurrence, f, of any rank, r, from $r = 1$ to $r = 29{,}899$, which is the terminal rank of the list, since the *Ulysses* contains only that number of different words.

It is evident that the relationship between the various ranks, r, of these words and their respective frequencies, f, is potentially quite instructive about the entire matter of vocabulary balance, not only because it involves the *frequencies* with which the different words occur but also because the terminal rank of the list tells us the *number of different* words in the sample. And we remember that both the *frequencies of occurrence* and the *number of different words* will be important factors in the counterbalancing of the Forces of Unification and Diversification in the hypothetical vocabulary balance of any sample of speech.

Turning to the quantitative data of the Hanley *Index* we can see from the arbitrarily selected ranks and frequencies in the adjoining Table 2–1 that the relationship between r and f in Joyce's *Ulysses* is by no means haphazard. For if we multiply each rank, r, in Column I of Table 2–1 by its corresponding frequency, f, in Column II, we obtain a product, C, in Column III, which is approximately the same size for all the different ranks and which, as we see in Column IV, represents approximately $1/10$ of the

260,430 running words which constitute the total length of James Joyce's *Ulysses*. Indeed, as far as Table 2–1 is concerned, we have found a clearcut correlation between the number of different words in the *Ulysses* and the frequency of their usage, in the sense that they approximate the simple equation of an equilateral hyperbola:

$$r \times f = C$$

in which r refers to the word's rank in the *Ulysses* and f to its frequency of occurrence (as we ignore for the present the size of C).

TABLE 2–1

Arbitrary Ranks with Frequencies in James Joyce's *Ulysses* (Hanley Index)

I Rank (r)	II Frequency (f)	III Product of I and II ($r \times f = C$)	IV Theoretical Length of Ulysses ($C \times 10$)
10	2,653	26,530	265,500
20	1,311	26,220	262,200
30	926	27,780	277,800
40	717	28,680	286,800
50	556	27,800	278,800
100	265	26,500	265,000
200	133	26,600	266,000
300	84	25,200	252,000
400	62	24,800	248,000
500	50	25,000	250,000
1,000	26	26,000	260,000
2,000	12	24,000	240,000
3,000	8	24,000	240,000
4,000	6	24,000	240,000
5,000	5	25,000	250,000
10,000	2	20,000	200,000
20,000	1	20,000	200,000
29,899	1	29,899	298,990

The data of this table give clear evidence of the existence of a vocabulary balance.

We must not forget that Table 2–1 contains only a few selected items out of a possible 29,899; hence the question is legitimate as to the possible rank-frequency relationship between the rest of the 29,899 different words. Although we cannot easily present in tabular form the rank-frequency relationships of all these different words, we nevertheless can present them quite conveniently on a graph, because we know that the equation, $r \times f = C$, will appear on doubly logarithmic chart paper as a succession of points descending in a straight line from left to right at an angle of 45°. And if we plot the ranks and frequencies of the 29,899 different words on doubly logarithmic chart paper, and if the points fall on a straight line descending from left to right at an angle of 45° we may argue that the rank-frequency distribution of the entire vocabulary of the *Ulysses* follows the equation, $r \times f = C$, and suggests the presence of a vocabulary balance throughout.[4]

As to the details of the graphical plotting of this particular equation (which will be repeated again and again throughout our study) we shall plot successive ranks from 1 through 29,899 horizontally on the X-axis, or abscissa. Then, in measuring frequency on the *Y*-axis, or ordinate, we

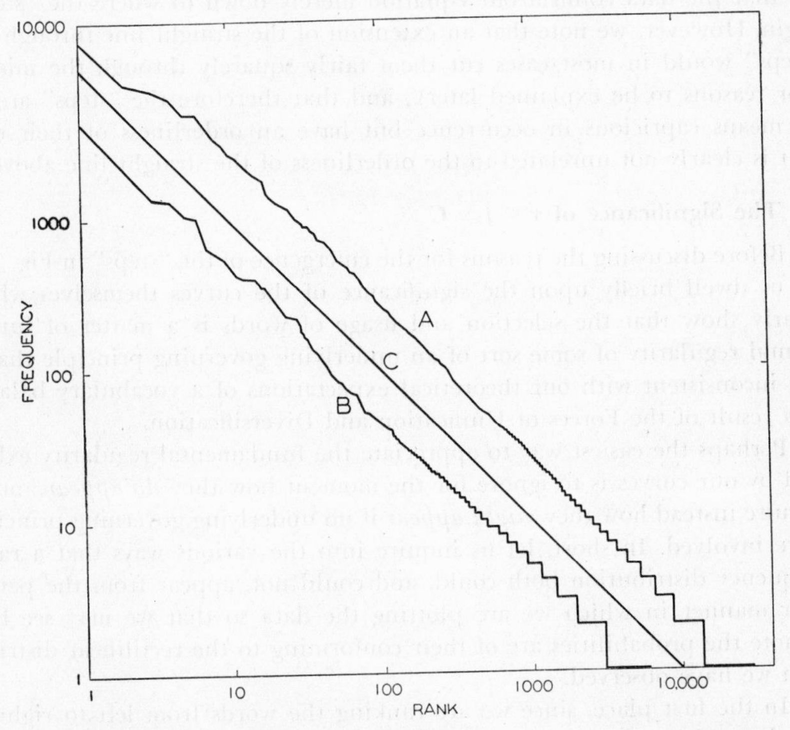

Fig. 2–1. The rank-frequency distribution of words. (A) The James Joyce data; (B) the Eldridge data; (C) ideal curve with slope of negative unity.

shall give for each rank a dot which corresponds to the actual frequency of occurrence of the word of that rank. After we have completed our graphing of the actual frequencies of our 29,899 ranked words, we shall connect the dots with a continuous line in order to note whether the line is straight, and whether it descends from left to right at the expected angle of 45°.

In Fig. 2–1 we present in Curve *A* the data of the entire *Ulysses* thus plotted, and the reader can assess for himself the closeness with which this curve descends from left to right in a straight line at an angle of 45°. In order to suggest that the *Ulysses* is not unique in respect of a *hyperbolic rank-frequency word distribution,* we include gratuitously in Curve *B* of Fig. 2–1 the rank-frequency distribution of the 6,002 different words in fully inflected form as they appear in a total of 43,989 running words of combined samples from American newspapers as analyzed by R. C. Eldridge.[5] Curve C is an ideal curve of 45° slope that has been added to aid the reader's eye.

Clearly the curves of Fig. 2–1 conform with considerable closeness to a straight line with the expected slope of 45°, except for the emergence of "steps" of progressively increasing size as the line approaches the bottom. Although we shall shortly see that these "steps" result from integral frequencies and are governed by the equation, $r \times f = C$, we may now only say that the data confirm our equation merely down to where the "steps" begin. However, we note that an extension of the straight line through the "steps" would in most cases cut them fairly squarely through the middle (for reasons to be explained later), and that therefore the "steps" are by no means capricious in occurrence but have an orderliness of their own that is clearly not unrelated to the orderliness of the straight line above.

B. The Significance of $r \times f = C$

Before discussing the reasons for the emergence of the "steps" in Fig. 2–1, let us dwell briefly upon the significance of the curves themselves which clearly show that the selection and usage of words is a matter of fundamental regularity of some sort of an underlying governing principle that is not inconsistent with our theoretical expectations of a vocabulary balance as a result of the Forces of Unification and Diversification.

Perhaps the easiest way to appreciate the fundamental regularity exhibited by our curves is to ignore for the moment how they *do appear* and to inquire instead how they *might appear* if no underlying governing principle were involved. In short, let us inquire into the various ways that a rank-frequency distribution both could, and could not, appear from the particular manner in which we are plotting the data so that we may see how remote the probabilities are of their conforming to the rectilinear distribution we have observed.

In the first place, since we are ranking the words from left to right in the decreasing order frequency, it is evident that the line that connects the succession of dots can at no point bend upwards, since an upward bend at any point would indicate an incorrect ranking of the data according to *decreasing* frequencies. On the other hand, the line can and, in fact, will proceed horizontally whenever adjacent ranks have precisely the same frequencies (as happens to be the case with the horizontal lines of the "steps" at the bottom of the curves of Fig. 2–1, as we shall presently see). Hence we may predict in advance that any rank-frequency distribution may never slope upward from left to right although it may be horizontal. But that is not all. We may also predict that a rank-frequency curve will never bend downwards in a true vertical, since the line must pass from left to right in order to connect the dots of adjacent ranks. The apparently vertical lines of the "steps" of Fig. 2–1 are not truly vertical, since they do in fact connect adjacent dots. On the other hand, as long as the line never becomes a true vertical, it can bend downwards with any slope at any point.

As far as our method of plotting our data is concerned, we may say in advance that the line proceeding from left to right in a rank-frequency distribution *may* twist and turn at any point on the graph paper as long as it *never* bends upwards and *never* bends downwards in a true vertical. In this connection the reader might take a pencil and paper and draw lines of various configurations and contortions that connect the upper left-hand corner with the lower right-hand corner—lines that avoid upward bends and true verticals—in order to assure himself of the vast number of possibilities that lie within the restrictions of our method of plotting. After completing his "random lines" the reader will appreciate the orderliness of the lines of Fig. 2–1; and he will see how this orderliness points to the existence of a fundamental governing principle that determines the number and frequency of usage of the words in the stream of speech, regardless of whether or not the speakers and auditors are aware of the existence of the principle, and regardless of whether or not our Forces of Unification and Diversification in vocabulary balance provide a necessary explanation of it. Since all the words of Fig. 2–1 had "meanings" in their respective samples, the reader may infer from the orderliness of the distribution of words that there may well be a corresponding orderliness in the distribution of meanings because, in general, speakers utter words in order to convey meanings.

III. THE ORDERLY DISTRIBUTION OF MEANINGS

Taking a temporary leave of the distribution of words in Fig. 2–1, let us now turn our attention to the question of the distribution of the *meanings* of words. We have previously argued that under the conflicting Forces of Unification and Diversification the m number of different meanings to be verbalized will be distributed in such a way that on the one hand no single word will have all m different meanings and that on the other hand there will be fewer than m different words. As a consequence, we may expect that at least some words must have multiple meanings. There remains then the problem of determining, first, which words will have multiple meanings and, second, how many different meanings these words of multiple meaning will have. In the solution of this problem, the Forces of Unification and Diversification will stand us in good stead.

Let us begin by turning our attention to the most frequently used word in the stream of speech, with special reference to the actual samples of Fig. 2–1. We shall arbitrarily designate the frequency of this most frequent word with the letter, F_1. The question now remains as to the m_1 number of different meanings which are represented by F_1. And here we may say that, regardless of the size of m_1, if we multiply m_1 by f_1, which represents the *average frequency of occurrence* of the m_1 meanings, we shall obtain F_1, since F_1 is made up of the total frequencies of its different meanings. Therefore we may write:

$$m_1 \times f_1 = F_1$$

With this simple equation in mind, let us recall our previously discussed Forces of Unification and Diversification and inquire into their respective influences upon the sizes of m_1 and f_1. Obviously, the Force of Unification which theoretically acts in the direction of putting all different meanings behind a single word will tend to increase the size of m_1 at the expense of the size of f_1. On the other hand, the Force of Diversification which theoretically acts in the direction of reducing the number of different meanings per word will tend to increase f_1 at the expense of m_1. Therefore the respective sizes of m_1 and f_1 of our previous equation will again represent the action of the opposing Forces of Unification and Diversification.

Of course, we do not know *a priori* what the comparative strength of these two Forces may be. Yet we have observed from the data of Fig. 2–1 that there is a hyperbolic relationship between the n number of different words in the samples and their respective frequencies of occurrence. Therefore we may suspect that our two Forces of Unification and Diversification stand, in general, in a hyperbolic relationship to one another, with the result that m_1 and f_1 will also stand in a hyperbolic relationship with one another, with the further result that m_1 will tend to equal f_1.

However if m_1 equals f_1 and since $m_1 \times f_1 = F_1$, then clearly m_1 will equal the square root of F_1, or $\sqrt{F_1}$.

But now let us note that the above argument will apply *mutatis mutandis* to the m_r number of different meanings of the word whose comparative frequency of occurrence is F_r, with the result that the following simple equation may be expected:

$$m_r = \sqrt{F_r}$$

This simple equation is of interest, for it means that if (1) we make a rank-frequency distribution of the words of a sample of speech, as was done for the *Ulysses* and Eldridge data of Fig. 2–1, and if (2) we find that this distribution yields the straight line of an equilateral hyperbola as found in Fig. 2–1, then (3) we may conclude from the nature of the above argument and equation that a rank-frequency distribution of the different meanings of those words on doubly logarithmic paper would yield *a straight line descending from left to right to the point, X = n,* yet *intercepting only ½ as much on the Y-axis as on the X-axis* (*that is, it will have what is technically called a negative slope of ½,* or *of* .5). The reason for this is that the m_r number of different meanings for each of the r-ranked words will be represented on doubly logarithmic paper by a point that is in each case ½ of the F_r of the respective ranked words. We shall call this the theoretical *law-of-meaning distribution.*

To determine empirically whether this theoretical law-of-meaning distribution exists, we could take the data of Fig. 2–1 and, after consulting a suitable dictionary, we could graph the m_r number of different meanings for each r different word, and note the resulting meaning-frequency distribution. The resulting meaning-frequency distribution would refer only to the particular *Ulysses* and Eldridge word-frequency distributions, and therefore would lack a more general applicability.

It would be of more general applicability and equally valid for our purposes if we selected the more comprehensive word-frequency distribution of

English as made and published by E. L. Thorndike on the basis of a count of 10 million running words.[6] Although Dr. Thorndike has published only the 20,000 most frequent words of his count, nevertheless these 20,000 words will represent the average frequencies of standard English better than the particularized vocabularies of the data of Fig. 2–1. It is true that Dr. Thorndike has for the most part ignored the inflectional endings of words; instead he has subsumed the frequencies of occurrence of practically all different inflectional forms of a given word under the dictionary form of that word (i.e., he used what is technically known as a *lexical unit*) ; however we have no reason to suppose that any "law of meanings" would be seriously distorted if we concentrated our attention upon *lexical units* and simply ignored variations in number, case, or tense. Nor need we be disturbed by the fact that Dr. Thorndike did not list the actual frequencies of the different words but merely noted the 1st thousand most frequent, the 2nd thousand most frequent, and so on down through the 20th thousand most frequent, with a further notation of whether a given word of the first 5000 words was among the first or second 500 words of its respective thousand. This lack of a precise numerical notation—far from invalidating his count —offers a genuine challenge to our thesis. For (1) if we are correct in generalizing upon the data of Fig. 2–2 by stating that the distributions are representative of English, and (2) if our theoretical *law-of-meaning distribution* be correct, then we may suspect, both (3) that Thorndike's 20,000 words would follow a hyperbolic rank-frequency distribution of words and (4) that the distribution of meanings of the 20,000 words when plotted on doubly logarithmic graph paper will yield a negative slope of .5 as previously explained. Therefore we may test our theoretical law-of-meaning distribution by turning directly to an analysis of the average m number of different meanings per word in each of the 20 successive sets of one thousand words.

Fortunately for the analysis of the meanings of the 20,000 words, we have available the *Thorndike-Century Dictionary* which selected the m different meanings to be presented for each word (*except for the 500 most frequent*) on the objective basis of Dr. Irving Lorge's *The English Semantic Count*.[7] Hence the m number of actually used different meanings for each word in the dictionary has been determined empirically, with the result that in making our meaning-frequency analysis we need not fear including archaic or obsolescent meanings which might well distort our distribution.

Thanks to the help of some of my students, who undertook the task of noting the number of different meanings in Thorndike's dictionary for each of the 20,000 words of the list, we present in Fig. 2–2 the average number of meanings per word (on the ordinate) for each successive set of 1000 words on the abscissa. Since the *average number of meanings per word* in each thousand refers in fact to the 500th word (or class-middle) of each thousand, the points on the abscissa represent these class-middles in all cases; that is, they represent the values of the 500th, 1500th, 2500th, . . . 19,500th words respectively.

A glance at the data of Fig. 2–2 suffices to show that the points descend in a strikingly straight line which is not far off from our theoretically expected negative slope of .5 (i.e., — .5). If we calculate by least squares the slope of the best straight line through the points, we arrive at the value — .4605 (± .0083) with the *Y*-intercept at 18.05 (antilog). This calculated value is not far off from our expected — .5 slope.[8]

The approximation may be even closer than that if we remember that *The English Semantic Count* was not used for the 500 most frequent words (whose differentiation of meanings is truly difficult for reasons that will be apparent in our following chapter). Because of this consideration the first point at the left of our chart is suspect. If we ignore it and recalculate the slope for the remaining 19 points we have a slope of — .4656 (± .0027), which is slightly nearer to the expected — .5 slope.

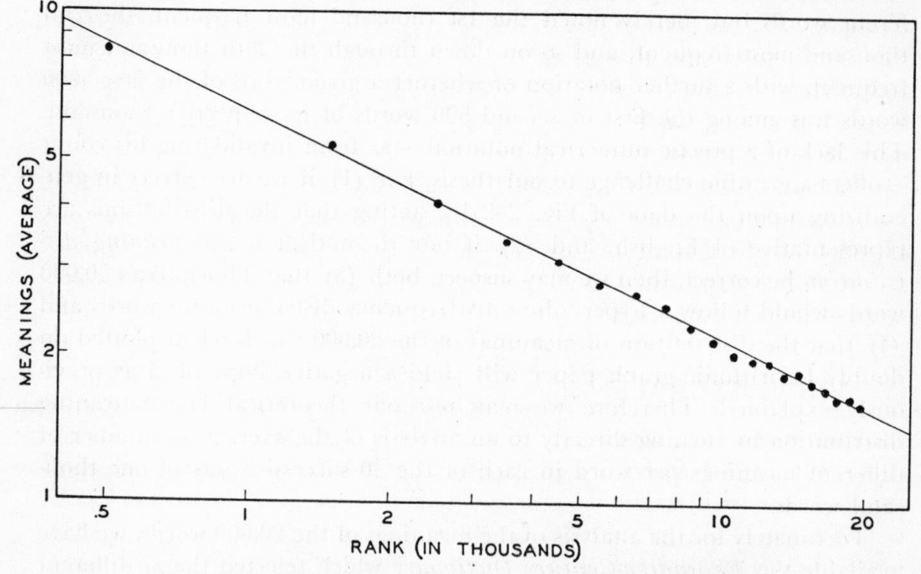

Fig. 2–2. The meaning-frequency distribution of words.

If we turn our attention now to the 10 successive sets of 500 words which constitute the 5000 most frequent words in the list, and if we again ignore the suspected first 500 words for reasons already presented, we have a slope of — .4899 (± .0030), with which we may scarcely quarrel as an approximation of a — .5 slope.*

It is of course regrettable that additional sets of data on this important point are not available. Nevertheless the results of even this one study are so striking that pending the future findings of empiric analysis we are not rash in concluding that a *law-of-meaning distribution* exists according to which the *m* average number of meanings per word of a thousand words (when ranked in the order of decreasing frequency) will equal the square

* This slope is probably the most reliable, since it refers to the most frequent 10,000 words that are likely to be found in an *optimum sample* of 100,000 running words. For a discussion of an *optimum sample* see below.

root of the average frequency of the words' occurrence (or will decrease according to the square root of the rank).

Although later we shall again return to the entire question of the "meanings of words" with the problem of defining the term *meaning*,[9] we may even now feel that our theoretical Forces of Unification and Diversification have led us to the empiric disclosure not only of a simple equation for the distribution of words (in the form, $r \times f = C$, with r an integer) but also of a simple equation for the distribution of the meanings of those words which may be put down in the form of the equation, $m_r = \sqrt{F_r}$, in which $F_r = C_r$.

Incidentally, the fact that we have no actual rank-frequency distribution for the 20,000 words of Dr. Thorndike's frequency list does not invalidate our above conclusion; on the contrary, we shall present so many word-rank-frequency distributions in our following pages that the reader will be more than ready to believe that, if we had a rank-frequency distribution of the 20,000 most frequent words of the Thorndike analysis, it would probably be rectilinear like those of Fig. 2–1, at least for the first 10 or 12 thousand most frequent words.

With the assurance of the *law-of-meaning distribution* of Fig. 2–2, let us return now to a study of the significance of the rectilinear distributions of Fig. 2–1, which descend with a negative slope of 1 except for the "steps" of increasing magnitude at the bottom, and which indicate the existence of a *vocabulary balance.*

IV. THE INTEGRALITY OF FREQUENCIES

Some pages back we implied that the "steps" at the bottom of the two curves of Fig. 2–1 emerge as a natural consequence of the fact that words cannot occur with fractional frequencies. Since "steps" of this sort will be found in the graphs of following chapters, we may profitably digress at this point to show the more precise relationship between the sizes of these "steps" and the equation, $r \times f = C$.

As far as the "steps" themselves are concerned, the upright lines (or "risers") are of no significance, since they merely connect the last dot of the horizontal line above with the first dot of the horizontal line below, and have been added to aid the reader's eye. On the other hand, the horizontal lines (or "treads") of the "steps" are quite significant, since they represent the number of different words, or ranks, that occur with the same frequency. Thus the horizontal line of Curve A that hugs the abscissa represents the 16,432 different words that occur one time in the *Ulysses;* the horizontal line of the next "step" above represents the 4,776 words that occur twice; the third horizontal represents the 2,194 words that occur three times, and so on up until the horizontal lines become so short that they no longer appear.

The reason for these horizontal lines becomes obvious if we remember that the frequency with which a word occurs can only be integral (or a whole number) in any actual sample of speech. Thus, in any actual sample of speech, a word can occur 1, 2, 3 or some other whole number of times but not $1\frac{1}{2}$, $2\frac{1}{3}$, $3\frac{1}{4}$ or any other fractional number of times. Yet since our equation, $r \times f = C$, as stated, will theoretically necessitate the fractional occurrences of words which are impossible in practice, it is quite evident that there will be no actual rank-frequency dots on those portions of the descending diagonal line which lie between integral frequencies (e.g., between 2 and 3). Instead it is quite conceivable that those frequencies which *theoretically should occur* with fractional frequencies *will actually occur* with the nearest integral frequency. That is, for example, those words which theoretically should occur from $2\frac{1}{2}$ to $3\frac{1}{2}$ times, according to the equation $r \times f = C$, will actually occur 3 times, since 3 is the nearest integral frequency. And that would also mean that the straight diagonal line above, if extended to the bottom, would cut approximately through the center of the horizontal lines of these steps, as an inspection of Fig. 2–1 shows is more or less the case. Hence the emergence of these "steps" is merely a natural consequence of the equation, $r \times f = C$, in terms of integral frequencies.

Indeed the equation, $r \times f = C$, which is responsible for the emergence of the "steps," will also determine both the positions and the sizes of the various "steps," as we shall now illustrate.

For it can be shown (and has been shown elsewhere) [10] that the N number of different words of the same f-integral frequency of occurrence (under the conditions of the equation, $r \times f = C$) will be inversely proportionate to the square of their frequency (approximately)—or, stated somewhat more precisely in equation form, that:

$$N\,(f^2 - \tfrac{1}{4}) = C$$

However instead of interrupting our demonstration in order to derive this new equation mathematically from the hyperbolic equation, $r \times f = C$, let us simply argue that if this new equation is true, we may expect to find in Joyce's *Ulysses* that when we multiply the N number of actual words of like f frequency of occurrence by the square of that frequency minus the constant $\frac{1}{4}$ [that is, when we multiply N by $(f^2 - \frac{1}{4})$], the resulting products will approximate the constant, C. And since the necessary data for this multiplication are available, let us proceed to it forthwith.

In Table 2–2 we present the actual products of our multiplication of the above factors for 15 arbitrarily selected frequency classes in the *Ulysses* (Column II); and also gratuitously for four Latin plays by Plautus (Column III), which we add for good measure to suggest that this number-frequency relationship is not uniquely characteristic of English.[11]

Inspecting in turn each of the two columns, II and III, of Table 2–2, we find that the calculated values of each column are approximately the same for the entire column, with the exception of the lowest two frequencies of the *Ulysses*. This means that both the *Ulysses* and the four plays of Plautus have approximately the number of different words of like frequency for the selected frequency-classes that we should expect theoretically on the basis of our equation. And that means in turn, more specifically for the *Ulysses*, that the horizontal lines of the "steps" of Fig. 2–1 are approximately of the right length to satisfy the equation $r \times f = C$ in the sense that the words which theoretically would have a fractional frequency do in fact have the nearest integral frequency.*

Since a more complete presentation of the above relationship is possible on a graph, we present in Fig. 2–3 the data for the frequency-classes from 1 through 50 for (*A*) the *Ulysses,* with each circle indicating the N number of different words (measured logarithmically on the abscissa) of

TABLE 2–2

The Number-Frequency Relationship, $N(f^2 - \frac{1}{4}) = C$, of (I) some Arbitrary Lower Frequencies of (II) Joyce's *Ulysses* and (III) four Latin plays of Plautus.

I Frequency (f)	Calculated $N(f^2 - \frac{1}{4})$	
	II Ulysses	III Plautus
1	12,324	4,075
2	15,410	4,490
3	19,193	4,280
4	20,239	4,750
5	22,424	3,985
6	22,773	4,504
7	23,546	4,241
8	23,651	4,399
9	24,063	4,366
10	22,145	4,289
15	21,576	2,922
20	27,844	5,996
30	18,000	3,600
40	25,600	4,800
50	22,500	5,000

like frequency, f (measured logarithmically on the ordinate). For full measure, we add gratuitously a set of data (*B*) for the same frequency-classes for a non-English language—this time for the Homeric Greek of the *Iliad* (plotted in black dots) as determined from Prendergast's *Concordance* [12] thereto by the patient and careful hands of my former student,

* The size of C of Column II of Table 2–2 should be the same as the size of C in Table 2–1 which was about 26,000. The slight difference between the two is ascribable to the fact that there is a very slight bend at the top and bottom of the *Ulysses* curve.

Dr. Harold D. Rose. (The Plautine material has already been published in full elsewhere.)

Inspecting the two curves of Fig. 2–3, we note that in each case they descend from left to right, on the whole, in such a fashion that the *X*-intercept is twice that of the *Y*-intercept, as is to be expected from the exponent, *2*, in $N\ (f^2 - \frac{1}{4}) = C$.* Dr. Joos informed me privately (September 16, 1937) that the calculated exponent of the *Ulysses data* falls between *1.99* and *2.01!* According to his calculation (Language XII [1936] 199) the least-square exponent for the Plautus data of Table 2–2 is *1.98*. These are remark-

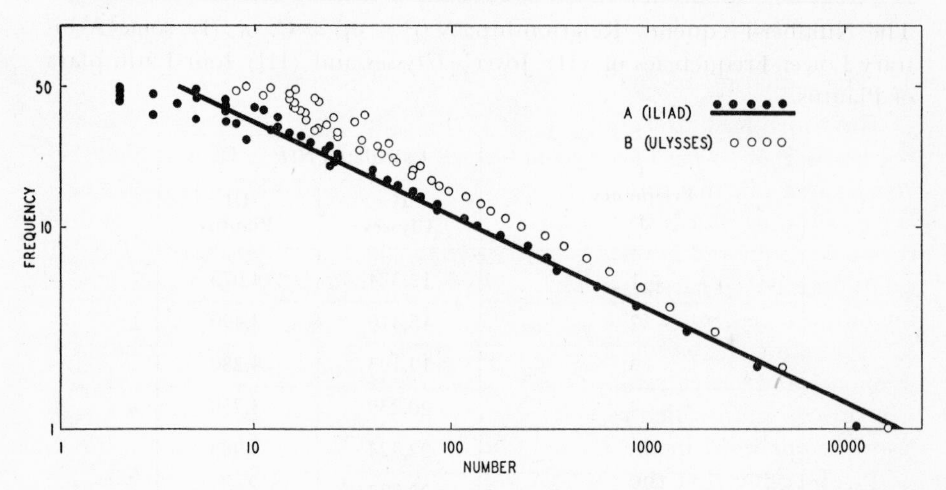

Fig. 2–3. The number-frequency relationship of words. (A) Homer's *Iliad;* (B) James Joyce's *Ulysses.*

ably close approximations to our theoretically expected 2. My least-square calculation of the *Iliad data* of Fig. 2–3 is 2.15 ± 501.†

In view of the orderly nature of the "steps" that emerge in a rank-frequency distribution of words, we may say that the two curves, *A* and *B*, of Fig. 2–1 closely approximate the equation of an equilateral hyperbola. Moreover, the gratuitously added information about the number, *N*, of words of like frequency in the lower frequency-range of other languages suffices to assure us that "vocabulary balance," in the sense of a general orderliness of word distributions, is not peculiar to English. In our following chapter we shall present further rank-frequency distributions from samples of many other languages, as we return again and again to a consideration of the Forces of Unification and Diversification. For the time being, however, we shall study the special case of English, which will also tell us much about the nature of *vocabulary balance* in general.

---

* We remember that the difference between f^2 and $f^2 - \frac{1}{4}$ is important only for very small values of *f*. Thus when *f* is even as large as *4*, the difference between f^2 and $f^2 - \frac{1}{4}$ is only a difference between 16 and 15¾. With $f = 10$, the difference is between 100 and 99¾.

† Since Prendergast does not give the frequencies of the most frequent words in the *Iliad* we cannot plot its rank-frequency distribution.

V. THE INTEGRALITY OF RANK

The rank that a word has must also be an integral number. Thus there may be a 1st, 2nd, or 3rd rank, but not one that is 1½, 2⅓, 3⅕ or any other non-whole number. This fact leads us to a very curious consideration, since our equation, $r \times f = C$, makes no provision for the integrality of r. Indeed, as far as this equation is concerned, both r and f may take on all values from positive to negative infinity which, in terms of speech, would be unthinkable. Hence the equation of the equilateral hyperbola is inadequate as a final description of what we have found. Let us now find a more adequate equation.

A. The Equation of the Harmonic Series

If we turn back to Table 2–1 and inspect the items of Column IV under the heading of *"The Theoretical Length of the Ulysses"* we note that the various items in this column approximate 260,430, which is the total number of running words in the novel. That is, when we multiply by 10 the constant, C (of $r \times f = C$), we arrive at the approximate total number of running words. That fact leads us now to an obvious and instructive consideration about *ranks* and *frequencies* which we have hitherto ignored.

In ranking the words of Joyce's *Ulysses* in the decreasing order of their frequencies, we have ranked them according to the simple integral series, 1, 2, 3, . . . n, in which n represents the terminal rank of the 29,899th and last different word in the Ulysses sample.

In observing that the product of a word's rank, r, when multiplied by its frequency, f, is a constant, C, (according to the equation $r \times f = C$), we may conclude at once that the different frequencies, f, of these ranked words will decrease in the order of the proportions of the following simple *harmonic series:*

$$1, \tfrac{1}{2}, \tfrac{1}{3}, \ldots 1/n$$

since every frequency, f, when multiplied by its rank, r, will yield a constant.

Now this harmonic series is interesting. For if we say that F represents the actual frequency of the most frequent word (i.e., the word whose $r = 1$), then it follows that F/r will be the actual frequency of any word of rank, r. Thus, for example, the 10th most frequent word (i.e., $r = 10$) will have the frequency $F/10$, and the nth most frequent word (i.e., $r = n$) will have the frequency, F/n.

Indeed, we may view the entire *Ulysses* as consisting of the following approximate sum of the n number of different words in terms of F and ranked in the order of decreasing frequency:

$$Ulysses = \frac{F}{1} + \frac{F}{2} + \frac{F}{3} + \cdots + \frac{F}{n}$$

an equation in which the denominators of the above fractions refer to the successive ranks of the respective words, and where $n = 29{,}899$.

But at this point a curious consideration arises. Since we may infer from Table 2–1 that the total number of running words in Joyce's novel is approximately equal to 10 times the frequency, F, of the word whose rank is one (i.e., $1 \times F \times 10 =$ about 260,000), we may say that $10F$ is approximately the length of *Ulysses.* Indeed we may even make the following approximate equation about all the words in the *Ulysses:*

$$10F = \frac{F}{1} + \frac{F}{2} + \frac{F}{3} + \cdot \cdot \cdot + \frac{F}{n}$$

When we inspect this equation, we note that in the last analysis we have merely multiplied by F the underlying simple equation:

$$10 = 1 + \frac{1}{2} + \frac{1}{3} + \cdot \cdot \cdot + \frac{1}{n}$$

and that, in turn, means that the *constant,* 10, of Column IV of Table 2–1 represents nothing more than the sum of the n harmonically seriated fractions of the right-hand member of the above equation.

Now the n fractions of a harmonic series, when added together, will yield a sum. This sum of the n members of a harmonic series can be represented technically by Sn (which means the sum, S, of the n members of the series). The size of Sn will obviously depend upon the size of n (i.e., the number of fractions added), with the result that we can calculate the approximate size of any Sn if we know the size of n (and vice versa).

But at this point we must be careful. Though the actual value, $Sn = 10$, may be significant for our understanding of *Ulysses*—and the same constant is found to be approximately descriptive of the Eldridge newspaper material of Fig. 2–1—nevertheless the particular value, $Sn = 10$, is of no vital significance for our understanding either of the harmonic series or of the equation, $r \times f = C$, or ultimately of the Forces of Unification and Diversification or the Principle of Least Effort that assumedly lies behind them. The size of Sn merely tells us the size of n (the number of different words that are used). Values other than 10 would do equally well. Indeed in Chapter Four we shall find that the limited vocabularies of children have an Sn that is characteristically smaller than 10. Therefore, in order to avoid relating our Harmonic Equation to any particular value of Sn, we shall present it in the following general form, which will suffice to describe many of our future sets of data:

$$F \cdot Sn = \frac{F}{1} + \frac{F}{2} + \frac{F}{3} + \cdot \cdot \cdot + \frac{F}{n}$$

Graphically, this preceding *Equation of the Harmonic Series* will appear as a succession of dots which, if connected by a line as in Fig. 2–1, will descend from left to right at an angle of 45° (technically a negative slope of 1) like the curves of Fig. 2–1. The size of Sn merely helps to locate the point on the X-axis which the rectilinear curve will intercept: the larger the size of Sn, the farther to the right the straight line will be located on the graph. Moreover, if we postulate that the above Harmonic Equation is *saturated* when the line intercepts equal distances on the X-axis and on the Y-axis (and this is important) then we may say algebraically that the above Harmonic Equation in saturated form refers to a condition in which $F = n$, or, if one will, in which $\frac{F}{n} = 1$. And that means, in turn, that the nth word occurs only a single time in the sample.

Now this Harmonic Equation in saturated form (hereinafter abbreviated to $F \cdot Sn$) offers a more faithful description of the approximate data of Fig. 2–1 than was the case with the hyperbolic equation, $r \times f = C$. For the Harmonic Equation, $F \cdot Sn$, tells us that r must be integral; and from it we can easily anticipate mathematically the "steps" that will emerge naturally from the fact that frequencies, f, can only be whole numbers.

And so let us remember that whenever in the future we find a rank-frequency distribution which, when plotted as in Fig. 2–1, reveals a slope of -1 (i.e., with the Y-intercept equal to the X-intercept) then we may infer that the distribution is that of the saturated harmonic series with $F = n$.

B. The Question of Sample Size and the Closure of Speech

Although we have already proceeded quite far in our analysis of the number and frequencies of occurrences of words, there remains one basic problem to which we shall now turn—the problem of the *optimum-size* of the sample of speech to be examined—that is, when the size of the sample is "just right" and not "too long" nor "too short." The nature of this problem can perhaps be most easily elucidated if we express it in terms of a simple mechanical tuning-fork analogy in which n different tuning-forks will represent our n different words, and where the frequencies, f, of the different forks will correspond to the frequencies, f, of our words.

Let us imagine that we have a long board on which are attached n number of different tuning-forks of such sizes that during a T interval of time they will all vibrate respectively according to the saturated harmonic equation, with $F = n$, *viz.:*

$$F \cdot Sn = \frac{F}{1} + \frac{F}{2} + \frac{F}{3} + \cdot \cdot \cdot + \frac{F}{n}$$

Thus far the group-behavior of our tuning-forks during a T interval will correspond to that of a vocabulary of words in the stream of speech, if we ignore momentarily as unessential the fact that the tuning-forks represent a synchronous phenomenon in the sense that they all vibrate at once, whereas the stream of speech is a diachronous phenomenon in the sense that only one word can be uttered at a time. The chief didactic value of this mechanical analogue will appear when we vibrate the board for a t-interval that is either shorter than T or longer than T.

If we vibrate it for a t-interval that is appreciably shorter than T, then the resulting frequency-distribution of the group-vibrations will be far removed from that of the saturated harmonic equation, $F \cdot Sn$, if only because the forks of lower frequencies will not have had time to round out their allotted few vibrations. Turning to the phenomena of words, we may remark that the same relationship will obtain also for an excessively short sample of speech—say 100 words—in which even some of the most frequent words might conceivably have no opportunity to repeat, not to mention the more rarely occurring ones which might not be able to occur at all. From so short a sample, in which most words would occur only once at best, we could scarcely detect the fundamental harmonic seriation which would only emerge as the size of the sample of running words approached that of $F \cdot Sn$.

On the other hand, if we extended the interval of vibration of the forks beyond T to $T + t$, we should overshoot the saturated series, $F \cdot Sn$. For although the summated vibrations during the T portion of the $T + t$ interval would represent the proportions of our equation, $F \cdot Sn$, nevertheless the summated vibrations during the entire $T + t$ interval might well yield graphically a very bent and distorted rank-frequency distribution (although much will depend upon the size of t). And similarly with an $F \cdot Sn + a$ sample of running words.*

Hence the $F \cdot Sn$ sample-length of words, like the T period of vibration of the tuning-forks, represents an *optimum* length in which the saturated harmonic equation will precisely reveal itself. Although we shall not tarry at this point to ask how a rank-frequency distribution might appear graphically if the sample deviates markedly from *optimum size,* we admit that it is extremely fortunate that early empiricists happened to examine samples of speech whose length approached *optimum size*. For if they had selected samples of very small or of very large sizes, the rectilinear rank-frequency relationship might have been disclosed only with great difficulty.†

Now that we have stressed the obvious—namely, that the harmonic equation that involves $F \cdot Sn$ running words will appear with close approximation only in samples whose lengths closely approximate $F \cdot Sn$ running words—let us proceed a step further. If the number and frequencies of words in the stream of speech are the resultants of the opposing Forces of Unification and Diversification (or of any other "forces" for that matter), then the *interval* of $F \cdot Sn$ running words may well have dynamic meaning as a unit, in reference to which a given speaker may be said to talk "too little" or "too much." That is, if we explicitly *assume* that the harmonic seriation, $F \cdot Sn$, represents a fundamental principle that governs the number and frequency of usages of words in speech, then we can only conclude that a given speaker "naturally" selects both the topics of his conversations and the words with which he verbalizes them in such a way that the resulting frequency-distribution of his continuing stream of speech will meet the exigencies of our equation, $F \cdot Sn$, without "too little" or "too much" talk. And this, in turn, means that inherent in the stream of speech is a

* As the interval of vibration takes on multiple values of T, the distribution becomes rectilinear, with the curve rising and with the nth rank having a frequency equal to the multiple value of T. The same is true of the increasing lengths of samples of speech; the chance of finding one of optimal length, or of multiples thereof, is very small.

† The relationship between the n number of different words in samples of different sizes with the same or different fundamental values of Sn for optimum sizes has been studied theoretically and empirically with great ingenuity by Dr. J. B. Carrol (*The Psychological Record,* II [1938], no. 16, 379–386). However, in this connection much may depend upon the *rate of repetition* in a sample. See below.

dynamic unit which we might call a *closure* (or a *cycle,* or a *rhythm*) which may be defined roughly as a length of speech during which a particular group of verbal tools has completed its collective behavior *once.* What else this *closure* may signify we do not yet know; in fact we happened upon its presence only by noting the particular fashion in which words (and the tuning-forks of our analogy) are used. In Chapter Seven we shall find that the stream of speech *can be organized* in such a way that *no closure* is inherent in it, and that schizophrenic speech may almost be characterized by the absence of *closure.*

But the concept of a *closure* leads to an even more important consideration which comes to light once we ask the following question, whose answer we have already partly foreshadowed: Suppose you could procure only *sub-optimum* samples for analysis; would you then never be able to discern the underlying regularity in the number and frequency of usage of words?

The nature of this question, which ultimately refers to a *rate of usage,* can be elucidated by stating it briefly in the terms of our erstwhile board of tuning-forks, which we shall now cause to vibrate for a *t*-interval that is so short that the harmonic seriation will not become manifest. This done, we face the problem of detecting the underlying harmonic seriation of the entire board by studying the few vibrations of the several individual forks of high frequency that have had the opportunity to complete several vibrations, and which thereby provide us with our only information about the organization of the total board. From an inspection of these few but frequent vibrations we should find that the higher the rate of vibration of a given fork is, the more nearly its cumulative vibrations, f, during the *t*-interval will approximate the proportions of the harmonic series:

$$\frac{f}{1}, \frac{f}{2}, \frac{f}{3}, \frac{f}{4}, \ldots$$

Whether we are able to deduce from these few harmonic vibrations that the entire board of forks was harmonically seriated would depend somewhat upon the length of the *t*-interval.

Turning now to the phenomena of speech, may we infer from the above mechanical analogue that the *rate* at which the words repeat in a very small sample will also give us a corresponding clue to the fundamental harmonic seriation of vocabulary usage? Obviously, we are not yet wise enough about the facts of speech to draw any such inference, for we know absolutely nothing about the rate with which words are repeated in the stream of speech, and therefore we may not assume that our tuning-fork analogue is a true analogy in this respect.

As far as the sheer harmonic equation, $F \cdot Sn$, for words is concerned, the sole matter of consequence is the *total* frequencies of occurrences of the respective words and not their *rate of occurrence,* or the length of intervals between their repetitions. For example, it makes no difference to the saturated harmonic equation, $F \cdot Sn$, whether the $F/1$ occurrences of the most frequent word are bunched together one right after another in the stream of speech, or whether they appear once in every *Sn* running words, or whether they occur according to some other scheme. For as long as the most frequent word occurs *F* times in $F \cdot Sn$ running words, it satisfies the harmonic equation, no matter how its *F* occurrences may be distributed over time. And *mutatis mutandis* with the remaining words of the series.

And so it becomes clear that the harmonic equation, $F \cdot Sn$—although obviously of great descriptive value for our verbal phenomena as far as it goes—is nevertheless not of final validity by itself as a complete description, since it tells us nothing about the *length of intervals between the repetition of words* in the stream of speech. Let us turn to this topic.

VI. THE LENGTH OF INTERVALS BETWEEN REPETITIONS

Perhaps the easiest approach to an understanding of the problem of the length of intervals between the repetitions of words is to find out what is actually the case in an extensive sample of speech like Joyce's *Ulysses,* whose adoption for this particular purpose seems to be recommended by the existence of Hanley's excellent *Index* thereto in which page references are given for the occurrences of all words that are used 24 or fewer times.

In 1937 my then student, Dr. Alexander Murray Fowler, as previously reported elsewhere,[13] undertook as a seminar topic the preliminary exploration of the number of pages that intervened between the repetition of all the different words that occurred 5, 10, 15, 20 and 24 times in Joyce's *Ulysses* (as determined from Hanley's *Index*). He found an interesting inverse relationship between the length of intervals on the one hand and the number of intervals having that length on the other.

Before discussing this inverse relationship, let us first discuss Fowler's methodological procedure which, though inescapably onerous, was analytically simple and essentially as follows. Each word that occurred, say, 5 times was considered to have 4 intervals, *I,* between its occurrences. And the length of each of these 4 intervals in terms of intervening pages was established by subtracting the respective page references from one another as given in the *Index*. More explicitly, the 1st interval was determined by subtracting the number of the page on which the word first occurred from the number of the page on which it occurred the second time; similarly the $n - 1$ interval was obtained by subtracting the page of the $n - 1$st occurrence from that of the *n*th for any word in question.

Naturally, if the word is repeated on the same page, the subtraction yields zero as the size of the interval. To avoid operating with zero in the calculations below, I subsequently added 1 page to all intervals so that, for example, if 20 pages resulted from the actual subtraction of two successive page-references, the resulting interval was nevertheless considered to be 21.*

---

* It would have been a somewhat better statistical practice, to have added ½ page instead of 1. However, in the onerous task of calculating slopes and errors, as presented below, by keeping *y* integral instead of fractional, I was able to use my tables for integral values and thereby save an enormous amount of work. If the reader substituted ½ page for 1 page for the below discussed calculation of slopes, he would increase all slopes by

After having determined the sizes of the intervals between each of the 5 occurrences of all the 906 words that occur 5 times in *Ulysses* (3624 intervals in all), Fowler next tabulated the number of occurrences of the various interval sizes, I, for all the 1st, 2nd, 3rd, and 4th intervals, both separately and combined. In all cases he found not only that short intervals were much more abundant than longer ones, but also that the N number of intervals of a like I size was inversely related to the size of I, or, in the form of a general equation:

$$N^p \times I_f = \text{a constant (approximate)}$$

In this equation f refers to the frequency of occurrence of the different words of like frequency whose intervals are being measured (in the present case, where we are treating all words that occur 5 times in the *Ulysses*, or $f = 5$, we may speak of I_5). Moreover, the exponent, p, represents graphically the absolute slope of the line fitted to the points when the data are plotted on doubly logarithmic paper with N on the abscissa and I_f on the ordinate as in Fig. 2–4.*

The reason for using the more general term, I_f, in the above equation instead of I_5, is that the same inverse relationship for the number and sizes of intervals was found in each of the classes of words that occurred 10, 15, 20, and 24 times respectively in the *Ulysses*. After submitting Fowler's observations to the usual routine checking and finding them accurate to a high degree, I extended the analysis to include words occurring 6, 12, 16, 17, 18, 19, 21, 22, 23 and 24 times in the *Ulysses,* which latter is the upper frequency limit for which page references are given in Hanley's *Index.* In all cases I noted the same inverse relationship although, in studying the data mathematically, I found significant differences in the size of the *constant* in the equation, as we shall presently see when we discuss the intercepts.

To illustrate graphically the nature of the above mentioned data, there are presented in Fig. 2–4, on doubly logarithmic paper with N on the abscissa and I_5 on the ordinate, the actual numbers and sizes of all intervals between repetitions from $I_5 = 1$ page through $I_5 = 50$ pages for all the 906 words occurring 5 times in the *Ulysses.* The negative slope of the line of best Y's (where $Y = \log I_f$) for the data of Fig. 2–4 as calculated by least squares is 1.25 (the root-mean-square deviation being $\pm$ .168). Hence we may describe these points mathematically by the equation:

$$N^{1.25} \times I_5 = \text{a constant}$$

if we remember that I_5 has only integral values from 1 through 50.

---

about .2. Thus specifically the negative slope of 1.15 reported below in Table 2–3 for words occurring 15 times (the arbitrarily selected 5th analysis) increases to 1.34 when the data are recalculated on the basis of an added ½ page instead of 1. The same would be found with the other sets of data. This slight difference in slope does not alter our argument.

* The measurement of N on the abscissa instead of on the ordinate, as is traditionally usual, was deliberately decided upon in order to bring the data of Fig. 2–4 into conformity with those of Fig. 2–5 which are plotted in the traditional manner. The relationship is not altered if the coordinates are reversed.

As to the remaining frequency classes (viz., the words that occur 6, 10, 12, 15, 16, 17, 18, 19, 20, 21, 22, 23, and 24 times respectively), we obviously cannot afford the space of presenting a graph for each of them. However, since we are interested only in the slopes and errors of our material, we can and shall give the complete information in tabular form for all the above frequency classes in Table 2–3. Referring to this table with its

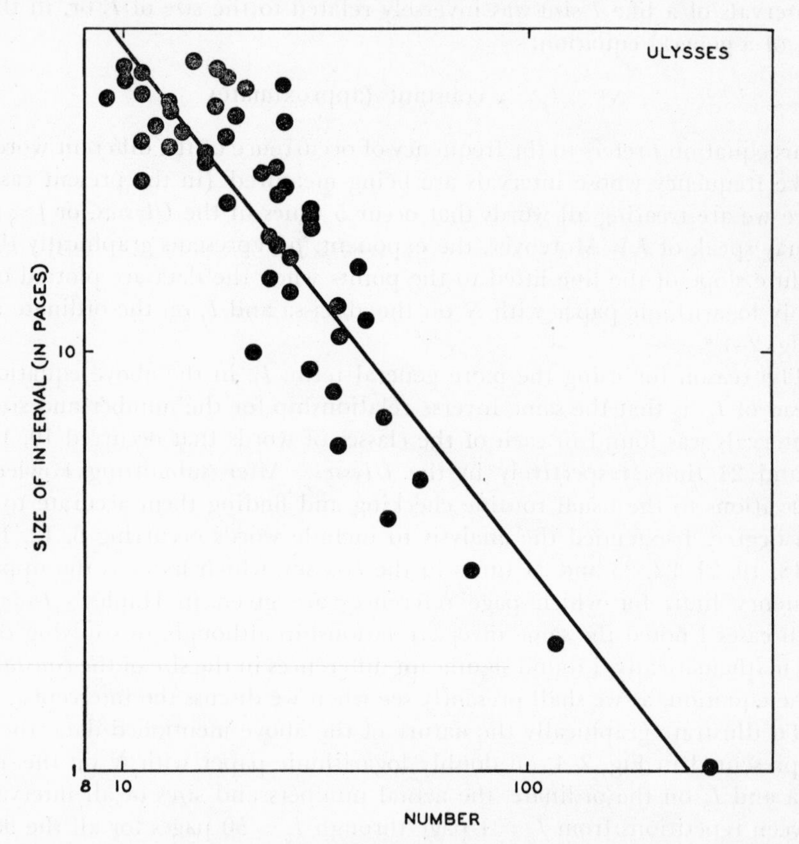

Fig. 2–4. The interval-frequency relationship. The number of different intervals of like size (in pages) between the repetitions of words occurring five times in Joyce's *Ulysses*.

15 different analyses as listed in Column I for the respective frequency classes of Column II whose number of different words are in Column III, we find the desired information about slopes, errors, and the like in Columns IV, V, and VI. In Column IV are the negative slopes of the line of best Y's as calculated by least squares; in Column V are the root-mean-square deviations of the lines of the slope; and in Column VI are the Y-intercepts of the best lines of Y's (actually the antilog of the Y-intercept). Analysis No. 14F is Dr. Fowler's analysis of I_{24}, while No. 15Z is mine; both are included to suggest the close correspondence between his and my analyses.

These calculations are based upon interval-sizes from 1 through 21 inclusive for all the 15 different analyses instead of for the intervals from 1 through 50, as was the case with the data of Fig. 2–4. The reason for restricting the calculations of the present material to the 21 smallest interval sizes is that some of the larger interval sizes in several of the sets of data had no occurrences (i.e., $N = 0$)—a fact that made calculation and comparison more difficult. And so in order to be able to compare all 15 sets of data the upper limit of I_f was reduced to an interval of 21 pages, for which all 15 sets of data had instances of intervals for all the units from $I_f = 1$ through $I_f = 21$. These 21 lowest units will suffice to reveal the presence of any tendency towards systematization in the entire tabular material.

TABLE 2–3

Calculated values of negative slopes, errors, and Y-intercepts of the number, N, of interval-sizes, I_f, between the repetition of words in 14 frequency-classes, f, as fitted to the equation $aX + Y = C$ where $X = \log N$ and $Y = \log I_f$, and where I_f has integral values from 1 through 21 inclusive.

I No. of Analysis	II Frequency of Occur. (f)	III No. of Different Words of like f	IV Slope of Best Line of Y's (negative) ($Y = \log I_f$)	V Error (root-mean-square)	VI Y-intercept (antilog thereof)
1	5	906	1.21	.151	716
2	6	637	1.20	.169	666
3	10	222	1.27	.106	677
4	12	155	1.24	.111	491
5	15	96	1.15	.096	328
6	16	86	.96	.124	153
7	17	79	1.22	.174	422
8	18	62	1.20	.120	264
9	19	63	1.21	.148	350
10	20	69	1.29	.124	944
11	21	52	1.05	.138	212
12	22	50	1.10	.117	264
13	23	44	1.24	.113	352
14F	24	34	1.01	.158	136
15Z	24	34	1.05	.147	153

Turning now to the entries of Column IV of Table 2–3 we find that the negative slopes range from .96 to 1.29 with the median at 1.20. The sizes of the errors in Column V show no marked correlation in their variations with the lower, middle, or upper frequency classes, but seem to be distributed without favoritism throughout the 15 analyses.

As to the slopes of Column IV with their median at 1.20, we may say without fear of contradiction that the high degree of correspondence between these values precludes the completely haphazard or random. *In fact they point unmistakably to the existence of a fundamental correlation between* N *and* I_f. And since this correlation will be found of importance for the balance of our study, we shall now briefly marshal conceivable objections to our acceptance of this correlation as of fundamental importance.

First of all, it cannot be objected that this correlation results merely from the fact that we have selected only the 21 smallest interval sizes, since in Fig. 2–4 we found for I_5 a negative slope of 1.25 with error of $\pm$ .168 for the 50 smallest intervals, which is not appreciably different from the slope of 1.21 with error of $\pm$ .151 for the 21 smallest interval-sizes of I_5, as given in Analysis No. 1, Table 2–3. Hence by more than doubling the range of interval sizes we do not appreciably alter the slope or error. Moreover, when in Fig. 2–5 we present the complete data for I_{24} we shall note by inspection that the correlation is valid for all of the interval sizes, including those that are far larger than 50 pages.

Second, the correlation between N and I_f cannot be ascribed to the fact that we decided to select a page as a unit of measurement, since the relationship would still hold if we took 2 pages, or $\frac{1}{10}$ of a page, or if we multiplied I_f by some other constant, or used words instead of pages as a unit (a course that would be advisable in the case of the repetition of words of highest frequency). Nor does the correlation result from the fact we have arbitrarily added one page to each interval-size in order to avoid operating with zero; such an addition might slightly modify the numerical value of each slope but not the essential correspondence between all slopes.

Third, the correlation cannot be dismissed on the ground that we have considered no frequency-class larger than I_{24} which, as we remember, is the highest frequency class for which the necessary page references are given in Hanley's *Index*. On the contrary, it is precisely the presence of this correlation among words of very low frequencies that is one of its most startling features. For we might conceivably expect to find some sort of principle governing the spacing of repetitions of the highly frequent words that occur 1, 2, or 3 times in every 100 *words* but not for those occurring 1, 2, or 3 times in every 100 *pages*.

And finally and most important of all, we may not overlook the obvious fact that the correlation is by no means an *a priori* necessity. For as a matter of fact an artificial sample of speech *could be fabricated* in which (out of many different possibilities) every interval was 1. Indeed the lack of any *a priori* reason for the necessary existence of the correlation between N and I_f alone suffices to justify our acceptance of it.

And so we shall continue on the basis of the belief that the relationship represented by the equation,

$$N^p \times I_f = a\ constant$$

is fundamental, and not a statistical artifact.*

In stating that $N \times I_f = a\ constant$ for the intervals between the repeti-

* As far as the *constant* in the above equation is concerned, its respective values for the 15 analyses of Table 2–3 are indicated by the antilogs of the Y-intercepts of Column VI, where we note a slight tendency towards an inverse relationship between the size of the intercepts and the sizes of the frequency classes of Column II. But clarification of this point should await the results of further quantitative investigations, particularly of the very highest frequency classes.

tions of all words of like frequency of occurrence, we must beware imputing to the equation more than it actually describes. For although it describes a hyperbolic preference for short intervals, it is noncommittal about whether (1) on the one hand, the shortest intervals will occur either early or late in the total repetition of words, or whether (2) on the other hand, the intervals of different sizes will tend to be distributed evenly over the entire sample of speech. Indeed, as we shall now see from the data of Table 2–4 and of Fig. 2–5, it is curiously enough this second eventuality (2) that is unmistakably the case.

To illustrate the above point (2) we present in Table 2–4 the dispersion of all the 1-page intervals (i.e., $I_f = 1$) among the $f - 1$ repetitions of all the words in each of 10 arbitrarily selected frequency classes which we have

TABLE 2–4

The dispersion of single-page intervals between the $f - 1$ repetitions of all words that occur with ten arbitrarily selected frequencies of occurrence, f, in Joyce's *Ulysses* (Hanley's *Index*).

A

The First 12 Intervals between Repetitions

No. of Sample	f	$f - 1$	Intervals between Repetitions in Order of Appearance											
			1	2	3	4	5	6	7	8	9	10	11	12
1	6	5	62	55	62	58	52							
2	12	11	7	19	15	16	9	12	18	16	12	15	14	
3	16	15	6	10	10	13	18	11	16	11	11	9	11	9
4	17	16	4	3	5	6	4	8	5	10	11	9	14	5
5	18	17	9	11	6	5	6	7	7	6	9	6	2	6
6	19	18	3	8	5	11	5	6	13	9	6	5	6	8
7	21	20	3	4	10	5	8	9	3	10	8	11	7	7
8	22	21	7	5	8	12	5	9	5	9	6	7	5	8
9	23	22	3	5	6	4	8	4	3	2	7	3	4	4
10	24	23	3	5	2	1	3	3	3	3	4	5	2	3

B

The Intervals from 13 through 23

No. of Sample	f	$f - 1$	Intervals between Repetitions in Order of Appearance										
			13	14	15	16	17	18	19	20	21	22	23
3	16	15	6	8	12								
4	17	16	8	6	7	8							
5	18	17	5	6	6	5	4						
6	19	18	2	7	10	5	7	4					
7	21	20	6	6	2	1	7	8	4	2			
8	22	21	6	6	7	10	7	10	9	5	2		
9	23	22	5	7	3	6	2	7	2	3	1	3	
10	24	23	7	3	2	2	0	1	2	2	2	8	3

analyzed. From this table it is evident that the shortest intervals show no preponderant favor either for the beginning, or for the end, or for any other part of the total sample. Indeed, they seem to be scattered more or less evenly among their respective succession of intervals. And the same is also the case for the interval sizes from $I_f = 2$ through $I_f = 21$, as well as for all other interval sizes for all our analyses (although limitations of space prevent our including the data here).

Moreover in Fig. 2–5, which is completely typical of all the 15 different samples of Table 2–3, we find a complete scatter diagram of the dispersion of *all* the interval sizes among all the words that occur 24 times in the

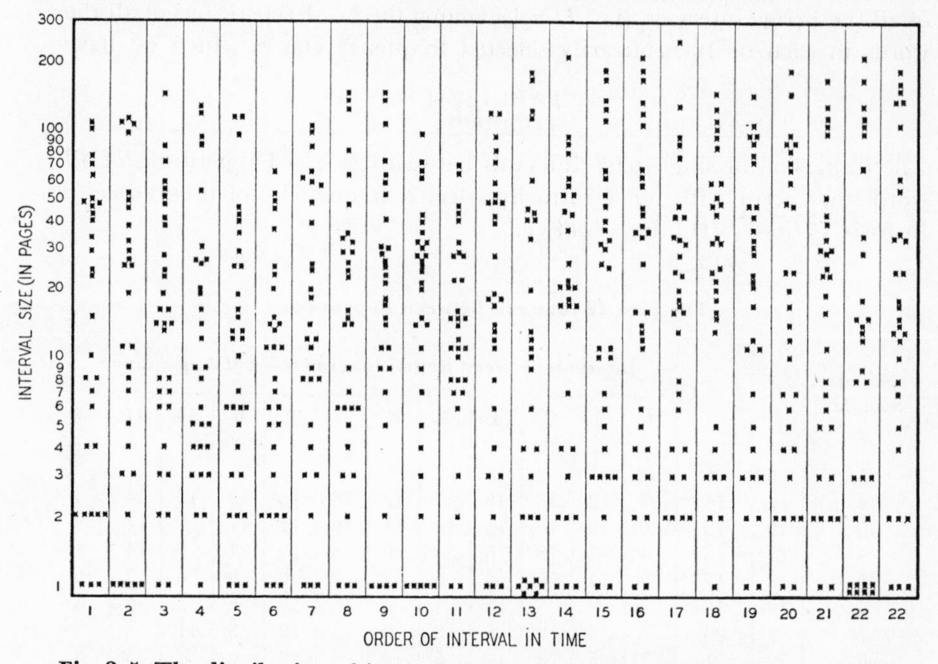

Fig. 2–5. The distribution of intervals between repetitions among the words occurring twenty-four times in James Joyce's *Ulysses*.

Ulysses. The 23 successive intervals between repetitions are indicated arithmetically on the abscissa while the actual sizes, I_{24}, of the intervals are measured logarithmically on the ordinate. The small crosses locate all intervals in respect of their size and of their position of occurrence. The data are from analysis No. 15Z.

As far as we can see, the crosses on Fig. 2–5 are distributed quite evenly over the scatter diagram, with no further systematization whatsoever. The same is also the case in the scatter diagram of the remaining 14 samples, although we cannot afford the space to present them here. Hence the equation, $N^p \times I_f = a\ constant$ (approximate), applies not only to *all the combined* $f - 1$ intervals of each given frequency class, f, but also *individually to each* of the $f - 1$ intervals of each frequency class. In other words on the basis of our analyses of the distribution of interval sizes we may say, in general: the inverse relationship between N and I_f is found to apply not only to the intervals of an entire frequency class, f, but also to each of the successive $f-1$ intervals of that class.[14]

Now that we have established the presence of this inverse relationship between the number and sizes of intervals between the repetition of words, the task remains of probing into the dynamic reasons for its existence.

VII. THE PROBLEM OF SPREADING WORK OVER TIME (THE EVEN DISTRIBUTION OF WORK OVER TIME)

For some pages now we have been so actively engaged in our quantitative study of the phenomena of words that we have allowed our interest in the Principle of Least Effort to slip into the background of our discussions. Now, however, as we turn our attention to inquiring into the dynamic reasons for the quantitative distributions, $N \times I_f = a\ constant$ (approximate), we should be well advised to begin by asking what this distribution *could mean* in terms of Least Effort; and if we remember from the data of Table 2–4 and of Fig. 2–5 that the various interval sizes, I_f, are distributed evenly over the entire time of the sample, we may suspect that the Effort involved in the spacing of words and their repetitions in the stream of speech may also be *evenly distributed over time.* This suspicion brings us to a consideration of the hitherto largely neglected concept of *time* during which all work is expended.

By the term *the even distribution of work over time,* we can mean only one thing: viz., that the total work, W, to be expended during the interval of time, T, will be expended at such a rate that during any unit interval of time, t, the same amount of work, w, will be expended, or $\frac{w}{t} = K$.

In terms of a sample of speech which consists of $F \cdot Sn$ running words, the *even distribution of work over time* will mean that the total work expended during the sample will be so distributed that the same amount will be spent during each of the two halves; or the same between each of the four quartiles, or, if one will, the same between each of the F number of Sn running words. That is, the rate at which work is expended must be as near constant as possible, regardless of the time unit selected.

Now that we have defined what we mean by the concept of the *even distribution of work over time,* the very immediate task remains of explaining theoretically the equation for words, $N \times I_f = a\ constant$ (approximate), in terms of the even distribution of work over time. To this end our first step (A) will be to construct a mechanical analogue (the Bell Analogy) in which minimized work will be distributed evenly over time and in which we shall find frequency distributions that can be described by the same equations as we have observed to be descriptive of the distribution of words in the stream of speech; this analogue will introduce the concept of *time-perspective.* Then (B) we shall tie the contents of this chapter together in a simple summary which will serve to orient us for the remainder of the book, in which the Principle of Least Effort will appear ever more as a fundamental governing principle in all biosocial phenomena.

A. The Bell Analogy and the Meaning of "Time Perspective"

In order to begin with our theoretical explanation of our various equations, let us take n bells that are equivalent in size and equally difficult to ring,* and let us attach them to a long straight board in such a manner that the bells are equally spaced along the board which, incidentally, will offer a constant resistance to all movement. At one end of the board we shall place a blackboard ruled with n columns for the respective bells; and we shall also station a demon there to act as the bell ringer. The demon must ring one bell each second of time, and after he has finished ringing a bell once he must return to the blackboard to record that fact in the bell's column. Thus in order to ring one bell ten times, or ten bells once each, he will in either case make ten round trips down the board and back in the space of ten seconds, and will have 10 marks therefor on the blackboard; and since we shall ask the demon to make his round trips over shortest distances, all his work will be thereby minimized.

This analogue is interesting for many reasons. First of all the demon's work, w, *in terms of making a round trip to ring a given bell,* will increase in direct proportion to the bell's distance, d, from the blackboard (or $w = d$). And since the distance of the respective bells from the blackboard increases integrally according to the series $1d, 2d, 3d, \ldots, nd$, it follows that the demon's work in getting to and from the respective bells will increase according to the series $1w, 2w, 3w, \ldots, nw$.

Now if we ask our demon to ring each bell with a frequency, f, that is inversely proportionate to the work, w, of running to and from it—or in equation form, $w \times f = C$—he will ring the closer (and hence easier) bells proportionately more often than the more distant (and harder) bells. And since the ranked frequency in decreasing order, r, with which each bell is rung will be equal to the bell's w above, we come upon the familiar equation:

$$r \times f = C$$

However, if we now ask the demon to ring all bells according to this equation, but to stop after he has rung the nth and farthest bell once, and after he has rung all other bells with their allotted frequencies, then the n bells will have been rung approximately according to the equation:

$$F \cdot Sn = \frac{F}{1} + \frac{F}{2} + \frac{F}{3} + \cdot \cdot \cdot + \frac{F}{n}$$

in which $F \cdot Sn$ represents the total number of round trips made (as well as the total number of seconds of time), and where F represents the total frequency of the nearest bell, with $F = n$. The above equation is only approximate since, for reasons presented some pages back, there can be no fractional frequencies.

The above equation, $F \cdot Sn$, puts no restriction upon the *order* in which the demon rings the bells. Thus he may ring the nearest bell its

* More specifically, we shall assume that it takes work to get to and from a bell, but that it takes no work to ring the bell itself.

allotted F times before ringing the second nearest bell its allotted $F/2$ times, and so on progressively down the board until he has rung the nth and farthest bell a single time. In short he may always ring "the easiest remaining bell first" while postponing as long as possible the more distant and hence more difficult bells. The chief drawback to ringing "the easiest first" is that the demon will be forced to run faster and faster, and therefore to work at an ever-increasing rate, as he proceeds farther and farther down the board, if he is to complete each round trip within the prescribed second. And in so doing he will be *unevenly distributing his work over time* with the risk of collapsing before he gets the nth bell rung.

To correct this uneven distribution of work over time, we shall ask the demon to distribute his work as evenly as possible over time while still ringing his bells according to the equation $F \cdot Sn$. Yet as soon as he does distribute his work evenly over time, he will automatically ring the bells in such a way that the sizes of the intervals, I_f, between the respective repetitions of the bells will approximate the general equation:

$$N \times I_f = a\ constant$$

The reason for the approximation to this equation is that from second to second the demon will be counterbalancing the cumulative work, w, with the cumulative frequencies, f; that is, he will try to expend half his total work in each half of the $F \cdot Sn$ seconds, ¼th in each quartile, and $1/F$th in each Sn seconds, and so on. Or, differently expressed, every time the demon rings a distant bell whose w is large, he will have to ring a succession or *cluster*, of nearer bells whose w is small.

Indeed, if we view the demon's entire activity as consisting of interspersing difficult bells with *clusters* of easier bells, we can perhaps most readily grasp why there will be proportionately more short intervals between repetitions than longer ones. For, to begin, we know that the larger the bell's w is, the rarer will its ringing be; so too, the longer the compensating *cluster* of easier bells is (that is, the greater the number of pealings of easier bells, when multiplied by their work), the rarer will be that *cluster's* occurrence. And just as more distant bells and longer *clusters* will be proportionately rare, so too will easier bells and shorter *clusters* be proportionately more frequent.

Now since the *clusters* consist of the easier bells (that is, they consist of proportionately more easier bells), and since the easier a bell is, the proportionately more often it will be rung, it follows that *within clusters* the bells will be rung with an above average high rate of repetition (that is, they will be rung at intervals that are much shorter than average). Indeed, there will be not only many above average short intervals between repetitions *within clusters,* but also proportionately so. Hence *within clusters* we may expect to find an approximation to the equation $N \times I_f = a\ constant$ (approximate).

The sizes of all intervals between repetitions are computed not only *within clusters* but also *between clusters.* However, since the sizes of *clusters* tend to vary inversely in proportion to their number, it follows also that *between clusters* there will be proportionately more shorter intervals between repetitions than larger ones. Therefore in measuring the number, N, of interval-sizes, I_f, between the ringings of the same bell (or of any frequency class of bells) we shall find an approximation to the equation

$$N \cdot I_f = a\ constant \text{ (approximate)}$$

and this will be true as aforesaid because our demon will be constantly counterbalancing the difficult but more rarely pealing bells at the farther end of the board with the rapid repetition of the easier and more frequently pealing bells at the nearer end of the board. A statistical analysis could reduce the accumulation of marks on the blackboard to a scatter diagram similar to that of Fig. 2–5. If we gave each bell a distinguishing name and recorded each bell's name when rung, then the frequency distribution of the succession of names would be approximately that of the succession of words in Joyce's *Ulysses.* That is, the succession of names rung out by the bells would constitute an artificial sample of running speech in which we should find approximately all the equations hitherto discussed in connection with Joyce's *Ulysses.*

Now from the equation, $N \times I_f = a\ constant$ (approximate), the other equations can be deduced, although the reverse is not the case. Hence in this sense the equation, $N \times I_f = a\ constant$ (approximate), may be considered to be primary to the others—a consideration to which we shall presently turn.

But before we turn to the primarity of the above Number-Interval relationship of our Bell Analogy, we should stress the point that other explanations of the workings of the Bell Analogy are quite conceivable. Thus the demon could ring the nth bell once and the 1st bell F times, and after that balance the rare but more difficult pealings of the bells at the farther end of the board with the frequent and easier pealing bells at the nearer end. Yet no matter how the analogy is explained, the demon would still be balancing the frequency of easy acts with the rarity of difficult acts so that during every Sn seconds he will expend as nearly as possible $1/F$th of his total work. For every Sn seconds during which an above-average amount of work is expended (i.e., one in which more than F/W has been expended —which can happen only by pealing an above-average number of harder bells) there must follow Sn seconds during which a corresponding below-average amount of work is expended (i.e., one in which less than F/W is expended—which can happen only by pealing an above-average number of easier bells), and *vice versa.* Hence there will emerge proportionately more shorter intervals between repetitions than longer ones.

Our demon, in facing the problem of our bell analogy, is working upon a true *group problem* in which every act influences every other act in bringing forth a population of successive acts in which minimized work is distributed at as nearly a constant rate as possible. In order to solve this *group problem* successfully, the demon must perceive it as a *group problem* which is cast in terms of *time;* or, as we shall say, the demon must have by definition a 100% *time perspective* which means, in terms of our bell analogy, not only the effective performance of acts with a frequency that is inversely proportionate to the work involved, but also the even distribution of that work over time.

This concept of *time perspective,* which refers to the demon's ability both to grasp, and to react to, a group problem successfully is of interest not only because it permits of future objective definitions of various kinds of psychotically unbalanced *time perspective* but also because it shows that the relationship, $N \times I_f = a\ constant$ (approximate), is not at all necessary to the stream of speech, since other distributions are quite possible.

Perhaps the easiest way to comprehend the meaning of a 100% *time perspective* is to reconnoiter a few possible theoretical cases of faulty time perspective in which by definition all work, though minimized, will be unevenly distributed, and where we shall not find an inversely proportionate relationship between N and I_f. One such case of faulty time perspective is that of the "easiest first," which we have already mentioned and which, as we remember, represents nothing more than ringing each easiest remaining bell its allotted F/r times in uninterrupted succession before proceeding to the next easiest bell. In this case all intervals between repetitions would be 1, with the result that the slope of the distribution on doubly logarithmic graph paper would be zero. Therefore we might describe the case of "easiest first" as one of zero time perspective.

Whether the time perspective, thus described, is *.00* or *1.00* the total amount of expended work, *W,* remains the same. The difference is the *rate* at which the work is expended. With a *1.00* time perspective, the rate of work expenditure is as nearly constant as possible, but with a *.00* time perspective, the demon works at an ever-increasing rate—running ever faster and faster—until he reaches a maximum velocity at the $F \cdot Sn$th second, only to drop precipitously again to minimum velocity at the $F \cdot Sn + 1$st second. Inherent in the case of the "easiest first" is an automatic emergence of cycles (as the result of our previously discussed *closure*) in the rate of work which may be of interest for neurological theory.

Thus, for neurological purposes, any time perspective that is less than *1.00* might be construed as being indicative of what might be called a *cyclothymic unbalance,* which would be characterized by an abnormal succession of "ups and downs" of activity.

Turning now to those hypothetical cases of time perspective that may be larger than *1.00,* we recall that the negative slopes of the samples of Joyce's *Ulysses* of Table 2–4 approximate the median value of 1.20. If for the sake of our more general exposition we ignore the errors of Column VI of that table, as well as the fact that we arbitrarily added 1 page to each interval, we may say that Joyce systematically tended to avoid repeating words. That is, in the terms of our Bell Analogy, in the *Ulysses* the acts of the past (whether of bells or of words) tend to be systematically treated as if they were more remote from the present than would actually be the case with a *1.00* time perspective (i.e., the events of yesterday were treated, say, as if they occurred day before yesterday). In short, in the *Ulysses* the present moment seems to engross and preoccupy Joyce systematically at the expense of past moments—a statement with which students of Joyce's "stream of consciousness" school of writing would have little to quarrel. In any event, we may feel that something is "wrong" with Joyce's time perspective if we define *1.00* as being "right."

Other hypothetical cases of faulty time perspective are thinkable, such as those in which the curve becomes markedly concave upwards or downwards as if the single group problem were either solved as several split problems or as an appendage to other and larger problems. But upon these hypothetical cases we need not dwell, since for our present purposes we are interested solely in illustrating the possible meanings of time perspective in terms of our equation, $N^p \times I_f = a\ constant$ (approximate), which we shall hereafter designate the *number-interval equation.*

The above illustrative cases of faulty time perspective show that different samples of speech, on the one hand, may reveal marked variations in the values of the *number-interval equation* which refers to the *rate of distributing work over time;* on the other hand, the same samples may closely approximate the harmonic equation, $F \cdot Sn$, which after all refers to the fact that *work is being minimized regardless of the rate at which the work is distributed.*

However, lest the reader doubt the general existence of a fundamental inverse relationship between the length and number of intervals between the repetition of words, we present in Table 2–5 the number-interval relationship of the words occurring 5, 10, 15, 20, and 25 times in the Old English epic *Beowulf,* and in Homer's *Iliad.* The *Beowulf* study was made by my former student, Mr. Allen Sorensen, who used the glossary of the Klaeber edition [15] of *Beowulf* for that purpose; the *Iliad* study was done by my former student Dr. Harold D. Rose, who used Prendergast's *Concordance* [16] and whose study of the *Iliad* we have previously mentioned. The methods of analysis were essentially those adopted by Dr. Fowler for the *Ulysses.* The data in both cases are in terms of intervening lines with the unit interval of 100 lines. We see from Table 2–5 that by and large there is an inverse relationship between the number and size of intervals in these two ancient texts which in time, style, and content are far removed from Joyce's *Ulysses.* The graphs of these several sets of points (which space limitations preclude presenting) do not yield a very satisfying rectilinearity throughout, although the scatter diagrams show no preference for any order of the interval. As to the *Iliad,* we remember that in Fig. 2–3 we also saw a remarkable rectilinearity in the *number-frequency relationship* of words. As to the *Beowulf,* we shall study its *rank-frequency* distribution in our next chapter.*

* In our next chapter, we shall also present linear rank-frequency data for the American Indian language, Nootka; we mention this now because in spite of the fact that the *Nootka* data represent only 10,000 running words, we nevertheless find a similar *number-interval equation* in terms of the number of intervening words. Thus the most frequent word which occurs 107 times in the sample has 31, 12, 15, 3 and 3 repetitions in the respective 5 classes of 1–10, 11–20, 21–30, 31–40, 41–50 *intervening words.* The 17 different words that occur 10 times have 35, 14, 9, 5 and 0 repetitions for the same 5 classes; and the 583 words that occur only twice have 131, 39, 34, 20 and 19 repetitions. The remainder of the data is similar. Therefore the *Ulysses, Iliad,* or *Beowulf* are similar in this respect to the American Indian language, Nootka.[17]

TABLE 2–5

The Distribution of the *Number* of the Repetitions of words occurring 5, 10, 15, 20, and 25 times respectively according to the *Length of Intervals* in terms of intervening lines in (*A*) the Old English of *Beowulf* (Sorensen count), and in (*B*) Homer's Iliad (Rose count).

Length of Interval in Lines of Verse	A. Beowulf					B. Iliad				
	Frequency Class					Frequency Class				
	5	10	15	20	25	5	10	15	20	25
1–100	91	57	63	29	30	284	227	206	116	164
101–200	51	30	23	13	9	115	99	79	53	84
201–300	40	21	7	9	3	67	71	64	35	59
301–400	36	17	14	1	3	72	59	59	31	41
401–500	32	7	3	4	1	54	54	41	24	25
501–600	31	6	7		1	55	55	40	17	22
601–700	11	4	1		1	53	36	47	21	29
701–800	11	7	1			47	42	38	14	19
801–900	18	4	7			57	32	22	14	15
901–1000	16					48	36	26	16	16
1001–1100	15	2				47	39	20	10	15
1101–1200	7	1		1		43	25	27	14	15
1201–1300	4	1				46	31	22	5	7
1301–1400	3					42	34	26	8	10
1401–1500	3					43	30	24	4	8
1501–1600	4	1				41	18	14	9	8
1601–1700	4					45	25	17	10	6
1701–1800	2					38	29	6	4	3
1801–1900	2					36	20	12	2	2
1901–2000	3					36	17	10	2	5
2001–3000	7					271	144	75	24	13
3001–4000						207	71	24	16	8
4001–5000						164	32	9	3	2
5001–6000						94	11	3	1	
6001–7000						73	9	6		
7001–8000						41	6	1		
8001–9000						25	3			
9001–10,000						17	1			
over 10,000						29	4	2		

None of these sets of data represents so extensive a sample as Joyce's *Ulysses,* and none is as clearcut in its rectilinearity. Just what the various deviations in slope may mean for the "personalities" of the individual writers or speakers in question is a problem that awaits future study. In the meantime, we shall continue in the belief that the extensive sets of *Ulysses* data, with their rectilinear correlations of negative slopes of nearly 1, were sufficient to justify an exploratory construction of our Bell Analogy.

Returning now to the Bell Analogy, let us remember that we have shown no further connection between the Bell Analogy on the one hand and the *number-interval equation* of word repetitions on the other, except for a similarity of mathematical description. Hence we have no right to conclude on the basis of our mechanical analogue alone that the *number-interval equation* of word repetitions does indeed represent the even distribution of minimized work over time.

On the other hand, the Bell Analogy is undeniably an objective picture of some of the salient features of the distribution of words. By using this analogy, and by refining upon it in our following chapter, we shall be in an ever better position to study the dynamics of speech without losing sight of the fact that words are a living phenomenon.

B. Summary and Prospectus

In the present chapter we have done two things.

In the *first* place we have presented quantitative data on the frequency of occurrence of words and of meanings in the stream of speech for the sake of showing the orderliness of the phenomenon. There was no *a priori* necessity for the particular orderliness observed, and the further corroborative data of subsequent chapters will ever more decrease the likelihood that the particular types of observed distributions are merely the result of chance.

In the *second* place, we have attempted to rationalize our empiric data on the basis of economy.* This attempt at rationalization is only a beginning, and is by no means offered in the belief that it is anything more than a preliminary orientation.

The chief step in the rationalization was the Bell Analogy in which we faced the question not only of minimizing work but also of the rate of distributing that minimized work over time. This question of distributing minimized work over time is fundamental to the thesis of this study, since it will lead in a later chapter to the concept of minimizing the average rate of work expenditure, and then to the concept of minimizing the *probable* (average) rate of work expenditure which, by definition, is *least effort.*

The Bell Analogy was deliberately constructed in such a way that the rate of work would be minimized over time with as little variation as possible from second to second. It was also constructed so that the distribution of the sounds of the bells would be similar to that of the distribution of

* Hyperbolic distributions of the type observed quite often suggest a governing consideration of economy, even as bell-shaped curves suggest a certain general kind of rationalization.

words in the stream of speech. Thanks to the objectivity of the Bell Analogy, we could see that the *number-interval equation* which referred to the inverse proportionality between the frequency and length of intervals between repetitions was primary to the *equation of the harmonic series* with which the present chapter started. That is, the latter equation can be deduced from the former, but not the reverse.

So much, then, in summary for what we have done in the present chapter.

Looking to the future, we can either continue the theoretical rationalization as we refine ever more upon our somewhat rigid Bell Analogy. Or we can present further empiric data. Or we can do both, as we alternate between the inductive and the deductive methods in the manner of the natural sciences.

In our following chapters we shall do both, as we present further sets of observation which we shall attempt to rationalize theoretically with an ever-increasing degree of refinement. By a consistent use of this inductive-deductive manner of analysis, we shall learn of the forms and functions of the large and small entities of the stream of speech, both from the view-point of the speaker and from that of the auditor, and we shall simultaneously learn more about their underlying principles of organization until we reach a point in Chapter Five where we can see that the entire phenomenon of speech is presumably subject to the Principle of Least Effort.

CHAPTER THREE

FORMAL SEMANTIC BALANCE AND THE ECONOMY OF EVOLUTIONARY PROCESS

In the last chapter there were three distinct aspects of our investigation. First we analyzed the frequency distributions of words in several extensive samples of speech and found regularities that were easily described by comparatively simple mathematical equations; this might be called the *formal aspect* of the investigation because it referred to the outward and perceptible forms of words. Second we analyzed the frequency-distribution of the dictionary meanings of the 20,000 most frequent words of English as determined by the Thorndike count, which is perhaps outstanding in the field, and again we found a regularity in the distribution of meanings that was susceptible of a simple mathematical description; this might be called the *semantic aspect* of the investigation because it dealt ultimately with the "meanings" of the words, regardless of their forms. And third we analyzed our data theoretically in the light of the Principle of Least Effort, beginning with a hypothetical set of opposing Forces of Unification and Diversification, and ending with the construction of a mechanical Bell Analogy whose work was not only minimized and spread evenly over time but was also described by the equations that we had found for the distribution of words; this was the *theoretical aspect* of our investigation.

Now we shall attempt to fuse more closely the *formal,* the *semantic,* and the *theoretical aspects* of our study as we seek to investigate the economics of human speech in particular, and of the personality in general.

Obviously, in the conduct of any such investigation both the ease of demonstration and the chances of success will depend to a considerable extent upon the *point of departure* and the *manner of approach.*

As to the *manner of approach,* we shall employ the same familiar inductive-deductive methods of exact science that we employed in the last chapter. More specifically, we shall argue theoretically what we may expect to find in critical situations if our Principle of Least Effort be true; then we shall determine empirically what is in fact the case in those critical situations, with the hope of checking the validity of our theoretical argument. In this fashion we shall simultaneously elaborate the details of the Principle under demonstration and also buttress it with factual support.

As to the *point of departure* we shall begin where we left off in our last chapter. That is, we shall begin with our mechanical Bell Analogy with its n-bells and demon. However, in order to avoid the inherent rigidity of the analogue, as well as to bring it more into line with everyday reality, we shall alter the n-bells into n different mechanical tools on a bench, while changing the demon into a flesh-and-blood artisan who will be obliged to survive by performing jobs as economically as possible with his tools. In this fashion our erstwhile Bell Analogy will become a Tool Analogy with its new owner-artisan confronted by problems of survival that are quite similar to those that confront us all in everyday life as we seek to match tools to jobs and jobs to tools.

To facilitate our demonstration we shall restrict our problem to the case of *fixed jobs,* where only the tools are variable; in this section we shall watch the artisan alter the number, forms, arrangements, and usages of his tools for the sake of saving as much work as possible in the performance of the fixed jobs upon which he is obliged to work. During these various alterations in the forms and functions of the tools, two primary principles of economy will emerge, (1) the Law of Abbreviation and (2) the Law of Diminishing Returns, which later will yield the three corollary principles of economy: (a) the Principle of Economical Versatility, (b) the Principle of Economical Permutation, and (c) the Principle of Economical Specialization. These principles will be found operative both in the Tool Analogy and in the stream of speech.*

But now that we have made clear both the manner of approach and the point of departure of our ensuing inductive-deductive analysis, there remain several points of view that may be taken towards the analysis itself. One is the more narrow point of view according to which we shall be concerned primarily with the laws of speech ways; this view will be respected at every turn as we seek to show that the stream of speech, even in respect of its tiniest minutiae, is organized out of deference to the primary exigencies of economy.

There is also the broader point of view, whose nature becomes apparent when we reflect that our Tool Analogy may be used as an analogue not only for speech ways in particular but also for all other human action that may be construed as being directed towards performing jobs for survival. Under this broader view, the speech process becomes only a special case of a much larger universe of action of *forms in function*—a special case which we have chosen for analysis because of its relative ease of quantitative handling.

By adopting this broader view, even at the risk of seeming at times to intrude extraneous material, we shall be able to set forth the basic theoretical construct for our entire book, with the result that all our ensuing chapters with their extensive sets of data will be only further illustrations and extensions of the fundamental principles of economy. Hence, in transforming our Bell Analogy into a Tool Analogy as the first step towards exploring the specific problems of the forms and meanings of speech entities, we are also simultaneously taking the first step in a much broader and

* In Chapter Five we shall remove all restrictions upon the jobs performed as we make the problem of the Tool Analogy a case of *variable jobs* as well as of *variable tools,* with the result that the artisan must thenceforth seek not only tools for his work but also work for his tools in a full-fledged *formal semantic* balance that will have its counterpart in the speech-process.

more general investigation that will ultimately involve the problems of formal semantic balance in general, and of the general economy of evolutionary process throughout the entire biosocial field.

In the closing portions of our preceding chapter we presented a Bell Analogy in which *n* equivalent bells were attached at equal distances to a straight board. A demon at one end made round trips to the various bells, which he rang in such an order that the rate of his work expenditure in terms of his running back and forth would be as nearly constant as possible. From the nature of the Bell Analogy we noted that the equation, $N \times I_f = a\ constant$ (approximate), represented what we termed the even distribution of minimized work over time. Although the Bell Analogy had the virtue of illustrating mechanically our empiric equations for the distribution of words, the palpable rigidity of its structure and operation makes it obviously unsuitable as a complete analogy of the verbal process, which is conspicuous for its continuous shifts in form, content, and arrangement. Let us therefore construct a new mechanical analogue, which we shall call the Tool Analogy, and which will do everything our Bell Analogy did without any of the latter's limitations of rigidity.

Our Bell Analogy consisted of a demon, *n* bells, a straight board and a blackboard. Except for the blackboard, which now becomes otiose, we can use the remaining equipment with a little conversion for the Tool Analogy. Thus the demon becomes a flesh-and-blood artisan; the *n* equivalent bells are melted down into *n* different tools of various sizes and weights just as the artisan sees fit; and the straight board remains unchanged except that it is now used as a bench which extends out in front of the artisan and on which the *n* tools are arranged one after another. The reason for this single line of tools down the bench is that we wish to preserve the properties of one-dimensionality because of the one-dimensionality of speech. In later chapters, when our problems involve areas or volumes, we may make the necessary dimensional alterations in the artisan's shop without any need of altering our mathematical equations.[1]

Now that we have set the stage for our Tool Analogy, we shall give some instructions to our artisan. In the first place, he must survive by performing certain jobs for us with his tools as economically as possible. Beyond that we do not care. Thus we do not care how many tools he uses, nor how he alters their size, shape, weight, and usage, nor how he arranges them on the board, as long as he performs the specific fixed jobs with a minimum of total work. Of course, if he chooses to alter his tools in any fashion, he must perform the work of alteration himself: in short *total work* will include not only the work of actually using the tools but also the work that is necessary for their procurement, maintenance, alteration, and—where need be—of their disposal. Hence the artisan must think his problems through carefully beforehand since he, like other men, has only a limited amount of work at his disposal each day and therefore must expend it with a maximum economy. So much then for our instructions!

Now let us launch our artisan on his career of *fixed jobs* by giving him raw materials and a large order for a number of like artifacts which he can fabricate by means of the n tools he possesses. Since our order solves the problem of jobs and raw materials for our artisan as long as he works at it, he is technically operating under the condition of fixed jobs, and therefore needs only to be concerned with so arranging, designing, and using his tools that his total work, W, will be reduced as far as possible. Let us watch him.

I. THE "MINIMUM EQUATION" OF ARRANGEMENT

To simplify matters, let us say that the artisan's work of using a given tool a single time consists exclusively of the work of transporting the tool a single time from its place on the board to the artisan's lap and back again to its place on the board. This definition corresponds more or less to the round-trip work of our erstwhile demon of the Bell Analogy. Moreover, as we watch our artisan with his tools we shall note that the frequency with which the tools are used, as well as the lengths of intervals between their repeated usage, will eventually approximate the equations of the Bell Analogy because of the exigencies of what we shall now describe as the basic *"minimum equation" of arrangement.*

The basic "minimum equation" is both simple to state and easy to remember because it is based upon the commonplace fact that the work, w, that is necessary to move an object of given mass, m, over a given distance, d, is equal to the product of the mass when multiplied by the distance, or: $w = m \times d$, if we assume a constant resistance, or friction.* Thus if we consider the distance, d, of a given tool to be its round-trip distance to the artisan's lap and return, then the work of using the tool a single time will be $m \times d$. Furthermore, if the relative frequency with which a given r tool is used in the shop during a given interval of measurement is represented by f, then we may say that the tool's *total work-usage* for that interval, w_r, is equivalent to the product of its $f \times m \times d$, or:

$$w_r = f \times m \times d$$

if we ignore for the time being the work of procuring, maintaining, altering, and disposing of the tool.

Obviously each of the n different tools on the board will have its own value of w_r depending upon the values of its f, m, and d, respectively. And the sum of these n different values of w_r will represent the total work-usage, W, of the n tools during the interval of measurement. In short, the total work-usage, W, of the n tools for a given interval of measurement is equal to the sum of the products of each tool's $f \times m \times d$. And this is true no matter how the artisan arranges his n tools, whether economically or not.

However, since the artisan is obliged to use his tools with a maximum economy *he must arrange the n tools of his shop in such a way that the sum of all the products of $f \times m \times d$ for each of the n tools will be a minimum.* This is, by definition, the "minimum equation" which we shall come upon repeatedly in the course of our entire study; and the "minimum equation"

* With a suitable choice of units, one does not need a constant factor.

describes the maximum economy possible for the given *n* tools of our artisan's shop.

The sense of the "minimum equation" is clear. Thus if two tools have the same mass, *m*, but differ in frequency, *f*, then the more frequently used tool is placed nearer so that the artisan will not have to reach so far for it. On the other hand, if two tools have the same frequency, *f*, but different mass, *m*, then the heavier tool is placed nearer to the artisan so that he will not have to reach so far for it, and so on. Under the static conditions of fixed frequencies, fixed masses, and a fixed number of tools, the arrangement of the different tools along the board according to the "minimum equation" becomes fixed and represents the most economical possible arrangement of the given *n* tools.*

But now that we have described what we mean by the "minimum equation," the question arises as to some of its consequences for the arrangement and usage of our artisan's *n* tools. Although the consequences are many, we shall restrict ourselves to a brief mention of (A) the Question of "Close Packing," (B) the Principle of Abbreviation of Size, (C) the Principle of Abbreviation of Mass, and (D) the Factor of Frequency of Usage. Then we shall turn from the problem of tools to the problem of words.

A. The Question of "Close Packing"

An important consequence of the "minimum equation" for our tools will be "close packing," in the sense that the *n* tools will be packed as closely together as possible down the board with just enough room to permit the removal and replacement of tools. This is true because "close packing" will at all times decrease the *d* distance of the tools and thereby decrease the work of using them, regardless of the size or mass of the tools in the shop. The effects of "close packing" are important, as we shall now see.

B. The Principle of the Abbreviation of Size

One effect of close packing is that the smaller the sizes, *s*, of our tools become, the more closely they can be packed together, and hence the shorter the distances, *d*, will be, with the result of a greater saving of work in general. Hence, there is an economy in a small size.

Since our artisan is perfectly free to redesign his tools, there is always a latent economy in reducing the sizes of his tools. Of course, as we shall later see in detail, a reduction in size, or a change in form of any kind, is economical for the artisan only when the work of making the change is less than what is saved in subsequently using the altered tool.[3] Then, too, for a given person there is probably a lower threshold of size below which the tool becomes so tiny that the work of using it increases; nevertheless in the course of dynamic process there remains within this restriction an

* Obviously, if two or more tools are precisely equivalent in *f* and *m* (as well as in other significant respects) and since one tool must be in front of the other (or others) on the one-dimensional board, there will be two (or more) alternative arrangements of tools that would represent equal work.[2]

urge to decrease, or *abbreviate,* the sizes of the tools. And this urge, or Force, towards an abbreviation of size is a direct consequence of the "minimum equation" and of the economy of "close packing."

But let us note well that this so-called Force of Abbreviation does not exert itself equally upon all n tools on the board. For under "close packing" the reduction of an inch in the size of the nearest tool will also save an inch in the d of all the remaining $n - 1$ tools, whereas an inch clipped from the size of the nth tool will reduce the d only of that last tool.

Therefore the magnitude of the Force of Abbreviation will tend to decrease in direct proportion to the distance of the tool from the artisan; the farther that a given tool is from the artisan, the proportionately less the comparative economy will be in reducing its size by a given amount. *Hence in redesigning his tools the artisan will lay a premium upon the reduction of the sizes of all tools in proportion to their nearness to him.*

As a result of the above, we may expect to find in our artisan's shop, as a consequence of years of redesigning, that there will be a tendency for the sizes of tools to stand in an inverse relationship to their nearness to the artisan (i.e., the nearer tools will be the smaller). We shall henceforth call this inverse relationship between size and nearness the Principle of the Abbreviation of Size.

C. The Principle of the Abbreviation of Mass

It is also economical to reduce the mass, m, of a tool, subject to the restrictions discussed in connection with reductions of size, because a decrease in mass will result in a decrease in work, w, since $w = m \times d$. Hence in dynamic process we shall have ever present a Force that operates in the direction of abbreviating mass. However, when we inquire into the particular tools that this Force will prefer for an abbreviation we find that there are two considerations.

One consideration is the factor of *distance* because an ounce clipped from a distant tool will save more work in a single round trip than an ounce clipped from a nearby tool. Therefore, there will be a preference for abbreviating the masses of distant tools as far as single usages go.

Nevertheless—and this is the second consideration—an ounce that is clipped from a nearby tool that is used *frequently* may be more economical of total work than an ounce that is clipped from a distant tool that is used only rarely because of the equation $w_r = f \times m \times d$. The factor of *frequency,* then, is also important.

If we choose to combine the factors of *distance* and *frequency* in stating the Principle of the Abbreviation of Mass we may say that there is a premium in reducing the mass, m, of those tools in proportion to the largeness of the size of their w_r $(= f \times m \times d)$. In short, there will be a tendency to abbreviate the masses of tools in proportion to the sizes of the products of $f \times m \times d$ regardless of the particular frequencies, masses, or distances involved. One effect of the Principle of the Abbreviation of Mass will be to tend to equalize the w_r of all n tools.

D. The Factor of Frequency

Thus far we have tacitly assumed that the respective frequencies, f, with which our n tools are used remain fixed for all time. Yet according to our instructions the artisan is at liberty to alter his tools in any way, including the frequencies with which he uses them—indeed he is under compulsion to alter frequencies of usage if in so doing he can save work. One way of altering the frequency of a given tool is to redesign the tool so that it can henceforth perform the tasks of some other tool or tools, thereby increasing its own frequency of usage.

As far as the economy of the factor of frequency is concerned, it is obviously most economical to use that tool most often which is easiest to use once—that is, whose product of $m \times d$ is smallest (if for simplicity we ignore its s). Hence *in redesigning tools it will be economical to redesign the easiest tool so that it may absorb the jobs of other less easy tools and thereby increase its own frequency still more.* (This statement presents our erstwhile Force of Unification in a new dress.) But although numerous consequences will be found to flow from the economy of increasing the frequency of usage of the easiest tool, none is more important than that of the reciprocal economy between increasing frequencies and decreasing masses that it effects. For if there is an economy (1) in increasing the frequency of the easiest tool, and also (2) in decreasing the mass of the most frequent tool, then (3) it follows (a) that the more frequently a tool is used the easier its use is made by abbreviation, and (b) that the easier the tool's use is made by abbreviation the more frequently it is used. In short, *greater frequency makes for greater ease which makes for greater frequency and so on.*

Furthermore, as the frequency of the easiest tool increases (while its mass decreases), the ever nearer to the artisan the tool will be moved because of the exigencies of the "minimum equation"; and the ever nearer to the artisan that the tool is moved the ever greater will be the Force of Abbreviation in reducing its size. Therefore after enough time has elapsed to permit our artisan both to explore the possibilities of a more economical redesigning and rearrangement of his tools, and also to effect the same, we may expect to find the following general condition in his shop:

As we proceed from the artisan down the bench we shall proceed from (a) the ever smaller, lighter, and more frequently used tools to (b) the ever larger, heavier, and less frequently used tools. In other words, there will be a direct relationship between distance, d, on the one hand and size, s, and mass, m, on the other, in the sense that they will all three tend to increase together. However, there will be an inverse relationship between these three factors (i.e., d, s, and m) on the one hand, and frequency, f, on the other in the sense that as d, s, and m increase, f will decrease. This entire relationship between d, s, m, and f, which we may theoretically expect to find in any set of tools as a result of the various described Forces in operation in dynamic process, we shall henceforth call the *Law of Abbreviation* which, as we shall shortly see, can be tested in speech, where it happens to be fundamental.

E. Summary: Formal Semantic Balance and the "Minimum Equation"

Let us briefly review some of the things that have taken place on the artisan's bench of n tools as time has passed and as he has redesigned and rearranged his tools to minimize his work in performing his job.

As we noted previously, the entire problem of redesigning and rearranging the tools may be expressed in terms of the "minimum equation" in which the sum of the products of $f \times m \times d$ for all the n tools was reduced to a minimum, provided that the increased work of alteration was more than offset by the reduced work of subsequent usage. This consideration has led us to suspect that in the course of time the different tools would be so altered in f, m, d, and s, that as we proceeded down the board away from the artisan we should find a correlation, or tendency, towards an increasing m and s and a decreasing f. This correlation we have called the *Law of Abbreviation.*

As a consequence of this Law of Abbreviation, a further consideration is worth noting in passing.

As a result of the artisan's redesignings, every one of the tools can have been altered in form and function from its original state beyond all present recognition. Some tools may have changed their form but preserved their usage; by definition this is a *formal change.* Some tools may have preserved their form and changed their usage; by definition this is a *semantic change.* And some may have done both and others may have done neither.

Nevertheless, whatever alterations were, or were not, undertaken from moment to moment in the course of the shop's history, they were all undertaken, or not undertaken, as a response to the minimizing of the total work of the shop according to the "minimum equation," which directly or indirectly refers to all form, function, and arrangement. Therefore, we may say that from moment to moment the shop was seeking to preserve by definition a *formal-semantic balance in the forms or usages of its tools.**

II. THE LAW OF ABBREVIATION OF WORDS

It is now time to test the validity of our Tool Analogy by inspecting the case of words, where we shall equate words and their frequencies and magnitudes on the one hand with the tools and their frequencies and magnitudes on the other.[4] From our foregoing argument, we should anticipate *mutatis mutandis* that there will be an inverse relationship between the lengths of words and the frequencies of their usage if we assume—quite correctly, I believe—that, under otherwise constant conditions, the work of uttering a longer word is greater than the work of uttering a shorter one.

A. Quantitative Data

To make a long story short, we present in Table 3–1 two sets of data, the one (A) from the American newspaper analysis by R. C. Eldridge, which

* This particular balance, which refers to an alteration in the forms and functions of the tools in order to *decrease* the rate of work expenditure in using them is obviously not an instance of pure *static equilibrium* as physicists understand the term, nor of *homeostasis* as biologists understand the term, but of *dynamic equilibrium* by present definition.

TABLE 3–1

The Frequencies and Average Lengths of Words (A) in terms of the number of phonemes, and (B) in terms of the number of syllables in (A) American newspaper English and in (B) the Latin of Plautus.

(A) AMERICAN NEWSPAPER ENGLISH
(According to R. C. Eldridge)

Number of Occur-rences	Number of Words	Average Number of Phonemes	Number of Occur-rences	Number of Words	Average Number of Phonemes
1	2976	(6.656)	31	6	
2	1079	(6.151)	32	4	
3	516	(6.015)	33	6	
4	294	(6.081)	34	2	
5	212	(5.589)	35	5	
6	151	(5.768)	36	3	
7	105	(5.333)	37	2	
8	84	(5.654)	39	2	
9	86	(5.174)	40	4	
10	45	(5.377)	41	1	(3.903)
11	40	(4.825)	42	7	
12	37	(5.459)	43	1	
13	25	(5.560)	44	4	
14	28	(5.00)	45	1	
15	26	(4.807)	46	2	
16	17	(5.058)	47	5	
17	18	(4.166)	48	1	
18	10	(6.100)	49	3	
19	15	(4.733)	50	3	
20	16	(4.687)	51	1	
21	13		52	3	
22	11		54	1	
23	6		55	1	(3.333)
24	8		56	1	
25	6	(3.455)	58	2	
26	10		60	1	
27	9		61–4290	71	(2.666)
28	6				
29	5				
30	4				

(B) LATIN OF PLAUTUS

Number of Occur-rences	Number of Words	Average Number of Syllables	Number of Occur-rences	Number of Words	Average Number of Syllables
1	5429	(3.23)	31	8	
2	1198	(2.92)	32	3	
3	492	(2.77)	33	4	
4	299	(2.05)	34	6	
5	161	(2.60)	35	3	
6	126	(2.53)	36	5	(2.05)
7	87	(2.39)	37	7	
8	69	(2.44)	38	2	
9	54	(2.35)	39	4	
10	43	(2.32)	40	3	
11	44	(2.29)	41	3	
12	36	(2.30)	43	4	
13	33	(2.30)	44	1	
14	31	(2.09)	45	1	
15	13	(2.07)	46	1	
16	25	(2.40)	47	3	
17	21	(2.09)	48	1	
18	21	(2.04)	49	1	(1.70)
19	11	(2.18)	50	2	
20	15		51	2	
21	10		53	4	
22	8	(2.08)	54	1	
23	8		55	1	
24	9		56	2	
25	11		58	1	
26	7		61	3	
27	9		62–514	71	(1.40)
28	12	(2.00)	33,094	8,437	
29	4				
30	4				

we have already mentioned in connection with Fig. 2–1; and the other (*B*) from the frequency list of Plautine Latin words, which we discussed in reference to Table 2–2. For each set of data of Table 3–1 we present both the number of occurrences and the number of different words of that occurrence. For the data of *A* we present the average lengths in terms of the average number of phonemes (roughly, a phoneme is a speech sound and will be defined later; the phonemes of *sit* are *s, i,* and *t*). For the data of *B* we present the average lengths in terms of the average number of syllables.[5]

In both sets of data of Table 3–1 we find an unmistakable inverse relationship between the lengths of words and their frequency of occurrence as we have anticipated theoretically on the basis of our Tool Analogy, which is thereby confirmed.

In view of the clearcut correlations in both sets of data of Table 3–1 there remain only the two questions, *first* as to the appearance of the correlation in other languages and *second* as to the extent of the correlation in a very large sample.

As to the first question, we can report that the same correlation was observed in the words of Peipingese Chinese as originally published,[6] and also (unpublished) in the American Indian languages of Nootka, Dakota, and Plains Cree, whose word-frequency analyses will be discussed later. Moreover the same correlation is apparent from frequency lists of the main Western European languages.[7] In fact, the correlation is so obvious to students of comparative philology that there is little incentive to pursue the matter further quantitatively.

As to the second question, which refers to the possible operation of the Law of Abreviation in very large samples, we quote the words of Dr. E. L. Thorndike, who in a brilliant study of the length of words of very rare occurrence, reported the following astonishing observation: "We have found evidence that differences in frequency even among words occurring less than two times in a million are related to differences in number of syllables or of phonemes."[8] Hence the correlation applies to samples aggregating virtually a million running words, or four times the length of the *Ulysses*. It would seem then that we are empirically on quite safe ground.*

B. The Mechanisms of Formal and Semantic Changes

In view of the foregoing data it is only natural to inquire, if only briefly, into the mechanisms whereby the above inverse relationship (between the lengths of words and their frequencies of usage) is maintained; for we

* Of course, the data admittedly refer to average lengths of words of the same or similar frequency classes. If we inspect the actual lengths of words that occur respectively once, twice, thrice, and so on, we find some variations in length whether in terms of phonemes or of syllables. Nevertheless without having actually calculated the factors, I report that the variations within the respective frequency classes are essentially symmetrical, with the mode moving to the left as the frequency increases, and with the kurtosis becoming less as the frequency increases. We mention these technical matters because, as we shall later see, exploratory studies suggest that the longer words *in a given frequency class* may be the newer or *nascent* words of the language, whereas the shorter may be the older or *senescent* words.

can easily see that as far as sheer possibilities are concerned, the longer words *could* also be the more frequent. Although these mechanisms have already been discussed in considerable detail in a previous publication,[9] and although we shall return later to their discussion in this book, we might point out that the *formal* and *semantic changes* of our Tool Analogy are also the mechanisms for altering the lengths of words.

As examples of formal changes, we need only to cite the cases of *phone, gas, bus, paratroop,* and the like for *telephone, gasoline, omnibus, parachute troop.* These are technically known as *truncations.*

As examples of semantic changes we need only to cite the substitution of shorter words, such as *car* for *automobile,* or *juice* for *electricity* in which the shorter substitute takes on the specialized meaning of the longer word and thereby undergoes a semantic change (i.e., after the semantic change, *car* means "automobile," and *juice* means "electricity," among other things). These are called *substitutions.*

Every language is demonstrably undergoing formal and semantic changes which act on the whole in the direction of shortening the sizes of longer words, or of increasing the frequencies of shorter words. Moreover, as far as we know, every language shows an inverse relationship between the lengths and frequencies of usage of its words—a relationship, which, as we have already said, is by no means an *a priori* necessity, since the longer words *could* be the more frequent ones. Therefore, without presuming to have exhausted the topic in these three paragraphs, we feel safe in viewing formal and semantic changes as at least two of the operating mechanisms of the Law of Abbreviation which is fundamental to speech.

However, the Law of Abbreviation is not the only law that is operative upon the speech process. But for our guidance let us first return again to the Tool Analogy.

III. THE LAW OF DIMINISHING RETURNS OF TOOLS

Up to this point we have not concerned ourselves about the size of *n*, which describes the number of tools on the artisan's bench. Even now we shall be concerned not with an absolute size of *n* but only with the consequences of increasing or decreasing the size of *n* for, as we remember, the artisan may alter the number of his tools if he can thereby decrease the total work of the shop.

It is obvious that as the size of *n* increases, the tools are pushed farther and farther down the board, with the result that the *d* of the farthest tool becomes that much greater. And since an increase in *d* will increase the work, *w*, of the new tool (i.e., $w = m \times d$), it is obvious that an increase in *n* is subject to what may be called a *law of diminishing returns.* Therefore there is an economic disadvantage in increasing the *n* number of tools and, conversely, an economic advantage in decreasing the size of *n*.

This problem of a larger or smaller *n* we have already discussed somewhat in our previous chapter under the terms of the Forces of Unification and Diversification.

At present we shall discuss several principles under which the size of n may be economically altered: (A) *The Principle of Economical Versatility,* which we have already foreshadowed; and both (B) *The Principle of Economical Permutation* and (C) *The Principle of Economical Specialization,* which are new. All three of these principles are simple and obvious.

A. The Principle of the Economical Versatility of Tools

In turning now to the Principle of the Economical Versatility of Tools, we are merely exploring the conditions for increasing the *versatility* (i.e., the number of different usages) of some tools in order to eliminate other tools from the board and thereby to decrease the size of n. In this connection it is quite obvious that (1) the farther down the board a tool lies, the more economical it is to get rid of it, and (2) the nearer to the artisan a tool lies, the more economical it is to increase its versatility of usage by having it absorb the tasks of the farther tools. Therefore, in general, the nearer tools will be the *absorbing tools* while the farther tools will be the *eliminated tools* because of the nature of the "minimum equation."

But now let us suppose that the 10 nearest tools are to be so designed as to absorb the tasks of the 10 farthest tools, which are to be eliminated (for convenience we shall assume that each tool on the board performs only 1 task).

The question arises as to which of the 10 nearest tools will absorb the respective usages of the 10 farthest tools. In this connection we remember that as we proceed down the board from the artisan we find that the frequencies of usage of tools decrease as their distances from the artisan increase; and that will be true not only of the frequencies of the 10 nearest tools but also of the frequencies of the 10 farthest. The question then arises whether the most frequent nearby tools should absorb the usages (and therefore the frequencies) of the most frequent distant tools, or whether some other scheme would be more economical.

We know from our previous discussion that it is economical to increase the frequency of tools in proportion to their nearness to the artisan. Therefore it is economical to increase the frequencies of tools in proportion to their frequencies. Consequently it will be economical to have the nearest (and hence most frequent) tool of the first 10 tools absorb the usage and frequency of the nearest (and hence most frequent) tool of the last 10 tools—and so on with the other tools, until the 10th nearest tool absorbs the usage and frequency of the farthest tool on the board.

As a result of the above absorption of the usages and frequencies of the 10 farthest tools by the 10 nearest tools let us note what has happened to the versatility and frequencies of these 10 nearest tools. As to their versatility, we know that each of these 10 tools now performs 2 different usages, instead of 1; hence they are equal in versatility. But as to their frequencies, we know that each tool has had its frequency increased in direct relation to its nearness to the artisan, with the result that the nearest tool has added more to its frequencies than has the 10th nearest.

If we were to continue the theoretical argument much further we should soon have a theoretical single tool of tremendous versatility, with all the remaining $n - 1$ tools eliminated from the board. In actual practice, our artisan might find it difficult to design so versatile a tool because of the brute realities of the physical-chemical properties of matter. For although we can easily think of versatile tools (like the corkscrew-can opener-jackknife-nail file-screwdriver gadget) which can perform quite a few different tasks, we feel intuitively that the process of an increasing versatility cannot be continued indefinitely because of what we may term an *increasing resistance to an increasing versatility,* which will make a continuing versatilizing ever more uneconomical (i.e., it will take more work of manufacture and usage * to increase the versatility of a tool from 10 to 11 usages than from 1 to 2). Let us postulate this *increasing resistance to an increasing versatility* and note its consequences for the versatility of the tools of our shop.

One effect of the *increasing resistance to an increasing versatility* will be that the nearer and easier tools can be made more versatile than the farther tools, because these nearer tools are the more economical ones to use in any way. More specifically, the nearer tools, in being the more economical ones, will be proportionately more capable of offsetting the increasing resistance than the more distant tools. Therefore as we proceed down the board from the artisan, we proceed from the most versatile to the least versatile tools (*that is, from the tools that perform the greatest number of different tasks to those that perform the least number*).

We remember from our preceding argument that the absorbing tools will tend to have their frequencies increased in direct relation to their nearness to the artisan. Therefore *the average frequency of usage for each tool* will decrease as the tool's distance from the artisan increases—a relationship that we shall call the *Principle of the Economical Versatility of Tools.* As we saw in Fig. 2–2, this Principle of the Economical Versatility of Tools has its counterpart in the number of different usages, or meanings, of words where we find that the average frequency of occurrence per meaning of a word decreases with the frequency of the word.

Without a precise knowledge of the actual rate of the *increasing resistance to an increasing versatility* of mechanical tools, we cannot formulate more precisely the relationship between the versatility of a tool and its relative frequency of usage. Nor is a more precise formulation necessary for our present purposes. At present we need only to know that our Law of Diminishing Returns will tend to decrease the size of n by increasing both the versatility and the frequency of usage of tools in direct relation to their nearness to the artisan, with the frequency being increased at a faster rate than the versatility. Obviously, at some point, an increase in versatility will become uneconomical, with the result that n will become stable.

* Consider the work of using a highly versatile gadget for the performance of any one of its many possible tasks! This work would presumably be greater than that of a specialized tool. Hence the resistance to an increasing versatility. For economy of specialized tools, *vide infra.*

This Principle of Economical Versatility is important because it provides an approach to an understanding of the all-pervasive Principle of Economical Permutation, which is quite similar in form and effect to the Principle of Economical Versatility.

B. The Principle of the Economical Permutation of Tools

We have just noted the economy of increasing the versatility (and frequencies) of tools in direct relation to their nearness to the artisan; because of this Principle of Economical Versatility, the size of n can be decreased. Now we shall note the presence of a second economy which is also connected with the tools' nearness to the artisan. This second economy we shall designate the *Principle of the Economical Permutation of Tools.*

This Principle, which makes possible a further reduction of n, is quite simple to explain. Instead of keeping a distant tool to perform a given task, the artisan can use two or more tools together to perform the task (e.g., the use of the mallet and chisel, or a ruler and pencil, or the saw and mortar box).* In this fashion two or more tools together may absorb the task of another tool so that this other tool may be eliminated, with the result of a decreased n.

The question now arises as to which tools should be combined for the purposes of absorbing usages, and which tools should be eliminated by having their usages thus absorbed. The answer is obvious, because it is merely a paraphrase of our argument in connection with the versatility of tools: *Tools should be permutated in direct relation to their nearness to the artisan, and these permutations of tools should absorb the usages of the most distant tools—with the easiest nearest permutations absorbing the most frequent usages of the distant tools to be eliminated.*

At this point we must be careful with our theoretical argument lest our theoretical first several tools in permutation theoretically absorb all the tasks of the remaining tools—an eventuality which, in actual practice, would scarcely occur. For just as the brute realities of the physical-chemical properties of matter will prevent an indefinite versatilizing of single tools, so too will the same realities of matter prevent the indefinite versatilizing of specific permutations of tools. With the permutation of two or more tools, as with a single tool, we may postulate an increasing resistance to an increasing versatilization of permutations. This postulate means that the artisan must employ ever more different permutations of tools to absorb the usages of an ever greater number of tools that are to be eliminated. Furthermore this postulate will also mean, in the long run, that the nearer

* The word *permutation* is used in preference to *combination* in order to emphasize the importance of the fixed order of the joint usage (e.g., the mallet hits the chisel and not the chisel the mallet). In an actual shop some tools can be used together only in one certain order, others cannot conceivably be used together at all. In speech we have permutations like *horse race* and *racehorse,* yet *doorknob* has no *"knob door."* We have *apt, pat,* and *tap,* but no *tpa, pta,* or *atp.* Hence our term *permutation* is to be viewed merely as descriptive of a tendency to combine together in a more or less fixed order, and nothing more.

tools will enter into a greater number of different and more frequently used permutations than the less near ones, as we shall shortly see more explicitly.

But first, by way of definition, we shall assume that in order to have a permutation perform a "permutation task" a single time, the respective tools of the permutation must each be brought a single time to the artisan's lap, and returned; and that the total work of bringing these tools to the artisan's lap and return will be the work of using the permutation a single time in performing the given task (i.e., the given "permutation task"). We shall also assume that each permutation can perform only one single task. For the sake of further simplifying our problem we shall finally assume that all n tools on the board are of approximately the same physical magnitude (or, if there is any difference, the smaller will be the nearer) and that the frequency of each tool will be inversely related to its distance. In short, we shall assume that our tools represent the effect of having been subjected for a considerable period of time to the abbreviatory and other Forces of the "minimum equation."

In view of the above assumptions and of the definition of the work of using a permutation, several matters become immediately obvious: (1) it is obvious that it is more economical to permute the nearby tools than the distant ones. Indeed, *the nearer to the artisan that the tools are situated, the more economical it will be to use them in permutations.* (2) It is obvious that the most frequent of the absorbed tasks should be performed, if possible, by the easiest permutation. (3) It is obvious that no permutation can be profitably used which will consume more work than a new specialized $n + 1$st tool.

As to the first point above (1) which relates to the economy of selecting for permutations tools in the order of their nearness to the artisan, we note not only (*a*) that the nearer tools are the more economical to permute, but also (*b*) that the nearer tools can profitably enter into a greater number of different, and also larger, permutations than the less near tools. Thus, for example, it is easier to use the first four nearest tools together in a permutation of a given size, than to use the next four nearest tools in a permutation of the same size; moreover, because of the increasing work of using tools that lie farther down the board, the amount of work that is necessary to use the first four tools together in each of 24 different possible permutations will be less than the work of using any two of the following four tools together in 2 possible permutations (if we assume that work increases in proportion to rank-distance); hence the nearer tools can economically produce not only easier permutations, but also a far greater variety of different permutations. Since the reader will find this point of considerable interest in understanding the inflection and compounding of words, phrases, clauses, and sentences, we shall generalize: *the nearer to the artisan that a tool is situated, the ever greater will be the number of different permutations into which it can profitably enter.* Obviously the degree of a tool's economical permutability in relation to its nearness to the artisan parallels the degree of its economical versatility.

But the parallel between the two Principles of Economical Permutation and Versatility becomes even more striking when we turn to the question of the comparative frequencies of the tasks to be absorbed, and ask (2) which particular permutations of tools can most economically perform the tasks to be absorbed. Here we see that the nearest and hence easiest permutations can most economically perform the most frequent of the tasks to be absorbed, just as we saw was the case with the nearest and easiest tools under the Principle of Economical Versatility, because we know that it is economical to increase the frequencies of tools in proportion to their nearness to the artisan. Therefore we may say (*a*) *that a given tool will enter into a number of different permutations,* and (*b*) *that these permutations will be frequently used* (*c*) *in direct relation to the tool's nearness to the artisan.*

However (3) as we have previously suggested, it is obviously uneconomical to use any permutation whose work is greater than that of a new specialized $n + 1$st tool. This has two important consequences for any actual set of n tools as n increases: (*a*) somewhere down the board there will be a *critical point* beyond which no tool can profitably enter into any permutation; and we shall say that this *critical point* separates the nearer *permutable* tools from the farther *nonpermutable* tools; (*b*) because of the existence of this *critical point* there is a restriction upon the number of different tasks that a given n number of different tools can perform. For with our postulate of an increasing resistance to an increasing versatility of single tools and of their permutations, the *critical point* will eventually be reached when the n tools will be in a saturated condition in respect of the usages that they can perform (we shall call this the *Z value of usages* for if given n tools, and it will refer to a complete saturation of single and permuted tools). Once this saturation point has been reached, the only way to increase the number of different usages of the n tools beyond the above *Z value* is to increase the n number of tools.

Hence we may say in summary that in addition to our initial Principle of Economical Abbreviation (in which magnitude is inversely related to frequency) we have two further Principles of Economy: (A) one in which the versatility of tools will decrease as their distance from the artisan increases; and (B) another in which the number, sizes, and frequency of usage of the different permutations into which the n tools can economically enter will decrease as the distance of the tools from the artisan increases. The actual size of n will be governed in the last analysis by the Z number of tasks to be performed and by the actual resistance of matter to versatilization and permutation. With a given Z, then n is a minimum.

However there is another Principle of Economy: The Principle of the Economical Specialization of Tools.

C. The Principle of the Economical Specialization of Tools; and the Question of Age

The Principle of the Economical Specialization of Tools can be immediately derived from the preceding Principle of Economical Permutation. Whenever the relative frequency of any permutation increases to such a point that its task can be performed more economically by a new single $n + 1$st tool, the adoption of that $n + 1$st tool will be economical. This new tool will be defined as a *specialized tool,* since it performs a task which can otherwise be performed only by a permutation of two or more tools.

Of course (1) whenever the frequency of a permutation increases, the constituent tools of the permutation will be moved *nearer to the artisan* because of the exigencies of the "minimum equation," thereby displacing the ranks of the tools that up to that time have lain between the new locations and the previous locations of the constituent tools that are to be moved nearer to the artisan. On the other hand (2) after the specialized tool has been adopted in lieu of the permutation of tools, then the constituent tools of the now abandoned permutation will have their frequencies decreased by amounts that are equal to the frequency of the erstwhile permutation; and according to the exigencies of the "minimum equation" these constituent tools of reduced frequency will be moved *farther away from the artisan.* In short, as the permutation is used more frequently, its constituent tools move nearer to the artisan; yet once the permutation ceases to be used, then the constituent tools have their frequencies reduced by an amount that is equivalent to the frequency of the erstwhile permutation, and therefore recede down the board from the artisan.

This alteration in the frequency and location of the constituent tools is interesting in the light of our Principle of Economical Abbreviation. Obviously, as long as the above constituent tools of a permutation are frequently used and lie near to the artisan their magnitudes will be reduced by abbreviation to a size that corresponds to the reduced sizes of their neighboring tools. Yet once these tools recede from the artisan—for whatever reason—then their reduced magnitudes will be smaller than the magnitudes of their new neighbors.

Therefore whenever we find a tool (or word) whose magnitude is smaller than that of its neighbors in the frequency range, we may conclude that the tool (or word) of below-average size is an older tool (or word) whose usage is on the decrease (hereinafter we shall call this a *senescent tool*).*

The new $n + 1$st specialized tool that has displaced the former permutation will be allocated a place on the board that is commensurate with its frequency, etc. Since this new tool will not yet have been subject to the grinding Force of Abbreviation, its magnitude may well be greater than that of its neighbors. Therefore whenever we find a tool (or word) whose magnitude is above average for its frequency, we may conclude not only that it is a newer tool (or word), but that its usage may well be directed towards an increase (hereinafter we shall call this a *nascent tool*).

Therefore, as a consequence of the Principle of Economical Specialization, there will be an inverse relationship between the *age and magnitude* of tools in the sense that the greater age will have the smaller magnitude. The presence of this correlation in any tool shop will be sufficient evidence of the operation of the Principle of Economical Specialization.

---

* The relationship between *age* and *size* of word will be found treated in Fig. 3–10.

D. Summary: Formal-Semantic Balance in Dynamic Process

If the Principles of the Economical Abbreviation, Versatility, Permutation, and Specialization of Tools are true, and if our artisan is always economical, then as time elapses all of the above Principles will be constantly operating simultaneously upon the number, sizes, forms, functions, arrangements, versatility, permutations, and frequencies of our set of tools in order to minimize the work of performing jobs. By way of definition we shall say that the Principles in thus operating upon a set of tools are attempting to preserve or restore a *formal-semantic balance* (or an *organic balance*) ; and we may say that the tools thus operated upon are changing *in dynamic process* for the preservation or restoration of a *formal-semantic balance.* Since all sets of tools that are engaged in performing jobs will at all times be in dynamic process, we may expect to find at any time certain tendencies, or correlations, in any set of tools which are organized in reference to the criteria of a fixed point for the discharge of fixed jobs.

Thus we may expect to find in general that *the more frequent tools will tend to be the lighter, smaller, older, more versatile tools, and also the tools that are more thoroughly integrated with the action of other tools because of their permutations with the same.*

Now if we sit back and reinspect the foregoing italicized generalization, we note a further attribute of the set of tools which relates to the *relative conservatism* of the *n* different tools. Thus we note that the most frequent tool, which tends to be the lightest, smallest, oldest, most versatile and most thoroughly integrated tool in the system, will also be the most valuable tool in the sense that its permanent loss would cause the relatively greatest cost of redesigning and of retooling. Hence it is most economical to *conserve* that most frequent tool. By extension of the above argument we see that the value of conserving any given tool is directly related to its relative frequency of usage. (For example, a carpenter should conserve his only hammer and saw with far greater care than his large, specialized, expensive, but rarely used lathe if no replacement of tools were possible.) *

Now that we have elaborated our Tool Analogy, let us turn to the case of words.

IV. THE LAW OF DIMINISHING RETURNS OF WORDS

Turning now to an inspection of the verbal aspect of our Tool Analogy we need to disclose whether words do in fact reveal (A) a Principle of Economical Versatility, (B) a Principle of Economical Permutation, and (C) a Principle of Specialization with the attendant concepts of *nascence* and *senescence* which will justify the conclusion (D) of a far-reaching

* Therefore in spite of the innovations of dynamic process we should expect to find a marked tendency towards the *preservation* of the more frequent (and older) tools and tasks because of the Principles of Economy that we have discussed (and not because of any love of antiquarianism, nor of any loathing of innovation). In short, frequency (and age) are the result of value and not the reverse.

Formal-Semantic Balance in Dynamic Process. But before we begin upon this trek there are two points about which we should become clear.

The *first* point is that the data we present cannot be described as representing the arbitrary case of fixed verbal jobs, but rather the more vital condition of variable jobs and tools; we need not worry about this point because we shall find our above four Principles in the samples we examine. In Chapter Five we shall understand why the selfsame Principles will be operative also under the conditions of variable jobs and tools.

However the *second* point cannot be so easily dismissed because it refers to the applicability of our Tool Analogy to words under any conditions. It is easy enough to say that words are to be equated with mechanical tools; but that still leaves the question of what in the verbal process is to be equated with the specific *usages* of mechanical tools. In short, what is the specific *task* that a word performs by means of a specific *usage?*

As far as anyone knows, different words in a given situation evoke different responses from the auditor; therefore we may suspect that the *tasks* of evoking particular responses in an auditor represent the specific usages of words. These different specific *usages* of words seem to be what lexicographers term the *dictionary "meanings"* of words. For if we take a dictionary and inspect the different *dictionary "meanings"* in it, we note that they are, in general, of two kinds. One kind of "meaning" is little more than a detailed direction for one or more of the word's *usages;* the "meaning" might be called a *definition of usage;* the "meanings" of English *a, he, and, it* are of this kind. Another kind of "meaning" is little more than an alternate set of words to be substituted for the word in question much like the substitution of a permutation of tools for a specialized tool; thus if you eschew the word, *castaway,* you can consider employing the alternatives of "thrown away," "cast adrift," "shipwrecked person," "outcast."

And so it seems that the *dictionary "meanings"* of words are parallels to the *usages* of mechanical tools in our general Tool Analogy. By *dictionary "meanings"* of words we refer to what is found in dictionaries.[10]

In adopting so simple and practical a view of the usages of words we may not have endeared ourselves to serious students of the age-old problems of *meaning* and the *meaning of meaning.* Nevertheless, in regard to the entire problem of meaning and definition in general we might point out to the above serious students that *in the exact sciences one defines entities in order to study properties; and, after having studied properties, one may return and redefine the entities in the light of his augmented knowledge.* Therefore our above use of *dictionary "meanings"* is only a beginning definition of what in the stream of words may correspond to the usages of mechanical tools—a beginning definition that in the course of our entire study will lead to better definitions in a problem that is truly age-old.

However, even this beginning definition must prove its merit before we may accept it. For the question arises as to whether the *dictionary "meanings"* of words behave in a manner that is analogous to that of the *usages* of mechanical tools.

A. The Principle of the Economical Versatility of Words

If dictionary meanings stand in the same relationship to words as that of mechanical usages to mechanical tools we should expect to find in a given sample of running speech that the number of different dictionary meanings of words will be directly related to their respective relative frequencies. For, after all, that is what we have anticipated theoretically to be the case with number of different usages of tools of different frequencies as explained under the Principle of the Economical Versatility of Tools.

As we have shown in Fig. 2–2, the average number of different meanings of the twenty successive sets of 1,000 words of the Thorndike Frequency Count of English, when ranked in the order of decreasing frequency, decrease in proportion to the square root of the *rank*. This, in turn, signifies that the number of different meanings of words will also decrease according to the square root of their *frequencies,* if we are correct in assuming that the 20,000 most frequent words of the Thorndike analysis are approximately distributed according to the harmonic series. The theoretical explanation of these data we presented in Chapter Two where we showed why a slope of −.5 was to be expected.

As far as our Principle of Least Effort and the Tool Analogy are concerned, we remember that neither the slope of −.5 nor the linear distribution is necessary. A nonlinear distribution would have answered our theoretical expectations just as well, in view of our ignorance of the precise nature of the law of increasing resistance to an increasing versatility. The fact that we have found a linear distribution in the ranked frequencies of meanings of words, with a slope that is ½ of the slope for words, suggests that for words there may be a "law of resistance" that operates against an increase of versatility of meanings in direct proportion to the increase. In Chapter Two we theoretically placed this resistance in the auditor's mind (i.e., the auditor's economy), and not in the speaker's, and in Chapter Five we shall find further reasons in support of this view.*

Before leaving the topic of the Versatility of Words let us think of possible objections to our use of the Thorndike data for this purpose. One is that Dr. Thorndike treated lexical units (i.e., words in noninflected form) and not words in their fully inflected form; however, because of the low degree of inflection of words in English this objection loses its weight, since the difference between a rank-frequency distribution of lexical units and of words in fully inflected form is not considerable. A second objection might be that we have presented in Fig. 2–2 only the average number of meanings for successive thousands of ranked words and not for the different individual words themselves. This second objection is not entirely without validity, and it is regrettable that a rank-frequency distribution of words

* In our subsequent chapters we shall see that in a very practical sense the speaker, while talking to the auditor, is attempting to use the auditor and his responses as a set of tools for the attainment of the speaker's objectives. Therefore the Tool Analogy is by no means invalidated by the introduction of the auditor.

and their meanings is not available. Nevertheless the correlation of Fig. 2–2 is unmistakable and the fact that Dr. Thorndike chose units of 500 and also of 1,000 words was quite arbitrary from the viewpoint of this study; there is no conceivable reason to suppose that the correlation could possibly disappear if smaller units had been selected.

Aside from the above, Dr. Thorndike's data are quite satisfactory for the purposes of this study. In the first place, he determined statistically from a vast number of samples of English just what the 20,000 most frequent words are, and these he used as the core of his dictionary. Then he and Dr. Irving Lorge consulted the Oxford English Dictionary to note all the historically different meanings of the 20,000 words as determined by the lexicographers from the entire range of English literature. Then Dr. Thorndike determined which of all the different historical meanings of his 20,000 words were actually used in the particular samples of speech which he had counted. These actually used meanings were alone included in the Thorndike Senior Dictionary. And we in turn have noted the correlation of Fig. 2–2, which scarcely can be ascribed to chance.*

It is regrettable that further data from other languages are not available. Nevertheless in view of the extent and unequivocalness of this one set of data we may say that the number of different "meanings" (or of different *kinds* of responses evoked) of words seems to be equal to the square root of the frequency.

This is in line with the Principle of Economical Versatility of Tools. Thus far our Tool Analogy has been validated.

B. The Principle of the Economical Permutation of Words and Other Speech Entities

The question of the economy of permutations in the stream of speech refers to the very core of speech structure. For, as we shall see from an extension of the argument used with our mechanical tools, the Principle of Economical Permutation will be found not only in the permutation of words into (1) holophrases and into (2) larger groups, but also (3) in the permutations of morphemes into words, as well as (4) in the permutations of phonemes into words. In order to treat our Principle in greater completeness we shall discuss in turn each of these three kinds of permutations, and in respect of the last two kinds (i.e., 3, and 4) we shall likewise show the presence of the Principle of Abbreviation in operation.

1. The Principle of the Economical Permutation of Words. If the Principle of the Economical Permutation of Tools applies *mutatis mutandis* to the permutations of words, we should expect to find in general that the number of different permutations into which a word enters, as well as the frequencies with which the permutations occur, will be directly related to the frequency of the word. Or, differently expressed, the more frequently that a word is used, the ever greater will tend to be the word's use in different

* Even the words in Thorndike's 20th thousand occurred several thousand times in his samples and therefore *had the opportunity* to represent as many different meanings as those found for the first 1,000.

permutations and the more often will those permutations tend to be used. This proposition, if true, should be verifiable by empiric test.

Yet before we may undertake an empiric test we must first ponder the question of an objective criterion for recognizing a *permutation of two or more words* (which for the sake of convenience we shall henceforth call a *holophrase*). For without some such objective criterion, a truly empiric test of our Principle would be impossible.

In some cases we might all agree that particular successions of words were holophrases; for example, *brother-in-law, hot-dog,* and *hit-and-run* driver. So too, perhaps, in regard to the phrases: *glad-to-meet-you,* or *how-are-you.* Yet in many cases it might be more difficult to decide. Thus in the sentence, "Is your brother in jail?", may we say that *brother in jail* is a holophrase like *brother-in-law?* And, if so, how about *father in the kitchen,* or *mother at the Women's Club?*

The problem of establishing objective criteria for the classification of the entities of the stream of speech is age-old.[11] In the case of holophrases a *criterion of inflection* has been suggested, which means that if a succession of words behaves like a single entity in respect of inflection, the succession is by definition a *holophrase.*[12] Thus, for example, English generally pluralizes nouns by affixing *(e)s* at the absolute end of the word, as in pluralizing *house* to *houses,* or *boy* to *boys.* Now, according to the above criterion, if we pluralize *brother-in-law* by saying *brother-in-laws,* we are treating it as a holophrase at whose final end we attach *(e)s.* On the other hand if we say *brothers-in-law,* we are treating it as a succession of discrete words, regardless of the hyphens, since the *(e)s* does not come at the final end.

This criterion of inflection is on the whole excellent, although in the case of languages which, like present-day English, use inflections only very sparingly, the criterion might often be of little practical help. Thus it would be of little help in determining the possibly holophrastic nature of the English adjective, *hit-and-run,* because in English the adjectives are never inflected to show the plural. On the other hand we need not forget that there also exist many languages that are so highly inflected that they use inflections virtually throughout their entire structure. Since we are interested solely in the test of our Principle of Economical Permutation, we are at liberty to select for our analysis one of these highly inflected languages where the criterion of inflection will be completely serviceable.

Our reliance upon this single criterion of inflection may seem offhand to ignore the question of the "meanings" of holophrases. But here let us remember that on the basis of our Tool Analogy we may expect theoretically that each holophrase will have one or more particular meanings of its own which will not be the same as the meanings of the constituent parts of the holophrase. Thus, for example, if English *hot-dog* is a genuine holophrase, it will have a particular meaning of its own which is not that of a "dog that is hot." Yet if each holophrase has its own peculiar meaning or meanings which differ from the meanings of its constituents, then that fact will have important consequences for our criterion of inflection. For whatever may be the actual meanings of the holophrases on the one hand in a given language, and of the constituent parts on the other, the native speakers of the given language will know them; and they will also know whether at a given moment in their conversation they are using a holophrase or a succession of independent words, since they will know the meanings that they are trying to convey. Therefore they will automatically know whether the given succession of speech entities should be inflected as a single holophrase or as a succession of independent words. The particular meanings in question will determine the speaker's adoption of inflections; and the adopted inflections will in turn convey to the auditor the particular meanings in question. Hence the manner in which the native speakers actually inflect the speech elements of their highly inflected language will serve to classify their verbalizations into holophrases and words respectively, so that a competent linguist in the field needs only to record samples of their speech in order to note which are the holophrases and which are the independent words. We in turn for our part need only make a rank-frequency analysis of these recorded samples in order to ascertain empirically whether the Principle of Economical Permutation is indeed in operation.

In short, by thus employing the above *criterion of inflection* in a highly inflected language we shall be in a position to verify our theoretical Principle of Economical Permutation by an empiric test. Our next step, then, is to select a highly inflected language for analysis.

Few languages are more highly inflected than some of our American Indian languages. Of these, none surpasses Nootka in the care with which it has been recorded, transcribed, analyzed, and published by the two eminent American scholars, Drs. Edward Sapir and Morris Swadesh.[13] Therefore we cannot do better than to select Nootka for our analysis.

The problem of testing our Principle in Nootka can be most simply solved if we take a sizable sample of Nootka and analyze it in two different ways, *A* and *B*.

One analysis (hereinafter the *A* Analysis) will be a rank-frequency distribution of the unpermuted running words in the samples selected, *after breaking all holophrases into their constituent parts;* that would mean in reference to English that the phrase, *his hot dog,* would consist of three different "words": *his, hot,* and *dog.* This *A* Analysis will correspond to the rank-frequency distribution of the *n* unpermuted tools of our Tool Analogy.

The other analysis (hereinafter the *B* Analysis) will be a rank-frequency distribution of the holophrases *plus* the independent unpermuted words. This *B* Analysis would treat the English phrase, *his hot dog,* as consisting of the unpermuted word *his,* and of the holophrase *hot-dog.* Incidentally, the Nootka texts are printed in this latter form—quite ready for the *B* Analysis. This *B* Analysis will be the equivalent of the rank-frequency distribution of the permuted as well as of the unpermuted tools of our Tool Analogy in performing the hypothetical *Z* different tasks.*

* We may say that a single independent "unpermuted" tool represents the permutation of a single tool once; so too we may say that a single independent "unpermuted" word represents the permutation of a single word once. We mention this point in order

Now let us turn to the practical steps of the analyses. Because of the form in which the Nootka texts are printed, the *B* Analysis was undertaken first. To this end a sample totalling 10,000 running holophrases and unpermuted words was taken from the texts in corrected galley proof as selected and transmitted to me for that purpose by Drs. Sapir and Swadesh. The rank-frequency distribution of holophrases and independent words of this *B* Analysis will be found in Curve B of Fig. 3–1. It will be remembered that the entire data of Curve B are ranked in the order of decreasing frequency without further discrimination as to the kind of entity.

The *B* Analysis completed, our next step was to send the rank-frequency list of the *B* Analysis to Dr. Morris Swadesh who, after eliminating to the point of negligible importance all errors that had crept into it, then undertook with great generosity the laborious task of splitting the holophrases into their constituent parts so that a rank-frequency study of the *A* Analysis could be made.

In reducing the holophrases of the *B* Analysis into their constituent parts, Dr. Swadesh was confronted by certain difficulties which can be best illustrated from analogous conditions in English. Thus, for example, the English entity, *gosling,* may be viewed as consisting of two parts, *gos* + *ling.* The first part means "goose" and the second part means "small." The question arises whether in making the *A* Analysis (1) the occurrences of the constituent part, *gos,* should be combined with the occurrences of the independent word, *goose,* on the ground that they are semantically and historically related; or whether (2) the forms *gos* and *goose* should be treated separately on the ground that they are different in phonetic form. The first course (1) would yield what may technically be called a *"morpheme"* rank-frequency analysis of Nootka; whereas the second course (2) would yield what we shall call a *"varimorph"* rank-frequency analysis (we shall later define these terms in quotation marks). Since there is no *a priori* reason for preferring the one type of analysis to the other, Dr. Swadesh was kind enough to make both. Hence Curve A_1, in Fig. 3–1, represents the "morpheme" rank-frequency distribution of Nootka in which the occurrences of *goose* and *gos* would fall together, while Curve A_2 represents the corresponding "varimorph" analysis in which the occurrences of *goose* and *gos* would be treated separately. Curve *B* represents the rank-frequency distribution of the *B* Analysis.

As we inspect the curves of Fig. 3–1, we note some interesting relationships. First of all, the two curves, A_1 and A_2, both approximate rather closely the straight line of the harmonic equation (as can be noted by comparing them with the line *C* which has been drawn with a negative slope of 1 to aid the reader's eye). This close approximation to linearity of the two *A* curves may be of interest apart from the considerations of this study,

---

to suggest that the *B* Analysis is fundamentally a rank-frequency distribution of permutations of words, with the smallest permutation consisting of a single word; that is, the *B* Analysis consists of completely homogeneous data. We have merely used the term *holophrase* in the sense of a permutation of two or more words, for the sake of a greater convenience of exposition.

for it shows that behind the elaborate holophrastic constructions of Nootka lies a fundamental rectilinearity.

As to the two curves, A_1 and A_2, the curve A_2 of the "varimorphs" (in which *"goose"* and *"gos"* would be kept apart) seems to approximate the harmonic distribution somewhat more closely than the "morpheme" count of A_1. In other words the *formal* classification of these speech entities yields a closer approximation than the *formal-semantic* classification; and that is fortunate because in our entire study of words up to this point we have

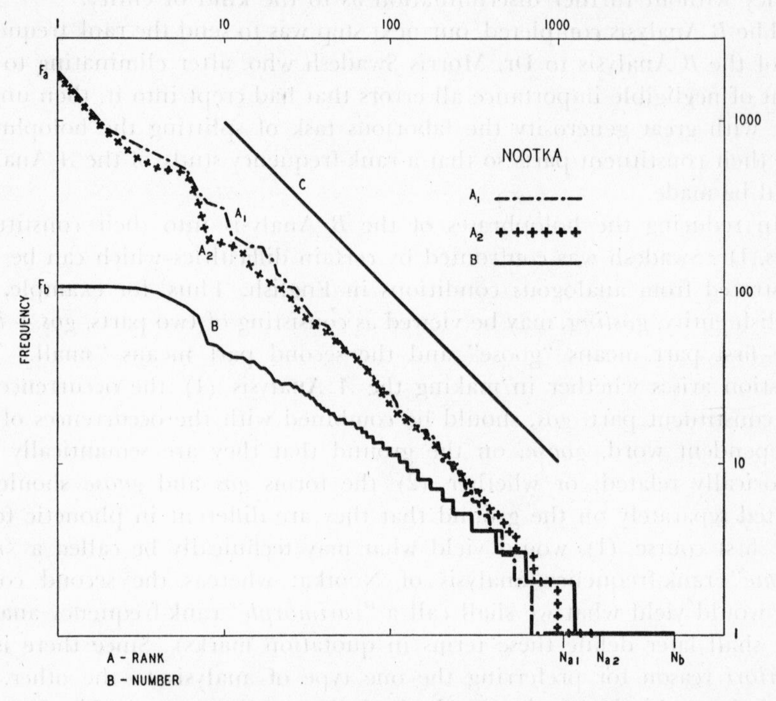

Fig. 3–1. Nootka. The rank-frequency distribution of (A_1) "varimorphs," (A_2) morphemes, and (B) holophrases.

consistently used formal distinctions (i.e., "different forms mean different words") and not *formal-semantic* ones except in the single case where we studied the frequencies of meanings (Fig. 2–2).

The fact that Curve A_1 has a smaller *X*-intercept (N_{a_1}) than that of curve A_2 is understandable from the fact that differences, such as that between *goose* and *gos,* which were preserved in A_2, were eliminated in A_1. On the other hand, the fact that these two curves intersect each other in the center has not been anticipated, and suggests that the splitting up of morphemes into their subsidiary formal varimorphs may itself be subject to a rigorous principle—as indeed would have to be the case if the Principle of Least Effort be correct.

Turning now to the *B* Curve, which represents holophrases plus independent words, we note that the difference between F_b and F_a is appreciably greater than the difference between n_b on the one hand, and either n_{a_1} (of the A_1 Curve) and n_{a_2} (of the A_2 Curve) on the other. It seems, in general, that as the A Curves are transformed into the B Curve, the A Curves sacrifice from their frequencies amounts that are *at least* equivalent to a power of the frequencies. In short, the more frequently an entity occurs on either of the A Curves, the *ever more frequently* it is used in holophrases. That much we may conclude from the nature of the curves of Fig. 3–1 without the need of knowing anything further about the particular entities involved. And that much is all we need to be able to conclude in order to argue that the data of Fig. 3–1 represent the Principle of the Economical Permutation of Words in reference to the permutation of the respective A entities into the B entities, as anticipated from our Tool Analogy. For we need only note that in changing from A to B, the upper portion of the left of either A Curve drops at a much faster rate than that at which the lower portion of the B Curve extends itself to the right on doubly logarithmic paper.

Hence the data of Fig. 3–1 provide an affirmative empiric test of the Principle of Economical Permutation.

Although the respective curves of Fig. 3–1 can apparently be explained only on the grounds that the A entities of greater frequency entered into ever more different and more frequently used permutations, nevertheless we might digress for a moment and, for didactic reasons, suggest how the B Curve might look if that were not the case. Thus if a sizable number of the most rarely used A entities were alone permuted, then n_b would not necessarily be much larger than n_{a_1} or n_{a_2}; this would be true because the A entities that occur once could at most enter into one-half as many B holophrases that occur once, whereas the A entities that occur twice could at most enter into the same number of B holophrases, which however could occur only once; moreover the upper left-hand portion of the B Curve would be congruent with one or another of the A Curves—depending upon the criterion adopted for the A Curve—until the point was reached down the B Curve where the permutations began; at this point the B Curve would drop suddenly and precipitously. The same sudden and precipitous drop would occur in the middle of the B Curve if the permutations were made only from the entities in the middle range of the A Curves. But we observe no precipitous drop in the B Curve, and very little change in slope after the first ten or dozen most frequent entities of the B Curve. Therefore the most frequent A entities were permuted.

Except for the first ten or a dozen of the most frequent entities of the B Analysis, the B Curve descends with a fairly close approximation to a straight line with a negative slope that is appreciably less than 1. This essentially rectilinear distribution we did not anticipate theoretically from the Tool Analogy, nor could we anticipate it without establishing many arbitrary *ad hoc* rules for the way that the mechanical tools should be permuted. Nevertheless, now that an essentially rectilinear distribution has appeared in the B Curve, we may properly ask why that should be the case. And in reply we can only suggest that the very Forces of Unification and Diversification which we discussed in our preceding chapter will apply also here. That is, as n_b increases, then the frequencies will decrease by a fixed power of their frequencies, if we assume, first, that the two Forces stand in a power relationship to one another, and, second, that the *A* Curves are genuine approximations of the harmonic series. Or, speaking more simply, we may suggest that an increase in n_b will be attended by the following: (1) the words of the *A* Analysis will in general be absorbed into holophrases of the *B* Analysis in the order of their frequency, and by amounts that are proportionate to a power of their frequencies; (2) the more frequent words will enter into progressively fewer different shorter holophrases with the progressively less frequent words; and (3) the relative frequency of the resulting holophrases will be such that their frequency of usage will tend

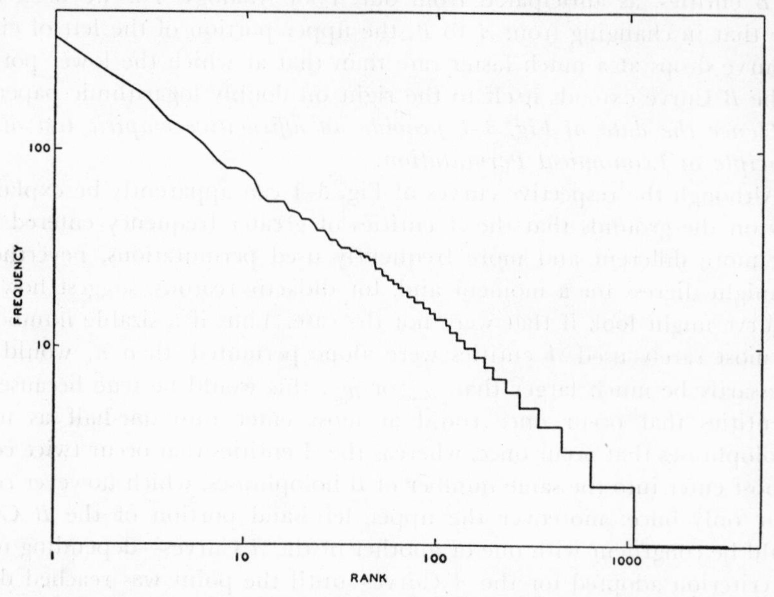

Fig. 3–2. Plains Cree. The rank-frequency distribution of holophrases.

to be directly related to the frequency of usage of their constituent parts.* Beyond this we cannot go for the present without introducing the concept of Economical Specialization. Nevertheless throughout our subsequent discussion of phrases, sentences, and morphemes, the above three points may profitably be borne in mind. Incidentally at a later and more opportune moment we shall discuss the *top-downward-concavity* † of the first ten or dozen words of the *B* Analysis which, as we shall then see, is quite generally characteristic of "informal" colloquial speech, as opposed to more "formal" studied verbalizations.

It is a pity that there are no complete sets of *A* and *B* data for other languages. Nevertheless *B* data are available for the very highly inflected American Indian language, Plains Cree. And in Fig. 3–2 we present the rank-frequency distribution of 10,000 running holophrases and independ-

* In Chapter Five we shall return again to a consideration of this Nootka material which we shall find of critical value for an understanding of semantic structure.

† By this term, we mean that at the top of the graph the curve is concave downward.

ent words as determined quantitatively by the present writer from samples taken from texts that were transcribed and published by Dr. Leonard Bloomfield.[14] The curve of Fig. 3–2 is to be compared with the *B* Curve of of Fig. 3–1.

In Fig. 3–2 we note a much closer approach to rectilinearity than was the case with Nootka, although the slopes are about the same. This means that a fundamental rectilinearity can be found in the *B* Curve of a very highly inflected language. Therefore we are not necessarily obliged to view the Nootka top-concavity in any other light than that in which we shall view

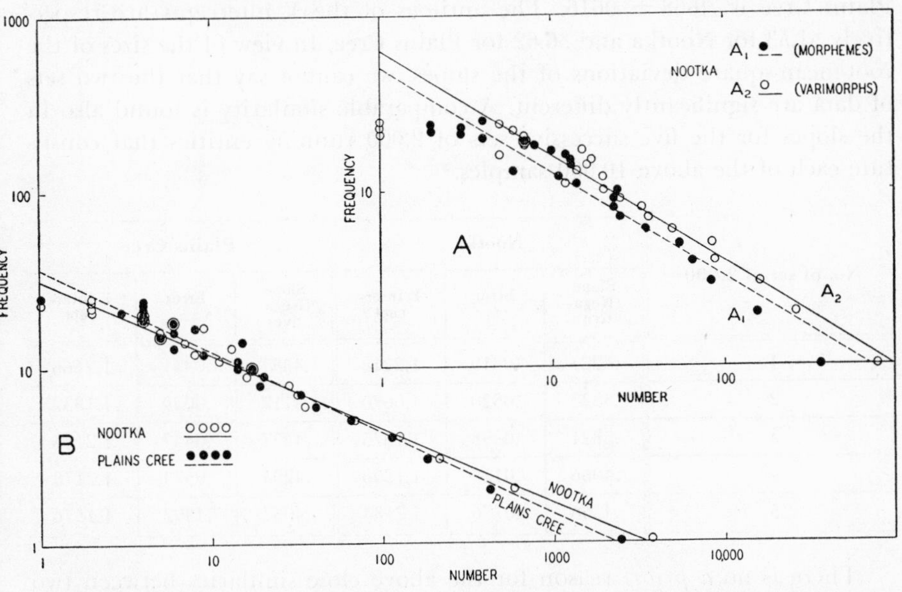

Fig. 3–3. The number-frequency relationship for Nootka and Plains Cree. (A) Nootka "varimorphs" and morphemes; (B) holophrases in Nootka and Plains Cree.

the comparable top-concavities in samples of colloquial English which we shall present and discuss later on.

Now that we have discussed the top portions of the *B* Curves for Nootka and Plains Cree we may turn to the lower portions where the "steps" appear, because the *N* number of different word-holophrases of like *f* frequency (or the "treads" of the "steps") will be linearly related to their respective *f* frequencies, *if the B Curves are fundamentally rectilinear.**

In Fig. 3–3, which consists of an upper right-hand section, (*A*), and a lower left-hand section, (*B*), we present in the lower left-hand section,

* The general equation will be $N \times (f^b - \frac{1}{4}) = C$. Since the size of *b* will be $p + 1 +$ *a small constant* if *p* represents the reciprocal of the slope of the rank-frequency distribution, it follows that the *b* of both *B* Curves will be larger than 2. We are presenting in the text the least-square slopes of the "treads" of the "steps."[15] The absence of least-square calculations for the full rank-frequency distributions in this and the preceding chapter is due to the enormous labor involved in fitting so many points. A fit of every 10th rank would tell us little more than we already know from the graphs. In the fourth chapter the reader will find plenty of least-square calculations of rank-frequency slopes.

(*B*), the *N* number of different word-holophrases of like *f* frequency of the *B* Curves of Nootka and Plains Cree with *N* on the abscissa, and *f* on the ordinate; circles represent Nootka and the dots represent Plains Cree. In each case the values of *f* are from 1 through 25, beyond which a considerable scattering begins, as is to be expected.

An inspection of the *B* data of Fig. 3–3 reveals an unmistakable linearity for both Nootka and Plains Cree. Moreover the two sets of data are not widely different in respect of slope and intercept. As calculated by least squares, the negative slope for Nootka is .4241 ± .0539, whereas that for Plains Cree is .4668 ± .0616. The antilogs of the *Y* intercepts are respectively 31.53 for Nootka and 36.62 for Plains Cree. In view of the sizes of the root-mean-square deviations of the slopes, we cannot say that the two sets of data are significantly different. A comparable similarity is found also in the slopes for the five successive sets of 2,000 running entities that constitute each of the above 10,000 samples.*

No. of set of 2,000	Nootka			Plains Cree		
	Slope (Negative)	Error ±	*Y* Intercept	Slope (Negative)	Error ±	*Y* Intercept
1	.4223	.0819	1.2218	.4557	.0441	1.2668
2	.3523	.0520	1.0670	.4112	.0099	1.1832
3	.3821	.0295	1.1375	.4237	.0447	1.2143
4	.4066	.0128	1.1890	.4294	.0574	1.2178
5	.4366	.0776	1.2584	.4057	.1992	1.1576

There is no *a priori* reason for the above close similarity between two widely separated and apparently unrelated languages. Indeed, apart from the Principles of Least Effort there is no *a priori* reason for the linearity at all, since it is *possible* to construct languages in which the number of words of like frequency increases with the frequency. Nevertheless the unmistakable linearity of the two *B* distributions of Fig. 3–3 is impressive, and tends to reassure us not only that the permutation of entities into holophrases is not a matter of caprice, but also that our Principle of Economical Permutation of Speech Entities is not fantastic. The general similarity in the slopes and intercepts of Nootka and Plains Cree may mean that the permutations of both languages have approached the limiting *Z* value discussed in reference to our tools. So much, then, for the *B* data at the lower left of Fig. 3–3.

There still remain for our consideration the data marked *A* in the upper right-hand corner of Fig. 3–3, which represent the number-frequency relationship of the "morphemes" (dots) and of the "varimorphs" (circles) respectively of the A_1 and A_2 Curves of Nootka as presented in Fig. 3–1, and

* The least-square negative slopes, errors and logarithmic *Y* intercepts of the five successive sets of 2,000 entities of Nootka and Plains Cree for *N* number of different words of like *f*, with values of *f* from 1 through 10.

as plotted like the *B* data of Fig. 3–3. The values of *f* are from 1 through 25 for the "morphemes," and from 1 through 25 for the "varimorphs," although the latter data are freakish from points 21 through 25. Nevertheless, in each case we find approximations to linearity. The least-square negative slope for "morphemes" (A_1) is .5996 ± .1049 with the *Y* intercept (logarithmic) at 1.70282; the negative slope for the first 20 points of the "varimorphs" (A_2) as represented by the line drawn is .6017 ± .0694 with the *Y* intercept at 1.7989. However, if the data are recalculated for the 25 lowest frequencies, the negative slope drops to .4716 ± .1212 with the *Y* intercept at 1.5883; although this line does not fit as closely as the line for the first 20 points, nevertheless the error is not greatly different from that for A_1.

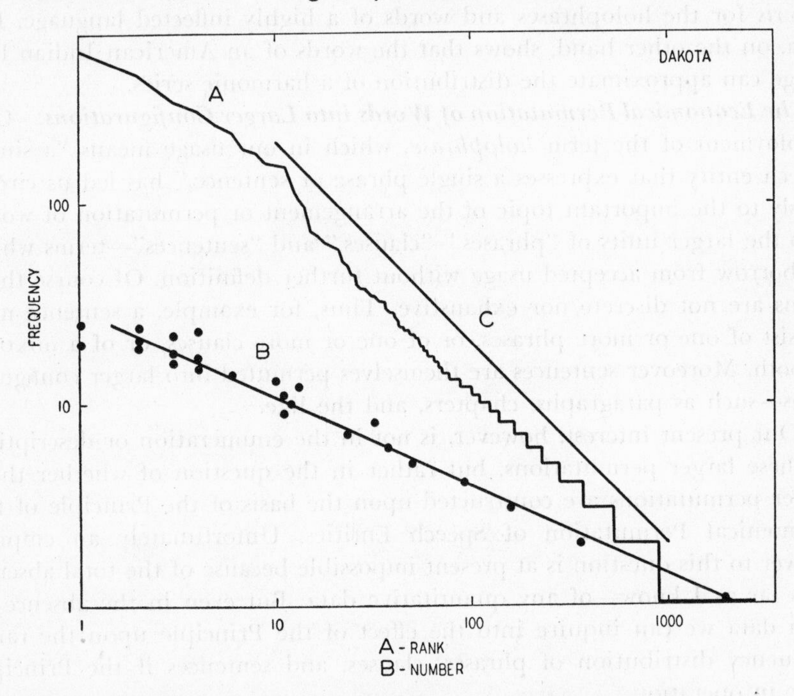

Fig. 3–4. Dakota words. (A) Rank-frequency distribution; (B) number-frequency distribution; (C) ideal curve with slope of negative unity.

Our concern for the niceties of statistical minutiae should not divert our attention from the obvious fundamental linearity of the various curves, which indicates that the classification of the stream of speech, whether into words-holophrases, or into "varimorphs," or into "morphemes," is subject to an orderly governing principle of the type which we have anticipated theoretically under the rubric of the Principle of Economical Permutation.

Before leaving the American Indian languages we present for good measure in Fig. 3–4 the frequency distribution of 10,000 running words of Dakota from the texts by Ella Deloria.[16] The *A* Curve represents the rank-frequency distribution with the line *C* of −1 slope drawn to aid the reader's eye; the *B* Curve represents the *N* number of different words of like *f* frequency for all words occurring from 1 through 25 times. In spite of the bends in the *A* Curve, we note in the *B* Curve a remarkable linearity for the number of different words that occur 25 or fewer times in the sample. The negative slope for the *B* Curve is .4373 ± .0663 with the antilog of the *Y* intercept at 29.360. These values, curiously enough, do not differ widely from the corresponding values of Nootka and Plains Cree.*

Viewing in retrospect the *A* and *B* Curves of Nootka we may say that all three curves are essentially linear—indeed markedly so in respect of the entities of 25 or fewer frequencies; and that the configurations of the *A* and *B* Curves are of the type that we expected theoretically from our Principle of Economical Permutation; and that the distributions of words that occur 25 or fewer times in Plains Cree show that the Nootka *B* Curve is not *sui generis* for the holophrases and words of a highly inflected language. Dakota, on the other hand, shows that the words of an American Indian language can approximate the distribution of a harmonic series.

2. The Economical Permutation of Words into Larger Configurations. Our employment of the term *holophrase,* which in our usage means "a single speech entity that expresses a single phrase or sentence," has led us circuitously to the important topic of the arrangement or permutation of words into the larger units of "phrases," "clauses," and "sentences"—terms which we borrow from accepted usage without further definition. Of course these terms are not discrete nor exhaustive. Thus, for example, a sentence may consist of one or more phrases, or of one or more clauses, or of a mixture of both. Moreover sentences are themselves permuted into larger configurations—such as paragraphs, chapters, and the like.

Our present interest, however, is not in the enumeration or description of these larger permutations, but rather in the question of whether these larger permutations are constructed upon the basis of the Principle of the Economical Permutation of Speech Entities. Unfortunately an empiric answer to this question is at present impossible because of the total absence —as far as I know—of any quantitative data. But even in the absence of such data we can inquire into the effect of the Principle upon the rank-frequency distribution of phrases, clauses, and sentences if the Principle were in operation.

Turning first to the question of *phrases,* we should expect theoretically that a few phrases, like *at home* or *with me* are used with a comparatively high frequency, whereas an increasing number of different phrases are used with an ever-diminishing frequency until we come to phrases of truly negligible frequency like *underneath the lorgnette.* Moreover we should also expect theoretically that all these phrases—whether frequent or infrequent—would consist of a small number of highly frequent words in permutation with words of diminishing frequency, as in fact seems to be the case, since practically all phrases consist of the highly frequent prep-

* The negative least-square (*a*) slopes, errors and (*b*) logarithmic *Y*-intercepts for the 5 successive sets of 2,000 running words that constitute the 10,000 word sample of Dakota are respectively: (1) *a*: .41097 ± .0510; *b*: 1.1415; (2) *a*: .42506 ± .0632; *b*: 1.17705; (3) *a*: .35499 ± .0612; *b*: 1.05386; (4) *a*: .40290 ± .0622; *b*: 1.12776; (5) *a*: .38461 ± .0576; *b*: 1.10316.

ositions in permutation with words of varying but of generally lesser frequency. Indeed the frequency of phrases might well be found to be related to the frequency of their least frequent parts; the phrase *with him* being more frequent than the phrase *with the whetlock,* even as *him* is more frequent than *whetlock.* Although no quantitative data are available to test the accuracy of the above theoretical deductions, nevertheless the deductions themselves do not strike us as being fantastic in the light of our common experience with speech.

As we have argued about phrases, so too we might argue to the same general effect *mutatis mutandis* about clauses and sentences—an argument which incidentally is susceptible to empiric test only by the stupendous labor of studying the relative frequency of these larger entities in samples of speech, which perforce would have to be truly enormous if the entities were to have an adequate opportunity to repeat.

It might be argued, however, that many words like *with, without, when, where, until,* and so on, occur very largely as constituent parts of the larger phrasal, clausal, and sentence entities to whose extensive usage the above words owe their general high frequency. In short, the words have a high frequency of usage because of their high frequency of usage in the larger entities to which they belong. But this argument by no means invalidates our Principle of Economical Permutation. On the contrary, in the light of our Principle of Economical Permutation we may theoretically view the stream of speech as consisting of permutations of permutations which are in turn permutations, and so on. According to the Principle, the comparatively more frequent members of the smaller permutations will be used comparatively more often as constituents of the larger permutations. It is this economy which lies in the Principle of Permutation which permits of a truly enormous diversity of activity from what are basically a very small number of primary speech entities.

Yet now that we have discussed theoretically the permutation of words into larger entities, the task remains of analyzing words into their constituent parts, in the belief that words too are permutations of smaller parts. For this analysis an abundance of quantitative data is available.

3. The Economical Permutation of Morphemes into Words. Let us say that a word consists of one or more *morphemes.* And we shall adopt the traditional definition of a *morpheme* as the minimal unit of speech which has a perceptible meaning. According to this definition the word, *un-tru-th-ful-ness,* may be said to consist of the five hyphenated morphemes, because these are the minimal units of meaningfulness. By the same token the word *mousetrap* has two morphemes; the word *cat* has one morpheme, whereas *cats,* or *cat's* or *cats'* each have two.

The question now arises as to whether morphemes are permuted into words according to the Principle of Economical Permutation. That is—in terms of the roots, affixes and endings of a fairly highly inflected language like present-day German—may we anticipate theoretically that a few different affixes and endings will be used with a high relative frequency in combination with a large number of different roots of comparatively low relative frequency? Surely on the basis of our feelings about German or any other similarly highly inflected language, the above theoretical anticipation does not sound bizarre, and indeed in the quantitative data that we shall shortly present it is distinctly realized.

Before turning to the actual sets of quantitative data, a few words of caution are in order. First of all, some languages, like English, have words that are difficult to morphologize; for example, we might not all agree as to the best manner of handling the hundreds of English words of Latin origin which, like *constitution* or *difficult,* are not morphologically transparent to the great majority of native speakers. This difficulty can be avoided by choosing those languages for analysis whose morphological structures are, on the whole, transparent.

A second difficulty relates to the *affixes* and *endings* of words even in these latter languages. For although there is rarely much doubt as to what the *root morpheme* of a word is, there is sometimes considerable doubt as to what the morphological components of the affixes and endings are. Thus in regard to the present-day German words, *wartete* ("waited") and *fragte* ("asked"), there might be some doubt as to how to analyze and compare the endings *ete* and *te*. Even though Germanic philologists might conceivably agree about this point, they would probably never agree about the comparable problems represented by the one-time identical endings which in Gothic had become under some conditions *jis* and under other conditions *eis,* and which could refer either to the second singular of verbs, or to the genitive singular of nouns: e.g., *nas-jis,* "thou savest," *sok-eis,* "thou seekest," *kun-jis,* "of the generation," and *haird-eis,* "of the shepherd."

As long as the root morphemes are on the whole quite easily isolatable, we can approach this problem of affix classification by first learning as much as we can about the distribution of the bare root morphemes. We shall begin our empiric analysis by inspecting the number-frequency of the bare root morphemes (and other morphemes) of several languages.

In Fig. 3–5 are presented three sets of data, *A, B,* and *C,* on doubly logarithmic paper. The points of *A* represent the *N* number of different "stem forms" (i.e., root morphemes) of like *f* frequency with values of *f* from 1 through 1,000 as determined by F. W. Kaeding in a count of approximately 11 million running words of German (with points above $f = 5$ calculated for the respective class-middles).[17] The *diamonds* of *B* represent the *N* number of different Chinese characters of like *f* frequency for values of *f* from 1 through 100 of the approximately 4,500 different characters in samples totalling nearly a million running characters as published by Mr. Ch'ên[2] Hao[2]-Ch'in[2] with the Commercial Press of Shanghai.[18] The *circles* of *C* represent the *N* number of different root morphemes of like *f* frequency, with values of *f* from 1 through 25 as determined by me from the Gothic Bible totalling 58,293 running words.[19] Before discussing in turn each of these three sets of data, we point out that each set of points is fundamentally linear and of roughly the same slope. We have not calculated the actual slopes of these sets of points because, as we shall see, some of them are incomplete. However, in the case of Chinese and Gothic we shall presently show (in Fig. 3–6) that their negative slope is approximately 1.

Now as to the *A* data for Kaeding's "stem forms" we note that the lowest 10 points which represent frequencies from 1 through 200 (or 77.81% of the stem forms) fall pretty closely upon a straight line whose negative slope seems to the eye to be not far off from 1. The upper two points, which represent frequencies from 201 through 1,000 (or 12.5% of the total), fall appreciably to the left of this straight line, much as if some members were absent from the classes in question; and that is understandable because

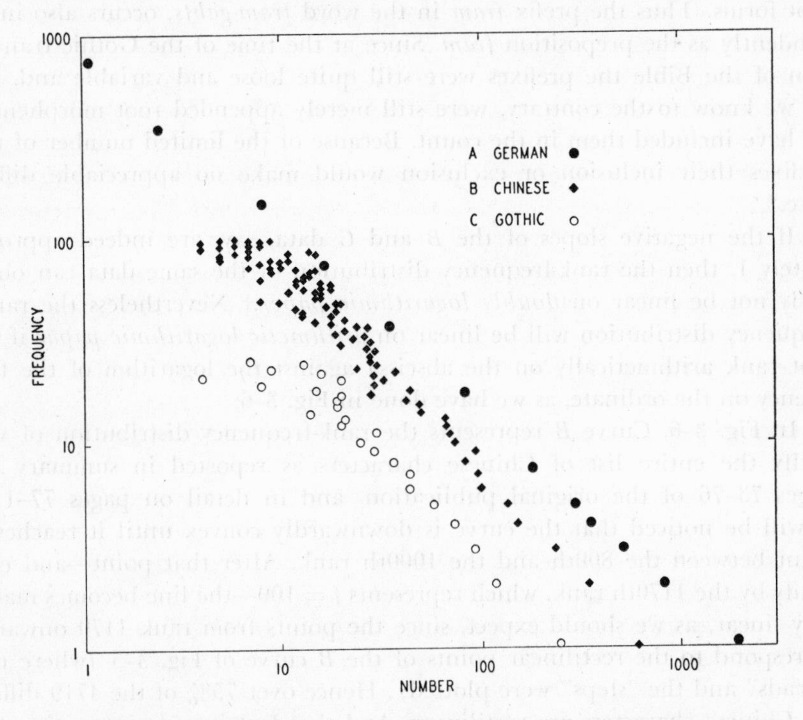

Fig. 3–5. The number-frequency distribution of (A) German stem forms; (B) Chinese characters; (C) Gothic root morphemes.

somewhere in this range would belong the least frequent affixes and endings which Kaeding excluded. As to the number of stem forms above 1,000, which we have not plotted, their points bend ever farther to the left of the straight line of the lowest 10 points. If the reader desires any further information about Dr. Kaeding's study, he may consult the original data, which are published in full. Our interest in his data is restricted to the fact that his stem forms (i.e., *Stammformen*), which for all intents and purposes represent root morphemes, are linearly related in respect to the *N* number of different stem forms of like *f* frequency.

As to the diamonds of *B* which refer to the *N* number Chinese characters of like *f* frequency, we again note a close approximation to linearity with a negative slope of 1. These Chinese characters are not the same as root morphemes (a term that is not applicable to Chinese). Rather do they represent different "ideas" on a syllabic morphological basis; two or more different characters may be represented by phonetically the same morpheme. For the present we are interested primarily in the linearity and slope of the distribution of characters.

As to the circles of *C* which represent Gothic root morphemes we note a linear distribution that is not radically different in slope from *A* or *B*. These root morphemes include not only the actual roots of the words, but also the "prefixes." These "prefixes" were included because some of them—and all of them occurring 25 or fewer times—have independent usage as root forms. Thus the prefix *fram* in the word *fram-gahts,* occurs also independently as the preposition *fram.* Since at the time of the Gothic translation of the Bible the prefixes were still quite loose and variable and, for all we know to the contrary, were still merely appended root morphemes, we have included them in the count. Because of the limited number of the prefixes their inclusion or exclusion would make no appreciable difference.*

If the negative slopes of the *B* and *C* data, say, are indeed approximately 1, then the rank-frequency distribution of the same data can obviously not be linear on *doubly logarithmic paper.*† Nevertheless the rank-frequency distribution will be linear on *arithmetic logarithmic paper* if we plot rank arithmetically on the abscissa against the logarithm of the frequency on the ordinate, as we have done in Fig. 3–6.

In Fig. 3–6, Curve *B* represents the rank-frequency distribution of virtually the entire list of Chinese characters as reported in summary on pages 73–76 of the original publication, and in detail on pages 77–116. It will be noticed that the curve is downwardly convex until it reaches a point between the 800th and the 1000th rank. After that point—and certainly by the 1170th rank, which represents $f = 100$—the line becomes markedly linear, as we should expect, since the points from rank 1170 onwards correspond to the rectilinear points of the *B* curve of Fig. 3–5 (where the "treads" and the "steps" were plotted). Hence over 75% of the 4719 different Chinese characters are rectilinear. And that fact is truly interesting because, as we have previously pointed out, these Chinese characters are by no means all phonetically different. Indeed when the 4719 different characters are reduced to a phonetic basis (i.e., varimorphs) they shrink in number to 1136, according to an analysis I had made.‡ Just what this arith-

---

* Foreign proper names, mostly from the Aramaic, that Wulfilus borrowed from the Greek Bible were treated as root morphemes unless they had Gothic endings, in which latter case, the form minus the ending was counted.

† In general, if p is the reciprocal of the slope of a linear *rank-frequency* distribution, then the reciprocal of the slope of the *number-frequency* distribution will be $p + 1 - a$ *small constant.*

‡ These characters when reduced to a *phonetic* basis are not too far off from linearity on arith-log grid from the point $f = 100$ to the point $f = 2{,}000$; for the higher frequencies the rank-frequency distribution is markedly convex downward; for the lower frequencies it is markedly convex upwards, thereby indicating a sample that is well above optimum size. With the removal of the differentiating phonemic tones, there were only 394 different "toneless" varimorphs. The linearity of the rank-frequency distribution of 20,000 running Chinese characters has already been reported elsewhere.[20]

metic-logarithmic linearity of Chinese characters implies remains an open question. In any event the linearity points to a regularity which is not unlike that for Gothic, as is clear from Curve C_1 of Fig. 3–6, to whose consideration we now turn.

Curve C_1 represents a rank-frequency distribution of the following combined entities (*a*) the root morphemes, which consist both of the roots and of the prefixes, and (*b*) the "bare endings," which are what remained of the

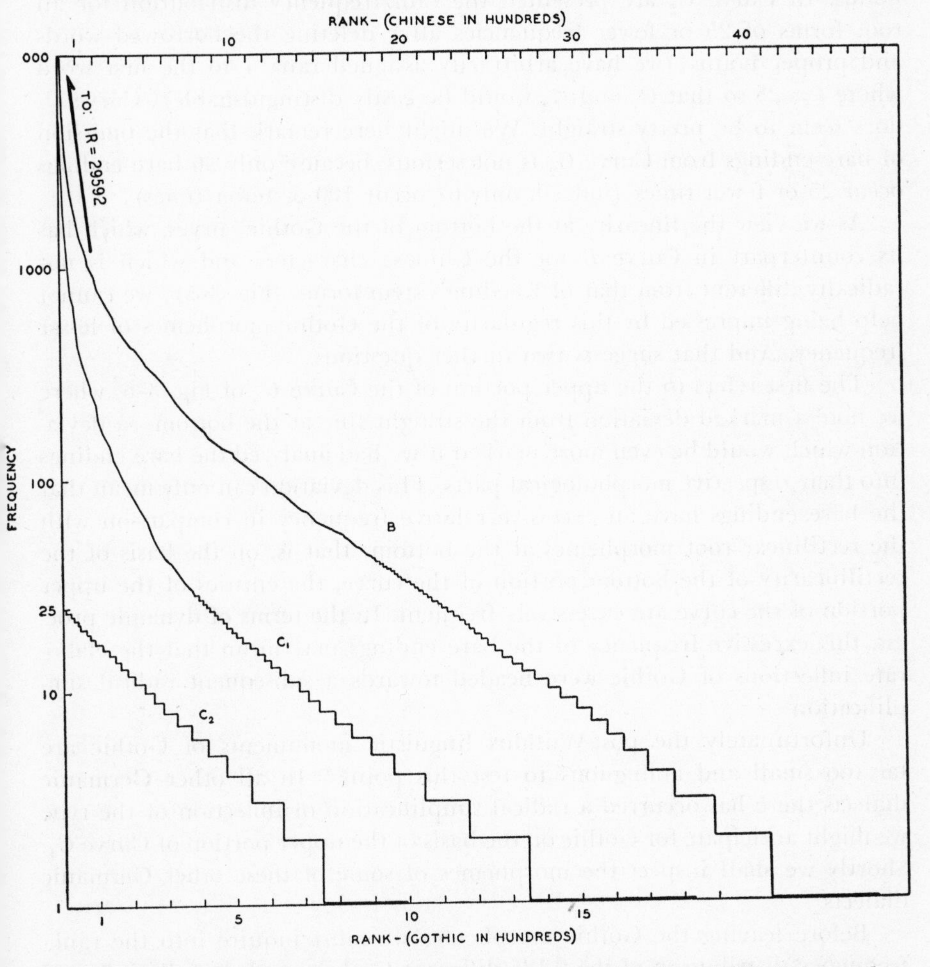

Fig. 3–6. Chinese and Gothic. The rank-frequency distribution of (B) Chinese characters and (C) Gothic root morphemes (see text).

words after the roots and prefixes had been removed. (Technically these "bare endings" consisted of stem-formant plus ending, e.g., *-jis, -eis,* etc.) We remember that in the case of foreign proper or common nouns (e.g., *Abrahamiis, praitoriaun*) we did not analyze the word into its foreign root and prefixes but treated it as a root morpheme.

In the rank-frequency distribution of the combined root morphemes plus bare endings, as presented in Curve C_1 we note a general similarity in configuration to Curve *B* for the Chinese data.

But if we inspect more closely the lower portion of C_1 of Fig. 3–6 (which represents the frequencies from 1 through 25 and corresponds to the circles of Fig. 3–5), we seem to detect a slight downward convexity. It occurred to me that the borrowed words and proper names of Biblical origin which were included among the root morphemes and which could not be analyzed into Gothic morphemes might be responsible for this slight convexity, which would disappear with the deletion of the borrowed words and proper nouns. In Curve C_2 are presented the rank-frequency distribution for all root forms of 25 or fewer frequencies after deleting the borrowed words and proper nouns (we have arbitrarily assigned rank 1 to the first word whose $f = 25$ so that C_1 and C_2 would be easily distinguishable). Curve C_2 does seem to be pretty straight. We might here remark that the omission of bare endings from Curve C_2 is not serious, because only 36 bare endings occur 25 or fewer times (indeed, only 62 occur 100 or fewer times).

As we view the linearity at the bottom of the Gothic curves, which has its counterpart in Curve *B* for the Chinese characters and which is not radically different from that of Kaeding's stem forms (Fig. 3–5), we cannot help being impressed by this regularity of the Gothic morphemes of lesser frequency. And that suggests two further questions.

The first refers to the upper portion of the Curve C_1 of Fig. 3–6, where we note a marked deviation from the straight line at the bottom—a deviation which would be even more marked if we had analyzed the bare endings into their respective morphological parts. This deviation can only mean that the bare endings have an excessive relative frequency in comparison with the rectilinear root morphemes at the bottom; that is, on the basis of the rectilinearity of the bottom portion of the curve, the entities of the upper portion of the curve are excessively frequent. In the terms of dynamic process, this excessive frequency of the bare endings may mean that the elaborate inflections of Gothic were headed towards a subsequent radical simplification.

Unfortunately the post-Wulfilus linguistic monuments of Gothic are far too small and ambiguous to test this point.* In all other Germanic dialects there has occurred a radical simplification of inflection of the type we might anticipate for Gothic on the basis of the upper portion of Curve C_1. Shortly we shall inspect the morphemes of some of these other Germanic dialects.

Before leaving the Gothic morphemes we must inquire into the rank-frequency distribution of the 9,125 different Gothic words in fully inflected form in the total bulk of 58,293 running words from which the morpheme distribution was obtained. For we remember that an empiric test of the Principle of Economical Permutation involves an analysis not only of the frequency-distribution of the morpheme-components of words but also of the frequency-distribution of the words themselves. Data on the "words" of the Chinese character study are apparently not available. Moreover,

* We have analyzed Gothic merely because out of all the recorded Germanic dialects, the Gothic is morphologically most transparent, with the exception of the Norse inscriptions of *ca.* 700 or earlier which are too sparse to be used statistically.

Kaeding's total bulk of nearly 11 million running words so far overshoots a sample of optimum size that it is of little practical use for us. The Gothic frequency-distribution of Gothic words is both available and usable, and is found in Fig. 3–7.

In Fig. 3–7 are two curves marked *A* and *B* respectively. Curve *A* represents the rank-frequency distribution of the 9,125 different words of Gothic in samples totalling 58,293 running words. As to the problem of what constitutes a word in Gothic, we merely remark that whatever was printed together and spaced as a word in the text was treated as a word; moreover

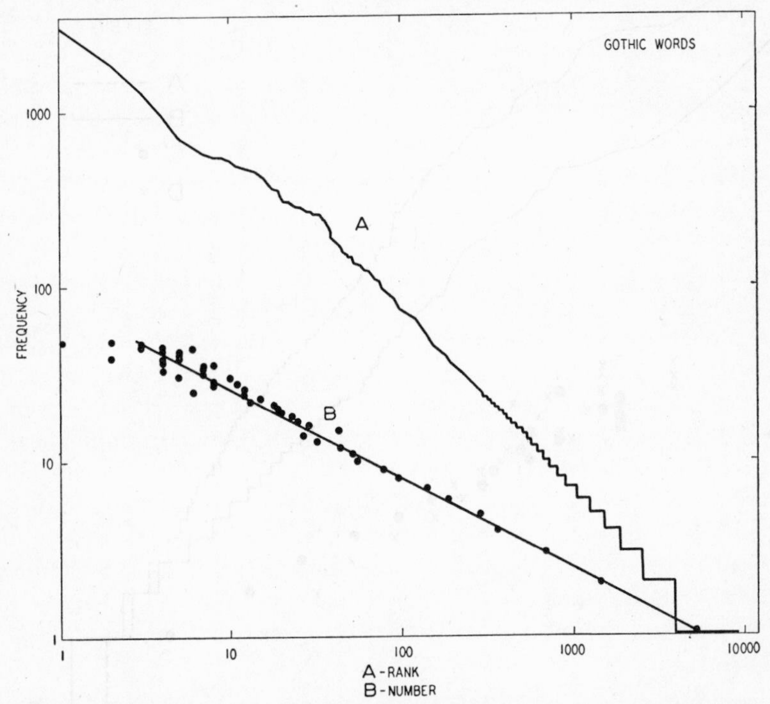

Fig. 3–7. Gothic words. (A) Rank-frequency distribution; (B) number-frequency distribution.

all words that were different in form we treated as different words, except for well-recognized scribal variations which had no phonetic significance (e.g., the traditional differences between *ei* and *e,* or between the final voiced and voiceless interdental spirants). Hence the analysis was made with virtually no tampering with the text.* We see from Fig. 3–7 that Curve *A* is fairly straight throughout, and notably straight for all but about the 40 most frequent words. Moreover, its slope is approximately that of a harmonic series.

Curve *B,* on the other hand, represents on the abscissa the *N* number of different words of like *f* frequency on the ordinate for all values of *f* from

* The statistical difference between an analysis of the words on a strictly formal basis and the one with the slight emendations above was found to be graphically indistinguishable.

1 through 49. No word happened to occur 50 times and there is a considerable scattering above 50. The line through these 49 points was calculated by least squares and is described by the equation $N \cdot F^{2.025} = 7040$. The exponent, 2.025, cannot be viewed as a wide deviation from 2.00, which is theoretically to be expected.*

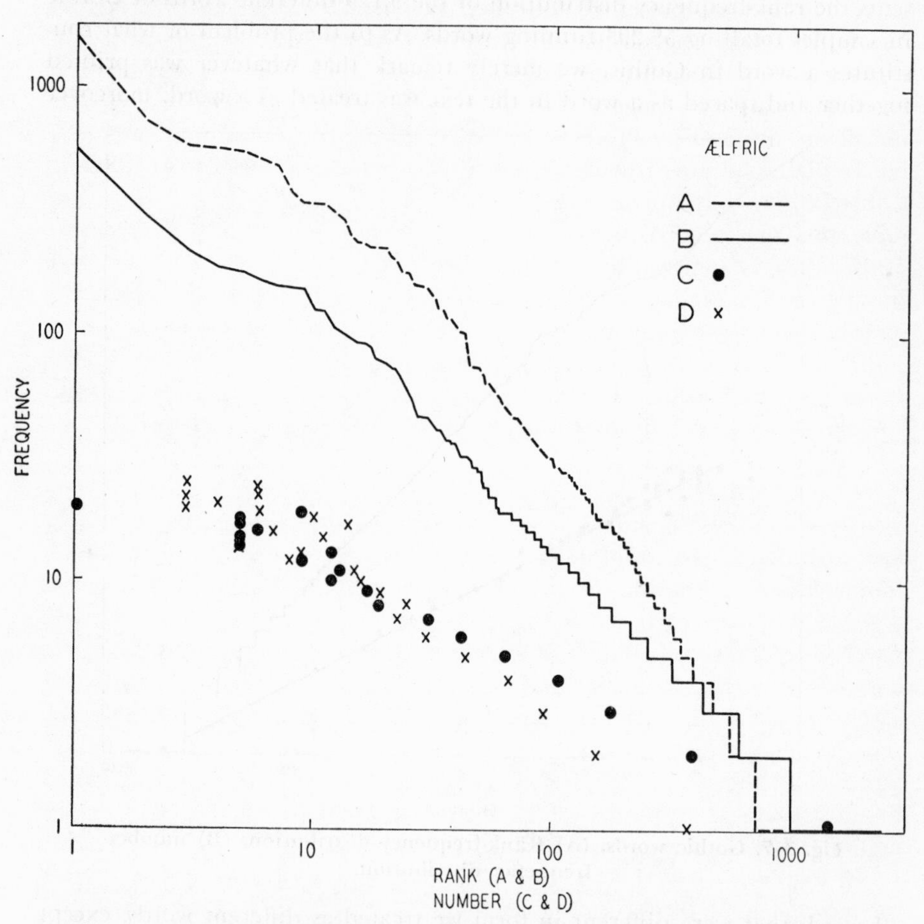

Fig. 3–8. Aelfric's Old English. (A) Rank-frequency distribution of morphemes; (B) rank-frequency distribution of words; (C) number-frequency distribution of morphemes; (D) number-frequency distribution of words.

In the light of the data presented in Figs. 3–5, 3–6, and 3–7 for the words and morphemes of Gothic, we are justified in saying, I think, that the Prin-

* The total sample of approximately 58,000 running words consisted of 5 different samples of 10,000 running words, 1 sample of 6356 words, and the *Skeireins* of 1905 words. The respective least square exponents and antilogs of the X-intercepts (in parentheses) are as follows: *1st,* 2.25 (2356); *2nd,* 2.13 (1923); *3rd,* 2.16 (2137); *4th,* 2.14 (1944); *5th,* 2.19 (1998); *6th,* 2.30 (1763); and *7th,* 2.41 (738). The increase in exponent with decrease in sample size can be anticipated theoretically. The rank-frequency distributions of the first 5 samples are similar. We may present these data in full in a future special publication, if desired.

ciple of Economical Permutation applies to the permutation of morphemes into words in Gothic, for the same reasons *mutatis mutandis* that we discussed in reference to the permutations of "word entities" into the holophrases of Nootka (Fig. 3–1).

Yet is Gothic unique in this respect?

In Fig. 3–8 are presented four different distributions, *A, B, C,* and *D,* for Aelfric's Old English. Curve *B* with the unbroken line represents the rank-frequency distribution of 10,000 running words from Sweet's *Selected Homilies of Aelfric* (page 2, line 1 through page 37, line 98) as made and put at my disposal by Professor F. P. Magoun, Jr.[21] The round dots of *C* represent the number-frequency relationship of the *N* number of different *words* of like *f* frequency for values of *f* from 1 through 20. Curve *A* represents the rank-frequency distribution of the *constituent morphemes* of the above as analyzed by my then student, Dr. Otto E. Schoen-René, with the help of Dr. Magoun. The crosses of *D* represent the number-frequency distribution of different morphemes of like frequency for values of *f* from 1 through 25. Curves *B, C,* and *D* are self-explanatory and are quite comparable to the Gothic. (Curve *A* was added in order to show the general configuration of all our rank-frequency curves of morphemes when plotted on *doubly logarithmic paper.*) Now let us turn to other data.

Thanks to the help of my former students, there are nine sets of data available for English and German which were originally gathered for the now abandoned project of a more comprehensive study of the dynamics of the evolution of English and German. Although space limitations preclude a presentation of each set of data in a separate figure like Fig. 3–8, we nevertheless present in Fig. 3–9 for all of them the *N* number of different *morphemes* of like frequency for all frequencies from 1 through 10 on the successive cycles of the logarithmic paper (hence the reader will make the shift, remembering that in all cases the value of *N* for $f = 1$ is between 100 and 400). Although the graphs give only the 10 lowest frequencies, we hasten to add that these 10 points are indicative of the slope and linearity of the higher frequencies.*

In Fig. 3–9, Curves *A* and *B* refer to older English. Curve *A* represents the morphemes of 6900 running words of the 12th Century *Holy Rood Tree* (Napier's text, EETS, 103) as selected and analyzed for this purpose by Mr. Russell F. W. Smith, whose further brilliant work on another topic we shall discuss in Chapter Seven. Curve *B* represents the morphemes of the first 10,000 words (omitting 139 Latin interpolations from the Vulgate,

* As to the German studies of Fig. 3–9, it should be pointed out that Professor John A. Walz recommended the German texts to be selected for the purpose, except in the case of Old High German where there is little choice. Each student did the complete job for his own sample; that is, he made the rank-frequency analysis of words (to be presented in a later figure), and he broke the words into what he considered to be their morphological components on the basis of the standard etymological dictionaries and comparative and historical grammars available. Then he broke the morphemes into their "varimorphs" (not charted) so that he might himself note how slight the statistical differences were in reference to some of the morphological details that often (and rightly so) are extensively treated in historical and comparative studies.

Christian commentators, and the ritual) of the 13th Century English *Ancren Riwle* (ed. James Morton, London: Camden Society, 1853) as selected and analyzed for this purpose by Mr. William M. Doerflinger; all borrowed Latin words like *Paternoster, Ave Maria, credo* which were integral units of the text were treated as one word and one morpheme.

As to the German studies: Curve *C* is a study of 4825 words in the Old High German of *Isidore "Contra-Judaeos,"* Paderborn, 1874 (representing late 8th Century at the latest) as selected and analyzed by Dr. A. Murray Fowler, whose other studies we have previously discussed. Curve *D* represents the morphemes in 9915 running words of the *Ackermann aus Böhmen* (1400 A.D.) as analyzed by Dr. Kenneth Lagerstedt. Curve *E* represents the morphemes of Dr. Arthur Watzinger's analysis of the 568 running words of

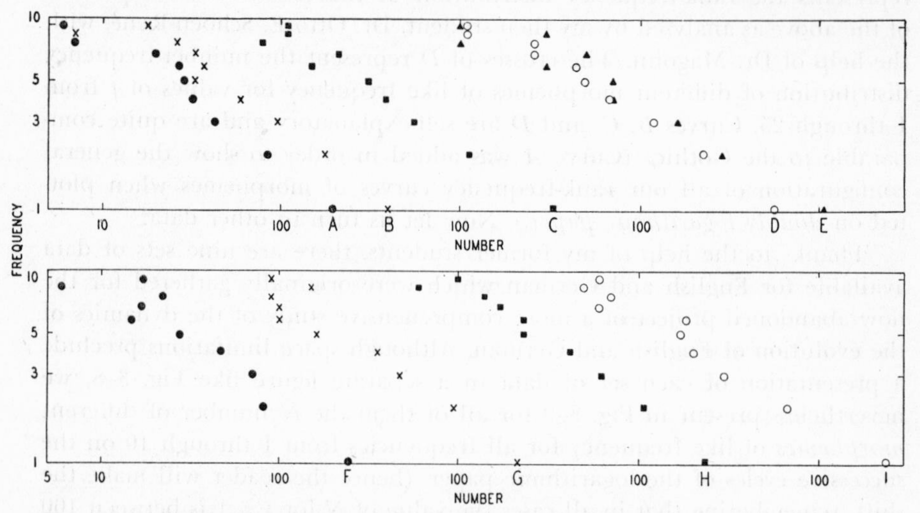

Fig. 3–9. English and German morphemes. The number-frequency distributions of nine different authors.

the *ca.* 10th Century *Lorscher Beichte* (Braune, W., *Althochdeutsches Lesebuch,* 1928, p. 120 f.). Curve *F* represents Dr. Caroline P. Riley's analysis of the morphemes in 10,000 running words of the middle 13th Century preacher Bertold von Regensburg (ed. Pfeiffer and Strobl, Wien, 1880, Vol. II, pp. 24–26; 145–153; 165–173; 233–237; 265, lines 1–7). Curve *G* represents Mr. S. A. R. Stephen's analysis of the morphemes of 4628 running words of the preacher, Geiler von Kaisersberg, 1445–1510 A.D. (ed. L. Dacheux, Freiburg, 1882, pp. 229–248). Curve *H* represents Dr. A. Watzinger's count of the morphemes in 5030 running words of previously mentioned Bertold von Regensburg's sermon (*op. cit.*) *"Von den fünf Pfunden."* Curve *I* represents Mr. S. A. R. Stephen's morpheme analysis of the famous *Wessobrunner Predigt* and *Otlohs Gebet* of the *ca.* late 11th Century (Braune, *op. cit.,* XXVI and XXVII).

In sum the nine sets of data of Fig. 3–9 refer to smallish samples of celebrated linguistic monuments which cover a time interval as large as that from Chaucer to the present, and which differ greatly in respect of region and dialect. They are purposely not ordered as to time. May the reader inspect them and try to find any truly significant differences! As far as I can see, the data are fundamentally linear with only slight differences in slope of a kind to be anticipated from differences in the sizes of the samples.* In addition to the above data, Dr. Lagerstedt analyzed the Old High German *Bamberger Glaube and Beichte* and Dr. Watzinger analyzed the Old Saxon *Beichte* (Braune, *op. cit.*, XXXXVII); the results are so similar to those presented in the graph that their inclusion did not seem to justify the crowded appearance that Fig. 3–9 would then have.

In view of these data (for which the corresponding rank-frequency analyses of *words* will be presented later) it is quite difficult to believe that we are not dealing with a primary dynamic regularity as far as the morpheme structure of words is concerned; after all there is no *a priori* necessity for such an agreement, since other morpheme-distributions are possible including the very reverse case of the frequent occurrence of many morphemes and the rare occurrence of few. If we compare on the one hand the *A* and *B* distributions for Nootka in Fig. 3–3, and on the other hand, say, the *B* and *D* distributions for Aelfric in Fig. 3–8, we note that the distributions are in all cases linear; yet as we pass from holophrases, to words, to morphemes, the slope systematically rises. This aspect of the Principle of the Economical Permutation of Speech Entities we should not overlook.

Now that we have shown that morphemes follow the Principle of Economical Permutation, may we also say that they follow the Principle of Economical Abbreviation? In reply, yes. The magnitudes of morphemes increase as their frequencies decrease. Data in support of this correlation have been presented in a previous publication,[22] and all the morphemes of the frequency-lists which we have mentioned in this chapter corroborate this earlier finding. In short, the same Principles of Economy govern the number, sizes, and frequencies of morphemes, as of words.

But do these Principles of Economy stop with the morpheme, or do they extend their influence even into the minutiae of the phonetic system, out of whose raw materials the stream of speech is constructed?

4. The Economy of a Phonetic System. Thus far we have inspected the economical permutation of "word entities" into holophrases, and also the economical permutation of morphemes into words. Now we shall turn to the basic *phonetic entities* that are permuted into morphemes (and words) and ask whether *phonetic entities* are also subject to the same principles of economy as are the others. That brings us to the question of a definition of a *phonetic entity*.

We might define a *phonetic entity* quite simply as "the minimal unit of distinctive significance" in the sense that it is the smallest unit that is dis-

* In this connection, least-square straight lines would tell us nothing new of importance. A "best straight line" can be drawn through a perfect cloud of points. Moreover slopes and errors would be merely curiosities because of differences in sample size and possibly in techniques of analysis. Figure 3–9 is presented for its gross graphical effect.

tinguishably functional in the speaker-auditor relationship.[23] The chief drawback to this definition is that we have no objective way of knowing for certain what speakers and auditors may or may not in fact be able to distinguish both consciously and unconsciously. Therefore we shall seek a unit that is philosophically less profound but which is operationally more serviceable.

By way of introduction to this more serviceable unit, let us take a pair of words like *fun* and *run,* which are completely homophonous except for their respective initial consonants. Other examples of such pairs are *babble* and *battle,* or *sin* and *sing.* We shall use the term "phonological opposition" to designate any such pair of words of different meanings that are homophonous except for a pair of different vowels or consonants; this pair of vowels or consonants we shall call *phonemes.* And we shall define a *phoneme* as "a minimal unit of distinctive significance *in keeping apart an otherwise homophonous pair of words.*" By means of this definition we can isolate the phonemes of any language for which the words are available.

A phoneme can obviously be defined only in reference to the actual vocabulary facts of a particular language, since *phonemic distinctions* in one language may not be so in another. Thus the phonological opposition of English *thigh* and *thy* shows us that the initial consonants (though written the same), are pronounced differently and do "keep apart otherwise homophonous words"; hence they are by definition different *phonemes.* However in Spanish these phonetically-acoustically identical sounds do not keep apart an otherwise homophonous pair of words; therefore in Spanish they are by definition not *phonemes* but *"variphones."*

Of course we cannot agree from a lack of suitable phonological oppositions that *variphones* are not also *phonetic entities* that are of significance in the entire speech process. On the contrary, the incorrect use of variphones may cause the speaker difficulties (witness the sorry fate of the 42,000 Ephraimites, *Judges* XII, 6, who had trouble with the initial variphone of the test word, *Shibboleth*). We may only say that we can agree about what *phonemes* are (and we can note that even phonologists seem to agree about what *variphones* are). After we have explored somewhat the dynamics of a phonetic system, we shall note not only why *variphones* can also be distinctively significant, but also why phonological oppositions may be expected to arise in a language so that, by and large, a language's stock of phonemes is its stock of significant phonetic entities.

With the above considerations in mind, we shall now inspect the dynamics of a phonetic system under the four headings: (*a*) the economy of permuting phonetic entities, (*b*) four fundamental principles of a phonetic system, and (*c*) miscellaneous considerations.

a. The economy of permuting phonetic entities. Although the permutation of phonetic entities into words is highly economical of human speech efforts, we must remember that such permutations are by no means necessary. Thus if we wanted a vocabulary of 10,000 different words, we could physiologically produce those 10,000 different words by means of 10,000 different unpermuted "word sounds." For example our American vowels could be so varied in length that vast quantities of different vowels could be produced to serve as word sounds.* If, in the midst of stretching a phoneme's length to make a word sound, it became necessary to take a breath, the speaker could introduce a stereotyped grace note to signal: "After I take my breath I shall continue with the same invariant word sound and not begin a new one." In addition to differences in length we could use differences in pitch and amplitude, from whispering to shouting (within the limits of the principle referred to under the "Weber-Fechner Law"). In short, a vocabulary of thousands upon thousands of distinguishably different word sounds is physiologically and acoustically possible.

Nevertheless, once we envisage a stream of speech that consists of unpermuted word sounds of the above kind, we comprehend its impracticability. Thus the "meanings" of Lincoln's *Gettysburg Address* which were delivered in a very short time by using words that were permutations of phonemes might well have lasted for hours or even days if word sounds had been used. Since in this case the extent in time is directly correlatable to the amount of physical work both for the speaker and for the auditor, it is evident that *the permutation of speech sounds (or phonetic entities) into words saves work.* Hence we find that our Principle of Economical Permutation, which applies to holophrases, words, and morphemes, may be expected to apply to the fundamental phonetic entities of speech (no matter how defined).

This consideration of the economy of permutations leads us to various interesting questions about the most economical number, frequencies, and kinds of phonetic entities to be permuted. Four of these questions we shall now inspect both theoretically and, where possible, empirically.

b. Four fundamental principles of a phonetic system. There are four characteristics of phonetic systems that point to the existence of four fundamental principles of economy. The *first* is that the actual number of different phonemes and variphones in a given phonetic system is generally between 20 and 60 and not in the hundreds, or thousands, or millions. A *second* is that out of the vast range of possible phonetic types, certain particular vowels and consonants (e.g., *a, n, m, s,* etc.) seem to be found quite consistently in widely diverse languages; hence in respect of some of the particular phonetic-types employed, languages seem to agree to an extent that is by no means justified on the grounds of "chance." *Third,* when different languages happen to use approximately the same phonetic entities, they tend to use them with approximately the same frequency. And *fourth,* whenever in a given language a particular phonetic entity changes its form under particular conditions in a given word, it tends to undergo the same change in every other word in which the same conditions prevail (this fourth well-known fact was first brilliantly elaborated by Karl Brugmann in the 19th Century).

---

* Sheer difference in duration can distinguish different phonemes, as with German short ă and long ā. Witness German *kan* (spelled *kann*) "is able," and *kan* (spelled *Kahn*) "boat"; or *man* (Mann) "man," and *man* (mahn!) "warm."

Now let us attempt briefly to explore the dynamics governing the above four characteristics, starting with the question why phoneme systems have about the same number of different phonetic entities.

First, we may say that adult human beings possess by and large the same vocal apparatus with the same range of variation, regardless of the particular ethnic or racial groups to which they belong. For example, negroes and whites have approximately the same speech physiology, with variations from the norm in the one being more or less duplicated by variations in the other. This fact of an approximate agreement in physiological givens leads us to an interesting consideration. For if the members of the different ethnic or racial groups have approximately the same vocabulary needs —say, from 10,000 to 20,000 different words—and if they all use the same Principle of Economical Permutation upon approximately the same physiological givens, the result will be an approximate agreement in the number of different phonetic entities in the various phonetic systems. (The problem is related to the one previously discussed in reference to the Z-value of the different usages that can be performed by n different tools.) Therefore it is by no means surprising to find that phonetic systems do not vary widely in the number of their different entities, so far as we know. And even if the vocabulary needs of different speech-groups should happen to vary quite widely, the variation in the size of the phonetic system would not need to be commensurately large because of the logarithmic nature of the Principle of Permutation.

The *second* principle of a phonetic system refers to the specific phonetic types of actual phonetic systems. The easiest approach to an understanding of this principle is to ask the following question: which particular phonetic types will the various languages select for adoption from the vast number of possible types? And the answer to this question, according to the Principle of Least Effort, is that each language will tend to pick those phonetic types which are easiest both to articulate orally and to discriminate aurally. Insofar as the physiological givens of the vocal apparatus are the same, the easiest phonetic types will be the same, and the various languages will tend to agree as to the phonetic types selected. If there are physiological differences in the speech apparatus of various groups, then there may be corresponding differences in the phonetic types of those groups. Moreover, if there happens to be a number of different phonetic types of approximately equal difficulty, then one language may select certain ones, and other languages may select others. Yet within these qualifying restrictions there will tend to be a substantial agreement in the phonetic types selected. As to an empiric confirmation of this agreement, we know of no actual quantitative investigation of the topic, although it lends itself to quantification. Thus one could select at random 100 different languages whose phonetic systems are reliably established. Then one could take the International Phonetic Alphabet and for each symbol tabulate the number of different languages whose phonetic systems contained the symbolized phonetic entity. And finally one would determine whether the distribution of entities throughout the 100 different languages was that of chance. This investigation is open. Yet even without the results of an actual investigation, we know that certain common vowels, diphthongs, nasals, and fricatives in Western European languages are quite general. Without the presence of this second principle it would be difficult to comprehend the data of the third principle, which now emerges from the one we have just discussed.

The nature of the *third* principle becomes clear if we ask the question: what are the most economical relative frequencies with which the different phonetic entities should be used? In reply, according to the Principle of Least Effort, we can only submit (1) that the easier phonetic entities will be the more frequently used, and (2) that if our preceding two principles are valid we may expect to find that similar phonetic entities in different languages will have similar percentage-frequencies. Both of these points (1) and (2) are empirically demonstrable.

To confirm this third principle empirically we shall proceed as follows. Our first step will be to select a set of corresponding pairs of phonemes in a given language where there is no doubt in the minds of competent phoneticists as to which is the easier member to pronounce; then we shall note if there is any positive correlation between greater ease of articulation and greater frequency of use. The phonemes selected for this purpose are the six pairs of voiceless aspirated stopped consonants, together with their nonaspirated counterparts in the Peiping dialect of Chinese as presented in Table 3–2.[24] The aspirated stopped consonant, which is indicated by a superscript *h,* is the more difficult of the pair because *first,* it has a tense or *fortis,* pronunciation whereas its mate has a nontense or *lenis* one, and *second,* its explosion is followed by a marked puff of air (*h*) that is lacking to its lenis unaspirated counterpart. Inspecting the percentages of Table 3–2 which refer to the phonemes in samples of 20,000 running Chinese syllables, we note that in all cases the easier unaspirated stop is almost twice as frequent as the more difficult aspirated stop. This confirms our hypothesis.

TABLE 3–2

Voiceless aspirated fortes and voiceless unaspirated lenes stops in present-day Peipingese.

(Percentages in reference to occurrences of all speech sounds in 20,000 running syllables)

	t^h/t	p^h/p	k^h/k	$cc_c{}^h/cc_c$	$tʃ^h/tʃ$	ts^h/ts
Aspirated Fortes Stops	2.56%	.56%	1.02%	1.04%	1.23%	1.40%
Unaspirated Lenes Stops.....	6.18%	2.37%	2.58%	2.69%	2.44%	2.63%

Data from other languages on aspirated and nonaspirated stops are in accordance with the above and have been published elsewhere with a detailed description of the phonetics involved.[25]

Turning now to the question of a possible correspondence in percentage-frequencies between similar phoneme types in different languages, we present data in Table 3–3 for the voiced and voiceless pairs of stops, *t/d, p/b,* and *k/g* in 17 different languages as previously published elsewhere. An inspection of the table discloses a rough correspondence between the magnitudes of each column. Thus the percentages for *t* are about 6%, those for *d* about 3%, and so on. In view of the differences in the sizes of the samples, the kinds of materials examined, and the methods of analysis employed by the various transcribers of texts, the presentation of mean-values and standard deviations may seem to be statistically dubious; nevertheless it is easier to include them than to explain their absence, nor is any harm done if they are not taken too seriously.[26]

Even more striking in Table 3–3 is the fact that the frequencies of the voiceless stops, *t, p,* and *k,* are with negligible exception greater than those of their corresponding voiced stops, *d, b,* and *g* in the 17 samples.* This is not to be anticipated from the law of probabilities. Indeed, the probability

TABLE 3–3

Percentage of occurrences of voiced-voiceless stops.

(Diphthongs counted as one unit.)

No.		t	d	p	b	k	g
1	Czechish	5.60%	3.73%	3.52%	1.86%	3.93%	.15%
2	Dutch	7.83	4.67	1.99	1.20	3.21*	.09*
3	English	7.13	4.31	2.04	1.81	2.71	.74
4	Hungarian	7.18	3.30	1.04	1.71	5.72	2.45
5	Lithuanian	5.76	2.61	3.71	1.35	4.61	1.36
6	North Russian	7.97	1.52	3.36	1.01	3.36	.67
7	South Russian	7.05	2.46	2.79	1.51	3.97	1.66
8	Wendish	6.26	3.02	2.55	1.56	3.29	2.41
9	East Ukrainian	3.83	3.24	2.82	2.11	4.11	
10	Bulgarian	7.54	3.55	2.82	1.32	2.98	1.46
11	Greek	7.58	2.87	3.38	.49	4.07	1.74
12	Sanskrit	6.65	2.85	2.46	.46	1.99	.82
13	Latin	8.66	3.12	2.54	1.32	4.34	.76
14	Italian	4.72	3.64	2.14	.52	3.38	.48
15	Spanish	4.46	1.56*	2.92	.46*	3.84	1.02
16	Portuguese	5.06	2.44*	2.68	.30*	3.44	.92
17	French	4.90	4.54	3.96	1.82	3.30	.36
	Average	6.36	3.14	2.75	1.22	3.66	1.07
	Standard Deviation	± 1.37	± .28	± .22	± .18	± .25	± .70

* Stops marked with an asterisk (*) are variphones (see text) and all others are phonemes.

that the voiceless stops will be more frequent than the voiced stops, as observed in the voiced-voiceless pairs in the above 17 languages, on the assumption of the null hypothesis that either kind of stop is equally likely

* A count of 5,000 Japanese phonemes in *Roomaziaki Tanpen Syoosetusyuu* (pp. 1–10) as romanized by Dr. N. Tanakadate revealed the following percentages: *p,* .26%; *b,* 1.52; *t,* 9.24; *d,* 2.86; *k,* 6.26; *g,* 2.20; *m,* 3.84; *n,* 5.92. Except for the *p,* these percentages are not far off. They are not included in the tables because I was not sure of the phonetic structure of some of the phonemes.

to occur, is about 5 chances out of a million [or, more precisely $P = (.5085)(10^{-5})$, according to Drs. Henry S. Dyer and John K. Dickinson, who very kindly calculated this probability]. Hence we are justified in asking whether, on the whole, the voiced stops are more difficult to produce than their corresponding voiceless ones. That such is indeed the case has been established by the brilliant experimental research of C. V. Hudgins and R. H. Stetson on the depression of the larynx in the voicing of consonants.[27]

The reader may wish to ask whether the correspondences of Table 3–3 are due to the *genetic relationship* of the different languages (except Hungarian). In reply, no. The Dutch and English stops, for example, are not historically the same as the others, if only because of the operation of Grimm's Law. The intervocalic *t* of Latin *vita* which is preserved in Italian *vita* is lost in French *vie* and has become a spirant (like *th* in English *thy*) in Spanish and Portuguese. Indeed in the course of the thousands of years that have elapsed since some of these languages could have constituted a common ethnic group, a fairly large shifting of phonetic forms has demonstrably taken place.

The reader may also wish to know whether data are available for other phonetic types. It should be pointed out that except for stops (i.e., explosive consonants) there is likely to be a considerable variation in the length and stress of utterance of speech sounds, as is notoriously the case for vowels, and somewhat the case for liquids, nasals, affricates, and aspirants. It so happens, however, that when short vowels on the one hand are compared with long vowels and diphthongs on the other, the short vowels are almost without exception markedly more frequent. The liquids (e.g., *r* and *l*) show a wide variation in frequencies among languages; and so too do the others, except for the nasals, *m* and *n*. As we note from the data for 22 different languages in Table 3–4, the *m* seems with negligible exception to be much less frequent than the *n* in the same language, and also to have approximately the same percentage-frequency in other languages widely different in region and time and, in some cases, not even remotely related.[28]

Although we have presented mean values and standard deviations for the data of Table 3–4, we again remind the reader that the underlying samples differed widely in size and technique of recording (e.g., there was no consistent treatment of what were vowels, diphthongs, triphthongs and this inconsistency would somewhat affect the size of the sample and hence the percentages); moreover, the percentages might well vary with styles of prose selected. If we had a dozen samples, each 10,000 phonemes long, for a given language, and each of these from different styles of speech phonemically transcribed with phonetic variations indicated, we might well obtain values of significance for the tongue in question which we could profitably compare with the results of similar undertakings with other tongues. Yet even then a certain amount of caution is in order. For after all, some phonemes in some languages may have excessive frequencies and be on the point of undergoing a corrective formal change (i.e., *phonetic change*); therefore a given above-average frequency may merely indicate the instability of the phoneme in question. This consideration leads us to the *fourth* principle of a phonetic system—*phonetic change*—which is intimately related to the other three.

TABLE 3–4

The frequencies (in percentages of the whole) of *m* and *n* in twenty-two languages.

Language	m (%)	n (%)	Language	m (%)	n (%)
Czechish	3.52	6.42	Burmese	4.72	4.15
Dutch	3.18	7.09	Swedish	3.28	7.32
English	2.78	7.24	Danish	3.18	5.70
Hungarian	3.35	5.74	Singhalese	3.12	7.40
Bulgarian	2.22	7.00	Old English	2.81	8.40
Russian	3.12	5.13	Old High German	2.91	10.85
Icelandic	4.37	7.77	Latin*	3.42	5.42
Greek (Attic)	3.19	8.55	Italian*	2.62	7.10
Sanskrit	4.34	7.04	Spanish*	2.98	5.62
Peipingese	2.18	10.18	Portuguese*	3.38	4.92
Cantonese	4.07	5.70	French*	3.42	3.04
			MEAN	3.28 ± .63	6.72 ± 1.78

* From F. M. Rogers' Analysis.

We approach the *fourth* principle by asking the obvious question: what happens to the percentages of frequency of phonemes in the dynamic process of evolution as old words are either abbreviated or eliminated while new ones are introduced? Obviously, unless all speech alterations are made within the severe restrictions of preserving the pre-existent phonetic percentages, these percentages will fluctuate—and even fluctuate quite widely. Differently expressed, unless some regulatory mechanism is present in the phonetic system to correct excessively high or low percentages, we should expect to find that the frequency of a given phonetic type will vary quite widely not only between different languages at a given time but also between different periods of the same language.

As a matter of fact a regulatory mechanism does exist in the form of *phonetic change.* Thus, for example, if a given long vowel becomes too frequent it may be shortened; a too frequent *d* may be weakened to a *t.* In general, whenever a phonetic entity undergoes an increase or decrease in frequency beyond the thresholds of toleration for its particular form, it may be expected to undergo a compensatory change in form.[29] Whenever such a phonetic entity undergoes a particular phonetic change—such as a *d* to a *t,* or the reverse—that change will occur in every word that contains the affected phonetic entity.* We shall call this the *orderliness of phonetic change.*

* As has been discussed in detail with copious illustrations in a previous publication, if the affected phonetic entity changes only in a particular set of conditions (e.g., in

Examples of the *orderliness of phonetic change* are literally legion, as the reader can determine for himself by consulting historical treatises on any language. This *orderliness* which Karl Brugmann and his school first established with rigor, and which, according to Dr. Clyde Kluckhohn, was the first disclosure of a rigorous law of action in the entire biosocial field, has served as the major premise for the exhaustive work of the historical-descriptive field known variously as *comparative philology* and *linguistics.* From this enormous stock pile we shall present only a few arbitrary examples.

Thus in Old English the phoneme, *ū,* changed to *ou* (sometimes written *ow*). Because of this change, *mūs* became *mouse, hūs* became *house, lūs* became *louse, cū* became *cow.* Although this change obliterated *ū* from Old English, the obliteration was only temporary. For subsequently the phoneme, *ō,* changed to *ū,* as *gōs* became *gūs* (written *goose*), and *mōna* became *mūn* (written *moon*), etc. These examples are particularly interesting because they illustrate how a given phonetic type, like *ū,* because of its instability, may change to *ou,* only to make place for a new *ū* which results from a change in the erstwhile phonetic type, *ō.* And after this second change from *ō* to *ū* had occurred in Old English, the erstwhile phonetic type, *ā,* took over the abandoned phoneme type, *ō* (e.g., Old English *stān, rāp,* and *gāt* appear today with *ō* pronunciation in *stone, rope,* and *goat*). So much then for the fourth principle of a phonetic system: the *orderliness of phonetic change.*

And so we may say in summary that a phonetic system alters the form of its component elements within the four principles of the phoneme system, as just explained. Thus (1) the phonetic system limits the number of its different phonetic types to approximately 20–60; (2) the phonetic systems of the earth seem to favor the use of the easiest phonetic types; (3) the frequencies of phonetic types are inversely related to their comparative work coefficient, with the result that like phonetic types tend to have like percentage frequencies; and (4) alterations in phonetic form occur in an orderly fashion throughout the entire vocabulary of a language in the sense that when a given change occurs under a given set of conditions in one word the same change will occur in all other words where the same conditions are found. Although phonetic changes are constantly occurring, we must not overlook the great antiquity of some present-day phonetic manifestations; thus the *m* and *s* of *mouse* are probably thousands of years old in that very word.*

c. Miscellaneous considerations. Now that we have outlined the four principles of the phonetic system, let us return to the question of the *phonetic entity, phoneme,* and *variphone.* We shall try to demonstrate first of all why a phoneme is not necessarily the exclusive minimal unit of distinctive significance (as some phonologists have argued); and second why

accented syllables, or finally, or intervocalically), it will change in all words where the conditions are found.

* Further detailed discussions of the effect of accent, analogy, assimilation, dissimilation, haplology, etc., have been presented in previous publications.[30]

a variphone can be a minimal unit of distinctive significance (as most phonologists deny).

Let us begin our demonstration by selecting a language like English, in which *d* is a phoneme (e.g., *bad vs. bat*). Then let us assume that because of a phonetic change all final *d*'s of words change to a form, *ɸ*, which is new to the language (e.g., *bad* becomes *baɸ*). Since the new form will occur only at the end of a word, and since no *d* will occur at the end of a word, it follows that no phonological opposition will exist in the entire language to show the difference between *d* and *ɸ*. Therefore by definition the new form, *ɸ*, will not be a phoneme but a *variphone* of *d*. Yet how do we know that *ɸ* is a *variphone* of *d* instead of a variphone of some other phoneme, like *l, m, n, o,* or *p?* Obviously we know that *ɸ* is a variphone of *d* only because we know that historically it developed from *d;* if this historical information were lacking we should not know it. Furthermore, before *d* changed to *ɸ* in final positions, those *d*'s in final positions were still phonemes which by definition were "the minimal units of distinctive significance." Yet after the change, what is *ɸ?* For us it is still a unit of distinctive significance, for we note a difference between a hypothetical *colɸ* (*cold*) and *cōl* (written *coal*).

Although we have defined *phonetic entities* as minimal units of distinctive significance, we have yet to be shown that an actual phonological opposition is necessary before phonetic entities can become minimal units of distinctiveness. As far as we are concerned, it is the permutation of the phonetic entities that is important. The existence of *phonological oppositions* is fortuitous. It is striking that practically all languages have *phonological oppositions* to illustrate most of the stock of different phonetic entities. But we submit that that is a result of the Principles of Economical Permutation. It is generally economical to make the small permutations of phonetic entities before making the larger ones; therefore *in the long run* small permutations are likely to arise to serve as *phonological oppositions* for most of the distinctly different phonetic entities of the given language's phonetic system.*

If we inspect further the "theory of the phoneme" we note a frequent belief which we express in Dr. Leonard Bloomfield's words (p. 83):[32] "the phoneme is kept distinct from all other phonemes in its language." This statement is in error. We have already pointed out, for example, that in

* As a final disproof of the phoneme as *the minimal unit of distinctive significance* (a definition that has become an article of faith in some quarters of American linguistics), let us take the case of Gothic *hausei!* "hear" and Gothic *hēr* "here" with a clear difference between *au* and *ē*. In Old English the respective words were *hīer!* and *her*—a true phonological opposition. But today they are the homophones, *hear!* and *here*. Unless one makes the ridiculous assumption that all phonetic change is instantaneous, we must conclude that for a long or short period between Old English and today the vowels of *hear* and *here* were ambiguous in respect of the phonological technique (i.e., phonologists would not know whether they were still different phonemes, or already the same phoneme). By extension of the argument, there may always be a phonologically unclassifiable residue in the stream of speech that is nevertheless not without distinctive significance either in light of the moment, or in light of what has been or is about to be.[31]

German short ă and long ā are different phonemes. Drs. Eberhart and Kurt Zwirner in a brilliant series of phonometric studies have found in phonographic recordings of actual samples of speech that the frequency distributions of the length of utterances of different vowel phonemes follow a "normal curve"; the only difference between ă and ā is in the mode of their respective distributions, because there are some longish utterances of ă that are in fact longer than some shortish utterances of ā.[33] Hence on a pure acoustical basis without a knowledge of the remainder of the permutation (or of the mode of the distribution), the phoneme ă is not always kept distinct from all other phonemes in its language.*

Penetrating even further into the minutiae of a phonetic system, and particularly into the question of varying lengths, we call attention to the brilliant empiric study of W. P. Lehmann and R–M. S. Heffner who found that the utterance of a given vowel tends to be longer before a voiced final stop than before a voiceless one (e.g., longer before *d, b,* and *g* than before *t, p,* and *k*).[34] Since, as the experimenters pointed out, the voiced stops are the comparatively less frequent ones, there is really a negative correlation between the length of a vowel and the frequency of the following stop—a correlation which they find valid also in reference to the decreasing frequencies of *d, b,* and *g.* Thus the vowel before the more frequent *d* is shorter than before the less frequent *g* (the reader can note the progressive lengthening of the vowel in his pronunciation of the successive syllables of *tot, tod, tog,* or in *pit, pid, pig*). This inverse relationship between the length of a vowel and the frequency of its following final stop (which the above experimenters ascribe without specific definition to differing "skills" in pronouncing the final consonants) ties up with the empiric research of Drs. Hudgins and Numbers.[35]

Thus Drs. C. V. Hudgins and F. C. Numbers in their pioneer work in investigating the speech of the deaf have observed that the errors made by the deaf in pronouncing vowels and consonants increase as the relative frequency of the vowels and consonants decrease. In this inverse relationship between error and frequency of occurrence the above experimenters propound a *pragmatic scale of difficulty.* Tying this observation to the previous Lehmann-Heffner observation, we might suggest that as a speaker approaches a rarer and more difficult final stop, his stream of speech slows down by way of preparation, with the result of a corresponding increase in the length of the preceding vowel. The Bonn phoneticist, Dr. Menzerath, and Dr. de Lacerda of Portugal, among others, have demonstrated the influence of a following phonetic entity upon the pronunciation of preceding ones.[36]

In discussing these various detailed phonetic problems as illustrations of an economy of effort, we must not overlook the basic problem of the

---

* The emergence of Zwirner's normal curve is interesting dynamically. We suggest, among other reasons, that it is the *speaker's economy* which tends to shorten the utterance, and the *auditor's economy* which tends to lengthen it. The result of these two opposing "Forces" might well be a normal curve. But see the following discussion of varying lengths and of errors. In any event the minimal magnitude of any phonetic entity would seem to be determined by what can be heard in normal speech situations.

selection of particular phonetic entities for particular permutations in order to save work for the auditor by making the succession of words of the stream of speech as different as possible, because obviously a too close juxtaposition of homophones, or even of "otherwise homophonous" words might confuse the auditor. Hence we may suspect the existence of a regulating principle that governs the distribution of phonetic entities among permutations so that the stream of speech will be richly variegated and completely unambiguous. As a result, successive words would be kept apart not by one but by many different phonetic entities in many different positions of permutation, so that the misarticulation of a phoneme would lead to little or no misunderstanding on the part of the auditor. This topic of the "phonetic variegation" of the stream of speech was kindly investigated by my then student, Mr. Frank Piano, who analyzed the 2,544 different words in a sample of 11,538 running words of R. C. Eldridge's list number 2. After reducing the 2,544 different words to the International Phonetic Alphabet, he found that 23 pairs of homophones fell together, leaving only 2,521 phonetically different words. With the removal of the phonetic difference between *l* and *r* (so that *call* and *core* would fall together) and also between *m* and *n* (affecting words like *some* and *son*), the number of different words dropped only to 2,481. With the further removal of all differences between short vowels (so that *bit, bet, bat, but, bought* would fall together) the number dropped only to 2,460. Then (in desperation) Mr. Piano let all long and short vowels and diphthongs fall together—with the result that without any vocalic differentiation whatsoever there were still 2,264 different phonetic forms. From this study it is apparent that, in actual samples of speech, words are kept apart not by one but by many differences, and that words that are phonetically very similar are not likely to appear often in the same context for obvious reasons of economy from the auditor's point of view. This problem seems to merit further investigation.[37]

There are many other inviting problems in phonetics, and many, many detailed studies which we have not mentioned. Thanks to Dr. W. Cabell Greet's careful editorship of *American Speech,* many key articles can be found in that publication, which also contains a complete running bibliography of the field from the experienced hand of Dr. S. Treviño. In addition, there is constant research by the Bell Telephone Laboratories, as reported in their publications. The empiric studies of Dr. Mark H. Liddell are still important. Abroad are the electroanalytic studies of Father A. Gemelli (Italy), the new ink-recording technique of Dr. A. de Lacerda (Portugal), the studies of Drs. D. and S. Jones (England), of Dr. Panconcelli-Calzia (Germany)—to name but a few not already mentioned previously. In the United States one may remember the important contributions and studies in progress of Drs. J. S. Kenyon, C. K. Thomas, F. H. Knower, A. A. Hill, H. L. Mencken, F. S. Cowan, C. M. Wise, W. A. Read, S. Newman, J. D. Zimmerman, K. Malone, H. Deferrari, Louise Pound, C. H. Voelker, C. E. Parmenter, R. C. Pooley, W. F. Luebke, and L. S. Hultzen—in addition to those whose research is discussed in the present text. Nor is this list exhaustive.

In calling attention to the enormous amount of excellent experimental and theoretical research in the broad field of phonetics, we venture to suggest that this growing body of careful observation and interpretation may have a value for biosocial studies to a degree perhaps not always envisaged even by some of the phoneticians themselves. And as far as we are aware of the studies, none is inconsistent with our Principle of Least Effort.

At this point one may feel that our interest in the structure and dynamics of a phoneme system is excessive to the point of pedantry. This feeling, however, may be abated if one views a phoneme system against the background of the entire organic world, and remembers that our discussion of a phoneme system is a discussion of the economy of a group of different *types* of physical action, and that there is apparently a "law of limited number" of these types. Such a law is by no means unique to a phonetic system. For example, in the all but endless variety of plants and animals, the whole range of observed numbers of chromosomes in germ nuclei is small; according to the haploid data of M. J. D. White, only 5% have fewer than 4 chromosomes, and 75% have fewer than 20.[38] Yet why should there be this "law of limited number" within whose narrow range there occurs an all but infinite chemical variability? Perhaps the reasons for the "law of limited number" of phonemes apply to the limited number of chromosomes, if we view chromosomes as *types* of physical action. In that event, the structure and behavior of speech is but a special case of the structure and behavior of all organic process (see Chapters Five and Six).

Hence the four principles of phonetic structure just discussed and illustrated may well apply beyond the domain of human speech. The same may well be true of the applicability of the Law of Abbreviation, and the Law of Diminishing Returns with its Principles of Economical Versatility and Economical Permutation that we have already discussed and illustrated in reference to speech. The same may also be true of the Principle of Economical Specialization which we have already described, and to whose more detailed discussion and illustration we now turn.

C. The Principle of Economical Specialization

During our detailed inspection of the Principle of Economical Permutation of words and other entities of speech we have somewhat lost sight of our Tool Analogy, which served originally to suggest not only the nature of the problems of speech structure but also their possible solution. There is no need for our recapitulating that portion of the Tool Analogy which referred to the "Minimum Equation" or to the Principle of Abbreviation, since the applicability of these points has already been tested in speech. But perhaps it is worth recalling that we are still concerned with the *Law of Diminishing Returns* which, as we remember, was discussed under the three rubrics, (*A*) *The Principle of Economical Versatility* (in which the different usages or "meanings" of a tool or word increase with its frequency), (*B*) *The Principle of Economical Permutation* (which we have just finished discussing), and (*C*) *The Principle of Economical Specialization* (which we shall now consider).

The chief features of the Principle of the Economical Specialization of mechanical tools were both few and simple. Thus whenever for one reason or another a permutation of several tools that performs a particular task is used with an increasing frequency, the point is eventually reached where it becomes economical to design and adopt a single specialized tool that will perform the particular task that has hitherto been performed by the permutation. This substitution of the single, specialized tool for the permutation of tools represents the operation of the *Principle of Economical Specialization.*

One important long-term consequence of this Principle in operation is that some of the older and abbreviated tools would tend to work their way down the board away from the artisan; these would be the "superannuated" or *senescent* tools. Another consequence would be that the newer, and not yet fully abbreviated specialized tools would work their way up the board; these would be the *nascent* tools. The net effect of both these consequences would be that as we passed down the board away from the artisan we should encounter a mixture of older, abbreviated *senescent tools* on the one hand, and of the newer larger *nascent* tools on the other, and, for reasons then given, this mixture would contain proportionately ever fewer *senescent* tools and ever more *nascent* tools.

If we now translate the above mechanical relationships into the terms of speech, may we say that as we pass into the domain of rarer words, these words will tend to consist ever more of the newer and longer words of the vocabulary, even as the Tool Analogy suggests? Let us see what the facts are.

My former student, Dr. Nai-Tung Ting, kindly undertook the arduous task of establishing both the date of adoption and the origin of adoption of the approximately 6,000 different words in R. C. Eldridge's frequency analysis (*op. cit.*) of about 44,000 running words of American newspaper English. To this end he used the Shorter English Dictionary (2 volumes, Oxford, 1933) and also consulted the New English Dictionary. Since the words of Eldridge's list are given in fully inflected form, the date and origin of the words were determined by their roots and not by their prefixes and suffixes (e.g., *build, real, promise* determined the age and origin of *builder, really,* and *promising*); the age and origin of a compound word was considered to be that of its accented component (see below). In the case of words of various dates and sources for different forms and meanings, the earliest were selected. Instances of doubtful origins and etymologies were duly noted. I checked sizable portions of Dr. Ting's analysis and found it without blemish.

The next step was the statistical analysis, the results of which are presented in Fig. 3–10 where we find four different graphs, marked A, B, C, and D respectively.[39]

In Graph *A* are fourteen vertical columns running from left to right. The first five columns together represent the first 499 most frequent words (from rank 1 through 499) which comprise all words occurring 10 or more times; in short, these successive five columns refer respectively to the most frequent successive sets of 100 ranks, except for the fifth column, which refers to 99 ranks (i.e., 401 through 499). After these first five columns come nine more columns which from left to right refer to the number of different words of like frequency from those occurring 9 times to those occurring 1 time as indicated; at the bottom of each column is given the frequency to

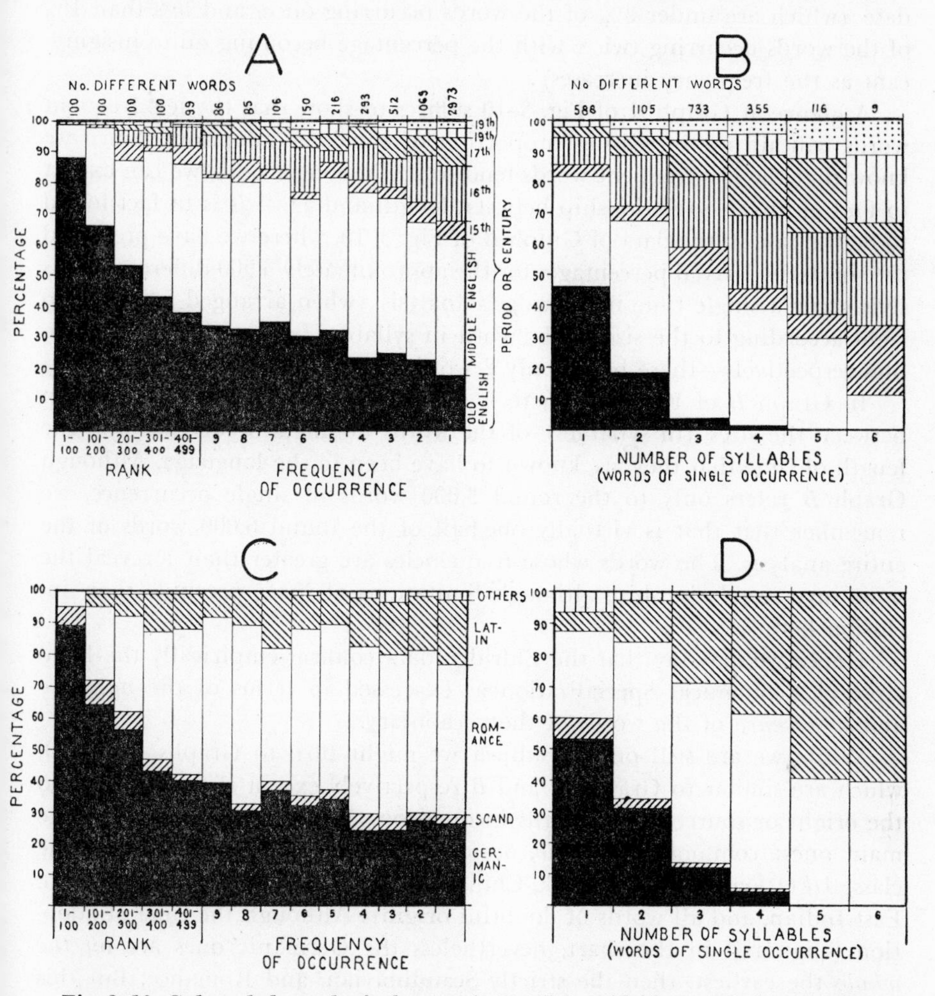

Fig. 3–10. Cultural-chronological strata in English (Eldridge analysis). (A) Chronological strata in words of all occurrences; (B) chronological strata in all words occurring once, according to size in syllables; (C) cultural strata in words of all occurrences; (D) cultural strata in all words occurring once, according to syllables.

which the column refers, and at the top is given the number of different words in the Eldridge list which have that frequency.

Each of the fourteen columns of Graph *A* represents *vertically* the percentages of the words according to their age in the language. Thus at the bottom (in black) is the percentage of words that were there in Old English times (including Late Old English); second (in white) are those that were adopted during the Middle English Period (including Early and Late Middle English); and above that, as indicated, are the percentages for the words adopted from the fifteenth through the nineteenth centuries inclusive. Twentieth century adoptions were statistically negligible. All percentages were reckoned on the basis of the total number of words for which the necessary information was available, and exclude all words of doubtful date (which are under 3% of the words occurring once, and less than 1% of the words occurring twice, with the percentage becoming quite insignificant as the frequency increases).

A glance at Graph *A* of Fig. 3–10 suffices to show that the less frequent words contain an increasing proportion of the later adoptions. Since we know that the less frequent words tend to be the longer ones, we can expect to find an inverse relationship between length and age—as is in fact found to be the case in the data of Graph *B* of Fig. 3–10, where we have presented the similarly derived percentages for the approximately 3,000 different words that occur a single time in Eldridge's analysis (when arranged from left to right according to the size of the word in syllables from 1 through 6 syllables respectively—there being only 2 words of 7 syllables).

In Graph *B* of Fig. 3–10 there is an unmistakable inverse relationship between the sizes (in syllables) of the words of single occurrence and the length of time that they are known to have been in the language. Although Graph *B* refers only to the round 3,000 words of single occurrence, we remember that that is virtually one-half of the round 6,000 words of the entire analysis. The words whose frequencies are greater than 1 reveal the same inverse relationship, although limitations of space preclude their inclusion here.

Hence we may say that the Eldridge data confirm empirically the Principle of Economical Specialization as expressed in terms of the *nascence* and *senescence* of the words of the vocabulary.

While we are still on the subject we might turn to Graphs *C* and *D*, which are similar to Graphs *A* and *B* respectively except that they refer to the origin or source of the words in question. The origins selected are the main ones: common *Germanic, Scandinavian, Romance,* and *Latin* (the class, *All Others,* includes Greek, Chinese, Hebrew, Celtic, American Indian, East Indian, and all words of doubtful origin). Although the time of adoption is ignored in the chart, nevertheless the Germanic ones are *on the whole* the earliest, then the strictly Scandinavian, and Romance. But this relationship is only "on the whole" since some Latin words were borrowed very early into the language and we are still borrowing Romance and Scandinavian terms.

The data of Graphs *A* and *B* are interesting in showing that the common Germanic matrix (i.e., the words of common Germanic origin already in the language at the earliest time) tends to be the shortest. The adoptions from Scandinavian, Romance, and Latin belong, on the whole, to the less frequent words. In this connection several notes of caution are in order. In the first place, borrowings from these various languages have been going on from quite early times; therefore we may not associate too precisely a particular period with a particular source of borrowings. In the second place, according to our manner of classification, any new compound word which was coined at a *later* date out of *earlier* parts would be ascribed to the *later* date for its *period* of adoption; yet the *origin* of the compound would consistently be the origin of that part of the compound which bears the chief accent: thus for example, the word *lineman* entered the language in 1858, as far as we know from the records, and since the accent is on the Romance component, *line,* instead of on the Germanic component, *man,* the word *lineman* is classed as a Romance adoption of the 19th century. By the same token *highwayman* is a Germanic trisyllable that entered the records in 1649. Of course these compound words are not abundant; our statistical observation would not have been significantly altered if they had been entirely excluded; for with or without the compounds, a vocabulary is enriched with new adoptions in its lower frequency range.

Before leaving the topic of the Eldridge vocabulary, it is perhaps worth presenting the actual percentages of new words from Germanic, Romance, and Latin during the five centuries from the 15th through the 19th (we ignore Scandinavian and the others because of their comparative rarity). These percentages are given in Table 3–5, where we find a considerable fluctuation from century to century for both Germanic and Latin, with a somewhat smaller fluctuation for Romance. Germanic hit a peak during the 18th century, after deferring to Romance and Latin during the three previous centuries; perhaps this upsurge of Germanic was connected with the Romantic Period which began in the late 18th, and which so frowned upon the Classical Latin of the preceding centuries.

TABLE 3–5

Respective percentages of new words whose roots or chief components were originally Germanic, Romance, or Latin, and which were incorporated into English during each Century from the 15th through the 19th.

Original Source	Century				
	15th	**16th**	**17th**	**18th**	**19th**
Germanic	14%	13%	10%	20%	12%
Romance	49%	42%	41%	50%	48%
Latin	31%	37%	44%	23%	26%

We must not go too deeply into details upon the basis of what is in fact a small sample of 6,000 different words in a total of 40,000 odd running words. A safer guide would be the information derived from Dr. Thorndike's 20,000 most frequent words (*op. cit.*). Although an analysis of the entire Thorndike list would be a very laborious undertaking, such an analysis might well provide students of cultural influences with a measuring scale of almost unimaginable value.*

* Thus if a correlation exists between the comparative frequencies of words and their comparative age in a given language, we might hope to be able to detect some of a folk's prehistoric cultural influences by simply examining the frequency distribution of its words in its earliest historical texts. In this way we might learn of its *cultural strata.*

Another example of the different origins of speech parts—this time for the root morphemes of our Gothic analysis—is given in Figure 3–11, which is comparable to the *C* diagram of the preceding Fig. 3–10 and refers to the origins of the *roots* of the words of Gothic exclusive of historically borrowed common and proper nouns. The roots of Gothic, as is well known, are very largely of *Indo-European origin* in the sense that many Gothic roots

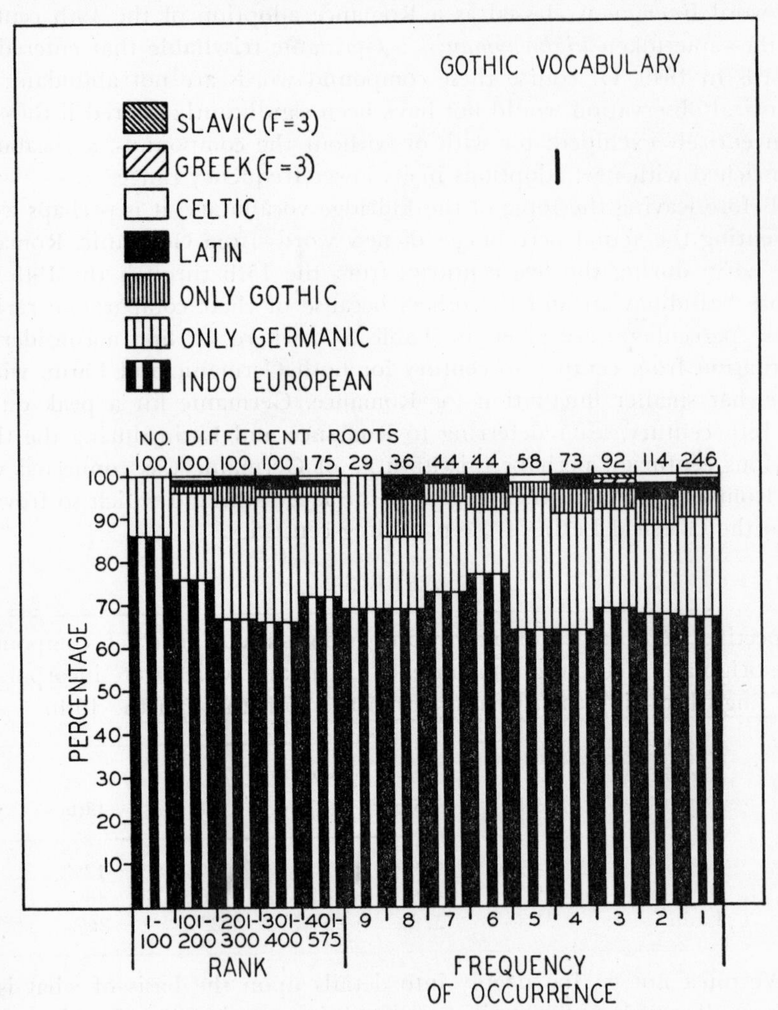

Fig. 3–11. Cultural strata in Gothic roots.

have counterparts in other non-Germanic Indo-European languages. There are also some roots that are of *Germanic* origin, in the sense that these *Germanic roots* are found only in the various Germanic dialects. Then there are some uniquely *Gothic roots* which are not found except in Gothic. And finally there are roots of words which were prehistorically borrowed from *Latin, Celtic, Greek, Slavic,* and which had subsequently been thoroughly absorbed and nativized much as early Romance words have been thoroughly absorbed and nativized in present-day English.

The percentages of these various roots, as determined from Feist's etymological dictionary,[40] are represented in the 1 diagram of Fig. 3–11, where the fourteen vertical columns refer to various sections of the rank-frequency list as represented by the notations at the top and the bottom. Thus, for example, the first column at the left represents the 86% *Indo-European roots* and the 14% *Germanic roots* of the 100 most frequent words; the second column represents the 76% *Indo-European,* the 20% *Germanic,* the 2% *Gothic,* the 1% *Latin* and the 1% *Celtic* roots; and so similarly for the remaining columns.

The question now arises as to how far we should dare to make a deduction about the prehistoric *cultural strata* of the Goths on the basis of these data (if we may assume that the same principle applies in general to roots as to fully inflected words). The first four columns, which refer to the 400 most frequent roots, do seem to suggest a slight trend towards an increasing Germanic stratum, at the expense of the older Indo-European stratum, much as if either a conquering or a conquered culture were beginning to assert itself. However the difference in this respect between the first and second sets of 7 columns is not great. A similar problem arises in respect of the purely Gothic, and of the Latin, Celtic, Greek, and Slavic roots, which increase slightly as we proceed from left to right down the frequency-list. Are these proportions indicative of the strength of the respective cultural influences? That is the problem, and a very exciting problem it may turn out to be for students of prehistoric cultural influences. Although there is no further Gothic text material to analyze, there are vast amounts of Old English and Old Norse that would serve almost as well.[41]

Taking now a permanent leave of our Gothic studies, let us turn to other languages to test whether the proportion of the specialized foreign borrowings into a tongue will in fact increase even more as the frequency decreases.* For if we find such to be the case, we shall learn about the relative conservatism of a vocabulary. The two languages we shall examine in this respect are, first, the vocabulary of the Old High German scholar, Notker Labio (died 1022), and, second, some present-day Pennsylvania Dutch (i.e., Pennsylwanisch).

For the purpose of instructing his pupils, Notker Labio, head of the St. Gall monastery school, "translated" certain Latin classics into a mixture of Old High German and Latin in such a fashion that the two languages are inextricably woven together—now the German translating the Latin, now the German commenting upon it or explaining it. Thus the 137th Psalm in Notker's translation begins as follows (we have put in italics the Latin text he was translating—*the Latin text being excluded* in our subsequent statistical analysis); the Old High German we render into English without altering the Latin loan words that Notker used:

"*Confitebor tibi domini in toto corde meo:* I confess thee, Lord, that is ecclesia, in all my heart. I praise thee manu forti. *Quoniam audisti*

* We already know from Fig. 2–2 that the number of different meanings of words decreases with the word's frequency; therefore we know that the rarer words will be the *less versatile* or *more specialized.*

verba oris mei: whenever you heard the words of my mouth. You heard me in the prayer prophetarum and justorum" etc.

In the above example we see that apart from the Latin text (i.e., *confitebor tibi domini in toto corde meo* and *quoniam audisti verba oris mei*) the actual "translation" is rich in Latin words such as *ecclesia, manu forti, prophetarum, justorum.* In fact, if we ignore the italicized portions of the Latin text in the "translations" and confine our attention to the mixture of Old High German and Latin prose (the famous *"Mischprosa"*) we probably see before us an example of what the students of the monastery really spoke: that is, an Old High German that was heavily garbled with words and clichés from Latin which the students were trying to learn. It was into this colloquial monastery *Mischprosa* that Notker translated the classics. Since his translations were well-known elsewhere at the time, we may suspect that his medieval German-Latin jargon was known and used in other monasteries in the neighborhood. This jargon perhaps had a counterpart in the United States in the 1920's when many girls at finishing schools assiduously interlarded their English with words and clichés from French purely for the social effect. However with the medieval novitiates and monks the reason for the *Mischprosa* may have been that they had not yet learned enough Latin or did not still remember enough Latin to "take the classics straight."

Fortunately for our present purposes the two American Notker scholars, Drs. E. H. Sehrt and Taylor Starck, made a card index of all the different occurrences of all the *Old High German words* in all of Notker's writings—a total of 17,196 different words in an aggregate of 195,821 running words. These cards they kindly put at my disposal for the purpose of making a rank-frequency analysis, the results of which are presented in Curve *A* of Fig. 3–12. The linearity of this curve is striking. And no less striking is Curve *C,* which represents the *N* number of Old High German words of like frequency that occur 50 or fewer times (the points are presented within circles). The equation for these 50 points, as calculated by least squares, is $N \times F^{1.68} = 9{,}832$, which is not a bad approximation * to the theoretically expected value of F^2. When the calculation is extended to include all frequencies that are less than 100, the equation becomes: $N \times F^{1.98} = 14{,}550$, which is a strikingly close approximation. Unfortunately, it is difficult to show graphically the points from 50 to 100 because of the logarithmic scale.

Now that we have seen the great orderliness with which the Old High German of Notker's *Mischprosa* follows our empiric equations, let us turn to the frequency distributions of the Latin words in the *Mischprosa* (and we remember that we are excluding from analysis the Latin headings that Notker took from the various works of the classics that he was translating). In this connection I took the Paul Piper edition of *"Die Schriften Notkers und Seiner Schule"* (Freiburg, 1883) and made a frequency analysis of all

* I find that although the *X*-intercept of the *C*-line is correct, the slope of the line in Fig. 3–12 has been incorrectly drawn by a very small degree. The correct slope fits the points even better, as the reader can determine for himself by substituting from the above equation.

the Latin words in the *Mischprosa* in Volume I and through page 346 of Volume II—a total of 7080 different words in fully inflected form in an aggregate of 21,766 words. The rank-frequency distribution of these Latin words is given in the broken line of Curve *B* of Fig. 3–12; their number-frequency distribution, with a straight line drawn by eye, for all words occurring 25 or fewer times is given in Curve *D* (represented by crosses). Both of these

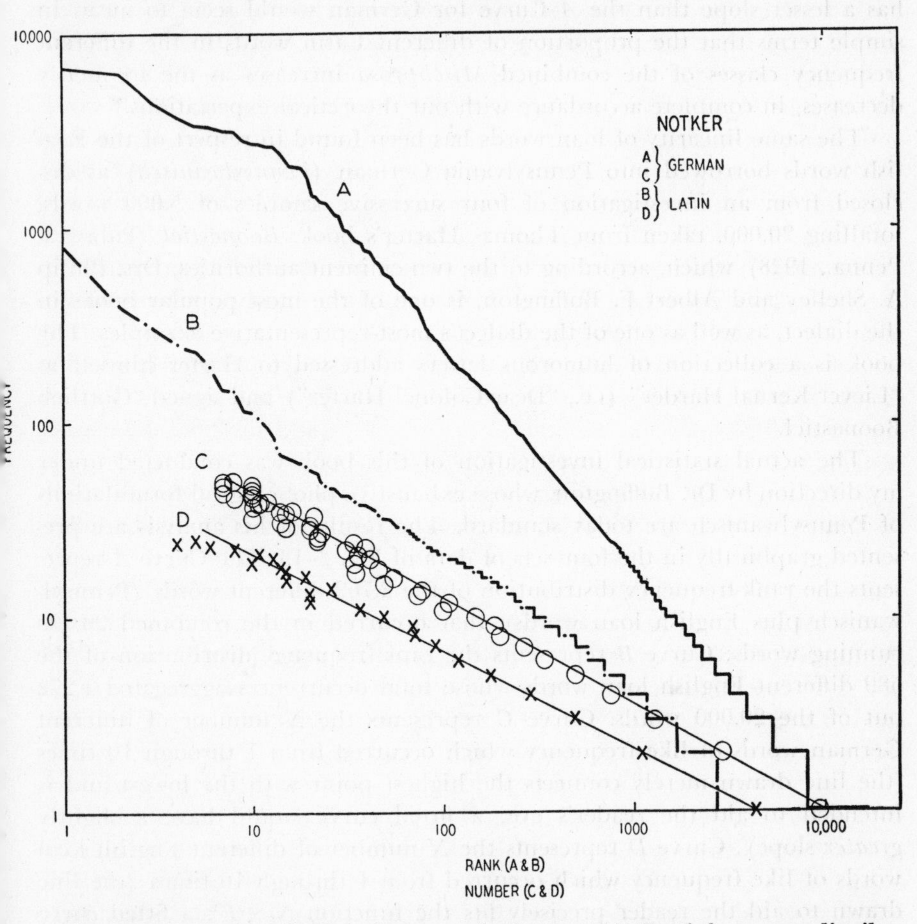

Fig. 3–12. Notker's Old High German mixed prose. (A) Rank-frequency distribution of German words; (B) rank-frequency distribution of Latin words; (C) number-frequency distribution of German words; (D) number-frequency distribution of Latin words.

lines are essentially linear, though of lesser slope than we find for Curves *A* and *C*. Although the sample of Latin is more than sufficient in size to justify a generalizing statement about the nature of the entire *Mischprosa*, it is regrettable that all the Latin was not counted so that a combined curve might be presented. But alas the writer's patience and sense of duty finally failed him on page 346 of Volume II (his intellectual curiosity about the topic having been thoroughly satiated back in Volume I). Because of the incompleteness of the Notker data, the slope of Curve *D* was not calculated;

however its linearity is unmistakable and would scarcely be altered by a complete analysis.

Viewing the linear curves of Fig. 3–12, we may say in sum that the *Mischprosa* is not inconsistent with our Principle of Economical Specialization. The fact that the Latin incorporations are linearly distributed shows that a geometric ratio is not absent. The fact that the *B* Curve for Latin has a lesser slope than the *A* Curve for German would seem to mean in simple terms that the proportion of different Latin words in the different frequency classes of the combined *Mischprosa* increases as the frequency decreases, in complete accordance with our theoretical expectations.*

The same linearity of loan words has been found in respect of the English words borrowed into Pennsylvania German (*Pennsylwanisch*) as disclosed from an investigation of four successive samples of 5,000 words, totalling 20,000, taken from Thomas Harter's book, *Boonastiel* (Palmyra, Penna., 1928) which, according to the two eminent authorities, Drs. Philip A. Shelley and Albert F. Buffington, is one of the most popular books in the dialect, as well as one of the dialect's most representative examples. The book is a collection of humorous letters addressed to Harter himself as "Liever Kernal Harder" (i.e., "Dear Colonel Harter") and signed "Gottlieb Boonastiel."

The actual statistical investigation of this book was conducted under my direction by Dr. Buffington, whose exhaustive phonological formulations of Pennsylwanisch are today standard. The results of his analysis are presented graphically in the four sets of data of Fig. 3–13. The Curve *A* represents the rank-frequency distribution of the 2,762 different words (Pennsylwanisch plus English loan words) that occurred in the combined 20,000 running words; Curve *B* represents the rank-frequency distribution of the 589 different English loan words whose total occurrences aggregated 1,272 out of the 20,000 words. Curve *C* represents the *N* number of different German words of like frequency which occurred from 1 through 10 times (the line drawn merely connects the highest point with the lowest and is intended to aid the reader's eye; a fitted curve would have a slightly *greater* slope). Curve *D* represents the *N* number of different English loan words of like frequency which occurred from 1 through 10 times (the line drawn to aid the reader precisely fits the function $N \times F^2$; a fitted curve would have a slightly *lesser* slope).

It is quite evident that all four curves of Fig. 3–13 are close approximations to linearity, with Curve *A* not far from a harmonic seriation except, first, for the *top-downward-concavity* which affects only the dozen or so most frequent words of this colloquial book and except, second, for the slight change in slope at about rank 200. Curve *B* for the English loan words has a lesser slope, suggesting that the proportion of loan words of like frequency

* If we glance back at the English distribution of Curve *A* of Fig. 3–10 we also note a "hollow curve" for Old English which, if it were graphed on doubly logarithmic paper, would approximate a straight line. Hence in spite of the comparatively small size of the Eldridge data when compared to the 200,000 odd words of the Notker *Mischprosa,* a linearity of the words of a given "cultural stratum" is not lacking in present-day English.

increases according to a fixed ratio as the frequency decreases; indeed that the loan words are the less frequently used words is evident from the fact that they constitute more than 20% of the different words yet only slightly more than 6% of the total occurrences. Curves *C* and *D* also confirm the fact that, with decreasing frequency, the proportion of German words (*C*) decreases while the proportion of the newly borrowed English loan words (*D*) increases. Hence the German and English cultural strata of the Pennsylwanisch of Fig. 3–13 substantiate our theoretical Principle of Economi-

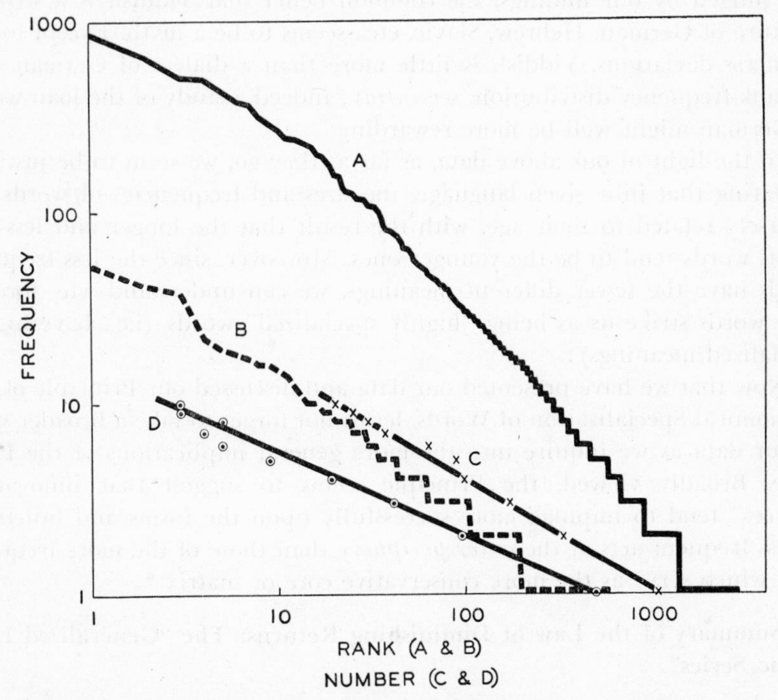

Fig. 3–13. Pennsylwanisch (Pennsylvania Dutch). (A) The rank-frequency distribution of Pennsylwanisch words, including English loan words; (B) the rank-frequency distribution of English loan words; (C) the number-frequency distribution of words of German origin; (D) the number-frequency distribution of English loan words.

cal Specialization as far as the comparative number and ages of its words are concerned. Moreover the correlation between length of word and recency of adoption is also not absent here, although space limitations preclude presenting a detailed chart.* It is also regrettable that we cannot present the entire list of 500-odd different English loan words which perhaps more than anything else represent words of the purely American cul-

* Similar limitations prevent our presenting graphically the data of the four component sets of 5,000 running words. Nevertheless an idea of the variability can be gained from the fact that the mean numbers of different words of frequencies from 1 through 4 with standard deviation for the four samples are: (1) 137.25, ±21.47; (2) 26, ±3.32; (3) 10.75, ±3.13; (4) 5.75, ±2.67. Above $f = 4$ the mean N number is around 2 or 1, as can be seen by inspecting Curve *D* of Figure 3–13.

tural stratum. Such a list of borrowings *from* our American culture *into* a foreign culture is as instructive as Dr. H. L. Mencken's studies of words that have been borrowed *from* a foreign culture *into* American.

Unfortunately we have no further conclusive quantitative data on loan words. An extensive investigation of present-day Yiddish, the supervision of which was undertaken by my former colleague, the eminent young scholar Dr. I. S. Stamm, was disappointing in the paucity of loan words to study. This may have been due to the literature selected for analysis. But judged by our findings, the common belief that Yiddish is a striking mixture of German, Hebrew, Slavic, etc., seems to be a myth. Except for its phonetic deviations, Yiddish is little more than a dialect of German (for its rank-frequency distribution, see *infra*) ; indeed a study of the loan words in German might well be more rewarding.

In the light of our above data, as far as they go, we seem to be justified in stating that in a given language, the sizes and frequencies of words are inversely related to their age, with the result that the longer and less frequent words tend to be the younger ones. Moreover, since the less frequent words have the fewer different meanings, we can understand why foreign loan words strike us as being "highly specialized" words (i.e., have highly specialized meanings) .

Now that we have presented our data and discussed our Principle of the Economical Specialization of Words, let us not forget to take a broader view of our data as we inquire into the more general implications of the Principle. Broadly viewed, the Principle seems to suggest that innovating "Forces" tend to impinge more successfully upon the forms and functions of less frequent acts at the *outer periphery* than those of the more frequent ones which serve as the more conservative core or matrix.*

D. Summary of the Law of Diminishing Returns: The "Generalized Harmonic Series"

Up to now we have analyzed the stream of speech from many different angles. We began by showing why the comparative lengths of words would be inversely related to their relative frequency of occurrence (the Principle of Economical Abbreviation) . Then we showed why the number of different meanings of words would increase with their frequency (the Principle of Economical Versatility) . The next topic was the Principle of Economical Permutation, which treated of various speech entities from phonetic entities on up through the large configurations. Finally we came to the Principle of Economical Specialization, which we tested by noting that the age of words was directly related to their frequency. The impulse behind these four principles was the economy that comes from a "close packing" of tools

* The comparative philologists have sensed this point in their genetic classifications. Thus for example, present-day Albanian with its vast stock of borrowings from Turkish, Greek, Italian, and Slavic is called an independent Indo-European language not because of an overwhelming preponderance of its own Indo-European roots, but because its few pronouns, numerals and other highly frequent entities (i.e., the proverbial "backbone of a language") are demonstrably of Albanian Indo-European origin.

and the reduction of their *n* number. Because of this impulse, *there is a tendency for old age, small size, versatility of meaning, and a multiplicity of permutational associations—all to be directly correlated with high frequency of usage.* The terms of this correlation may be worth remembering, because the correlation may be expected to appear in any biosocial organization that follows our Tool Analogy (cf. Chapter Six).

However, there is one risk in the manner of our exposition up to this point. For although we have treated the above Principles one after another, we must remember that they are all constantly operating simultaneously for the preservation of a dynamic equilibrium with a maximum of economy. That is, in dynamic process, words are constantly being shortened, permuted, eliminated, borrowed, and altered in meaning, while at the same time the four principles of the phonetic system are operating upon the number, forms, frequency, and spacings of the basic phonetic entities. As a result of all these factors we may anticipate that in any sample stream of speech in any language at any time in any place there will be marked indications of the various kinds of distributions which we have been describing under the general heading of Formal-Semantic Balance.

Perhaps nothing is so illustrative of this constant drive towards a Formal-Semantic Balance in dynamic process than to view in rapid succession a series of the rank-frequency distributions of the words of samples of speech selected from various periods in the development of the same language, as we shall shortly do with data for English and German (Figs. 3–14 and 3–15).

But before turning to these data, which represent nearly two dozen separate samples of speech of different sizes ranging from about 5,000 to about 20,000 running words, we must briefly point out certain problems of variation that are bound to appear in samples of differing sizes. In the first place, with samples that are as small as some of these are, we may anticipate a certain degree of divergence from our expected linear norm in the form of a kind of waviness in our straight lines, a waviness that will tend to disappear as the sample size increases. In the second place, we may expect that the slope of the line will tend to increase somewhat with an increase in the size of the sample for reasons already mentioned in Chapter Two; of course, insofar as the sizes of the samples are approximately the same, the slopes will be approximately the same. In the third place we must be prepared to find cases of unstable equilibrium in which—even with due regard for the sample's size—the slope is either too gentle or too steep; and here we must look for a subsequent correction in the historical development of the language, as a more stable equilibrium emerges. Since this third point is important for our entire study, it is fortunate that we have several illustrative cases of a temporarily unstable equilibrium.

But none of these three points will be as conspicuous in our data as that of the striking bend at the top of the curves with the concave side downward, the *top-downward-concavity,* to which we have already alluded and which generally represents only the dozen or so most frequent words. The appearance of this particular bend means nothing more than that the sample in question was taken from "colloquial speech" of the kind that one finds in intimate personal letters (as well as in plays, exhortative sermon material, and the like); it is not found in more formal material.*

As to the reason for the emergence of a *top-concavity,* say, in intimately personal (i.e., not formal) letters it might be suggested that in such cases the writer and reader have a certain commonness of experience and therefore may dispense with the high degree of articulation that is otherwise necessary in writing to a nonintimate who is a stranger to the topic. Thus the articles and other short highly frequent words which are necessary for coherence when writing to the nonintimate about an unfamiliar topic, are no longer necessary with the intimate who will know without being told that Mary, John, and Ned refer to the cat, the chauffeur, and the dog respectively, and who also will be able to guess the persons or things referred to by "he," "she," and "it." In general, in samples of speech with a *top-concavity* we find without exception that the normally frequent articles and the like have yielded part of their frequency to the more personal pronouns, with the result of a concave bend at the top.

With the above several considerations in mind let us turn now to Fig. 3–14, where we find fifteen different sets of data ranging in time from the early Old English of *Beowulf* (Curve *A*) to the recent poems of T. S. Eliot (Curve *O*). For the reader's convenience these curves are distributed among three successive cycles of the logarithmic paper, as will be seen by inspecting the top portions of each curve, which in each case begins with rank 1.

On the first cycle four rank-frequency curves begin: Curves *A, B, C,* and *D.* Curve *A* represents the words of *Beowulf* in fully inflected form as established from Dr. Fr. Klaeber's glossary by my former student, Mr. Allen B. Sorensen. This curve is on the whole quite straight; nevertheless its slope is less than 1, and hence may point to a condition of unstable equilibrium, although the slope may also result from the poetic nature of the material. In any event it is worth noting that in curves *B, C,* and *D,* which represent later periods of Old English, the harmonic slope has been restored, and that subsequent to the time of *Beowulf* Old English had undergone a certain small amount of morphological simplification. Curves *B, C,* and *D* respectively represent samples of 10,000 running words each from (*B*) the anonymous Old English *Letter of Alexander the Great to Aristotle* (late 10th century), from (*C*) Alfred's translation of *Orosius* (9th century), and from

* In regard to intimate personal letters, as early as 1936 the *top-concavity* was found to be quite general by Dr. J. C. Whitehorn, who was the first to note its presence at all. And that the top-concavity is associated with the intimacy, or the colloquialness of the letters, rather than merely with an epistolary literary form, was further illustrated by Dr. Whitehorn's analysis of the published correspondence of George Bernard Shaw and Ellen Terry; here Shaw's letters approach the harmonic seriation more closely (as if he were composing his letters with great care for a number of different readers) whereas the actress' language revealed the expected *top-concavity*. The Whitehorn finding has been subsequently confirmed by the investigation of my three former students, Messrs. W. A. Burnham Jr., H. Shippen Goodhue, and Kermit Roosevelt, who carefully analyzed the frequency distributions of words in extensive sets of intimately personal letters and found a top-concavity in all cases.

(*D*) the late *West Saxon Gospel of John*—as determined statistically in all three cases by Dr. F. P. Magoun Jr., who kindly put his data at my disposal for this purpose. We note that in spite of the time difference, Curves *B, C,* and *D* are quite similar.

Turning now to the second logarithmic cycle, we find six different curves (from *E* through *J*). Curve *E* represents the approximately 7,000 running words of *The Holy Rood* (*ca.* 1170 A.D.) as analyzed by my former student, Mr. R. F. W. Smith; this is very early Middle English and represents a period during which many structural changes were occurring. Curve *F* represents a sample of 10,000 words of the English text of the *Ancren Riwle*

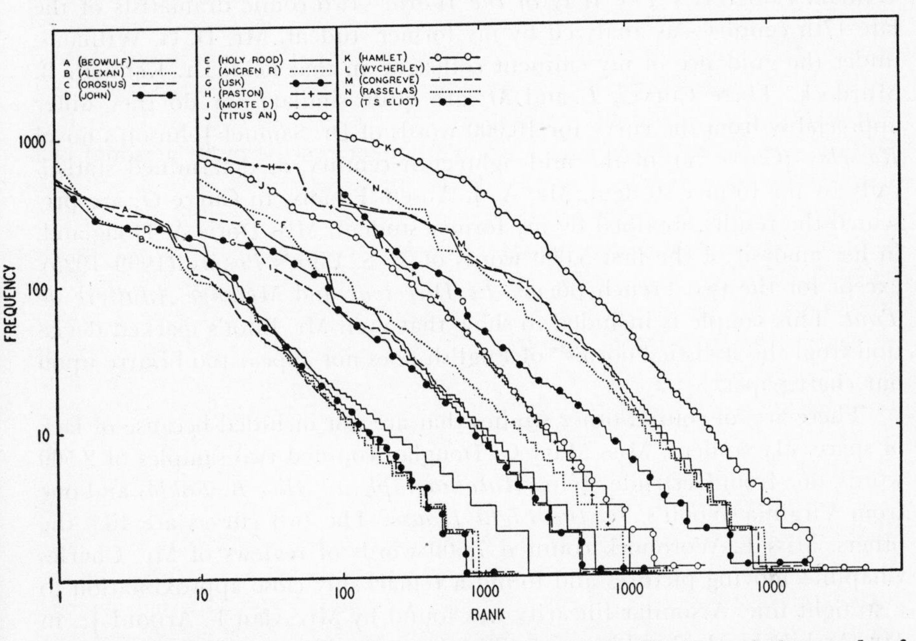

Fig. 3–14. Beowulf to T. S. Eliot. Rank-frequency distributions of the words of fifteen English writers from early Old English to the present day.

(*ca.* 1230–1250 A.D.) as determined by my former student, Mr. W. M. Doerflinger; and we remember that to the readers of the 12th and 13th centuries, *Beowulf* or the writings of Alfred or of Aelfric would have appeared as completely foreign languages—so great had been the intervening morphological, phonetic, and semantic changes. Curves *G, H,* and *I* are from the detailed studies of my former student, Mr. Elmer R. Best, and refer to the 15th century: *G* represents 10,000 words of Usk's *Testament of Love, H* represents 20,000 words of Sir John Paston's letters, and *I* represents 10,000 words of Mallory's *Morte d'Arthur*. Curves *G* through *I* are not greatly different despite differences of style and in sizes of sample; moreover the top-concavity of the *Paston Letters* (*H*) is to be expected because of the intimate nature of the personal letters. Similarly intimate and colloquial are the data of Curve *J,* which represents an analysis of Shakespeare's *Titus Andronicus,* as undertaken by my former student, Mr. G. Blakemore Evans;

it is on the whole quite linear, and represents a closer approximation to the harmonic series than the *Paston Letters* of more than a century earlier. By the time of Shakespeare the Old and Middle English inflections had become greatly simplified while numerous loan words had been incorporated from Latin and Romance.

Turning to the third cycle, we have five more sets of data. Curve *K* represents Shakespeare's *Hamlet* as analyzed by my former student, Mr. W. H. Bond; except for the first dozen or so words the curve is quite straight; we shall return to the data again in connection with Figure 3–15. Curves *L* and *M* refer to 10,000 words each from William Wycherley's *Country Wife* and William Congreve's *The Way of the World*—two comic dramatists of the late 17th century—as analyzed by my former student, Mr. D. G. Williams, under the guidance of my eminent colleague in that field, Dr. Kenneth B. Murdock. These Curves, *L* and *M,* are quite similar, nor do they differ appreciably from the curve for 10,000 words of Dr. Samuel Johnson's novel *Rasselas* (Curve *N*) of the mid-eighteenth century, as determined statistically by my former student, Mr. A. J. Ansen. Finally, in Curve *O,* are presented the results obtained by my former student, Miss Doris A. Hoagland, in her analysis of the first 5,000 words of T. S. Eliot's *Poems* (1909–1925) except for the two French poems, *Le Directeur* and *Mélange Adultère de Tout.* This sample is included to show that even Mr. Eliot's marked deviation from the stylistic "norms" of English does not appear too bizarre upon our chart paper.

There are, of course, other studies that are not included because of lack of space. My student, Miss Mary G. Douglas, counted two samples of 2,500 words, one from Gertrude Stein's *Autobiography of Alice B. Toklas* and one from Virginia Woolf's *To the Light House.* The two curves are like the others. Miss E. Woronock counted 7,500 words of reviews of Mr. Charles Chaplin's moving pictures and found a remarkably close approximation to a straight line. A similar linearity was found by Mr. Alan F. Arnold Jr. in Mr. Archibald MacLeish's article *The Irresponsibles.*

Let us now inspect the 15 charts of Fig. 3–14 as a whole while remembering that they represent the elapse of over a 1,000 years in the life of English, and refer to such widely different personalities as those of King Alfred and Mr. T. S. Eliot. In many cases there is a top-concavity which at most is conspicuous for the first few dozen words, and which generally represents fewer than 1/10 of 1% of the total number of different words. But as we inspect the curves of Fig. 3–4, we should ask whether they are not fundamentally similar as they "spill down" from left to right—far, far more similar than the actual writings which the curves represent. (Of course, the reader is perfectly free to reach to his own bookshelves for some other writer, and analyze a sample of five or ten thousand words in order to check our Principles.)

Now with the above fifteen sets of English data in mind, let us turn to the eight-rank frequency distributions of German and Yiddish as given in the lower left-hand corner, marked 1, of Fig. 3–15. Six of the eight analyses are from those that have already been discussed in connection with the distribution of morphemes as illustrated in Fig. 3–9. More specifically, Curve *A* represents the rank-frequency distribution of the 4,825 words in the Old High German of *Isïdore* as determined by Dr. A. Murray Fowler. Curve *B* represents the 1,726 words of the Old High German *Wessobrunner Sermon* and *Otloh's Prayer* as studied by Mr. S. A. R. Stephens. Curve *C* represents the 2,556 running words of the Old High German *Bamberger Creed and Confession* according to the analysis of Mr. Kenneth Lagerstedt, who also analyzed 10,000 running words of *Der Ackermann aus Böhmen* (*ca.* 1,400 A.D.) represented by Curve *E*. Curve *D* represents 10,000 running words taken from Berthold von Regensburg's *Sermons* (*ca.* 1,250 A.D.) as investigated by Miss Caroline P. Riley (because of limited space we shall not pre-

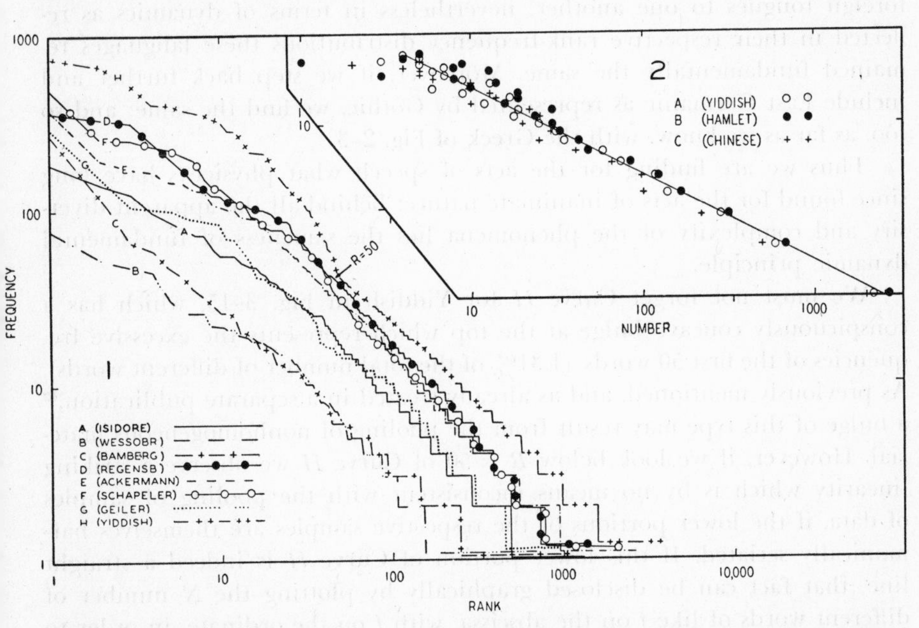

Fig. 3–15. Comparative curves. (1) Rank-frequency distributions of the words of seven Old High German or Middle High German authors, and of Yiddish; (2) the number-frequency relationship of Yiddish, Hamlet, and Chinese.

sent the data from Dr. Watzinger's study of 5,000 words from another part of these sermons because their curve is the same as Miss Riley's). Curve *F* represents a sample of approximately 10,000 running words from the Countess of Nassau-Saarbrücken's *Hug Schapeler* (1437) as studied by my former student, Mr. Warren Meredith. Curve *G* represents the approximately 5,000 words of *"Der Pilger"* from the writings of Geiler von Kayserberg (1445–1510) as studied by Mr. S. A. R. Stephens. In Curve *H* we present the 20,000 word data of a study of *Yiddish* as supervised by Dr. I. S. Stamm; it consists of excerpts from Ab. Kahan, *Blätter von mein Leben* (Vol. II, New York, 1926); Z. Levin, *Kopolovitz und andere Erzählungen* (New York, 1919); J. J. Zevin, *Chayim der Customer-Pedlar* (New York, 1926); Z. Schnaiur, *Vetter Zhome* (Wilna, 1930); and newspaper articles. Curve *H* is added here also for didactic reasons to warn the reader of what may be expected when nonhomogeneous material of the above sort is combined and treated as if it were a homogeneous population.

It is evident that except for Curve *H* for Yiddish, the German curves of Fig. 3–15 might just as well have been placed on the fourth cycle of Fig. 3–14 for English, since there is no fundamental statistical difference between the German curves from the 9th through the 16th century, and the English Curves from the 9th century to the 20th. In short, although the original West Germanic had split apart long ago into the various dialects of England on the one hand and of Southern Germany on the other, and although with passing centuries these dialects changed phonetically, morphologically, semantically, and syntactically until they appeared as completely foreign tongues to one another, nevertheless in terms of dynamics as reflected in their respective rank-frequency distributions these languages remained fundamentally the same. Moreover, if we step back further and include East Germanic as represented by Gothic, we find the same; and so too, as far as we know, with the Greek of Fig. 2–3.

Thus we are finding for the acts of speech what physicists have long since found for the acts of inanimate nature: behind all the apparent diversity and complexity of the phenomena lies the sameness of fundamental dynamic principle.

We must not forget Curve *H* for Yiddish in Fig. 3–15, which has a conspicuously concave bulge at the top which represents the excessive frequencies of the first 50 words (1.31% of the total number of different words). As previously mentioned, and as already treated in a separate publication,[42] a bulge of this type may result from the pooling of nonhomogeneous material. However, if we look below $R = 50$ of Curve *H* we observe a striking linearity which is by no means inconsistent with the pooling of samples of data, if the lower portions of the respective samples are themselves harmonically seriated. If this lower portion of Curve *H* is indeed a straight line, that fact can be disclosed graphically by plotting the N number of different words of like f on the abscissa, with f on the ordinate, in order to see whether the familiar linear *number-frequency relationship* appears; and this we have done in the upper right-hand corner of Fig. 3–15 (marked 2) where we present *in circles* the N number of different Yiddish words of like f frequency for all values of f from 1 through 25; here we also present *in dots* the N number of different words of like frequency, for values of f from 1 through 25, in the approximately 30,000 running words of *Hamlet* as determined by Mr. William Henry Bond. The arbitrarily drawn straight line of exponent, *2*, has been added to aid the reader's eye. But that is not all. For we have also added in *crosses* the N number of different words of like f frequency for values of f from 1 through 23 (since none occurred 24 and 25 times) as they appeared in samples of Peipingese Chinese totalling 13,248 running words, as discussed in a previous publication.[43] These three sets of data do not differ greatly in slope either from those for Homer's *Iliad* and Joyce's *Ulysses* in Fig. 2–3, or from those for the Gothic Bible in Fig. 3–7. If the *circles, dots,* and *crosses* of Fig. 3–15 (2) are sometimes too close to be easily distinguishable, the reader must blame the Principle of Least

Effort, because the underlying samples of speech upon which the Principle had been operative were so similar in size that the results likewise are quite similar. In spite of the stupendous differences in time, space, and culture between Yiddish, Shakespeare, and Chinese the dynamic difference is not significant.

There are further frequency lists for other languages. A selected bibliography up to the year 1939 for the chief modern European languages will be found in the *English Word Lists* of C. C. Fries and A. A. Traver. Since 1937, and under the influence of Dr. Hanley's *Word Index* to James Joyce's *Ulysses,* a series of important indices have appeared at the University of Wisconsin with the University Press. They are: W. T. Bandy's *A Word Index to Beaudelaire's Poems* (1939),* R. M. S. Heffner and W. P. Lehmann's *A Word Index to the Poems of Walther von der Vogelweide* (1940), A. R. Hohlfeld, Martin Joos, and W. F. Twaddell's *Wortindex von Goethes Faust* (1940), Alfred Senn and W. Lehmann's *Word-Index to Wolfram's Parzival* (1938). In addition, there is the recent (1942) monumental *Norwegian Word Studies* in two volumes by Einar Haugen which indexes (a) Sigrid Undset's novels of medieval life and (b) her early stories of modern life, (c) Ivar Aasen's writings in New Norse, (d) the vocabularies of Henrik Wergeland (1808–1845), and (e) the vocabularies of the Old Norse Sagas. We remark incidentally that this invaluable study has been published in mimeographed form in an edition of only 100 copies (*verbum sapienti*). It contains (pp. 20 f.) a bibliography of previous Scandinavian word counts. Although we may not devote further space to German frequency lists, particularly when they are publicly available in print, nevertheless we do present Dr. Haugen's modern Norwegian material in Fig. 3–16 on which there are 5 curves: Curve *A* represents Undset's novels of medieval life, Curve *B* represents her early stories of modern life, Curve *C* represents Ivar Aasen's writings in New Norse, Curve *D* represents Wergeland's writings. In the original publication, values are not given for frequencies less than 10 for *A* and *B,* nor for less than 100 for *D.* Incidentally, in regard to Curve *N* (which has been added for the sake of its silent commentary), this curve *N* represents the Old High German words of the South German monk, Notker Labeo (–1022) which we have already presented in Curve *A* of Fig. 3–12. Except for the top-concavity, the curves are essentially parallel, with slopes slightly less than 1 (probably because of the enormous sizes of the samples).

In looking at Fig. 3–16 we should remember that the language of Curve *N* for Notker is separated from that of the other four by at least eight hundred years. Moreover Curve *N* represents West Germanic, whereas the other four represent North Germanic.

Because of the foregoing charts, with their approximations to the slope of a harmonic series (except for the top concavities), we must not overlook

* My colleague, Dr. James Richard Reid, is studying Dr. Bandy's statistics in conjunction with those for French privately collected and transmitted to him by Mr. J. Autrey Dabbs. See his disclosure of the harmonic distribution in French, and his own further important contribution in *Language,* XX (1944), 231–237.

the possibility that sometimes what are called "words" will have a rank-frequency slope that is less than 1. Such was the case with the "holophrastic words" of Nootka and Plains Cree, as we saw in Figs. 3–1 and 3–2. To refresh our memories of this type of slope that is less than unity, let us present in Fig. 3–17 the rank-frequency distribution of 5,000 running words of present-day Palestinian Hebrew, as analyzed by my former student, Mr. Bernard Siegel, together with a sample of 2,000 running words of the American

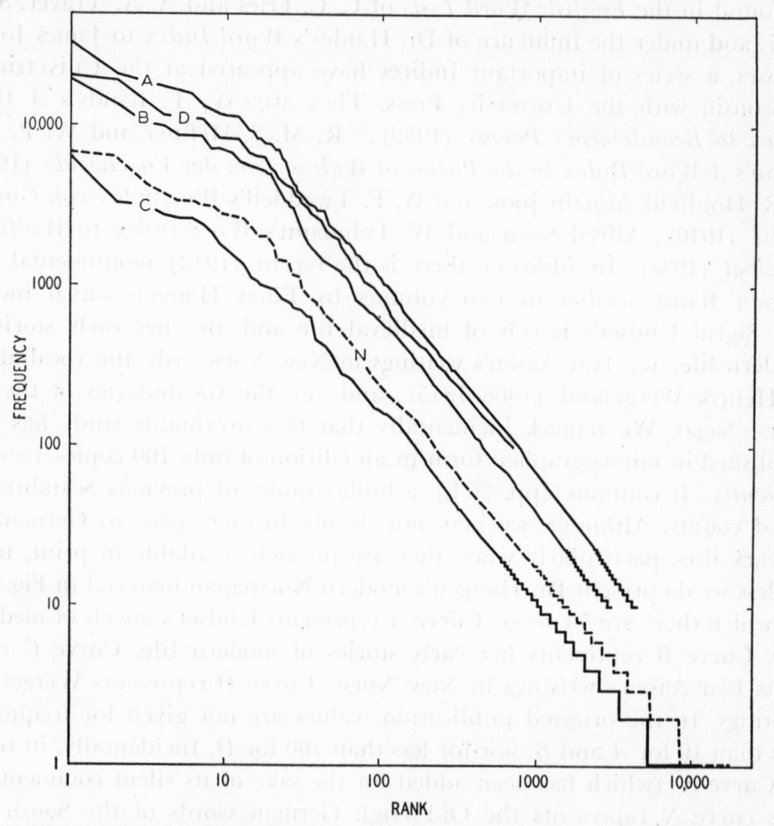

Fig. 3–16. Norwegian (Haugen analyses) and Notker rank-frequency distributions of words. (A) Undset's novels of medieval life; (B) Undset's early stories of modern life; (C) Aasen's New Norse; (D) Wergeland's writings; (N) Notker's writings, from Fig. 3–12.

Indian language, Plains Cree, which we add for comparative purposes. The curve for Hebrew is the first of four samples of 5,000 words which unhappily Mr. Siegel never had the opportunity to combine into a single sample of 20,000 words as originally planned. The curve for Plains Cree is the first of five samples of 2,000 words which were presented in combined form in Fig. 3–2.

It is evident that the two curves of Fig. 3–17 are linear, more or less parallel, and of a slope that is appreciably less than one. Moreover the respective *circles* and *crosses* of the number-frequency relationship for words occurring 15 or fewer times are fundamentally linear and parallel (no word occurred 11 times in Plains Cree nor 13 or 14 times in Hebrew). And so it would appear theoretically from our statistics that Palestinian Hebrew, like Plains Cree and Nootka, is structurally of the nature of a holophrastic language—as is in fact the case. For the Hebrew "words" of Fig. 3–17 include what in Hebrew are technically known as the "inseparables." Incidentally, the task of removing the "inseparables" and of studying the resultant rank-frequency distribution (such as we did for the A_1 and A_2 distributions of Nootka in Fig. 3–1 was also undertaken by Mr. Siegel but not completed; however insofar as the resolved data of Hebrew with "inseparables" removed are available, their rank-frequency distribution is by no means inconsistent

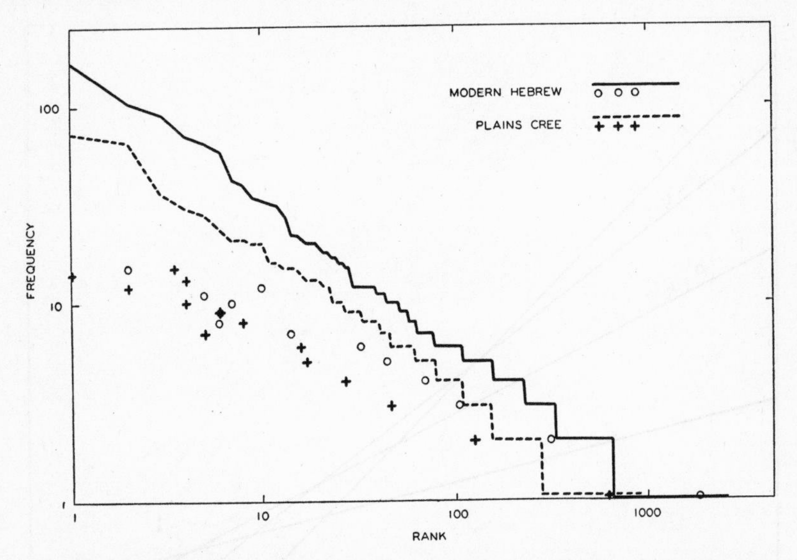

Fig. 3–17. Hebrew and Plains Cree. Rank-frequency distributions (broken and unbroken lines); and number-frequency distributions (circles and crosses).

with a linearity of unit slope, although a very marked tail is present. In this connection we remember that Palestinian Hebrew, unlike Nootka, is to a considerable extent an "artificially constructed" language; and this fact may explain the variations of the resolved data.*

By now we have presented enough data to suggest that the rank-frequency distributions of words, and also of holophrases, tend to be linear on doubly logarithmic paper, even though the distributions may not always have a negative slope of 1 (as we have just noted in the data of Fig. 3–17). Per-

* Without pretending to completeness we might remark by way of illustration of present-day Hebrew that if we undertook to revive classical Latin by coining new words for new cultural ideas and artifacts by manipulating the stock of original Latin morphemes within the framework of Latin grammar, the result would be an "artificially constructed" language analogous to Palestinian Hebrew. Naturally in either case many of the classical terms would be preserved. The artificiality of the language might be expected to reveal itself in the frequency-distribution of morphemes and phonetic entities. Incidentally the reader should not confuse Palestinian Hebrew, which has a Semitic base, with Yiddish, which has a Germanic base.

haps by way of conclusion we might digress momentarily upon the topic of these variations in slope—treating first the mathematics of it and then the theory. In either case the problem is elementary.

As to the mathematics of the variations in slopes, we present in Fig. 3–18 five different straight lines, the size of whose absolute slopes is in each case indicated by the fraction after the letter p. Thus the bottom horizontal line has no slope and is marked $p = 0$; since the second line from the bottom intercepts only ¼ as much of the vertical axis as it does of the horizontal, its p is ¼. And so on up the list. Obviously we could increase the slopes of these lines indefinitely; yet regardless of the steepness of the slope, the

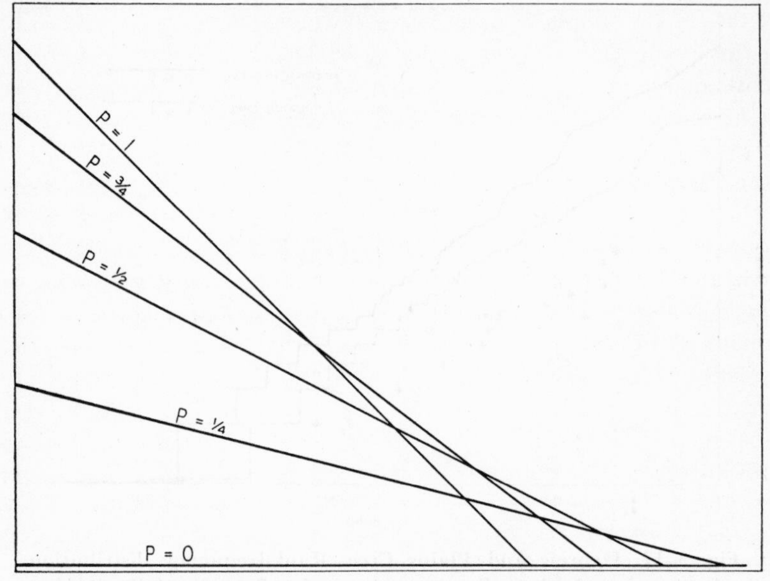

Fig. 3–18. The generalized harmonic series. Various values of p.

amount intercepted on the vertical axis, when divided by the amount intercepted on the horizontal axis, would yield a numerical value of p which would be the absolute slope.

No matter what the value of p is, the points on a straight line of a given p slope on doubly logarithmic paper can be described algebraically with the following simple equation,

$$r \times f^{1/p} = C,$$

in which r, representing *rank*, is plotted on the abscissa, and f, representing frequency, on the ordinate. When $p = 1$, as happened to be the case with the data of Fig. 2–1, then we have the familiar equation, $r \times f = C$, which we discussed in Chapter Two.

Moreover the value of p is important when we view a set of rank-frequency data as a *series of fractions,* as we did with the Equation of the Harmonic Series in Chapter Two which we now write as follows:

$$F \cdot Sn_{}^{} = \frac{F}{1^1} + \frac{F}{2^1} + \frac{F}{3^1} + \cdot \cdot \cdot + \frac{F}{n^1}$$

The reason for the exponent of 1 in the denominators of the fractions at the right becomes clear when we write the *Equation of the Generalized Harmonic Series,* which is as follows:

$$F \cdot Sn = \frac{F}{1^p} + \frac{F}{2^p} + \frac{F}{3^p} + \cdot \cdot \cdot + \frac{F}{n^p}$$

This *Generalized Harmonic Series* (a fundamental equation in our entire book) describes any set of rank-frequency data whose points fall on a straight line on doubly logarithmic paper. The size of n will be the antilog of the X-intercept; the size of F will be the antilog of the Y-intercept; the size of p will be the result of dividing the Y-intercept by the X-intercept. In the case of the simple harmonic series with which we have been dealing up to this point, the X-intercept has been equal to the Y-intercept, with the result that $p = 1$ (and we hence omitted the exponent entirely). Our simple *harmonic series,* therefore, is but a special case of the *generalized harmonic series.*[44]

With the above simple mathematics in mind we could now return to Figs. 3–1, 3–2, and 3–17 for Nootka, Plains Cree, and Hebrew, and calculate the slopes and the values of p; with these values we could describe the data approximately in the form either of the generalized harmonic series, or of the equation $r \cdot f^{1/p} = C$. And so we see that the mathematical aspect of our entire book will be quite elementary as long as our distributions are linear, since the size of the slope tells us everything.*

Turning now to the theoretical meaning of changes in slope according to the Generalized Harmonic Series, we remember that our theoretical Force of Diversification "pulls" the slope in the direction of a zero slope, whereas our theoretical Force of Unification "pulls" it in the direction of a true vertical, with the slope becoming infinitely great. The absolute slope of 1 of our harmonic series seems to indicate the point of dynamic equilibrium between these two hypothetical Forces. This is the slope of a great number of rank-frequency distributions of *words,* as we have seen.

It is only natural to ask why the value, $p = 1$, should be of critical significance for *words,* since obviously other slopes are possible and, indeed, for Plains Cree and Palestinian Hebrew, other slopes (less than 1) have been observed. This question we shall attempt to answer in Chapter Five.

V. SUMMARY

In the preceding pages we have presented a sizable amount of empiric data which we have attempted to rationalize by appealing to the economy of a mechanical analogue (the Tool Analogy).

As to the empiric data themselves, we have presented enough, I think, to establish beyond doubt the presence of orderliness in human speech. Thus, regardless of the particular physical words used, and regardless of their particular meanings, the ratio between the n number of different words and their f frequencies is apparently the same for all speech groups,

* If we designate the actual slope (positive or negative) as λ, then $p = -\lambda$.

even, presumably, if the different groups have no two physical words and no two meanings in common. This entire orderliness we shall later define as *mind* into whose dynamics we shall inquire more particularly in Chapters Five and Seven.

All our formulations refer clearly to a person's organization and usage of *n* different classes of physical stimuli in reference to *m* different classes of responses (i.e., meanings), in terms of the conventions of the speech group in question (*m* is the equivalent of the *z* different usages of our mechanical tools).

Throughout our discussion, we pointed out two consistent tendencies of speech. The *first* tendency was in the direction of reducing the magnitudes of the speech entities by correlating the entities of smaller size with the classes of more frequent occurrence; we called this tendency the Law of Abbreviation.

The *second* tendency was in the direction of decreasing, or minimizing, the *n* number of different classes of activity performed; we called this tendency the Law of Diminishing Returns (later we shall call it simply the "*n* minimum"). As devices for minimizing the *n* diversity of the classes used, we spoke of the Principles of Economical Versatility, of Economical Permutation, and of Economical Specialization, which we merely mention here without reviewing their definition.*

For the sake of rationalizing our data we invented our Tool Analogy with *n* different tools whose structure we shall not review here beyond saying that we derived our above Laws and Principles from it. It is legitimate to ask, however, whether there is any closer relationship between speech and the Tool Analogy than that of a mere analogue. In this connection and in anticipation of our argument in later chapters, we submit that *speech* refers to the organization of *n* different classes of physical action which have only a *conventional,* or *cultural, correlation* between stimulus and response. Our Tool Analogy, on the other hand, refers to the organization of *n* different classes of physical action which have a *physical correlation* between stimulus and response. The significance of this difference will be made amply clear in Chapters Five, Six, and Seven. In these chapters, in the course of discussing the question of probable work (Effort), we shall see that there is no dynamic difference between speech and the Tool Analogy; and that in general an important economy of the organism lies in its minimizing its *n* different classes of action of all sorts.

Having discussed in the present chapter the general topic of formal-semantic balance, we shall turn in Chapter Four to a brief inspection of the structure of the speech of children, where we shall find a confirmation of much of our foregoing argument. Then, in Chapter Five, we shall turn our

* In the light of our later argument in Chapter Five we might state even now that the Principle of Economical Permutation—that is, the principle of combining two or more different *classes* of action to make a third *class*—seems to be quite fundamental to speech structure. Indeed, both the Principles of Economical Versatility and of Economical Specialization may be inherent in the Principle of Economical Permutation for reasons that can be inferred from the argument of Chapter Five.

present argument around and view speech as a sensation of the auditor, into whose general economy we shall inquire. In Chapter Five, where we shall be working with an entirely different type of problem, we shall once again come upon the economy of the generalized harmonic series in the organization of mentation.

CHAPTER FOUR

CHILDREN'S VERBALIZATIONS AND THE "ORIGIN OF SPEECH"

In our foregoing discussion of word-usage we noted the importance of the size of n—the number of different words in a given person's vocabulary. Now we shall investigate empirically and theoretically the question of variations in the size of n. Since it has long been known that the vocabularies of children vary quite widely in size, we shall concentrate our interest in the present chapter exclusively upon the verbalizations of children. This concentration will be the easier because the topic of children's speech has been considered of such prime importance by many skilled investigators in the general field of child development that we shall find in the fruits of their research the necessary raw materials for our entire statistical analysis.[1]

In investigating now the vocabulary sizes of children, we do not approach the problem from the background of the entire field of child development. Rather do we come to it fresh from a study of cases of adult English speech in which we found, among other things, the presence of the Hyperbolic Equation, $r \times f = C$, as well as its corollary Equation of the Harmonic Series, $F \cdot Sn$.* Moreover in our ensuing treatment of children's speech we shall become only incidentally concerned with the non-linguistic background of the entire field of child development, since from the viewpoint of our main interests the speech ways of children are recommended for study only because they happen to offer us an excellent opportunity for studying certain aspects of the Principle of Least Effort which apparently cannot be explored elsewhere with equal ease.

I. THE PROBLEM

In turning to the problem of children's speech we do well not only to recall what we said in our discussion of the basic Forces of Unification and Diversification at the opening of the second chapter, but also to remember what we did not say. For although we discussed at length the conflicting economic advantages of a large and small vocabulary for a given *speaker,* we never placed the restriction that the given speaker should be an *adult* and not a *child.* Hence for all we know to the contrary the entire argu-

* We shall not present information about the distribution of interval sizes between the repetition of words ($N_f \cdot S = a\ constant$) not only because of the very great expense of such analyses but also and more particularly because this equation is primarily useful for a study of personality differences (as we saw in discussing the cases of unbalance at the end of Chapter Two) in which we are not at present interested. For our present purposes the Harmonic Equation suffices.

ment about the Forces of Unification and Diversification can be applied automatically and *in toto* to the verbalizations of children, with the result that we may turn immediately to the quantitative aspects of our problem.

By itself the sheer fact that children may have smaller vocabularies than adults does not render impossible either the Hyperbolic Equation, $r \times f = C$, or the Equation of the Harmonic Series

$$F \cdot Sn = F/1 + F/2 + F/3 + \ldots + F/n$$

For in decreasing the size of n, we merely decrease (1) the size of Sn, and (2) the size of C which equals n, as well as (3) the size of F which we always assume is equal to n (i.e., $F/n = 1$). The same applies conversely when we increase the size of n.

In this general connection, however, we should perhaps bear in mind that as n increases or decreases arithmetically, Sn will correspondingly increase and decrease only logarithmically, with the result that differences in vocabulary size, n (as well as in the size of $F \cdot Sn$), will be more strikingly apparent to the observer than the subtler but no less critically important differences in Sn. Indeed because of the ultimate importance of the relationship between n and Sn not only for the present chapter but also for the entire book, we may profitably digress for a moment and, for the purpose of illustration, present in the adjoining Table 4–1 the approximate number of different words, n, and the approximate optimum size of the sample, $F \cdot Sn$ (with $F = n$) that will be necessary to satisfy the Equation of the Harmonic Series for a few arbitrarily selected values of Sn.

Even a glance at the three columns of Table 4–1 suffices to show the enormous changes that may result both in the number of different words in a vocabulary and in the optimum size of a sample from comparatively slight changes in the size of Sn. For practical purposes of analysis that can be quite perplexing, for we may not calculate a slope except from a sample of optimum size, and yet we cannot tell what a sample's optimum size is unless we know the size of its Sn. And we cannot calculate Sn except from a sample of optimum size. So we find ourselves in a minor dilemma.

Nevertheless, there is a way out if we are willing to be patient. Thus for a given child we can select different samples of running words whose respective sizes, Σ, will vary appreciably in length. After reducing the words of each sample to a rank-frequency distribution, we can plot each one graphically and note which one seems to approximate most closely the slope of -1, because the sample that approximates -1 most closely will also presumably approximate most nearly a condition of optimum size with which we may safely operate.

Once we have a sample that is approximately of optimum size, we can calculate the actual slope of its best straight line, which should be close to -1. On the basis of this information we can also calculate the Y-intercept of the best straight line; this Y-intercept will be the theoretical frequency, F, of the most frequent word (i.e., the word, $r = 1$). Then working on the assumption that the sample size, Σ, is approximately $F \cdot Sn$, we can divide

TABLE 4–1

The approximate number of different words, n, in a vocabulary and the approximate optimum size, $F \cdot Sn$, of a sample of running words (with $F = n$) that will be necessary to satisfy the equation,

$$F \cdot Sn = \frac{F}{1} + \frac{F}{2} + \frac{F}{3} + \cdot \cdot \cdot + \frac{F}{n}$$

for a few arbitrarily selected values of Sn.

I Size of *Sn*	II Number of Different Words *n* (Approximate)	III Optimum Size of Sample *F* · *Sn* (Approximate)
5	81	405
6	227	1,362
7	610	4,270
8	1,670	13,360
9	4,550	40,950
10	12,370	123,700
15.3	2,560,000	39,168,000
17.5	22,400,000	392,000,000

Σ by our calculated theoretical F and thereby gain an insight into the size of Sn for the child, and thus extricate ourselves from our dilemma.

After eliciting this information about Sn for the verbalizations of one child, we can extend our analysis to the verbalizations of a group of children of various ages with the intention of exploring into the extent to which the verbalizations of children can, in general, be appropriately described by the equations, $r \times f = C$ and $F \cdot Sn$.

II. QUANTITATIVE DATA

As we turn now to a quantitative study of the rank-frequency distributions of the words of children's speech, we shall divide our study into two sections. In the first section (A) we shall study the word distributions of one child's speech at various moments of sampling from the age of 5 through 7 years (hereinafter, the *Uhrbrock Material*). In the second section (B) we shall study the word distributions of samples of the respective streams of speech of a group of children at various ages between 22 and 59 months inclusive (hereinafter, the *Fisher Material*).

A. The Uhrbrock Material

In Fig. 4–1 are presented graphically nine rank-frequency distributions of the different ranked words (on the X-axis) with their respective frequencies (on the Y-axis) of samples of connected speech as dictated into an Ediphone by a girl on or about her 5th, 6th, 6½th, and 7th birthdays as noted by R. S. Uhrbrock, who kindly put at my disposal not only the manuscript of the word frequencies and the statistical tabulations of the

5-year-old sample which he himself reported, but also the manuscript of the girl's dictations at the approximate age of 6, 6½, and 7 years.[2]

On Fig. 4–1, Curve *A* represents an aggregate of approximately 24,000 running words of the 5-year-old material; Curve *B* represents the first 10,000 running words of the same; Curve *C* represents 10,000 running words of the

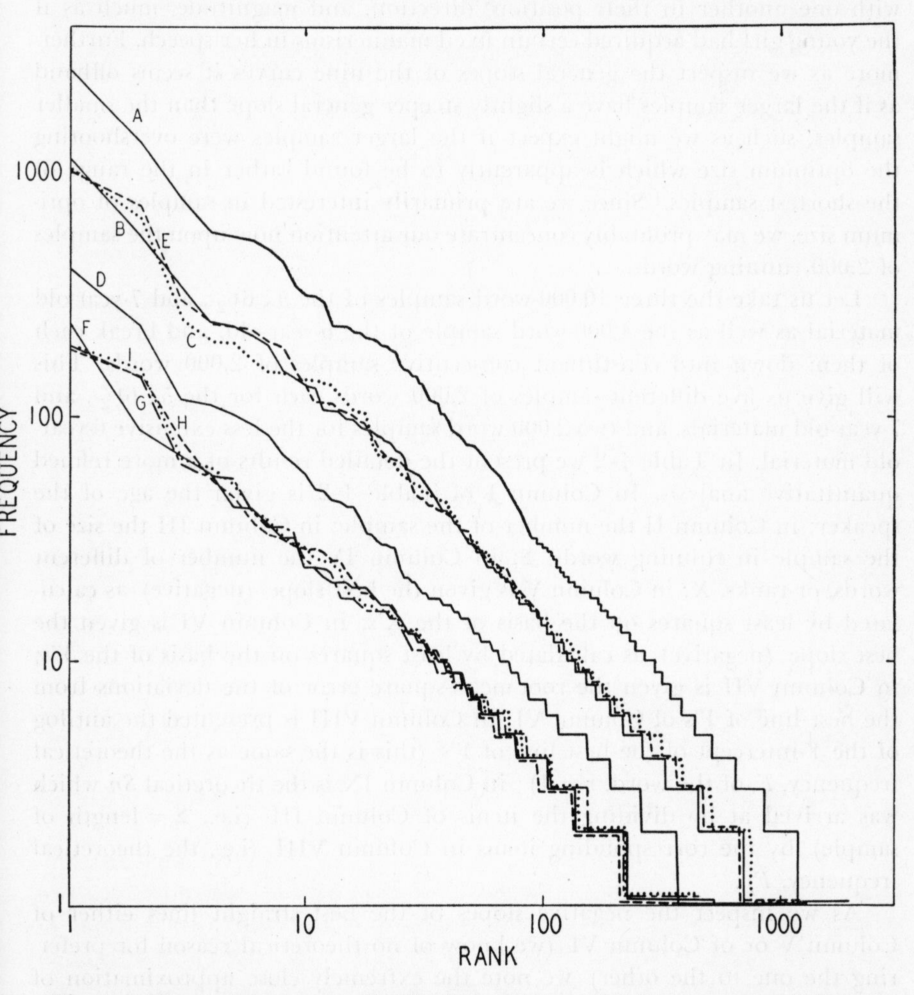

Fig. 4–1. The rank-frequency distribution of the words of a young girl (Uhrbrock material) at different ages: (A) 24,000 words at 5 years; (B) 10,000 words at 5 years; (C) 10,000 words at 6½ years; (D) 4,000 words at 6 years; (E) 10,000 words at 7 years; (F), (G), (H), and (I) 2,000 words at each of above ages (numbers refer to lengths of samples).

6½-year-old material; Curve *D* represents 4,000 running words of the less extensive 6-year-old material; Curve *E* represents 10,000 running words of the 7-year-old material; while Curves *F, G, H* and *I* refer respectively to the first 2,000 running words of the 5-, 6-, 6½-, and 7-year-old samples.

As we inspect the nine curves of Fig. 4–1 we note that they descend from left to right in a manner that is both *on the whole* similar and *on the whole* reasonably close to an approximation of the slope of -1 (thus, for example, they approximate -1 more closely than -2 or $-\frac{1}{2}$). True, they exhibit more marked bends from a straight line than was the case with the *Ulysses* and Eldridge curves of Fig. 2–1; moreover some of the bends of the different curves seem to be systematic in the sense that they correspond more or less with one another in their position, direction, and magnitude, much as if the young girl had acquired certain fixed mannerisms in her speech. Furthermore as we inspect the general slopes of the nine curves it seems offhand as if the larger samples have a slightly steeper general slope than the smaller samples, such as we might expect if the larger samples were overshooting the optimum size which is apparently to be found rather in the range of the shortest samples.[3] Since we are primarily interested in samples of optimum size, we may profitably concentrate our attention now upon the samples of 2,000 running words.

Let us take the three 10,000-word samples of the 5-, 6½-, and 7-year-old material as well as the 4,000-word sample of the 6-year-old, and break each of them down into constituent consecutive samples of 2,000 words. This will give us five different samples of 2,000 words each for the 5-, 6½-, and 7-year-old materials, and two 2,000-word samples for the less extensive 6-year-old material. In Table 4–2 we present the detailed results of a more refined quantitative analysis. In Column I of Table 4–2 is given the age of the speaker; in Column II the number of the sample; in Column III the size of the sample in running words, Σ; in Column IV the number of different words, or ranks, *X;* in Column V is given the best slope (negative) as calculated by least squares on the basis of the *X*'s; in Column VI is given the best slope (negative) as calculated by least squares on the basis of the *Y*'s; in Column VII is given the root-mean-square error of the deviations from the best line of *Y*'s of Column VI; in Column VIII is presented the antilog of the *Y*-intercept of the best line of *Y*'s (this is the same as the theoretical frequency, *F,* of the word, $r = 1$); in Column IX is the theoretical *Sn* which was arrived at by dividing the items of Column III (i.e., $\Sigma =$ length of sample) by the corresponding items in Column VIII (i.e., the theoretical frequency, *F*).

As we inspect the negative slopes of the best straight lines either of Column V or of Column VI (we know of no theoretical reason for preferring the one to the other) we note the extremely close approximation of the calculated negative slopes to the theoretical negative slope of 1. And from the comparatively small size of the errors of Column VII we may believe that our calculated best *Y*-lines come pretty close to the actual points. Therefore without further ado we may say on the basis of our discussion in Chapter Two that the Hyperbolic Equation, $r \times f = C$ and its companion Equation of the Harmonic Series, $F \cdot Sn$, will describe on the whole quite accurately the verbalizations of this girl at the ages of 5, 6, 6½, and 7 years respectively.

If we inspect the different sizes of the theoretical *Sn* in Column IX, we note that they vary between the extremes of 8.9 and 5.1, with the median

TABLE 4–2

Rank-frequency distribution of the Uhrbrock recordings of the speech of a girl.

I Age	II No. of Sample	III Size of Sample Σ	IV No. of Different Words X	V Best X-Slope (Negative)	VI Best Y-Slope (Negative)	VII Error (Y)	VIII Theoretical F of r = 1 (Y-intercept)	IX Theoretical Sn
5 Yrs.	1	2,002	513	.97	.92	.086	240	8.3
	2	2,000	501	.95	.93	.055	247	8.1
	3	2,003	496	.96	.92	.077	232	8.6
	4	2,000	484	.97	.94	.078	254	7.9
	5	2,000	475	1.00	.95	.091	254	7.9
6 Yrs.	1	2,000	466	1.00	.96	.080	282	7.1
	2	2,000	459	.99	.96	.081	282	7.1
6½ Yrs.	1	2,000	467	.99	.95	.082	269	7.4
	2	2,000	500	.97	.93	.077	238	8.4
	3	2,000	413	1.02	.99	.074	327	6.1
	4	2,000	404	1.02	.99	.074	332	6.0
	5	2,000	476	.96	.93	.069	258	7.7
7 Yrs.	1	2,000	437	1.02	.99	.074	312	6.4
	2	2,000	440	1.01	.98	.074	301	6.7
	3	2,000	398	1.04	1.01	.076	358	5.1
	4	2,000	457	.98	.95	.070	262	7.6
	5	2,000	487	.95	.92	.073	225	8.9

at 7.6. Although we shall return later to a detailed discussion of the variability of theoretical *Sn,* nevertheless in passing we may even now refer to Table 4–1, where we see that with *Sn* equal to 7 we may expect to find *approximately* 600 different words in a sample of about 4300 running words. This is interesting because the actual number of different words, *X,* of Column IV, and the actual lengths of our samples, Σ, of Column III are both of the general order of magnitude to be expected when *Sn* is about 7. True, our samples show in Column IV consistently fewer words than the theoretically estimated 600 words for $Sn = 7$. But this discrepancy can be explained by a glance at the bends in the curves of Fig. 4–1, where an upward convexity in the middle of the curves reveals a certain tendency towards an excessive frequency of usage of the words of medium frequency. Clearly any such tendency towards an excessive frequency of usage of some of the words in the middle range of frequency may be compensated for by a diminution either in the size of *F,* or in the size of *n,* or in the sizes of both, as was apparently the case with our 17 samples.

In spite of all these considerations, the salient fact remains that the calculated best slopes (Columns V and VI) are practically those which we expect theoretically.* Hence we have delivered thus far an amazingly precise empiric confirmation of the Hyperbolic Equation, $r \times f = C$, with all that that implies.

B. The Fisher Material

Now that we have examined the rank-frequency distributions of one girl at various moments of recording from her 5th through her 7th birthdays, with the result of a positive confirmation of our Hyperbolic Equation and its implications, it is our immediate duty to examine the rank-frequency distributions of other children in order to determine the extent to which we may generalize upon the basis of the Uhrbrock observations.

Happily, Dr. Mary Shattuck Fisher put on file at the Child Development Institute of Teachers College, Columbia University, her recordings of children's speech that served as the basis of her excellent monograph on the speech of the preschool child.[4] Dr. Lois Hayden Meek, the Director of the Institute, generously and hospitably allowed my research assistant to make a transcription of Dr. Fisher's recordings (the Fisher Material).

The Fisher Material, as described by Dr. Fisher in her monograph, consists of written recordings of the speech of children at a play school. The samples necessarily varied in length, and the verbalizations of some children were recorded again at a later date. For exploratory and comparative purposes we analyzed in some cases (1) not only the frequency distribution of the entire sample of a given child's speech on a given date, but also (2) constituent portions thereof of different sizes, as well as occasionally (3) the combined samples of several children of like age.

The results of our statistical analysis we now present in Table 4–3. Here Column I represents the age of the child in the number of completed months of life (thus, for example, 22 months includes every day from 22 months up to the day of the 23rd month). In Column II we present the number of each consecutive sample in the entire table. Column III gives an identifying number to each child (to disguise its identity) plus either the letter *m* or *f* to denote whether the child was a male or female; by means of these numbers we can also note when a given child's speech is being sampled again at a later date. In Column IV is given the date that Dr. Fisher made the recording. In Column V is given the size of the sample, Σ, in the terms of the number of running words it contains. In Column VI are the number of different words (ranks) in the sample. In Columns VII and VIII are the negative slopes of the lines (least squares) of the best X's and Y's respectively; and in Column IX the Error (root-mean-square deviation) of the line of best Y's. In Column X is the theoretical frequency, F, of the most frequent word (antilog of the Y-intercept of line of best Y's); and in Column XI is the theoretical Sn (obtained by dividing the items, Σ, in Column V by corresponding items, F, in Column X).

* As far as the question of bends from the straight line are concerned—a question to which we shall return again and again in later chapters—we might remark at this point that the child was using adult words in her limited discourse and hence might understandably reveal a suggestion of awkwardness therein.

Whenever the same date is given for different samples of the same child (e.g., sample nos. 64, 65, 66, 67), that indicates that a large recording of the child's speech on that date has been broken down into smaller consecutive parts which may or may not be of equal size; this breakdown was undertaken not only in the hope of approximating more closely the optimum size but also with the desire to study the differences in slope that may attend differences in sample size, Σ. The same hope and desire led also to the pooling of different samples of the same child at about the same time; such instances of pooling are indicated by the insertion in Column IV, under Date, of the sample numbers of the different combined samples (cf. sample nos. 3, 11, 16, 26, 43, 49, 53, 56, 62, 71). Therefore whenever the reader finds in Column IV numbers instead of a date, he will know that he is dealing with a combination of the samples to which the numbers refer.

Finally, in three cases (sample nos. 17, 23 and 45), the samples of different children were combined, and the children's identifying numbers will be found in Column III; these combinations of the speech of different children, which were undertaken to illustrate the danger of combining a diversity of samples, can even now be ignored on the grounds that they are statistical artifacts.

In inspecting the data of Table 4–3, the reader will note the presence of comparatively small errors where the combination of samples of a given speech is not exactly the same as the sum of its parts (e.g., sample no. 34 has 4052 running words instead of 4047). As far as we know, these errors are neither frequent nor significant. In view of the scope of the statistical task involved, we ask the reader to be lenient with these errors of calculation as well as with any others which he may find in the entire book.

As we inspect the data of Table 4–3, concentrating our attention upon the negative slopes of Columns VII and VIII, we note the astonishing closeness with which they approximate the theoretically expected negative slope of 1. The median of the 72 different slopes of best Y's is 1.02. Moreover, if we ignore the second decimal point of these 72 different slopes, we find that the mode is negative 1.0 (the negative slopes in *italics* are distributed as follows: *.6,* 1; *.7,* 2; *.8,* 6; *.9,* 19; *1.0,* 27; *1.1,* 12; *1.2,* 5).

In view of the nature of the disclosures in Table 4–3, we need have little hesitancy in saying that Dr. Fisher's material, like that of Dr. Uhrbrock, reveals the extreme closeness with which children's speech approximates the Hyperbolic Equation as well as the corollary Equation of the Harmonic Series.

Of course there are differences in slope, as we should expect from the differences in the sizes of the samples, if we remember our discussion in Chapter Two of saturation and the optimal sizes of samples. On the whole, the size of the slope (Column VII or VIII) tends to increase with the size of the sample (Column V), although we observe little tendency of the Error (Column IX) to vary either with the size of the sample (Column V) or even, say, with the ratio of different ranks to sample size (items in Column VI divided by corresponding items in Column V).

TABLE 4–3

Rank-frequency distributions of words in samples of speech of various children at various ages (the Fisher material)

I Age (Months)	II No. of Sample	III No. of Child	IV Date	V Size of Sample (Σ)	VI No. Different Words (*X*)	VII Best *X*-Slope (Negative)	VIII Best *Y*-Slope (Negative)	IX Error (*Y*)	X Theoretical *F* of (*r* = *1*)	XI Theoretical (*Sn*)
22	1	1*m*	10/7/29	363	71	.99	.93	.095	64	5.7
	2	1*m*	10/23/29	318	74	1.00	.94	.087	62	5.1
	3	1*m*	1; 2	681	124	1.05	.97	.108	132	5.1
23	4	1*m*	11/6, 20/29	356	94	.88	.83	.081	50	7.1
27	5	2*f*	5/5, 12, 20/30	1771	235	1.16	1.06	.140	453	3.9
	6	3*f*	11/27/29	64	27	.76	.64	.101	9.2	7.0
	7	3*f*	1/8, 17/30	684	188	.95	.91	.083	102	6.7
	8	4*f*	4/15/30	313	110	.85	.77	.098	36	8.7
	9	4*f*	4/23/30	363	89	.95	.90	.082	61	6.0
	10	4*f*	4/30/30	293	74	1.00	.95	.091	60	4.9
	11	4*f*	8; 9; 10	977	191	1.01	.93	.112	148	6.6
	12	5*m*	5/6/29	36	12	1.21	1.08	.119	12.6	2.9
	13	5*m*	5/12/29	86	23	1.03	.97	.081	22.9	3.8
	14	5*m*	5/17/29	118	31	1.12	1.06	.090	31.8	3.7
	15	5*m*	5/24/29	212	42	1.13	1.09	.076	53.5	4.0
	16	5*m*	12; 13; 14; 15	468	75	1.20	1.16	.079	136	3.4
	17	3, 4, 5	Combined	1473	252	1.08	1.02	.103	313	4.9
28	18	6*f*	5/1/30	1077	195	1.08	.99	.121	226	4.8
	19	6*f*	18; 5/15/30	1479	241	1.12	1.02	.136	328	4.5
	20	7*f*	11/13/29	833	190	1.01	.94	.108	144	5.8
	21	7*f*	12/10/29	1222	185	1.16	1.11	.099	293	4.2
	22	8*f*	4/13, 16, 17/34	1655	257	1.18	1.15	.085	541	3.1
	23	6, 7, 8	Combined	3912	467	1.21	1.14	.115	130	30.0
29	24	9*m*	3/18, 29/29	1425	322	1.04	.99	.096	271	5.3
	25	9*m*	4/16/29	1448	266	1.10	1.02	.115	306	4.8
	26	9*m*	24; 25	2873	463	1.17	1.11	.108	835	3.5
	27	10*m*	4/14; 5/2/30	1010	122	1.31	1.17	.165	357	2.8
	28	11*m*	4/11, 16; 5/2/30	288	91	.99	.82	.091	40.7	7.1
	29	12*m*	4/14, 18/30	2733	328	1.30	1.23	.116	1163	2.4
30	30	13*m*	2/15/29	699	174	.99	.94	.086	110	6.4
	31	14*m*	5/11/34	1303	281	1.09	1.03	.106	280	4.7

	32	14*m*	5/14/34	1481	302	1.09	1.04	.089	331	4.5
	33	14*m*	5/16/34	1263	353	1.09	1.03	.104	280	4.5
	34	14*m*	31, 32, 33	4052	509	1.27	1.22	.107	1693	2.7
	35	15*f*	5/1/36	892	209	1.02	.98	.078	162	5.5
	36	12*m*	4/25/30	798	184	1.06	1.01	.113	167	4.8
35	37	16*f*	4/10/34	1118	215	1.11	1.05	.098	264	4.2
	38	16*f*	4/11/34	1920	324	1.18	1.10	.118	542	3.5
	39	16*f*	4/12/34	1929	313	1.13	1.09	.094	492	3.9
	40	17*m*	10/11/29	1516	276	1.11	1.05	.109	357	4.2
	41	17*m*	10/22/29	1539	240	1.02	.98	.126	450	3.4
	42	17*m*	10/29/29	2035	296	1.19	1.12	.116	612	3.3
	43	17*m*	41; 42	3586	390	1.28	1.21	.122	1481	2.4
36	44	18*m*	2/18/29	805	223	.95	.89	.096	115	7.0
	45	17*m*, 18*m*	Combined	4339	481	1.26	1.20	.112	1760	2.5
42	46	19*m*	4/15, 28, 30/30	1449	293	1.06	1.02	.085	291	5.0
	47	19*m*	4/15, 28, 30/30	1571	317	1.08	1.03	.093	337	4.7
	48	19*m*	4/30/30	1472	314	1.06	1.01	.101	296	5.0
	49	19*m*	46; 47; 48	4492	551	1.22	1.21	.051	1875	2.4
	50	20*m*	1/31/30	664	192	.94	.88	.092	93	7.1
	51	21*m*	1/24/30	786	247	.90	.85	.092	94	8.4
	52	21*m*	1/24/30	782	252	.89	.85	.083	91	8.6
	53	21*m*	51; 52	1568	382	1.02	.97	.098	271	5.9
	54	22*f*	10/8/29	762	184	1.04	.98	.103	147	5.2
	55	22*f*	10/8/29	756	202	.99	.95	.083	133	5.7
	56	22*f*	54; 55	1518	286	1.14	1.08	.108	395	3.8
48	57	23*m*	4/8/35	1313	350	1.11	1.06	.098	670	2.0
	58	23*m*	4/8/35	2892	525	.97	.92	.088	186	5.5
	59	24*m*	5/2/34	1738	387	1.06	1.01	.096	335	5.2
	60	18*m*	2/4/30	1056	225	1.09	1.03	.122	224	4.7
	61	18*m*	2/4/30	1346	268	1.10	1.03	.107	293	4.6
	62	18*m*	60; 61	2402	382	1.21	1.14	.118	758	3.2
	63	25*f*	4/1/30	1904	377	1.10	1.04	.105	430	4.4
49	64	26*f*	3/4/30	1599	238	1.24	1.17	.116	559	2.9
	65	26*f*	3/4/30	1223	229	1.12	1.06	.103	293	4.2
	66	26*f*	3/4/30	1612	276	1.16	1.09	.113	453	3.6
	67	26*f*	3/4/30	1455	295	1.12	1.06	.108	345	4.2
53	68	27*m*	5/22/35	867	224	.96	.90	.093	132	6.6
54	69	28*f*	3/10/30	1253	310	.99	.95	.079	205	6.1
	70	28*f*	3/26/30	1605	335	1.08	1.02	.107	340	4.7
	71	28*f*	69; 70	2861	485	1.15	1.10	.099	766	3.7
59	72	29*f*	5/7/35	567	198	.83	.79	.076	56	10.0

In order to give a slightly more precise idea of the relationships between slope, sample size, error, and rank-sample-size, let us divide the data of Table 4–3 into the following three age-groups: I, 22–29 months; II, 30–42 months; and III, 43–59 months. Then in Table 4–4 let us present the results of a study of the possible correlations between: (1) the slope (from Col. VIII, Table 4–3) and the sample size (from Col. V, *ibid.*); (2) the error (from Col. IX, *ibid.*) and the sample size (from Col. V, *ibid.*); and (3) the error (from Col. IX, *ibid.*) and the result of dividing respective ranks (Col. VI, *ibid.*) by sample sizes (Col. V, *ibid.*).

An inspection of Table 4–4 reveals (1) that on the whole the slope is positively correlated with the size of the sample; that is, the larger a sample is, the steeper its slope is likely to be (as we might have anticipated more or less from our discussion of subsaturation, saturation, and supersaturation). On the other hand, the Error (*2.3*) tells us little of interest.

TABLE 4–4

Correlation Study of the Data in Table 4–3

Study No.	Correlates (Roman Numerals in Parentheses Refer to Columns in Table 4–3)	Group I 22–29 Months	Group II 30–42 Months	Group III 43–59 Months	Groups I, II, III
1.	Slope (VIII) and Sample Size (V)	+ .41	+ .82	+ .65	+ .67
2.	Error (IX) and Sample Size (V)	+ .41	+ .02	+ .28	+ .20
3.	Error (IX) and $\frac{\text{Ranks (VI)}}{\text{Sample Size (V)}}$	− .40	− .11	− .56	− .42

Although Table 4–4 disposes of the minor points in reference to the slopes and errors of Table 4–3, there still remain the items in Column XI of Table 4–3 (the theoretical *Sn*) which merit passing consideration. These, like the corresponding items for the Uhrbrock material, vary considerably. Nevertheless with the exception of sample nos. 23 and 72, *Sn* falls appreciably short of 10 and even 9, with only three samples that are larger than 8. The conspicuous case of $Sn = 30$ of sample no. 23, in the probable event that it is *not* a miscalculation, represents the risk of combining samples of speech of different persons (but note the apparent conformities of the combined samples of nos. 17 and 45). Sample 72 with its abrupt 10.0 is probably little more than an "accident." * But in spite of all this the upper limit of *Sn* in the Fisher material in Table 4–3 is approximately that of the upper limit of the Uhrbrock material in Table 4–2, although the lower limit of *Sn* in the Fisher material is well below the lower limit of

* We must remember in general, however, that our theoretical *Sn* will vary with the slope; thus as the negative slope increases, the size of theoretical *F* not only increases but also represents a greater share of the total number of running words, Σ; hence with a constant Σ an increasing slope will mean a decreasing *Sn*.

the Uhrbrock material—perhaps because there are lower age groups in the Fisher material.

As to the rest of the possible correlates, such as the difference in slope and the sex of the child, we leave them in the hands of any interested person, since our primary interests are still in the disclosure of the Principle of Least Effort, whose operation we suspect is responsible for the nature and orderliness of the data of this chapter.

The Fisher material has firmly buttressed our empiric findings by showing how closely even infant speech can approximate the slope of − 1. The sizes of some of the errors suggest that the children may have been at times somewhat awkward in using adult "word tools" with a close approximation to the Hyperbolic Equation.[5]

C. Children's Echolalia (Fisher material continued)

In retrospect we must confess that the Fisher material presented us with not a few difficulties of classification. By that we mean chiefly the difficulties of classifying some of the children's recorded utterances into the categories of formal words.

These classificatory difficulties were of two kinds. The first and less serious difficulty was that of classifying such utterances as *"brabrabrabra"* which incidentally happened to be repeated twice in sample no. 3 (and there were 26 other similar *acultural utterances* in that sample which, with the preceding, had however only a combined total frequency of occurrence of 42 out of 680 running words).

The second and more serious difficulty was that of treating the immediate repetitions of formal words (i.e., *echolalia*). Thus, for example, in sample no. 3 there was the most frequent word, *"grandma"*; this occurred a total of 97 times, of which 85 instances were bunched together into twelve different sets of immediate repetitions whose respective sizes in terms of juxtaposed *grandma's* were as follows: 33, 14, 10, 8, 4, 3, 3, 3, 2, 2, 2, 2 (the approximation of the harmonic proportions may be accidental). The second most frequent word, *"duck"* had 51 occurrences of which there were three clusters of 27, 7, and 3 juxtaposed utterances respectively. The third was *"daddy,"* whose total of 30 occurrences included clusters of 9, 9, 3 and 2; the fourth was a proper name which occurred 27 times with clusters of 6, 5, 2, 2, 2, 2, 2, and 2. And so on down the list. Indeed we shall present for its didactic value the opening of the text of the sample of 1*m,* October 7, 1929 at the age of 22 months (not yet two years!) where the *echolalia* is conspicuous (*echolalia* is normally defined as the automatic and "purposeless" repetition of words).

> Grandma. Grandma. Buggy. Baby. Baby crying. Baby crying. Baby crying. Grandma. Grandma here. My ball. Baby girl. Munner. All through. Yes. Grandma. Grandma. Grandma. Grandma. Grandma. Grandma. Grandma. Grandma. Stand up. Stand up. Grandma. Grandma. Grandma. Grandma. Grandma. Grandma. Grandma. Grandma. Grandma. Grandma. "Bill's" hat. Coat. Coat. Put my sweater on. Put my sweater on. Grandma sit down. Grandma sit down. Grandma. Grandma. Grandma. Grandma. Grandma. Grandma. Grandma. Grandma. Grandma. Grandma. Grandma.

Grandma. Grandma. Grandma. I got blocks. I got blocks. Hat. My ball. Look. Look. Look. Ball. Ball. "Mary." Ball. Ball. Ball. Ball. Grandma. Grandma. Grandma. Grandma. Hat. Hat on. Mmmmmmmm. Paper. Paper. Paper. Paper. Munner—mandeet, mandeet, mandeet, mandeet, mandeet, mandeet—seebeesh, seebeesh, seebeesh, seebeesh, seebeesh, bubabubububububububub. oooooo oo oooo. Grandma (repeated to a total of 33 times). Grandmah (repeated to a total of 11 times).

And so on through samples no. 1 and 2 (which, combined, yield sample no. 3).

How should the elements of this "gibberish" be classified? We don't know. We only know that we counted *all* like "words" including repetitions as like "words" and *all* like "acultural utterances" as like "words." And we found that the best X slopes (negative) of this "gibberish" as reported, for example, in sample nos. 1, 2, and 3 were respectively .99 and 1.00 and 1.05 (Y slopes were .93, .94, and .97 respectively). Hence we may say that the lad whose speech was recorded was not only consistent in his "gibberish" throughout the entire sample, but that he also revealed in his infantile verbal "workshop" a hyperbolic economy of word usage that is quite comparable to the hyperbolic economy of James Joyce in Joyce's adult verbal "workshop."

Perhaps we should ask whether we should have eliminated from our tabulations all nonverbal entities as well as all instances of echolalia on the grounds that these are not *"words."* We can only remark that in spite of our perusal of many words on the subject of *"words"* we have yet to find out what a *word* is, though more will be said on this subject in our following chapter. As far as we know, *seebeesh* and *bubabubu,* etc., in the above sample which sound like the "bow wow" of a dog, bear the same relationship to the infant's verbalizations as the adult's formal words do to the adult's verbalizations. Hence *seebeesh,* and the like, may be only nonadult acultural utterances which under no consideration should be eliminated (after the age of 30 months the "nonadult acultural utterances" rapidly become statistically insignificant; and even in sample no. 3 they amount to only 42 out of 680).

But even if we retain the "nonadult acultural utterances" in our samples, should we perhaps eliminate the echolalia? It is easy enough to eliminate the echolalia by simply deleting it from the samples and then recalculating the best Y slopes with errors. In this case the number of different words (ranks) of Column VI of Table 4–3 will remain the same, although the size of the sample, Σ, of Column V (Table 4–3) will shrink by an amount that is equal to the number of repetitions removed (in sample no. 1 the removal of echolalia will decrease the sample from 363 to 219 running words).

In order to show the effect of the deletion of echolalia in the first 29 samples of Table 4–3 (the age groups from 22 through 29 months, after which echolalia is statistically insignificant) we present in Table 4–5 the calculations by least-squares of the best Y slopes (negative) and the Y error (root-mean-square deviations) of the above samples after all echolalia has been eliminated. In Table 4–5 Column I we find the age group, and in Column II the sample number from Table 4–3. Column III *A* gives the

TABLE 4–5

The first 29 samples (ages from 22 through 29 months) of Table 4–3, *supra*, in which are compared the differences in sample size, Σ, and best *Y* slopes and *Y* errors, first (A) with echolalia included, and second (B) without echolalia.

I Age (mos.)	II Sample Number	III Sample Size (Σ) A With Echolalia	III B Without Echolalia	IV No. Different Words (Ranks) X	V Best *Y* Slope (Negative) A With Echolalia	V B Without Echolalia	VI Error (*Y*) A With Echolalia	VI B Without Echolalia
22	1	363	219	71	.93	.81	.095	.102
	2	318	199	74	.94	.80	.087	.074
	3	681	418	124	.97	.85	.108	.109
23	4	356	256	94	.83	.72	.081	.086
27	5	1771	1208	235	1.06	1.00	.140	.127
	6	64	56	27	.64	.56	.101	.100
	7	684	635	188	.91	.89	.083	.081
	8	313	263	110	.77	.68	.098	.100
	9	363	277	89	.90	.79	.082	.083
	10	293	268	74	.95	.93	.091	.090
	11	977	804	191	.93	.92	.112	.097
	12	36	26	12	1.08	.92	.119	.145
	13	86	72	23	.97	.95	.081	.071
	14	118	95	31	1.06	1.00	.090	.131
	15	212	169	42	1.09	1.06	.076	.095
	16	468	373	75	1.16	1.11	.079	.082
	17	1473	1231	252	1.02	1.00	.103	.092
28	18	1077	1034	195	.99	.99	.121	.119
	19	1479	1419	241	1.02	1.04	.136	.108
	20	833	765	190	.94	.92	.108	.101
	21	1222	1165	185	1.11	1.10	.099	.090
	22	1655	1644	257	1.15	1.15	.085	.085
	23	3912	3782	467	1.14	1.14	.115	.112
29	24	1425	1373	322	.99	.98	.096	.089
	25	1448	1393	266	1.02	1.01	.115	.097
	26	2873	2766	463	1.11	1.10	.108	.113
	27	1010	846	122	1.17	1.14	.165	.140
	28	288	230	91	.82	.76	.091	.090
	29	2733	2690	328	1.23	1.23	.116	.116

size of the sample *with* echolalia (the same as Column V of Table 4–3) while Column III *B* gives the size of the sample *without* echolalia. Column IV (from Column VI of Table 4–3) gives the number of different words (ranks), which remains the same with or without echolalia. Columns V *A* and V *B* give the respective best *Y* slopes (negative for the samples first *with* and then *without* echolalia). Columns VI *A* and VI *B* give the respective *Y* errors for the samples first *with,* and then *without,* echolalia.

As we inspect the two sets of sample sizes in Column III, we note that by and large the proportional differences between the corresponding items in the *A* and *B* columns tend to be less pronounced with an increase in age. That is, as the child grows older, the proportion of echolalia in his total speech tends to decrease, until by 29 months it is practically negligible. Moreover when we turn to the individual items under *A* and *B,* both for the slopes in Column V and for the errors in Column VI, we again note that differences between corresponding items become less pronounced with increasing age, as is to be expected from the fact that with increasing age the underlying *A* and *B* samples themselves differ less and less. Indeed, even by the age of 28 months the differences in slope between *A* and *B* are so comparatively insignificant that it is perhaps useless to make any other remark than that by 28 months the *B* slopes without echolalia are by and large either the same or merely slightly smaller than the corresponding *A* slopes with echolalia.

Up through 27 months the differences between the *A* and *B* slopes are appreciable. Moreover in every case in these early age groups the *A* slopes are larger (steeper) than their corresponding *B* slopes. In all but 6 cases out of the 17 (*viz.,* sample nos. 5, 12, 14, 15, 16 and 17) the *A* slopes are equally close or closer to 1; and with the exception of sample no. 5, the nearer the sample is to 22 months the more remote the *B* slope is from negative 1.

Therefore if we assume on the basis of our empiric observations that the negative slope of 1 represents a condition of equilibrium between our Forces of Unification and Diversification, we may conclude that not only the "nonadult acultural utterances" of childhood but also the echolalia of childhood constitute somehow or other a dynamically integrated part of the total verbal expression. Although this conclusion is both simple and obvious, it nevertheless leads us to some theoretical considerations which will ultimately be of great value for our entire investigation of the reciprocal economy of tools and the Principle of Least Effort, as we now ask what all these curves and data may mean.

III. THEORETICAL DISCUSSION OF THE "ORIGIN" OF SPEECH

The data of the above Tables 4–2, 4–3, and 4–4 are unequivocal in one important respect. They reveal that samples of children's speech of the same order of magnitude can agree in rank-frequency distributions whose calculated best slopes are virtually − 1. And that means two things: First, that the selection and usage of "words" by children is subject to a law and not to capriciousness. Second, that this law is quite probably the same as that which governed the distribution of words both in Joyce's *Ulysses* and in the Eldridge material of Chapter Two, with the result that we may henceforth safely operate with the empiric equations, $r \times f = C$ and its corollary for $F \cdot Sn$ (with the full awareness that anyone who is still doubtful is free to test objectively our formulations upon the verbalizations of the millions of talking children in the country). But that is not all.

The combined data of Tables 4–2, 4–3, and 4–4 have revealed two further factors in children's speech, one of which we have just mentioned. They have revealed that both the "nonadult acultural utterances" and the echolalia of childhood may be dynamically an integral part of the child's stream of speech, in the sense that their presence makes the distribution more nearly hyperbolic. Second, they have revealed in the variations in the size of *Sn* that a given child (or children of a given age group) uses speech in a way that is by no means constant in respect of optimum size. Since both of these two factors are of interest to our general purposes, we shall discuss each in turn in A and B below.

A. Echolalia and "Bow-wow"

We have just said that any person who doubts the general validity of our observations in this chapter is free to resort to further objective tests. The results of such further objective tests would be so welcome that we shall here outline an ideal experimental setup for just such a test, although in so doing we are guided primarily by its didactic value for our present theoretical discussion.

To begin, let us suppose that the primary objective of the experimental setup is the study of the vocalizations of children of all ages, including children who are even younger than 22 months. This could be done by putting the children in a situation where their spontaneous vocalizations would be electrically recorded without the children's awareness (in this connection we remember the perfected method of observation of Dr. Arnold Gesell of the Child Development Clinic at Yale University). After we have accumulated recordings of significant length for our various children we should turn to the task of analyzing them statistically.

On the basis of our general experience with children, we might expect to find two things as we progressed backwards from the vocalizations of the older children to those of the youngest infants. First, we might expect to find that the proportion of echolalia would tend to increase as the age group became younger and younger. Second, we might expect to find that the proportion of "nonadult acultural utterances" would also increase with decreasing age until we reach the complete "gu-gu-ga" condition of infancy in which the echolalia would refer to the repetition of undiluted "nonadult acultural utterances." In short, as we went back from childhood into earliest infancy, we should expect to find a condition which became increasingly one of general echolalia and of "nonadult acultural utterances" not much unlike the pleased, pained and ambiguous vocalizations of the puppy, or of many other animals.

Conversely, if we started with the small infant and observed his vocalizations as he grew older, we should expect to find the reverse of the above, as the infant's nonadult acultural echolalia became on the one hand increasingly more adult and culturally verbalized, while on the other hand the proportion of echolalia to nonecholalia diminished as a whole—quite unlike the puppy or other animals whose vocalizations rarely seemed to alter appreciably after a certain age.*

If we concentrate our attention first upon the general economy of speech, we may suspect that the growing infant comes ever more into the possession of a set of tools which are useful in getting a fellow man to do things for him. Or, more precisely stated, his vocalizations become increasingly more efficient in utilizing a fellow man as an instrument for the attainment of objectives (i.e., the use of man as *a social instrument*). Of course, even the early babblings of childhood are effective in utilizing a fellow man as a social instrument; witness the baby's outcry and the response of the mother as a social instrument (and there is often a parallel in the dog's barking and his master's response). Indeed we may suspect that there is a general economy that is latent even in the most "physiological" outcry of a baby, although the infant may not always be aware of the presence or nature of the economy from which he profits.† Thus if we may imagine that the spontaneous "physiological" birth cry of the infant's expanding lungs has some time in the history of mankind called attention to a newborn baby whose birth at the loins of a dead mother would otherwise have passed unnoticed, we should have therein an example of a vocalization which, however automatic, nevertheless accomplished socially in the job of survival practically everything that a formal word or sentence could have done. Hence the *general economy* of speech is potentially present even in the most autonomic noises.

Passing now from the *general* to the *internal economies* of speech as discussed in the terms of our Forces of Unification and Diversification, we must remember that at no time did we restrict our argument exclusively to the selection and usage of *formal* adult words in contradistinction either to infant babblings or *to anything else that wittingly or unwittingly conveys an "idea" to, or otherwise evokes a response in, a fellow man or a fellow-anything-else.* Therefore we may infer that our Forces of Unification and Diversification are at least potentially present also in the babblings of infants in the sense that it is potentially economical even for the infant to have both a single "babble" of 100% frequency and also a repertory of n "babbles," depending upon the nature of the verbal job to be performed.

Naturally, as the child grows older and faces more complex verbal jobs, he may find it much more economical if he articulates his babble into formal classes (i.e., words) which will be stereotypes that are socially understandable. This will also be more economical of the efforts of the listener

---

* If we plotted the Y-size of Sn for a group of children of various ages against their respective X-ages, and fitted a curve to the same, it would be interesting whether the calculated X-intercept was closer to zero months or -9 months.

† We here merely mention in passing the entire problem of the association of ideas with acts which has been investigated with brilliant results by I. P. Pavlov, D. K. Adams, C. L. Hull, George Humphrey, E. L. Thorndike, L. L. Thurstone, and others. Ernest R. Hilgard has recently published a valuable critical analysis of the chief theories of learning with a very complete bibliography.[6]

(as well as for the student of biosocial dynamics who has to classify it). Hence the formal words of adulthood in which we have found the hyperbolic relationship may be viewed as nothing more than babble that has been organized into social stereotypes for the sake of using fellow men more effectively as social instruments.

Of course, if a child happened to have no need for using a fellow man as a social instrument, then he would also find no economy in formalizing his babble for a fellow man. And, in general, there is never an economy for an individual to formalize his "babble" beyond the exigencies of his more economical survival. Thus, for example, an adult may well find it economical to know so unusual a word as *logarithm* if he finds it economical to become an engineer; but a hod carrier, like the newborn baby, will have no need for this word or for any other new word unless his present stock of "babble stereotypes" turns out to be inadequate for the jobs at hand.

As babies grow, their jobs grow, and so, apparently, do their capacities for handling the available tools for performing their jobs, including the tool of a fellow man who is useful as a social instrument in the general job of self-support, self-defense and self-propagation. And as fellow man looms up ever more as an economical social instrument of survival, so too does the more highly articulated "babble" of formal adult language recommend itself as a more economical device for manipulating fellow man as a social instrument. Hence we may suspect that on the whole, as a human being becomes more social, his speech becomes more socialized in the sense that it becomes more formally stereotyped into "grown-up words" (and the same may be true of other animals which, like dogs and many birds, often have stereotyped outcries to which a fellow responds in a more or less stereotyped manner).

B. The "Origin" of Speech

The above discussion of the babble of infancy brings up the stock question as to the origin of speech, a question to which a more or less categorical answer has often been tendered without always a preliminary definition of the terms *origin* and *speech*.

If by *speech* is meant any particular kind of noise that is made by one individual and which evokes a particular kind of response (or association) in another individual, then the first of our remote ancestors to correlate a particular kind of physiological noise of a fellow with another kind of his action was the first to discover speech. Thus, for example, if ages ago an individual made a stereotyped outcry of pain or flapped a fin with spontaneous joy at the sight of food, and if some other individual of the same species inferred therefrom what kind of action was happening or impending, then speech, in the above restricted definition, will have occurred. According to this definition, a cough, a sneeze, an audible flatulence, a death rattle are all speech. This view is essentially that of the "bow-wow" theory of speech, and all animals with stereotyped cries (or smells or gestures) indulge in speech. In our usage in later chapters we shall call this the language of the species, or the *language of physiology*. It refers to a more or less correct understanding of automatic physiological responses such as an understanding of the growling of an angry dog.

On the other hand, as soon as a dog barks, or lifts up his paw, for example, in order to evoke a particular kind of response, and if the bark, or paw-lifting, is not the result of an automatic physiological act, then *cultural speech* has occurred if any other individual understands it correctly. Thus when the dog barks in order to beg for his supper, and his master understands, then the two have a cultural vocabulary in common (cf. Chapter Seven), and *cultural speech* has occurred.

The difference between physiological and cultural speech may be a fine line, but it is an important line, since once the second step of emitting a *conventional* signal has occurred, then there is no dynamic difference between that single conventional signal and the most highly elaborated syntactic speech of man, except for the size of the n number of different signals. In either case the principles elaborated in our preceding chapter will apply. In our usage, speech will always mean cultural speech with no necessary physiological connection between the signal emitted and the response evoked.

As to the origin of cultural speech, we can only say that the first of our remote ancestors to give a comprehended conventional signal in the above sense was the first to speak. When that happened may never be known. But there is no reason for supposing that it was not long before our ancestors became human (whenever that was). Nor is there any reason for supposing that man has a monopoly upon cultural speech. The difficulty is that cultural signals can in time become automatic physiological actions (e.g., the apparently automatic *ouch!* is by no means a universal human signal of pain). The pollen dance of bees may have originally been cultural if it is no longer so. It would seem offhand that any living social system whose members co-operatively pursue like objectives with like rules might well evolve a cultural language out of the original assortment of physiological givens.

A commonplace example of the "origin" of human speech in an individual is found in the small baby's outcry. Although the baby may at first cry merely because of a touch of colic, yet the moment he discovers that his mother will come to his sheer cry, he has discovered human speech: one word and one meaning. This discovery has been made independently by virtually every baby. Can we say that the offspring of no other species has *ever* made a corresponding discovery? No little monkey has *ever* screamed at its ma to attract her attention?

In any event, the above discussion makes clear our conception of at least the nature of the problem of the "origin" of speech. After the individual has discovered the first word, it is easy to increase the n size of the vocabulary, perhaps by associations of the kind suggested, say, by E. L. Thorndike in his babble theory. Human cultural speech may have "originated" many times and independently.[7]

In the discussion of the "origin" of speech of the species, the origin of speech in childhood is clearly instructive.

C. The "Law of Recapitulation" in Children's Speech?

Some light may be shed upon the "origin" of speech by studying the chronological strata of children's speech in the manner employed for adult speech in Chapter Three, Fig. 3–10. Thus, for example, when a child learns to speak does he show a greater preference for the older shorter words of the cultural vocabulary, such as would be expected under the so-called "Law of Recapitulation" of biology, according to which the individual tends to recapitulate ontogenetically the phylogenetic history of his species? *

In order to investigate this question my former student, Mr. Marshall G. Pratt, examined the date of adoption of the words in the following three samples of children's speech: (1) the combined thirty-six-month-old material represented by Sample 45, Table 4–3, representing 481 different words totalling 4339 running words; (2) the five-year-old Uhrbrock material totalling 10,000 running words; and (3) the seven-year-old Uhrbrock material totalling 10,000 running words. The procedure of analysis was the same as that employed for the chronological strata in Chapter Three.

As to the quantitative presentation of the data, there were difficulties of comparison in view of the differing sizes of the samples, since the first sample (36 months) is only one-half the size of the second and third samples (5 and 7 years) which in turn are only one-fifth as large as that of the Eldridge material whose strata we studied in Fig. 3–10 and which we shall present again in Fig. 4–2 for comparative purposes.

Several methods of comparing the different samples are possible. Thus, for example, we can view the total number of ranked words in each sample as 100%, and then study the chronological strata of each successive 5% or 10% of the different ranked words in the four samples (including Eldridge's). In that case, according to the data, the younger children would clearly use an overwhelmingly greater proportion of older (and shorter) words, with the proportion being the highest for the 36-months-old material.

A more conservative method, and the one we have adopted in Fig. 4–2, is to compare the chronological strata of the successive sets of 100 ranked words for each of the four samples. Any difference in the percentages of chronological strata that appears with this more conservative method of comparison will be instructive.

In Fig. 4–2 are plotted in successive hundreds of ranked words—up to 10 hundreds where available—the percentages of the chronological strata for Old English, Middle English, and all the later chronological strata combined, of *A,* the 36-months material, of *B,* the 5-year material, of *C,* the 7-year material, and of *D,* the Eldridge material. These are only approximate (e.g., the 5th hundred of *A* represents the percentages for only 81 different words). When a given hundred included fractions of one or two different integral frequency classes (e.g., the eighth successive set of 100 words might consist in part of a fraction of the words occurring 8 times and a fraction of those occurring 3 times), the percentages of the strata in

* This topic is discussed in greater detail in Chapter Six.

the entire integral frequency classes in question were computed; these percentages were considered to apply to those portions of the given 100 words that consisted of the fractional part (s) of the integral frequency class (es).

Inspecting Fig. 4–2, we note little difference in the percentages of the chronological strata for the first 2 hundreds, much as if even small children used the articulatory articles, pronouns, auxiliaries, prepositions, and the like, with a virtual adult frequency. But beginning with the third hundred, the *D* column for Eldridge has a smaller percentage of Old English words in all cases. Moreover the *A* 3-year-old material has the highest percentages

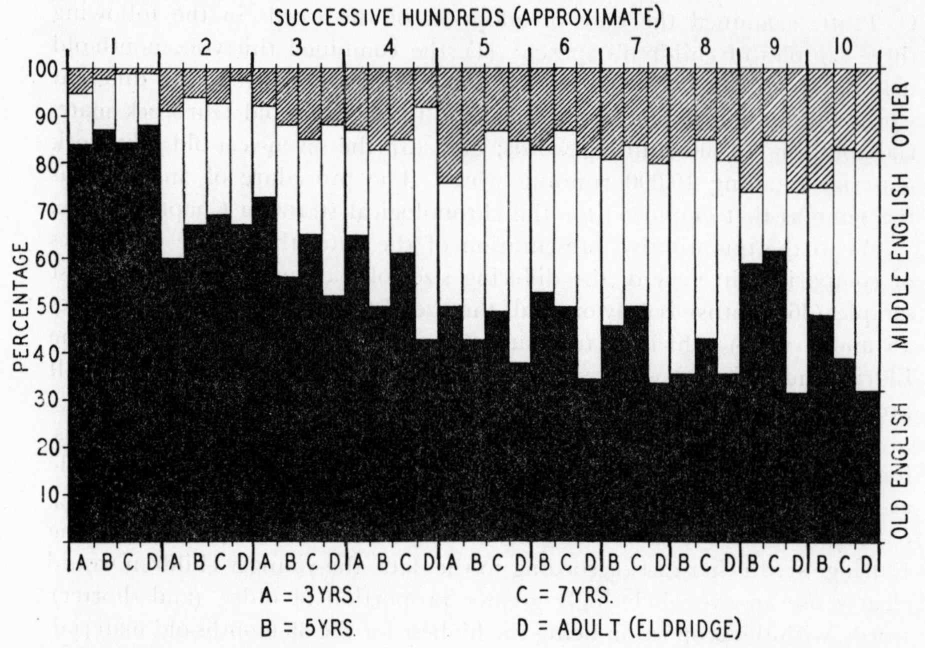

Fig. 4–2. Cultural-chronological strata of the ranked words (in hundreds) of the speech of persons at various ages: (A) 3 years; (B) 5 years; (C) 7 years; (D) adult (Eldridge material).

of Old English words in all cases except for the first and second hundreds. The variations of the *B* and *C* material render difficult any comparisons of their Old English strata. Moreover there seems to be no conspicuous difference between the percentage-usage of the Middle English and "other strata" in all four samples.

How far we may generalize upon the basis of these few data is questionable, beyond simply stating what we all suspected already: younger children tend to use a greater proportion of the older and shorter words in their speech. Yet this simple statement suggests the possible value of far more extensive analysis of the chronological strata of children's speech in shedding light on the "Law of Recapitulation."

While still on the subject of children's verbalizations and the possible tendency of older children to use a slightly increasing proportion of the longer and newer words in the vocabulary, let us call attention to the brilliant research of Dr. Mary Shattuck Fisher and many others into the structure of children's speech.[8] Thanks to their research, we know that in general the length and complexity of sentences used increases with the age of the child, even as does the diversity of the vocabulary; all of this is to be expected theoretically from the discussion of Chapter Three. Equally interesting is the disclosure that the relative frequency of usage of the word *I* tends to decrease with the child's age as he becomes ever more accustomed to, and interested in, the other actors of the group and their common conventions.

IV. SUMMARY

This chapter has been devoted largely to a presentation of empiric data for the verbalizations of childhood, in which we found the proportions of the harmonic law over the entire range of studies from the age of 22 months to 7 years.

This harmonic distribution referred, however, to the entire vocalization of the children in question, including the echolalia and the spontaneous acultural utterances (gibberish) that occurred in increasing amounts in the younger age brackets. Indeed, when the echolalia was removed (and inferentially the gibberish) there was no longer an approximation of the harmonic distribution. Therefore we conclude that the echolalia and gibberish of childhood are a part of the child's total verbal expression, and a part that disappears with passing months as the child becomes ever more conventionalized—or culturized—in his behavior. If this conclusion be correct, then we may view the conventions of culture of the social group as an alternative vocabulary of action that is substituted for the earlier individualistic vocabulary of action without, however, any alteration in the underlying principles of dynamics.

As to the stock question of the "origin" of speech we have suggested the need for a definition of terms. If by *speech* is meant the *language of physiology* as an interpretation of the apparently automatic physiological behavior of others, even as one interprets the action of inanimate nature in the light of his experience (e.g., a dog's reaction to a thunderstorm), then speech may well be as old as life. But if by speech is meant the *language of culture* in the sense of uttering a conventionally stereotyped noise for the purpose of evoking a conventionally stereotyped response in another individual without any necessary physiological connection between the type of action and the type of response, then the first of our forebears who made a squeak in order to tell his mother or mate where he was, was the first to speak, with a vocabulary of 1 word ordered to the equation, $F \cdot Sn = 1$. After the individual has taken this initial step of getting $n = 1$ cultural words in his vocabulary, an increase in the size of n can proceed according to the principles discussed in Chapter Three.

Apparently, in the development of a child's speech there is a tendency for the proportion of older and shorter words in the language to decrease, much as one might expect from the "Law of Recapitulation" of biology.

CHAPTER FIVE

LANGUAGE AS SENSATION AND MENTATION

Up to this point we have treated the speech process largely as the expression of a speaker who did the acting—that is, who manipulated the elements of the speech vocabulary in order to evoke responses in another person; during our argument we repeatedly inquired into the economy of the speaker in his speech expression. When, in Chapter Three, we developed our mechanical Tool Analogy with its artisan and *n* different kinds of tools, we kept stressing the viewpoint that the artisan was manipulating his environment, and not the reverse.

Now, however, we shall turn the proposition around and treat speech—and language—primarily as a sensory impression, as we observe the auditor as someone who is verbally acted upon. The economy into which we shall inquire is that of the auditor. But though we are shifting our emphasis, let us hasten to remark that we shall not be obliged to retract any of our previous statements, even though we shall have the opportunity to refine upon some of them.

Before proceeding further, let us remember that the topic of language as a sensation is only a part of the more general topic of gaining any sort of sensory information about one's environment. Since we are interested ultimately in the general economy of gaining information, our present problem of sensation (and mentation) of language becomes, in general: *what is the most economical information to have, what is the most economical means of procuring it, and what is the most economical means of utilizing it?* Without a very precise knowledge of the general meaning of our question, we shall be at a disadvantage in inquiring into the more particular economies of language.

Therefore in the present chapter we shall begin with the more general, and work towards the more particular. Before even broaching the question of language, we shall first (I) inquire into the particular kinds of information that the artisan of our Tool Analogy will need, as he competes for survival with other artisans. For convenience we shall assume initially that the artisan must produce goods and services of a certain quantity and quality with least effort. This elaboration of the Tool Analogy, in which we shall borrow from the terminology of traditional economics,[1] will provide the background for inquiring into (II) the economy of sensation, and (III) the economy of handling all sensory information (i.e., mentation). Subsequently (IV, V, and VI) we shall inquire into related matters, such as the economy of a semantic system, the meaning of consciousness, the possible source of mental conflict, and so on.

I. THE COMPARATIVE CONSERVATISM OF TOOLS IN THE RISKS AND OPPORTUNITIES OF THE ENVIRONMENT

The artisan of our Tool Analogy—and theoretically every organism—in seeking to exist in his environment with maximum economy, must be on the alert for all those kinds of events in his environment whose presence or absence may affect the economy of his shop. Thus, for example, he must watch out for those raw materials which are necessary for the construction, maintenance, and operation of his tool shop. So, too, he must beware those things that may in any way harm or impede the functioning of his shop. And, of course, he must continually give a thought to possibilities for a greater efficiency of his shop.

These various kinds of environmental events whose presence or absence will seriously modify the economy of the artisan's shop one way or the other may be called the relevant events of his sensory activity; all other kinds of events are *otiose,* as far as he is concerned, unless they are helpful in predicting the emergence of relevant events. Later (III and IV) we shall have much to say in general about relevant and otiose events.

A. The Problem of the New Kind of Job

One threat that continually confronts our artisan is that he may lose his present job and be forced to seek a new one. If he can find another job that is just like his old job, he is fortunate, since he can perform the new job with his old tools. On the other hand, if he must seek a new kind of job—and our present argument is restricted to the case of a new kind of job—then he will be obliged to seek that particular new kind of job that will be most economical for him. What factors will govern our artisan's decision in his selection of a new job, now that he can seek any job and use any kind of tools to perform it?

In the first place, his selection of a new kind of job will be restricted to those kinds of jobs which are either available or can be made available to him, and of whose existence he is aware.

In the second place, his selection will be governed by the probable duration of the new kind of job. Often a somewhat more difficult kind of job that lasts appreciably longer is economically preferable, since it postpones the day of seeking a still different kind of job.

In the third place, his selection of a new kind of job will be governed by the comparative cost of reconversion of his tool shop in order to perform the new job efficiently.

There are a few other considerations that enter into his selection of a new kind of job, as will appear in the course of our discussion.

Now clearly, in selecting a new kind of job, our artisan must, by hypothesis, ponder various factors, particularly since he is compelled to behave at all times with maximum economy. Let us therefore reinspect his tool shop (i.e., the Tool Analogy) as we formulated it in Chapter Three when, incidentally, we were concerned only with the most economical toolage for performing the given kind of job which we assumed would last forever (i.e., the case of variable tools and a fixed job). From now on the artisan can alter both his tools and his jobs (i.e., the case of variable tools and variable jobs).[2]

B. The Tool Analogy and the Comparative Value of Tools

In Chapter Three we elaborated a Tool Analogy in which our artisan had an n number of different kinds of tools with which he performed the fixed m number of different tasks of a given kind of job. To minimize his work by availing himself of the economy of close packing, the artisan set out to minimize the size of n. This he accomplished, *first,* by designing his tools so that each tool would perform as many different tasks as possible (the principle of economical versatility), *second,* so that "permutations" of these tools could also perform specific tasks without the need of introducing new specialized tools; and *third,* he arranged his tools so that the most frequently used tools were nearest and therefore easiest to reach. Finally he kept redesigning his tools so that their sizes and masses would be reduced —with a premium upon the reduction of the sizes and masses of the nearer and more frequent tools.

As pointed out, the artisan's task of saving work consisted of minimizing the sum of the products of all tools' respective masses, sizes, frequencies, and distances over a sizable interval of measurement. As a result, when we proceeded down the bench from the artisan, we tended to pass *from* the smallest, lightest, most versatile, most permuted, and most frequently used tools, *towards* the larger, heavier, less versatile (or more specialized), less permuted, and less frequently used tools. In so proceeding we also tended to pass from the comparatively *oldest* kinds of tools to the comparatively *newest.*

If we now assume that the artisan must alter his set of tools for the sake of performing some new kind of job selected at random, the question arises as to the particular tools he is likely to preserve intact as he sets out to alter his tool shop.

Clearly he is *likely to preserve those tools intact in proportion to their comparative versatility and permutability,* since those tools will be most likely to be usable in any new kind of job by reason of the above-average number of different tasks that they can perform whether alone or in "permutation."

These tools will also tend to be the comparatively *older* kinds of tools; *hence the longer that a given kind of tool has been in a shop, the more likely it is to remain there.* And since the older kinds of tools tend to be the smaller, lighter, and more frequently used tools, we may suspect that *the smaller, lighter, and more frequently used tools of a shop will tend to be preserved in the face of changing jobs even if the new jobs are selected at random.*

If we choose to call the older and more versatile and permutable tools the "core" of the system, and the others the "periphery"—the two terms being by no means discrete—we may say that the "core" tends to be more conservative over time than the "periphery"; and that, in turn, means that the rate of innovation or desuetude of a system's tools with the elapse of time will tend to be appreciably greater as the tools lie farther out in the periphery, and ever less as they lie farther within the "core."

C. The Comparative Economy of Jobs

In our previous section we considered the condition in which the artisan was obliged to perform a new kind of job selected at random. We noted that the smaller, older, more versatile, and more permuted tools at the "core" would be less likely to be altered than those at the "periphery."

With the above in mind, let us now assume that the artisan does not simply turn to a new job that is selected at random, but instead that he selects for himself a new job from the available jobs at hand. The question then arises as to which jobs would be comparatively most economical for him to select.

1. The Ease of Conversion of Tools. In the first place, if we assume that all available jobs will last equally long, and that they will involve the expenditure of work at an equal rate, then that job will be most economical which demands the least work in altering the old set of tools.* In other words, that particular new kind of job that can be performed most nearly completely by the already extant set of tools, will tend to cost least in retooling and, therefore, will be the most economical job to select.

Insofar as different kinds of tools are needed either to replace or to augment the tools already there, these new tools are more likely to be placed farther out towards the periphery than closer in towards the core, for reasons already given.

Once the new kind of job has been selected, then the Laws of Abbreviation and of Diminishing Returns will begin to operate, with the result that in time the structure of our Tool Analogy will become the same as that of Chapter Three. We mention this in order to point out that all the speech data of our preceding chapters apply to the present case of our Tool Analogy, in which both tools and jobs are variable. Indeed, our present more general case of the Tool Analogy is obviously more appropriate to the facts of speech than the more restricted case in Chapter Three.

2. The Rate of Amortization of Tool Conversions. It may happen, however, that some of the new kinds of jobs will last longer than others.

If (1) some of the new kinds of jobs last longer than others, and if (2) the cost of conversion of tools is the same for all jobs, and if (3) the rate of work expenditure is the same, then (4) the artisan should select that kind of job that is likely to last the longest, so that he can amortize the cost of retooling at a lower rate.

This factor of the comparative rate of amortizing capital changes in a system is by no means new to economics. We are merely pointing out that if the new kind of job is of shorter duration, the artisan will have to earn more from it in order to justify (i.e., pay for) the capital changes. Hence there is a premium upon jobs of longer duration, because the lower rate of

* In Chapter Three we amply explored the case of jobs of different rates of work expenditure.

amortization (or the lower rate of *necessary earned surplus,* if one will) means he will have to devote a proportionately smaller amount of his work to paying for his new tools.

To select such a job of long duration, the artisan must have *information* about the opportunities of his environment, and he must also be able to *predict* the length of the various jobs. Hence he must have a sensory system and a predicting mechanism; or, as we shall say, he must have a sensory-mentational system (II and III below).

There is an additional economy, however, in a longer job. The longer a job lasts, the greater opportunity the artisan has for redesigning and rearranging his tools in order to benefit from the economies of the Laws of Abbreviation and of Diminishing Returns.

D. Optimals, Ideals, and Regression

It is evident from our above discussion that the selection of a new kind of job depends upon the particular tools that are already at hand.

For any given set of tools in a field of different kinds of available jobs of whose existence the artisan knows, that particular kind of job is *optimal* which can be performed with the least average rate of work, including an amortization of the cost of retooling. Since the actual duration of a job is a matter of estimation, however, it is more correct to say that the optimal job is the job of least (average) probable rate of work—or simply *least effort*—as estimated by the artisan.

In addition to optimal jobs for tools, there is also the possibility of *ideal jobs* for a given set of tools. An *ideal* job for a given set of tools is the most economical job of which the artisan can conceive. Thus, for example, if an artisan has just finished a kind of job, *A,* which is no longer present, then *A* is not the optimal job for the given tools, though it may be the ideal job.

Obviously, when the ideal job is not available it is not optimal. There may, however, be a strong incentive to alter the environment in order to realize the ideal. This concept of an ideal that exists only in the artisan's "mind" is interesting for several reasons beyond the provision for a "mind" or "knowledge" whose structure will be discussed later (Sections III and IV *infra*).

In the first place, the concept of an ideal provides for the artisan's altering his environment to suit the economy of his given tools (i.e., the alteration of jobs to suit tools), even as he can alter his tools to match jobs. This consideration is obviously important for any study of human behavior.

In the second place, with the elapse of time, the optimal job at which the artisan works, and to which he adjusts his tools, may become also the ideal job for his tools. That is because an ideal is defined in terms of a given set of tools. As the tools change, so too the ideal changes. Hence a person who, while waiting for the emergence of the ideal job, temporarily accepts a makeshift optimal job to which he automatically adjusts, may be surprised to find that the optimal job has become ideal, whereas the erstwhile ideal job ceases to be ideal. Thus, for example, some men marry their wives because they are in love with them (i.e., their ideal); others may fall in love with their wives because they have married them (i.e., by adjusting to their wives, their wives become ideal).

Since, in general, optimals tend to become ideals, one's present job, or mode of behavior, tends in time to define one's economy. Hence one's evaluations of the good or the bad for one's self, tend to refer to the exigencies of one's present status and not to a former status; a change in job can entail a "change of mind."

Nevertheless, since we select a future *B* optimal job on the basis of our past *A* toolage, the past, *A*, will bias our selection. For that reason, at the end of our present *B* kind of job, there is a certain bias towards the previous *A* job, since some of the tools that are necessary for *A* will still be residual in the *B* shop. This tendency to revert to an earlier *A* status when one is frustrated in one's newer *B* status may be called the *economy of regression.*

We mention these matters of optimals, ideals, and regression which are meaningful in everyday experience in order to show that they can be defined in terms of our Tool Analogy which, after all, is designed to objectify living action.

E. Tools, Jobs, and Operations

Our use of the well-known terms, *tool* and *job,* has been recommended by considerations of easier exposition. Nevertheless, there is an inherent awkwardness in the terms since, as we have already pointed out,[3] tools are usually defined in terms of jobs, while jobs are defined in terms of tools. Although we shall continue to use these terms—and even the term, *tools-jobs,* for the sake of emphasizing the urge to match the two—we shall nevertheless digress briefly now in order to state the *tools-jobs* relationship in more fundamental terms.

We have said that our artisan must use his *n* different mechanical tools with maximum economy of effort (i.e., minimizing his average probable rate of work over time).

To this end, he must procure an *n* number of different kinds of matter-energy which will perform *m* different kinds of operations upon matter-energy so that he can get enough energy to support himself. That is what the problem is in simplest terms. The *n* different kinds of matter-energy (whether conceived of as material kinds, properties, configurations, or combinations) are *tools* in our usage. The *m* different kinds of operations that these tools can perform on matter-energy can be called *tasks.* The matter-energy upon which the tools operate in order to get energy for the artisan's survival can be called the *job.*

By definition, the artisan must procure sources of energy (work). Moreover he must expend the least amount of work. In order to do so he must predict his future—and he may make some sorry mistakes in doing so, as we all know from actual experience; hence, he expends least probable (average) work, or *least effort.*

In taking this path of least effort, the artisan may use any kinds of matter-energy (tools) that he can find. And he may use them in any *m* different manners (tasks) of operation upon other kinds of matter-energy (jobs) for the sake of procuring the necessary energy (work) for his survival. And he must expend least effort (i.e., least probable work) in doing so. He must reckon the costs of procuring, maintaining, and operating his shop (tools, tasks, and jobs) to his total cost of production, hence these probable total costs must also be minimized.

In the above usage, we may say that tools perform jobs by means of tasks. If the artisan has a given set of tools and tasks, he must seek jobs. If he has a given job, he must seek tools and tasks.

As a matter of fact, the artisan, if he be an organism, will always have a set of tools to start with, even if it be his genetic donum at conception (discussed later). The problem, then, is one of so altering jobs and tools (including tasks) that he can minimize effort while maintaining production.

This problem is clearly fundamental to an understanding of all organic evolution, if our Principle of Least Effort be correct. Closely connected with this problem are two considerations: (1) the concept of the probable future, and (2) the concept of the *n* minimum. Let us briefly inspect each in turn.

1. The Probable Future. In the eyes of our artisan at any moment, the events of the future are solely a matter of his own predictions, since he has no knowledge of the future other than his calculations. Hence we may call *his* future *his probable future.*

Obviously, as the artisan looks ever *further* into the future, the future becomes relatively ever less predictable (i.e., relatively less determinate) and proportionately so. Conversely, as the artisan looks into the future that is ever *nearer* to the present, the future becomes proportionately more determinate or predictable.

Since the artisan must govern his present selective action on the basis of the probable future, it follows clearly that as events lie ever further off in the future they exert an ever decreasing weight upon his calculations, because they become increasingly less determinate. And conversely.

Even though we assume that the passage of time is a constant, it will not necessarily seem to be a constant to the artisan to whom the future is only a probable future. On the contrary, he will tend theoretically to weight the importance of the events of the future ever less as those events lie ever further in the future. Regardless of the constancy of time, the artisan will act, for example, as if two weeks from today is much more than just twice as far off as one week from today. Thus those events which, like interest payment, taxes, seasonal changes, and the like, are more or less fixed in calendar time will seem to arrive much sooner than expected. The summer vacation that seems so far off to the small boy arrives sooner than expected; and so, too, its end. The actual rate at which we discount the future is something to be disclosed empirically.[4]

A life of least effort, therefore, is always limited by what we may call the "cone of an increasingly indeterminate future" with the "cone's vertex" at the present instant. Regardless of the accuracy of his predictions at every moment, the artisan will, nevertheless, look back upon a life of missed opportunities and wasted work.

There seems also to be a corresponding "cone" for the past with the "vertex" again at the present as we view the events of the past as the determinants of the present. The further off an event lies in the past, the increasingly less determinate of our present it seems to be, and the increasingly less we consider it in estimating the future. As a result, we feel that two centuries ago are far more remote from us (say, four times as remote) as one century ago. Hence to the average person the remote events of history seem very remote indeed, and the vast periods between them, only a moment of importance.

This quasi "hourglass" (the two "nappes") of indeterminacy will always influence our predictions by introducing what might be called the bias of the near present and the near past in all our calculations. Yet the "hourglass" presupposes a basic constant physical time, as we shall see in greater detail later in this chapter.*

As a result of this quasi "hourglass," the artisan will be continually altering his predictions, as the future becomes present.

*2. **The Economy of Minimizing n.*** We have previously argued that the artisan should show preference for the more frequently occurring kinds of materials in his environment, in order to decrease the risk of being unable to find them when needed. The relatively rarer the materials are that he uses, the greater will be the need for carrying inventories of these materials as an insurance against a shortage of the same. These inventories will increase the cost of the shop, and hence the rate of amortization (or the rate of necessary earned surplus).

Yet even after the artisan has made his *n* different kinds of tools out of the most frequently occurring kinds of materials, it is economical for him to decrease the size of *n* because *in any random spot he is more likely to find a smaller n number of different kinds of materials than a larger n number, and hence by decreasing n he decreases the probable work (i.e., effort) that will be necessary to look for and procure a larger n number.* Hence by decreasing the *n* different kinds of matter-energy that he employs, the artisan minimizes his probable work (effort).

The same argument applies to the *n* number of different kinds of material-chemical properties that the artisan uses in his shop. By decreasing the *n* number of different properties, he increases the probability of finding materials with those properties in any given spot, thereby minimizing the probable work of the shop.

The same argument applies to the *n* number of different configurations or combinations of matter-energy and of their properties; by decreasing their *n* number he increases the probabilities of finding the prerequisite materials.

---

* Our concept of faulty time perspective discussed in Chapter Two can be expressed by considering increases and decreases of the angle of the cone at the vertex.

The same argument applies to decreasing the amounts of the different kinds of materials used, since small amounts of given kinds of materials are more likely to be found in a random environment than larger amounts. By minimizing the amounts of materials used, the artisan increases the probability of finding them. There is a premium, then, on small size.

Hence, by and large, the shops of comparatively greater efficiency are the comparatively smaller shops with the comparatively fewer different kinds of tools, whether the tools are conceived of as different kinds of matter-energy, or as different kinds of configurations and combinations thereof, or as different kinds of action. By minimizing the *n* kinds of tools, the artisan increases the probability of finding the material prerequisites for them in his immediate environment, and thereby minimizes the likelihood of expending work in searching for them elsewhere.

Consequently the artisan will prefer jobs that can be performed with a smaller *n* diversity of toolage, since those jobs will be the easier ones in terms of his shop. Conversely, small tool shops with a comparatively small *n* diversity of different tools will be the comparatively more economically organized shops in terms of effort (least probable average work). Theoretically, therefore, all organisms will seek to decrease their size, mass, and complexity (i.e., their *n* number of different classes of action), in order to minimize effort.

It may happen, of course, that size and/or mass can be decreased only by increasing the *n* diversity, or *vice versa.* Since effort is the minimum, the artisan will take such courses of action as will minimize the sum of the products of probable masses when multiplied by probable distances and probable frequencies in order to procure enough energy to keep his shop in operation (including the amortization of capital alterations).

If we imagine that our artisan is competing for materials with countless numbers of other artisans, and that each artisan's shop is a potential raw material for other predatory artisans, then we can understand how all artisans will be driven to reduce the size and complexity of their shops as far as possible upon pain of extermination. Those that survive are the comparatively more efficient tool shops. In them we should find fairly close approximations to the conditions of our Tool Analogy.

Since the sole purpose of every shop is to preserve itself as a physical system, there will be a tendency for simpler shops also to be smaller shops, and *vice versa,* since nothing is gained by increasing either the size or the complexity (i.e., the *n* diversity of tools) unless one is driven to do so by competition (see Chapter Six).

Our present insistence upon the economy of a small *n* number of different kinds of tools (i.e., classes of operations) to which we shall refer again and again, springs from the belief that the *n* minimum, if correct, can be explained *only* on the grounds of least effort (i.e., least probable work).

F. Least Effort and Least Work

As autumn advances, the squirrel becomes fat and scurries about to hide acorns. The added mass of fat is not necessary at the time and hence increases the squirrel's rate of work expenditure. The same applies to his work in collecting and hiding acorns for which he has no immediate need.

If this squirrel survived solely by least work from instant to instant, without any time perspective, he would do neither of these things, particularly during the time of autumnal abundance.

Yet the squirrel's activity is understandable if viewed as one of least effort, since he is expending present work to build up an earned surplus that will serve as an *insurance* against his predicted future when he will be "out of work."

The squirrel's case is instructive for many reasons. It shows us the economic liability of living under variable conditions and the economic asset of a more constant, or homeostatic environment. It suggests that an increased size may indicate a less favorable situation in the environment.

But more than anything else, the squirrel's activity raises the question of the nature of the calculating machine whose existence is obvious, not only in the squirrel—or in the ape which, in leaping from tree to tree, solves correctly and apparently easily and relatively unconsciously enormously complicated physical problems, often under penalty of death—but also in all organic nature.[5] As to the physical structure of these mechanisms, we shall have nothing specific to say.

Nevertheless we all feel that sensory information about the environment is a prerequisite for the calculating machine; so too the capacity to estimate the probable consequences of the items of sensory information. In short, *sensation*—and estimation (*mentation*)—are necessary to any survival with least effort. Let us inquire into some of their economies.

II. THE ECONOMY OF SENSATION

The general steps of our ensuing discussion of the economy of sensation[6] are simple to state in advance. We shall begin (*A*) by pointing out that the artisan can minimize the likelihood of environmental disturbances to his shop by insulating it against the same; through this insulation he will have sensory peepholes by means of which he will take sensory samplings of his environment. Then (*B*) we shall inquire theoretically into the most economical manner of taking these sensory samplings. This theory of sensory sampling will then (*C*) be tested empirically. After that we shall consider (III) the problem of mentation.

A. Insulation and Sensitivity

As long as the artisan lives in a physical environment, his shop will react to the forces of his environment in order to establish a general physical equilibrium with the same. This reaction may be both dangerous and beneficial for the shop.

The reaction may be dangerous because the shop can be damaged or destroyed by an environmental bombardment of particles and waves beyond the degrees of tolerance of the tools of the shop. Hence the shop must expend work to procure, maintain, and operate an insulation against the most likely kinds of deleterious environmental impingements.

On the other hand, the environmental bombardment of particles and waves can be beneficial to the shop, since the particles and waves can bring news of the outside world and therefore are potentially valuable as sources of information. All sensation depends upon reaction to environmental impingements. The economy of sensation depends upon selecting the most informative elements of the bombardment whereas mentation—which is essentially a part of sensation—involves a classification and correlation of the selected impingements.

Naturally, the more the artisan exposes his shop to environmental bombardment for the sake of gaining information, the more his shop may suffer from a lack of insulation, and *vice versa*.

1. Insulation and Homeostasis.[7] The actual amount of insulation that any shop needs will depend upon two factors: the *degree of tolerance* of its tools and the *variability of its environment*.

As the degree of tolerance of the tools to variations in temperatures, pressures, chemical constitution of the environment, etc., becomes ever greater, the need for insulation becomes ever less in a given environment, because the only purpose of the insulation is to protect the tools and worker from environmental disturbances. Since insulation costs work, there is a premium upon increasing the degree of tolerance of the tools.

Even after the degree of tolerance of the tools is given, the artisan still has various courses of action to insure his tools against environmental disturbances.

In the first place, he can seek a constant environment in the sense that the range of environmental variation will fall within the degree of tolerance of his tools. In the second place, he can avoid extreme variations by migrating seasonably, like many birds, to other environments where conditions are tolerable. In the third place, he can shut up shop and live off of his earned surplus, like a hibernating animal, until extreme variations have passed. And fourth, he can insulate himself permanently or seasonably in a suitable fashion, like a sheep, in order to protect himself against the intolerable acts of his environment.

Or he can do any two or more of the above in combination.

The above considerations lead us to the concept of *homeostasis* as defined by Dr. Walter B. Cannon,[8] in the sense of a physically-chemically constant *milieu intérieur* of an organism in the presence of a physically-chemically different, or variable, *milieu extérieur* of the environment (the latter two terms having originated with Claude Bernard). All devices, including emergency devices, that are used to preserve a condition of homeostasis within the degree of tolerance of the shop may be called homeostatic devices, among which are to be included migration and hibernation and the alteration of tools.

Yet the preservation of homeostasis is not the goal of an organism, as Dr. Cannon seemed at times to imply. Rather is homeostasis an economical device for survival. The upper and lower thresholds of homeostatic range are determined primarily by the physics and chemistry of the tools-operations in question, and not the reverse.

2. *Homeostasis and Sensitivity.* Theoretically as the need for more elaborate homeostatic devices increases, the need for sensory information *tends* to increase correspondingly, since both insulation and sensitivity are directed towards an environment that tends to vary beyond the degrees of tolerance of the tools. For that reason we may expect theoretically that comparatively small, simple organisms in what seem to be reasonably stable physical-chemical environments (e.g., some marine animals) will have comparatively few homeostatic and sensory devices because they have little need of them. And the reverse.

3. *The Localization of Sensory Peepholes.* From our preceding discussion it follows that as our artisan finds himself in an environment whose range of variation ever more surpasses the degree of tolerance of his tools, he will be obliged to expend ever more work in increasing both his insulation and his sensitivity, both for the sake of protecting himself against environmental vicissitudes, and for the sake of gaining as much advance information as he can about those which are impending.

Since, however, in insulating a surface, the artisan makes the surface generally less sensitive, and vice versa, the only means he has for increasing both his insulation and his sensitivity is to localize his sensitivity in narrow areas.

The localization of sensitive surfaces to narrow areas without an appreciable loss of information is quite possible. For example, if we take the case of a flat tin roof, it is evident that virtually as much visual, auditory, and olfactory *information* will hit a small area of the roof as will hit the entire roof. If we think of the roof as a delicate sensory surface whose elaborate sensory mechanisms must be built, maintained, and operated by the expenditure of work, we can see the economy of restricting the sensory surface to small areas. Moreover, by decreasing the area of the sensitive surface, one can increase the area of insulation.

When we take the case of human eyes, we have theoretically an example of the economy of localized sensitivity. Yet to the general economy of the eye we must reckon both its movability in its socket and the movability of the head—devices that permit of an increased visual range without increasing the area of visual sensitivity.

When, on the other hand, there is no contradiction between insulation and sensitivity, as may sometimes be the case with the sense of touch, then the areas of touch sensitivity are determined solely by the problem of having a sufficient dispersion of touch peepholes for receiving those touch stimuli that will probably be instructive.

Although one may not be dogmatic on the subject, the economy of sensation involves a minimizing of sensitive areas—that is, a minimizing of the number and sizes of peepholes. This economy is fortified by the economy of insulation.

Since it takes work to manipulate a sensory mechanism, one can save work by reducing the extent of sensitive areas. Moreover, since it takes work to screen out different kinds (or classes) of sensory stimuli, there is an economy (as we shall see later (III) in detail) in minimizing the *n* number of different kinds (or classes) of stimuli that are screened.

B. The Economy of Sampling

Even after the artisan has decreased the number and sizes of his sensory peepholes to the least amount commensurate with his receiving adequate information for his shop, he still has before him the tasks (1) of selecting actual kinds of sensory mechanisms, and (2) of then using his selected mechanisms for sampling.

1. The Selectivity of Sensory Mechanisms. As to the actual sensory mechanisms for obtaining information about the environment, they all relate in the final analysis to physical reactions to physical stimuli, as has been repeatedly pointed out by students of sensation and perception. The stimuli may be those of corpuscular bombardment, as in the case of touch; or they may be the bombardment of light and heat waves, or of air waves, or the chemical bombardment of gases and liquids. Since both the stimuli and reactions are physical, we assume without further ado that the entire mechanism of sensation is physically correct.

Nevertheless, as the artisan reacts to an ever greater *n* diversity of stimuli, he increases the cost of his sensory machinery. Therefore, in order to save work, he will select his kinds of sensory stimuli on the basis of their relative information value. Thus in an environment of little or no light, the artisan may find it economical to ignore visual sensation, while relying instead upon sound, smell, and touch, without the expense of a photosensitive apparatus; or he may trust to sight for short ranges, and to sound and smell for long ones, and so on.

The sheer possession of a sensory apparatus is not economical *per se*. An economical sensory apparatus for one individual need not be economical for another. A fish may need a sense of pressure to a degree that is totally unnecessary for man; an arbored animal may need a sense of balance to a degree that is totally unnecessary for an earthworm; a migratory bird may even need a sense of lateral thrust to help it locate itself in latitude and longitude, for which man apparently has no particular need.*

Just as there is no absolute virtue in any particular *kind* of sensation, so too there is no absolute virtue in any particular *degree* of sensory discrimination; for that, too, is relative to the individual's customary needs. Thus the eye of an eagle that can discriminate at vast heights is unnecessary for the housefly. Though the loss of one sense may call for a greater power of discrimination in others—as is apparently the case with man (e.g., the sensitive fingertips of the blind)—nevertheless nothing is gained from the sheer sharpening of sensation. It is doubtful whether a given person with otherwise normal human senses would be more strategically situated if he

* This suppositional sense of lateral thrust which is introduced for illustrative purposes only may be basic to a bird's homing instinct; it could be tested empirically by noting whether homing pigeons, in getting their bearings, all circle clockwise north of the equator, and counterclockwise south of the equator.

possessed a highly sensitive set of fingertips, or the bat's capacity to hear supersonics, or the setter's fine nostrils, or the ability to see radio waves or waves far beyond the violet.

Instead we may suspect that our usual senses and their usual degrees of discrimination provide us with a range and degree of discrimination that is sufficient for the information needs of our environment and tool shop. Indeed the probable information needs of any Tool Shop in a given kind of environment will determine the kinds and degrees of discrimination of the sensory machinery. Naturally, after a specific sensory machinery has been developed, then the artisan's life is largely committed to that kind of environment for whose risks and opportunities the sensory machinery is sufficient, unless he wishes to expend the work of altering his sensory tools.

The selection of *particular kinds* of sensory apparatus with particular ranges and degrees of discrimination, already represents a sampling of the total activity of the environment. Yet even with the given particular sensory apparatus, the economy of sensory sampling can be carried much further.

2. The Number and Sizes of Samples. The artisan, in desiring information about his environment for the ultimate purposes of discerning opportunities for, and dangers to, his tool jobs, has two possible courses of action. In the first place, he can conceivably try at all times to procure *complete information* about his environment, subject only to the limitations of his sensory mechanisms whose kinds and ranges, after all, can be increased. This attempt to obtain complete information would cost an untold amount of work.

In the second place, the artisan can content himself with what we shall call *representative samples* of his environment at a cost of considerably less work. Theoretically, if either work or effort is minimized, this second alternative will be adopted, as seems indeed to be the case. Hence we shall ignore the first possibility of his trying, Godlike, to know everything about everything, and instead we shall restrict our attention to the economy of taking representative sensory samples.

Once the artisan has his given sensory peepholes, he can procure at the most, as an upper threshold, only that certain definite amount of sensory information of which his sensory mechanism is capable in a given interval of time; the case is like that of a moving picture camera which can procure only an upper threshold of samples in a given interval of time. Beyond this threshold the artisan cannot go without elaborating upon his machinery. The more he falls short of this upper threshold, the more economical is his sensory operation.

But now let us note that—with a fixed upper limit to the total amount of possible sensory sampling—as the artisan increases the s sizes of his samples, he must decrease their n number proportionately, and *vice versa,* during an interval of measurement, because sensory sampling is cast in terms of time and space.

However as he increases the s sizes of his samples, and decreases their n number, he increases the amount of his knowledge about a smaller n number, or diversity, of different things (thus, for example, the longer a person looks to the south, the more he senses about the south, and the less about all other directions). Conversely, as he increases the *n* of his samples at the expense of their *s* size, he increases the diversity of his knowledge at the expense of its extent in any one field.

The *n* number and *s* sizes of sensory samples, therefore, would seem to be intimately related to the dynamics of all sensation. Let us inspect more closely the problem of *n* and *s* in connection with actual cases where, incidentally, we shall note that our familiar opposite Forces of Diversification and Unification are in operation in their conflicting attempt to increase *n* and *s* respectively.

C. Empiric Data on Sensory Sampling

To study empirically the inverse relationship between the *n* number and *s* sizes of sensory samples, let us first take the case of the *n* number of different news items in a newspaper, together with their varying *s* sizes. A newspaper, after all, represents sensory samples of information, even though the sensory samples may have been gained by the collective efforts of many persons. Indeed one may visualize the reporters and editors of a newspaper as the auxiliary "eyes" and "ears" of the paper's readers. As long as the size of the paper is fixed, these auxiliary "eyes" and "ears" must select both the *n* number of different items to be reported and their *s* sizes.

1. Some General Determinants of the Structure of Publications. The pages of a newspaper have the properties of a limited plane surface. Hence the organization of the contents of a newspaper is subject to the properties of a two-dimensional surface. Just how large the total surface will be (i.e., its total number of pages) need not concern us at present. Suffice it to say that as the paper increases in size, it can include more news; yet with an increase in size goes a corresponding increase in printing costs and in the cost to the reader's time in reading it; eventually, therefore, an optimal total size will be reached in the light of the paper's costs, circulation, and advertising.

In the ensuing argument we shall assume that the size of the paper is given, and so too the amount of space that is to be devoted to news items. We shall further assume that it is the news that sells the paper, and that the purpose of the paper is to print such news as will increase the circulation of the paper in order to make money for its owners.

The problem then becomes: what kinds and amounts of news should be put in a paper's given news space so that the paper's circulation will be increased for the purpose of increasing its owner's profits?

As to the amount of news that *could* be printed, let us be clear about two points at the very start. In the first place, a virtually infinite number of different events do occur, so that a virtually infinite number of different items are available for publication. In the second place, an all but infinite amount of space could be consumed in discussing the ramifications of any one single event. Hence the *n* number of different items *could* be virtually infinite, and so too the *s* space of any item.

The problem, therefore, that faces any editor in organizing his news space includes (1) the problem of selecting the particular *n* events to be reported at all, and (2) the problem of determining the actual *s* space to be allotted to the news items selected. In the organization of the news space of a paper, both *n* and *s* are clearly important factors.

If there were no other principle involved in the organization of the given news space than that of cutting up a limited plane surface into parts—much as a child cuts up a newspaper with his scissors—then virtually any frequency distribution of the different news items of like *s* size is possible, as long as they add up to the total news surface, and as long as the smallest *s* size is no smaller than a line of readable type (however small that may be).

If we reflect, however, that the manner of selecting and presenting the news affects the size of the paper's reader population, then we can understand how the news desires of the actual or potential reader population will impose their restrictions both upon the items to be selected and upon their spatial treatment. The nature of these restrictions of the reader population becomes particularly clear when we ask why persons buy and read newspapers at all.

For if we assume that individuals will at all times try to minimize effort, then it follows that the reason for their buying and reading newspapers is that such conduct is an economical method of learning of those events in their environment that may be of positive or of negative value for their particular economies. In response to these economic needs of the reader population, the editor of a paper will find it profitable to select those news items that will be of greatest interest to the members of his reader population.

If the reader population happens to be homogeneous in its interests in regard to a specific range of topics—as is largely the case with trade journals or learned journals with their limited reader populations—the editor will rigorously select his items with complete deference to those interests.

With the general public, however, to whom newspapers are sold, there is no marked homogeneity of interests: what interests one will not necessarily interest another. Therefore in order to lure these potential buyers into the paper's reader population for the sake of increasing the circulation, the editor must increase the *diversity* of his news items. *This economic urge to increase the diversity of news items will act in the direction of increasing the n number of different news items to be included; and, with a given amount of news space, this increase in n can only be accomplished by decreasing the average s size of the items.* This urge to increase *n* at the expense of the average *s* size of the items we may call the *Force of Diversification* (a quite familiar term, by now!).*

On the other hand, as the average *s* size of the *n* items decreases with an increase in *n* under the Force of Diversification, each item will contain an ever shorter account of the events it reports, and thereby will be decreasingly valuable in satisfying the news needs of its readers. Hence the Force of Diversification, though profitable for the editor in increasing the size of the reader population, is by no means necessarily profitable for each indi-

* In terms of an individual's own sampling, this Force of Diversification represents the economy of a wide range of different samples.

vidual reader in that population, since each reader has his own news needs to be met with satisfactory fullness.

From the viewpoint of the individual reader who thinks only of his own individual and collective economy, there is every reason for restricting the size of n to include only those events of primary concern to himself with a copious treatment of each such event (as might well occur in a newspaper that is edited solely for the breakfast table of an absolute monarch). In other words, for each member of the reader population there is an economy in *unifying* the news contents of the paper into a very few n number of different items of very large average s sizes. We shall call this economy the *Force of Unification* which is opposite to the Force of Diversification.*

As a result of the above opposite Forces—both of which are quite familiar to our argument—an editor is compelled not only to diversify his paper by increasing the n number of items selected, he is also compelled simultaneously to respond to the Force of Unification of each of the members of his reader population by allotting proportionately more space to those items that are of primary interest to the largest number (regardless of whether the primary interests are a presidential election, a ball game, or a strawberry festival). Any sensational "bad news" or "good news" for a large number of his reader population will make life easier and more profitable for an editor, particularly if he is the first to print it (i.e., a "scoop") and satisfy the population's interests.

Even in the absence of any sensational news, or of any news that a resourceful editor can make sensational, there still remain the opposing economies of the Force of Diversification, which increases n at the expense of s, and the Force of Unification, which increases s at the expense of n.

Now these opposing Forces of Diversification and of Unification will have precisely the same effect upon the n number and s sizes of different news items as they had upon the n number of different words and their f frequency of usage (as discussed in Chapters Two and Three). As a result of the opposing Forces there will be a comparatively few news items of large size, and an increasing number of news items of diminishing size.

As to the more precise relationship between the size of news items and their number, let us first remember that a given area of plane surface, A, when divided into smaller areas of size, a, will yield a number of smaller areas that is inversely proportionate to a.

Since, however, each news item can increase its s size (or length) only at the expense of the number and/or the sizes of others, we can understand how the inverse relationship between the Forces of Unification and of Diversification may be logarithmically rectilinear (just as in the case of the diversity and frequencies of words).

For that matter, by the very nature of the problem, *if* the above Forces are of *equal* magnitude and of *opposite* direction, then an equilibrium between them will be established in such a way that when the n number of

* In terms of an individual's own sampling, this Force of Unification represents the economy of a single very large sample.

different items are ranked (r) in the order of their decreasing s sizes, they will be distributed according to the simple equation of an equilateral hyperbola: *

$$r \cdot s = n$$

in which the r of a news item represents its ordinal rank according to its s size—with r taking only positive integral values from $r = 1$ (the largest item) through $r = n$ (the smallest item).

This equation, which is similar to the equation, $r \cdot f = c$, discussed in Chapter Two, will, for reasons there set forth, lead to the following corollary equation that refers to the N number of different news items of like s size:

$$N \cdot s^2 = C \text{ (approximate)}$$

This corollary equation is recommended for its greater ease of curve fitting.

And so, as we bring to an end our theoretical discussion of the economies, or Forces, that govern the number and sizes of news items in a newspaper, we find ourselves in possession of the same kinds of equations that apply to the number and frequency of usage of different words.

Moreover if we wish to test empirically our theory of the structure of socially gained information, we need only to ascertain the N number of different news items of like s size in samples of newspapers, in order to note whether they are in fact distributed according to the preceding equation.

2. The Case of News Items. The question now arises whether the N number of different news items of like s size (in terms of column length) in newspapers that meet our previously enumerated conditions are in fact approximately proportionate to the square of their s sizes.[9]

Since, in alphabetical order, (A) *The Chicago Tribune,* (B) *The New York Herald Tribune,* and (C) *The New York Times* are all profitably managed newspapers that meet our previously enumerated conditions, these were selected for analysis.† In all three cases the actual lengths of all news items were first measured for each of the arbitrarily selected issues of September 13 and 14, 1926, April 5, 1930, and April 6, 1940, which were combined for each paper in order to achieve a larger sample (there being, however, no significant difference in exponents of s between the whole and the parts).

In Fig. 5–1 we see graphically the combined data for each paper as labelled. The N number of news items of like s size is plotted logarithmically on the abscissa, and their s size in 3-inch intervals is plotted logarithmically on the ordinate. The lines represent the best straight lines as calculated by least squares with respective negative slopes and errors as follows: (*A*) $.4975 \pm .0893$; (*B*) $.4495 \pm .1200$; (*C*) $.4153 \pm .0837$. These observed values are not far off from the theoretical .5000 negative slope.

---

* Lacking a precise measure of the magnitudes of the Forces, we might better argue that if they are in equilibrium they are equal and opposite.

† The statistical measurements of the above papers were undertaken by my then students, (*A*) Mr. C. W. Joyce, (*B*) Mr. F. P. Hamilton, and (*C*) Mr. Walter S. Spike.

In equation form we have: (A) *Chicago Tribune:* $N \cdot s^{2.0101} = 245.5$; (B) *New York Herald Tribune:* $N \cdot s^{2.2246} = 513.9$; (C) *New York Times:* $N \cdot s^{2.4079} = 962$.

The differences in the sizes of the constant at the right-hand side of the equations relate to differences in total news surface. Yet despite these differences, the actual *organization* of the given news surface follows the same principle for all three papers.

Although, in view of the size of the errors of the slope, all three papers may be said to approximate the inverse-square rule,* nevertheless, of the three, *The Chicago Tribune* with a calculated exponent of 2.0101 (against a theoretically expected 2.0000) can in particular not be accused by its

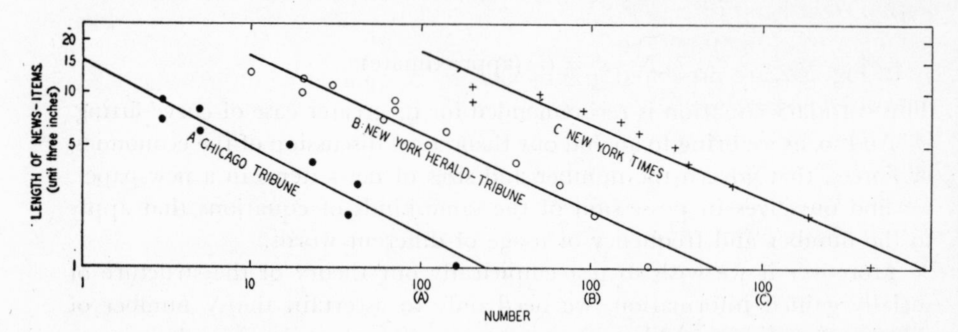

Fig. 5–1. The number of different news items of like length. (A) The Chicago Tribune, (B) The New York Herald-Tribune, (C) The New York Times. For each successive journal the origin is moved one cycle to the right.

reader population of ignoring the individual and group economies of its readers. Nor do the other two papers lag far behind according to our admittedly small samplings.

These distributions do not mean that the managing editors sit down with slide rules and calculating machines to organize their newspaper surface. They mean rather that in selecting one news item and excluding another, expanding here and cutting there, the editors are unconsciously responding to a very subtle "law of the inverse square." Further, they mean that the entire surface devoted to news is organized as a whole. The degree to which the newspaper management can procure the comparatively most valuable news items for its reader population, and select and space them in accordance with the exigencies of our hypothetical Forces of Unification and Diversification, would seem to be the degree to which they are great newspapermen.†

3. The Case of the Encyclopaedia Britannica. Upon reflection, it is clear that our above argument about the opposing Forces of Unification and

* Technically only the first two (*A* and *B*) have a probable error that is large enough to include the theoretical − .5000 slope.

† Although one often hears of how papers select their news, one can only submit, in all candor, that all publications by their very nature must select their news items. The day they refuse to respond to their reader-population's news needs—whatever the needs may be—is the day they go bankrupt while a competing paper flourishes.

Diversification will also apply, say, to the *Encyclopaedia Britannica,* since the editors of an encyclopaedia are faced by a similar problem of balancing a large spatial treatment of individual articles against a large n number of different articles in a total space whose amount cannot be increased indefinitely if the publication is to be a profitable venture.[10] Since the 14th edition of the *Encyclopaedia Britannica* was reportedly intended by its publishers to be a more profitable and popular venture than its predecessors, it was selected for analysis in the following fashion.

For each of the 23 different volumes, the articles were measured, starting with the first article to begin on or after page 500 (about the middle of the volume) and continuing page after page through the article that was on the bottom right-hand corner of the 50th page from the page of departure (thus making a total sample of about 1150 pages in all).*

In Fig. 5–2 are presented graphically the N number of different articles (measured logarithmically on the abscissa) of the same s size (measured logarithmically on the ordinate), with s size measured in inches of column length with all values plotted for the class middles which were in units of 2 inches up to 30 inches (30 inches equals about 1½ pages), then in units of 10 in. from 30 to 100 in. (100 in. is about 5 pages), and finally in units of 100 in. up through 500 in. (500 in. is about 25 pages)—there being only 7 articles beyond that (4 between 500 and 1000 in., and 3 between 1000 and 1500 in.) which were ignored because of their fewness. (The value of N is .8 for $s = 750$, or the class middle, 500–1000.)

An inspection of the data reveals a remarkable approximation to linearity, except for the bottom value, which falls short probably because of the tendency of all publishers to use fillers and either to expand or prune articles for the sake of making the page look better.

A calculation of the slope of these points by means of least squares yielded the astonishingly close approximation of $-.5068 \pm .1590$ (against a theoretical $-.5000$), or in equation form:

$$N \cdot s^{1.9732} = 2888.7$$

which is an almost unbelievably close approximation to our theoretical $N \cdot s^2 = a\ constant$. This indicates that the entire 14th edition of the *Encyclopaedia Britannica* was organized as a whole and, according to our theory, with consummate skill.†

Since there is a widespread belief that the 11th edition of the *Encyclopaedia Britannica* was "a more scholarly and less popular" edition than the

* The task of measuring the lengths of the individual articles was undertaken by the following seven students in my course at Harvard University and Radcliffe College: the Misses Rulan Chao, L. Mitchell, A. Porter, and Elizabeth White, and the Messrs. A. S. Cook, F. F. Lamont, Jr., and M. J. Schleifer.

† The mean number of articles for the seven successive sets of three volumes of the first 21 volumes for the first ten 2-in. class-intervals and their standard deviations are respectively: (1) 124 ± 44.32; (2) 78 ± 31.30; (3) 32 ± 7.67; (4) 16 ± 3.57; (5) 9 ± 1.69; (6) $7\ 4/7 \pm 2.74$; (7) $4\ 1/7 \pm 2.23$; (8) $3\ 1/7 \pm 2.25$; (9) $3\ 6/7 \pm 2.61$; (10) $2\ 5/7 \pm 3.86$. From these it is clear that the variation is considerable. A comparable variation was found in the 11th ed. (*Vide infra.*)

14th edition, it seemed wise to investigate the lengths of the articles in the 11th edition. For if the 11th edition is "more scholarly and less popular"—with the implication of a more extensive treatment of numerically fewer articles—then we should expect a negative slope that is greater than .5, and correspondingly an exponent of s that is less than the square.

In investigating the 11th edition of the *Encyclopaedia Britannica*, precisely the same methods were used, even to the point of beginning the sampling of each volume on page 500 (the pages of the 11th edition used were of approximately the same size as those of the 14th). The same persons undertook the investigation, of which the results are presented graphically

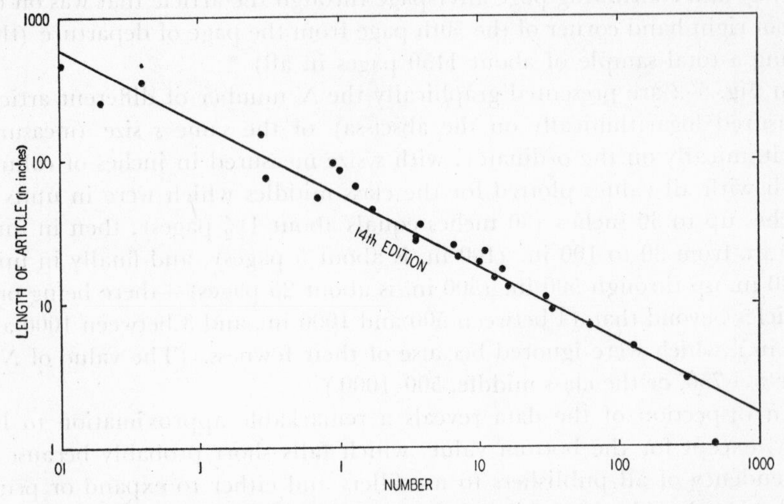

Fig. 5–2. The number of different articles of like length in samples of the 14th edition of the *Encyclopaedia Britannica*. Lengths in inches.

in Fig. 5–3 for all articles up to 1000 in. (with the uppermost point representing the class middle of all articles of from 500 to 1000 in.).[12]

The linearity of the distribution is unmistakable for all articles except for those whose length are 2 in. or less, a result which is perhaps understandable in an encyclopaedia—and notably in the 11th edition, which tends to avoid cross references.

The negative slope of the best least-squares line of Fig. 5–3 is .5956 ± .132 which, in being larger than .5000, is not inconsistent with the widespread belief that this earlier edition was "more scholarly and less popular" (in the sense of a more extensive treatment of numerically fewer articles). In the terms of our equation the distribution is:

$$N \cdot s^{1.6790} = 1081.2$$

If we ignore the lowest two points and recalculate by least squares, however, the negative slope drops to .5578 ± .08, with the exponent of s increasing to 1.7928. In view of the size of this error (or even of ⅔ of its size) we may *not* say that the 11th edition does not closely approximate the inverse square. (The standard deviations of the means were comparable to those of the 14th edition.) In any event the logarithmic linearity of the distribution of Fig. 5–3 again indicates that this edition too was well organized as a whole.

4. The Case of the Union Catalogue at Harvard University. At this point it is only natural to inquire into the *N* number of different books of like *s* size. This problem (like the problem of the length of journal articles, upon which work has not yet been completed) is difficult, first because of the definition of a book, second because of variations in the size of pages and fonts of type of books, and third because of the nonhomogeneity of almost any actual population of books in any library (for example, the dif-

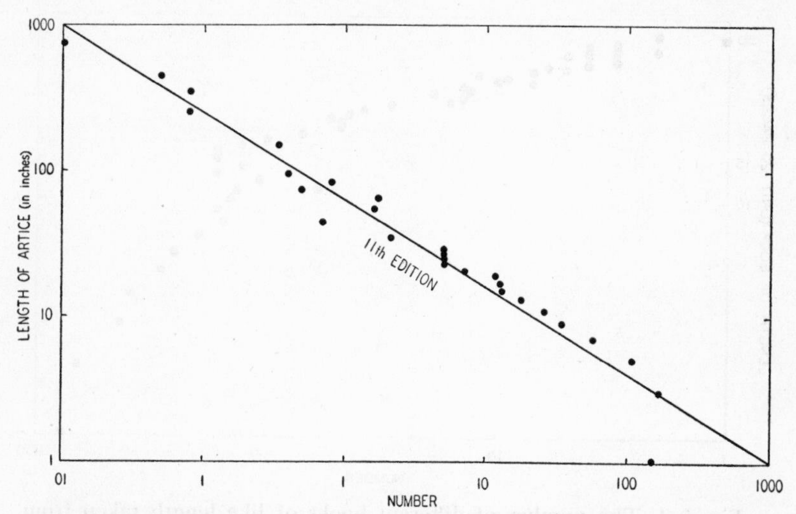

Fig. 5–3. The number of different articles of like length in samples of the 11th edition of the *Encyclopaedia Britannica*. Lengths in inches.

ferences of years of publication, different languages) . Moreover some books are "popular" and profitable while others are not.

In view of the fact that we are apparently dealing with an inverse-square relationship, it would seem theoretically that there should at least be some sort of an inverse relationship between the *s* number of pages of books and the *N* number of books of like *s* pages. To test this point, it was decided to investigate from the cards of the Union Catalogue of the Harvard College Library the first 200 first editions of the publications in English at the beginning of each letter, except X, of the alphabet—5000 different publications.*

In Fig. 5–4 we present the distribution graphically, with the length of the books (exclusive of prefaces) in units of 20 pages plotted logarithmically on the ordinate, and the number of different books of like length plotted logarithmically on the abscissa. From this figure we see that there is an inverse relationship between the sizes and numbers of books, even

* The actual number counted was 5050; hence the degree of accuracy was very high in this tedious job. The aforementioned Misses Mitchell, Porter, and White, and the Messrs. Cook and Schleifer undertook the task of making the tabulation.

when books (including reprints) of widely separate dates and different sizes of page and font are lumped together.[13]

Even though the distribution of Fig. 5–4 refers admittedly to a very small sample of rather heterogeneous material, nevertheless it is perhaps worth noting that the curve itself might be said to consist of two linear parts of different slopes which join at about $s = 15$ (which refers to books of about 300 pages). Since 300 pages represent to many the optimal size of a book beyond which a second volume becomes feasible, we need not be surprised at a bend at about that point. Above that point the curve is markedly linear, with a negative slope of about ⅓—much as if the popula-

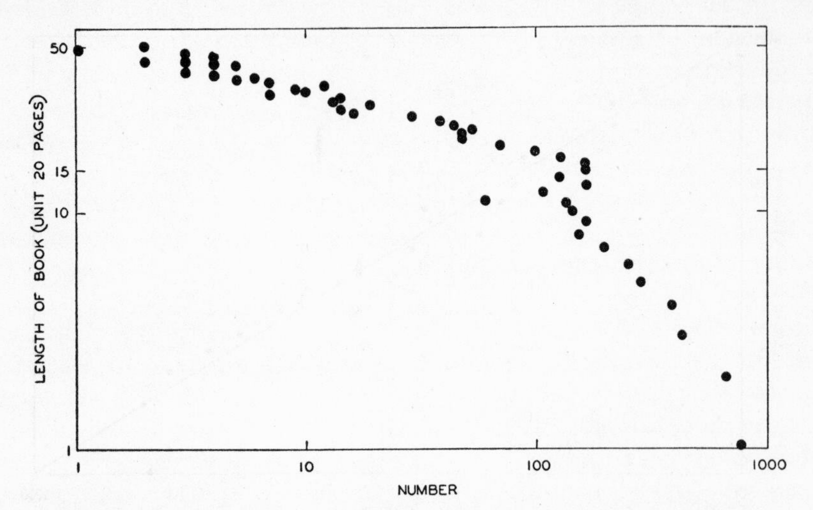

Fig. 5–4. The number of different books of like length taken from the Union Catalogue of the Harvard College library. Lengths in 20-page units.

tion of readers and writers of books were divisible into those who are interested in two or more volumes and those who are not.

Below the point of $s = 15$ (i.e., books of 300 and fewer pages) the curve is again practically linear, with a negative slope that is even greater than unity. Yet this lower portion of the curve is the part that may rightly be suspected, since periodical publications such as *Harpers,* or even such weekly news journals as *Time,* might appropriately be added here. As to the products of the journalistic world, it would seem that smallish journals outnumber larger ones and hence might decrease the slope of the lower part of the curve of Fig. 5–4.

For our purposes, however, it is interesting to note that an inverse relationship does exist between the number of library catalogue items of like size and their size.

5. Miscellaneous Cases. This same argument can be applied to other kinds of socially gained information such as radio news, or moving picture news, for which empiric data are unfortunately lacking.

For that matter, the argument can be applied to the course offerings of a college in which the students have largely free elections. Thus, for example, there is an economy in taking a course of "general" informative value whose content can be applied to many different problems; this is the economy of the versatile tool and is the Force of Unification. On the other hand, there is an economy in taking a specialized course of detailed informative value for a limited range of specific problems; this is the economy of the specialized tool and is the Force of Diversification. Curiously enough, the courses of Harvard College for each of various years in the 1920's and the 1930's, when ranked in the order of the decreasing number of enrolled students, have a rank-frequency distribution that is a reasonably close approximation to linearity on doubly logarithmic grid. And so it seems that the Harvard Faculty's learned ponderings about concentration versus distribution, or about "general education in a free society," [14] all refer to the opposite economies of gaining versatile information of wide applicability on the one hand, and of gaining specialized information of comparatively narrow but detailed applicability on the other. The data in question may be published elsewhere.*

6. Summary of Socially Gained Sensory Samples: The Hypothetical "Law of Winks." As long as it is economical to learn about an increasing n number of different things, and to learn an increasing s amount about each different thing, then—with a given sensory surface during a given interval of time—there will be a Force in the direction of increasing n, and another Force in the opposite direction of increasing s. In the foregoing data, their respective magnitudes seemed to be equal.

It must be conceded that the foregoing data represent socially gained information for the probable news needs of a definite social group. Nevertheless, the above basic principle of selecting and of organizing news does not seem to be uniquely social.[15]

The problem of sensation does not involve merely a physical reaction to physical stimuli, such as the reaction of a photosensitive film to light. It involves also a sampling of the environment, as by a moving picture camera in the hands of a newsreel photographer who turns the camera hither and yon.† Indeed, the editor of a newsreel, in selecting what is to be photographed at all and at what length, exemplifies the sampling aspect of sensation.

If we choose to define a span of attention with a given focus as a *"wink,"* then there is a putative *"law of winks"* that may be basic to sensation: a few long "winks" and an increasing number of shorter "winks." According to this usage, we may perhaps call a news item a "wink," as we admonish the managing editor to give us sufficiently long "winks," and lots of different "winks" in our daily sample of daily news. The same admonition applies to novelists, scenario writers, and dramatists who are trying to hold our attention (see Chapter Eight).[16] Although "brevity is the soul of

* See Chapter Twelve for the data on the rank-frequency, number-frequency, and interval-frequency distributions of the performances of musical compositions and of composers as played by the Boston Symphony Orchestra over a ten-year period.

† The lengths of scenes of a successful moving picture, like the speeches of a play, seem to merit quantitative study (see Chapter Eleven).

wit," a balance between unification and diversification is the prerequisite of being listened to at all, according to the theoretical "law of winks."

The question is only natural as to whether there is a "law of winks" for sampling in accordance with our equation, $N \cdot s^2 = C$. As we shall see in turning to the topic of mentation in Section III following, the existence of such a law seems highly likely in view of our argument about the economy of mentation.

In Section III we shall develop a theoretical reason why all sensory samplings will approximate the equation, $N \cdot s^2 = C$.

III. MENTATION: THE CORRELATION OF SENSORY DATA

In previous pages we concentrated our attention upon the n number and s sizes of sensory samples that are used as a basis for estimating the probability of future risks and opportunities for a given system. We noted the respective economies of a few large samples and of many smaller ones, as the artisan reacts to the impingements that his environment makes upon his system.

In the present section we shall attempt to penetrate more deeply into the same topic as we inquire into the methods whereby the artisan uses the data of his sensory samples. But instead of continuing our foregoing discussion, we shall approach the problem from an entirely new angle—the angle of classification.

We shall attempt to show that the n different classes into which experience is redacted is a minimum.

A. The Economy of Class Criteria

Presumably the only method whereby the artisan can predict the future is for him to assume that the frequencies with which particular events have occurred in particular associations in the past are the frequencies with which they are likely to occur in the future. Prediction, therefore, will depend upon frequencies of occurrence. Yet before the artisan can note the frequencies of particular events, he must be able to *define* what the events in question are; that is, he must *classify* the contents of his sensory samples so that he can determine whether the *same kind* of event or association is occurring, or whether there is a *different kind* of event, or *different kind* of association, and so on.

This question of *sameness* and of *difference* brings up the entire question of classification, which is basic to logic and to science. Our interest in classification, however, is solely in its economy—that is, in the more economical and in the less economical manner of classifying data. As far as our artisan is concerned, any particular classification of *likes* and *unlikes* is otiose unless the classes in question refer directly or indirectly to the solution of one or more of his actual or potential problems. In other words, classes are selected on a utilitarian basis.

Thus, for example, the sheer question of whether or not a piece of wood that is 47 inches long is the same as one that is 48 inches long is a foolish question, since our artisan knows that he can never measure length, or anything else, precisely enough to compare absolutely. Instead the artisan will inquire into the particular problem that the pieces of wood are intended to solve. If the problem is that of stacking cord wood in 4-foot lengths, then the two pieces are similar enough to be the same *in reference to that particular problem.* If, on the other hand, he is making a cabinet that is four feet long, then the two sticks are not the same, but are different. In other words—as we shall argue again in Chapter Seven—the decision as to what is the same and what is different depends entirely upon some definite problem as a frame of reference. And that applies to the entire field of sensation—to hues, intensities, frequencies, masses, temperatures, linear dimensions, areas, volumes, forms, chemical mixtures, and all else. If two things are the equivalent in solving a problem, they are the same; and our artisan is interested only in solving his problems.

With the above in mind, let us now note that there is no economy in *narrowing* a class beyond the needs of the actual problem, since the *narrower* the class is, the less frequent are its members likely to be. For example, the artisan is more likely to find a piece of wood that fits the class of 45″–50″ than he is to find one that fits the class 47″–48″, since all that fits the second *narrower* class will also fit the former *broader* class, but not the reverse. Hence he should state his problem in terms of *broadest* permissible tolerance and, of course, he should try to cast his life in terms of problems that can be stated comparatively more *broadly.*

In using the term "narrower" in relation to classification—with its opposite, "broader"—what do we mean? In order to explain, let us first illustrate.

If, in classifying our sensations, we use the class *furniture* and the class *chair,* then *furniture* may be said to be a *broader* class than *chair,* because it includes the class, *chair.* Obviously, the terms, *broad* and *narrow,* are only comparative: one class is broader than another because it includes it.

Let us now note that the broader classes are likely to occur more often in experience (and cannot occur less often) than the narrower classes—and by the *occurrence of a class* in experience, we mean the occurrence of one or more members of that class in experience. That in turn will mean that the broader classes will tend to be found present in a greater number of random samples of the same size, and also that they are more likely to be found in a smaller sample.

Hence, *it is economical to have broader classes for predictions, since they can be found both in a comparatively fewer number of different samples and also in comparatively smaller-sized samples, thereby decreasing the work of sampling.**

Now that we have argued about *broader* and *narrower* classes illustratively, let us point out that these two terms denote nothing more or less

* Incidentally, with a fixed *n* number of different classes in a given experience, the *broader* the classes are, the greater amount of experience will be positively classified. Thus, for example, if a person has only the single class, *furniture,* then he will divide his experience into the positive class, and its negative, *not furniture.* More of his experience will thereby tend to be classified positively than if he had only the single narrow class, *chair.*

than what is commonly understood under the traditional terms, *generic* and *specific,* which we shall henceforth use. Thus the broader class, *furniture,* is the more generic class, while the narrower class, *chair,* is more specific. The terms, *generic* and *specific,* in our usage will always be comparative, and relative to the solution of one or more problems of one or more artisans.

But though we are using the traditional terms, *generic* and *specific,* let us unfailingly remember that they are comparative.

For, as we add to the n number of different criteria of classification of a given class, the class becomes less generic and more specific by definition. Moreover as we thus add to the n number of criteria of a class (*thereby making it less generic and more specific*) *we decrease the probabilities of finding that class in a random sensory sample of given size at a given interval of measurement, if the events of the environment are random as far as the artisan is concerned. Therefore, to increase the n number of criteria of a class is to increase the probable need for larger samples or for more frequent samples, or both. Since it consumes work to increase the size and/or frequency of sensory samples, the n number of criteria of classification used will be a minimum under the Principle of Least Effort.*[17] *That is, he will use the fewest possible different classes* (i.e., *the smallest n number of different classes*) *that are consistent with adequately predicting his future.**

As a result of this n minimum, the artisan will forever strive to classify his environment to a given degree of probability with a smaller n number of different classes. He will always prefer generic classes to specific classes (hence man's love for sweeping generalizations and for oversimplifications).

B. The Specific versus the Generic

In the light of our preceding argument, the artisan will have n different classes of *relevant* environmental events whose emergence he must predict because he either fears or wants them. This n number of different classes of *relevant* events is determined by the particular n_2 classes of different tools in his shop.† Let us for convenience restrict our attention to the n different classes of *relevant* events and assume that they are given. We shall inquire into how they can be most economically predicted. Some of our preceding argument will be repeated from a different angle.

As we have previously pointed out, the artisan can predict the emergence of any one or more of the relevant kinds of events in his environment by assuming that all classes of events will occur in the future with the same frequency with which they have occurred in the past. Furthermore, he will seek to find those particular classes of *telltale* events that will betoken the emergence of the relevant events. In short, he will seek *correlations* between

* The above paragraph is italicized in the belief that it may be a basic first principle of the dynamics of all actual sensory (or mentational or semantic) systems.

† In speaking of n_2 different classes of tools or of n different classes of sensory events, we have already classified. Hence theoretically the artisan (organism) will always have an antecedent set of n classes. Whatever the actual n classes may be, he will theoretically minimize n by trying to reduce them further. To this end he may seek fewer, more versatile tools.

each of his *relevant* events on the one hand, and the respective *telltale* events on the other.

But now let us inquire into what we mean by a *correlation* between two different classes of events. Let us assume that the artisan is continually taking random samples of his environment—all samples of like size. In these samples let us say that class *A* occurs with a percentage-frequency of *a* while *B* occurs with a percentage-frequency of *b*. In that case, the product, *ab,* is the probability that the two classes will both occur together in the same sensory sample if the two classes of events are unrelated. As their observed occurrence together (or in any other fixed relationship) increases above *ab,* the artisan infers that they are ever more positively related, with the result that the emergence of *A* presages the emergence of *B,* and he can use *A* to predict *B* to the degree of the correlation. On the other hand, as the observed occurrence together decreases below *ab,* the artisan infers that the events are negatively related, with the result that the emergence of *A* presages that *B* will not emerge, and he can thus predict to the degree of the correlation. If, however, *A* and *B* occur together neither more nor less often than *ab,* then there is a zero correlation between them, and from the emergence of *A* he can make no prediction about the emergence, or non-emergence, of *B*. A zero correlation may be called *otiose.*

Obviously, the only classes of events that are of value to him are those that enter into positive and negative correlations with his relevant events (all others can be dismissed as being *otiose*). The values of the positive and negative correlations increase with the amounts of their coefficient of correlation. Naturally the artisan will seek to find correlated telltale events of a greater coefficient of correlation than what he already possesses.

1. The Economy of the Specific Correlation. If completely successful with the above procedure of correlation, the artisan will possess an aggregate of specific correlations for what we shall call his E_1, E_2, E_3, . . . E_n different classes of *relevant* events. But until he is thus completely successful, he will continue to analyze and compare and correlate the data of his experience in order to procure larger coefficients of correlations for his specific classes of *relevant* events, in obedience to what we shall call the *economy of specific correlation.*

This aggregate of specific correlations will be *logically self-consistent* in the sense that the classes throughout will be unambiguous, and so too the correlations. Thus a correlation between *A* and E_1 will not be confused with a correlation between *B* and E_2 or with any other correlation.

Though logically self-consistent, the aggregate of specific events will by no means necessarily be *semantically integrated* in the sense that all the different classes used are comparable. Thus, though there is a correlation between the classes *A* and E_1 on the one hand, and a correlation between *B* and E_2 on the other, there will not necessarily be any logical connection between the several classes of *A,* E_1 and *B,* E_2. Thus, for example, the artisan might see that (*A*) wind makes (E_1) waves, and that (*B*) lightning makes (E_2) thunder, without seeing any connection between wind and lightning, etc. These correlations are logically self-consistent but not semantically integrated.

2. The Economy of Generic Correlation. Although the economy of the specific correlations is obvious if the artisan is to predict his future and minimize his effort, nevertheless a further economy is still possible. This further economy we shall call the *economy of the generic correlation.*

The economy of the generic correlation rests upon the analysis of all telltale classes of events and all relevant classes of events into *intersections* and *unions* of two or more classes that are more generic. Thus, for example, the peculiar quadruped, *A,* can be classified as the *intersection* of the two more generic classes, *white* and *elephant* (or, *white* × *elephant* = *white elephant*). And the peculiar procession of objects down the street can be classified as the *union,* say, of the two classes, *people* and *vehicle* (or *people* + *vehicle* = *procession,* etc.).*

This analysis of classes into their more generic components consists essentially of comparing the different classes in order to find class criteria that they may have in common. These common class criteria will be both more generic and tend to be more frequent in experience than the specific classes that they constitute (e.g., the classes *white* and *elephant* will each be more generic and tend to be more frequent than the single class *white elephant;* so, too, with unions).

Since the more generic class is more frequent, the artisan is more likely to find it in a sensory sample of given size that is taken at random.

As the artisan succeeds in reducing his aggregate of correlations of relevant and telltale classes to the intersections and unions of ever fewer generic classes (or criteria), he sacrifices nothing from the logical self-consistency of his aggregate of classes, as previously defined. But he gains what can be called a *semantic integration,* or a *semantic unification,* in the sense that more of his classes and correlations can be compared in terms of common classes.

As a result of analyzing his sensory classes into the intersections and unions of an ever smaller *n* number of frequently occurring generic classes, the artisan will not need to take so many nor so large sensory samples in order to find the *n* classes, since a more generic class tends to be more frequent in experience, and therefore more likely to be found in fewer and/or smaller samples. This is the *economy of the generic correlation* which is attended concomitantly by an increased semantic integration.

Naturally, in order to keep the telltale and relevant classes discrete for the sake of prediction, the artisan must have sufficient generic criteria to provide intersections and unions of sufficient number to discriminate between the telltale and relevant classes. Any criteria beyond that number are otiose, and it is economical to ignore them.

Since the relevant classes, like the telltale classes, will also have been analyzed into their generic components, and since relevant classes may be correlated with other relevant classes, the entire semantic system of classes

---

* A definition is only a statement in terms of the intersections of classes, such as "a *square* is a rectangle whose sides are equal."

and correlations will be relevant to the artisan either because a given class represents a need or threat, or because it is useful in predicting a need or threat. As a result, the artisan will tend to look upon his universe of sensory experience as a unit causal whole.

If the artisan is successful in correlating all his relevant classes to a satisfactory degree of probability in terms of a minimum n number of different generic classes with no otiose criteria, then his *semantic system* is presumably a system of logic which is *semantically packed* in the sense that all classes are defined discretely in terms of a minimal set of generic criteria without redundancies or tautologies, and without any noncomparable class or classes.

3. Specific-Generic Balance. The entire preceding argument about the economies of specific and generic correlations can be meaningful only if there is a fixed number of different classes of relevant events to be predicted. Once this fixed number is given—even though it is a function of the n toolage—then the concept of a minimum n number of criteria of classification is meaningful.*

The value of a *more specific* correlation lies in the fact that it describes *more completely* a very small number of isolated classes of events. The value of a *more generic* correlation is that it describes a *larger number* of different classes—or greater amounts of experiential data—but describes any portion thereof less completely. Thus, for example, the specific correlation, *shrimps always make grandma sick,* is quite precise about shrimps and grandma, but little else. On the other hand, the more generic gravitational correlation between mass and distance has a far wider applicability to experiential data, yet says little that is characteristic of any particular class that is selected at random.

The economy of the more generic class or correlation is the economy of our erstwhile Force of Unification discussed in Chapter Two; it is the economy of the single all-inclusive class or correlation that refers to everything. The economy of the more specific class, like the Force of Diversification, is the economy of a class or correlation that refers quite precisely to certain special portions of experience and therefore not to all of experience. The more you have the one, the less you have the other. Both are necessary. Thus, for example, one must be able to view and treat grandma as a member of the more generic classes of human being, mammal, organism, matter-energy—for she belongs to all these classes and many more. One must also be able to view and treat her as a class of her own, *sui generis,* since she is that too.

From the above considerations, it follows theoretically that there will be a balance between the specific and the generic, as the artisan tries to generalize upon the basis of his specific correlations, and to particularize upon the basis of his generic correlations for the sake of minimizing n. If he

* To avoid the appearance of a double superlative, let us note that the n number of different tools is a minimum in one frame of reference. Yet this n number provides the fixed number of relevant events of a second frame of reference whose n number of different criteria of classification is minimized. One can decrease the n criteria by decreasing the n tools.

reduces n too far, the relevant facts of his environment will abruptly force him to a greater semantic precision. These relevant facts of the environment in reference to the actual positive and negative needs of his shop are the final determinants of the structure of the artisan's sensory-mentational system.*

In other words, the n number of classes used is a balance between the "too few" generic correlations and the "too few" specific correlations in an actual semantic system of an artisan.†

C. The Question of Empiric Proof

It is one thing to point out theoretically the economy of the n number of different sensory classes, and quite another to demonstrate that the n classes are minimized in actual practice. Since we are contending that an organism always does in fact behave economically and that to minimize n is an economy *with a given degree of probability of prediction of the future,* we are faced with the problem of empirically testing the theory of the n minimum in an actual sensory-mentational system (i.e., a *semantic system*). Several empiric tests seem possible.

1. The Test of Human Speech. A class is traditionally defined as the *name* of an abstract quality that different entities have in common. This view is basic to all logic. Hence our problem refers ultimately to class names that are more or less generic or specific, and that impinge upon our senses with varying degrees of frequency. Is the n number of class names minimized?

A person's vocabulary of words is nothing more than a set of conventional names of conventional classes of experience; and by *conventional,* we mean that a group of persons agree as to the particular classes of experience that are to be correlated with the particular arbitrary classes of noises. Hence a person's (or a given group's) vocabulary may be viewed as a special case, or a particular set, of the general domain of the person's (or the group's) field of sensation-mentation.

The question then arises as to whether the n number of different classes of a vocabulary is a minimum. The problem clearly refers to an auditor's sensation of a given person's vocabulary; therefore the problem refers to the occurrence, or usage, of the vocabulary in its owner's stream of speech.

In exploring this problem, let us note that the specific class, *white-elephant,* is defined by the intersection of two more generic classes. The still more specific class, *the-white-elephant,* is the intersection of three classes. The even more specific class, *the-white-elephant-takes-a-peanut-from-*

* The reader will note the applicability of our argument in Chapters Two and Three to the problem of the n number of different classes that describe, say, a fixed m number of different relevant events. This refers only to the usage of classes. See discussion of speech below.

† This concept of the n minimum is the only part of the preceding argument that may be new—at least I have never heard of it before. And, if true, it may be of considerable practical value. All the rest can be found formalized in the algebra of classes (Boolean algebra) and is presumably germane to lattice theory and symbolic logic, about whose more precise details the writer claims to know virtually nothing.

my-little-boy's-hand, is an intersection of eleven classes (if we ignore the inflectional endings). Indeed, a sample of speech, however long, may be viewed as an *inclusion* (by means of intersections and/or unions) of other classes which may themselves be *inclusions* of further classes.*

The question now arises as to whether, in the formation of larger inclusions of classes in speech, the more generic speech classes are preferred to the less generic speech classes. Since we have argued that the more generic classes tend to be the more frequently occurring classes, the question becomes whether the more frequent generic speech classes are preferred to the less frequent and more specific ones in constructing the more specific inclusions. To this question the answer is quite definitely affirmative, if we remember the rank-frequency distribution of Nootka holophrases and their parts (Chapter Three).

Indeed our speech data, insofar as combinations of elements are concerned, show an unmistakable balance between the more frequent generic and the less frequent but more numerous specific, of precisely the kind demanded by our theory, with the n number of different classes a minimum. This n minimum, we remember, was basic to our Principles of Economical Permutation and Specialization under the general theoretical Law of Diminishing Returns.

Furthermore, let us recall at this point that the rank-frequency distribution of words and of holophrases was rectilinear with differing slopes. This difference in slopes is instructive in view of our present theory.

The negative slope for words in English (Fig. 2–1), as well as for some other tongues, was 1, thereby indicating theoretically that words represent an equilibrium in class inclusions between the opposite economies of the generic and the specific in the particular case where the magnitudes of the two opposite economies are equal. Indeed a *word* might almost be thus defined. Since classes are discrete and integral, words will be discrete and integral (i.e., no fractional words).

As we turn to the more specific inclusions represented by the holophrases of Nootka, and presumably by those of Plains Cree (Chapter Three), we note that the negative slope decreases, though the rank-frequency distribution remains rectilinear. In other words, as the elements of the speech population take on a higher degree of specificity, the linear logarithmic relationship remains, as the magnitude of the specific (in terms of rank-

* It may be difficult to determine what the particular *inclusions* of classes are. But if we remember that, according to our theory, logical redundancies are avoided, then in the sentence, *this is the man that hit the ball,* there must be at least two different inclusions because the class, *the,* occurs twice; if there were only one class *the* would be redundant. For, in the definition of classes in terms of other classes, nothing is added by repeating a class (Boolean algebra: $a \times a = a$; $a + a = a$). Thus the class, *rose rose,* must represent two inclusions [e.g., (*My daughter*) *Rose rose* (*this morning*)]. Therefore in the repetition of speech elements we *may* have objective criteria for defining the inclusions of classes—or better still, the inclusions of inclusions of inclusions. Words, phrases (in the most inclusive sense), clauses, sentences, etc., may therefore be definable in terms of the repetition of inclusions. This is a promising field in the semantic-dynamic aspect of biosocial dynamics that is not particularly emphasized in this book. Some pseudo redundancies occur: *the red red rose* meaning "the very red rose." These are intensives.

order) increases at the expense of the magnitude of the generic (in terms of frequency). If we argue speculatively that holophrases represent a sort of mid-point between word units and sentence units (i.e., statements), then, theoretically, the negative slope of the rank-frequency distribution of sentences will become still gentler though the rectilinearity will remain. Somewhere in the rank-frequency distributions of elements of increasing specificity, the slope will theoretically become zero, which means an extreme specificity and no repetition. Let us call this hypothetical unit a *patch,* which is characterized by the absence of repetition in the stream of speech. A *patch* is a very specific class, like a paragraph, that deserves to be disclosed empirically. It may very well increase in size with the speaker's age.

So much then for the negative slopes between 1 and 0 for words and larger speech units.

Turning now to those speech units called morphemes, which, as discussed in Chapter Three, are fewer and less specific classes than words, let us remember that their rank-frequency distribution is rectilinear on arithmetic-logarithmic co-ordinates (i.e., $\log. f + \text{rank} = C$), and not on logarithmic-logarithmic co-ordinates, if we may trust the evidence of Chinese and Gothic. This may mean in terms of the generalized harmonic series that the morpheme (as phonologists have long claimed) is indeed the minimal unit of the *semantic* system of speech—though not of the phonetic system—since in the rank-frequency distribution of morphemes, the p-exponent of the generalized harmonic series tends to become infinite. If this interpretation be correct, then morphemes are generic classes that cannot be further defined in terms of the inclusions of still more generic classes. Therefore no morpheme is more specific than another, according to our definition.*

Though the morpheme's rank in terms of decreasing frequency is meaningless as far as degrees of specificity are concerned, it may have real meaning in terms of relative age since, as every experienced philologist knows, and as we have shown in Chapter Three, the more frequent morphemes in the language tend to be those that were adopted earlier in the history of the language.

This factor of relative age of adoption of morphemes may be instructive for our theory of the generic-specific equilibrium. For it implies, in brief, that those classes that are experienced earlier in life will tend to be used as the generic components in forming the intersections and unions of those classes that are experienced later in life. In other words, we use the terms of our early experience to define the terms of our later experience; hence phylogenetically and ontogenetically the present environment tends to appear to us primarily in terms of our entire past sensory experience with it.[18]

Consequently an earlier experience class, x, including an earlier experienced correlation (e.g., *gravitation*) between two classes, p and q (say, $p \rightarrow q$), will tend in time to enter definitively into an increasing number of

* Nevertheless the rectilinear frequency distribution of morphemes on arithmetic-logarithmic co-ordinates indicates that the economy of preferring to use the fewer morphemes more frequently is still present.

the inclusions of other classes and correlations that are constructed subsequently. If we define as an *association of ideas,* or as a *complex, com. x,* the number of different inclusions into which the class, *x,* enters in a given individual's semantic system, then, dynamically viewed, *com. x* will tend to increase with time (this definition may describe what neurologists call a neurological complex). And we can easily understand the extensive work of resampling that will be necessary later in life to re-analyze, or to "restructure" logically, a complex of earlier formation (cf. discussion of *intellectual rigidity* below). If we proceed further and define as a *conflict* the logical contradiction between *x* and *y* in a given person's semantic system, we can understand how disturbing a conflict can be if *com. x* and *com. y* are large.*

The structure and behavior of speech classes seem not only to confirm our hypothesis of a balance between the specific and the generic with the *n* minimum, they seem also to proffer a useful unifying frame for defining some current neurological theories.

In our foregoing discussion we have not mentioned the Law of Abbreviation of Size, which we found in Chapter Three to be so patent in speech. Is the Law anything else than the effect of deleting otiose classes in the intersections and unions of inclusions? [19]

We have also not spoken of phonemic balance—the balance between the frequency and magnitude of complexity of the submorphemic elements, *phonemes* (discussed in Chapter Three). In view of the discussion of the morpheme as a lower limit of the speech semantic system, may we perhaps suggest that phoneme balance is an evidence of the *n* minimum in the person's total semantic system of which the speech semantic system is only a part? In other words, the *n* number of different phonemes is minimized because theoretically man minimizes all his different classes of action of whatever sort, and therefore minimizes his different classes of phonetic action. Cultural meanings (in the sense of stereotyped cultural responses that are "permuted") are attached, however, only to the "permutations" of phonemes into morphemes.

Clearly this discussion, if continued, would simply lead to a recapitulation of our entire Chapter Three, from whose data the concept of the *n* minimum was originally developed. Instead, let us merely remark that the speech data presented there seem to confirm our thesis of the *n* minimum in general and of the balance between the generic and the specific in particular.

It may be objected quite reasonably that the *n* minimum may be a peculiarity of human speech without applicability to any other part of the organic world. To meet this quite reasonable objection we shall devote our following chapter to a demonstration that the *n* minimum is present in all organic action, of which the *n* minimum of speech is but a special case. If our demonstration be correct, then the structure of human speech may represent *par excellence* a field where the sheer classifying and correlating

* A conflict of this sort may arise between an individual's own early experience and that of his culture, as defined and described more fully in Chapter Seven.

activity of sensation-mentation can be studied objectively and quantitatively with comparatively great ease. In other words, speech may offer an almost unique advantage for studying the economy of sheer classification where physical factors enter but little.

2. The Test of Sample Size. There is another empiric test of the n minimum and the balance between the generic and the specific. This test relates to our previous argument that the more generic class will occur more often in the environment and, therefore, both can be found in a smaller sensory sample, and hence will be sought for in a smaller sensory sample, since smaller samples are easier than larger ones.

Now if it is true (1) that there is a balance between a few frequently occurring generic classes and many rarely occurring specific classes, as previously argued under the economy of classification and the n minimum; and if it is true (2) that sample size tends to decrease as the class sampled becomes more generic; and if it is true (3) that the artisan is continually sampling for his various classes in order to predict relevant events, then (4) there will be a few small samples of frequent occurrence, and an increasing number of larger samples of decreasing frequency of occurrence.

Indeed, if the opposite economies of the generic and the specific are of equal magnitude, then the N number of different sensory samples of a given s size will be inversely proportionate to s^2, for reasons presented earlier in this chapter, where we saw that the N number and s sizes of newspaper items, encyclopedia articles, and the like, do follow the relationship, $N \times s^2 =$ *constant*.

This empiric test of sample size differs from the previous empiric test of the frequencies of speech entities, since it is based upon an inferred correlation between the comparative degree to which a class is generic and the comparative size of the sensory sample in which it is likely to be found. If this correlation is sound, then the number-size relationship of sensory samples should be the same as the number-frequency relationship of words, if the rank-order of words is a criterion of the degree to which they are generic-specific.

Although our data on sample sizes seem to confirm our hypothesis, it may rightly be objected that these data refer to socially gained sensory samples and not to individually gained samples. Although this objection could perhaps be met, let us rather prefer to let our critics view the data as a mere coincidence (forgetting that socially gained information must be individually economical if it is to be accepted), while we urge instead the need for further empiric research into the topic.

According to our view, our artisan is at all moments continually concerned with getting information about the needed and feared classes of environmental events. Hence he is continually taking sensory samples (even though he may not be consciously aware of it). Regardless of the particular kinds of sensory samples taken (e.g., whether visual, auditory, etc.), and regardless of the use of more refined news gathering devices (e.g., social newspapers and encyclopedias), the relationship, $N \times s^2 = c$, will theoretically still hold, if our n minimum and our argument about the balance between the specific and the generic be sound. Hence $N \times s^2 = c$ is the "Law of Winks."

At this point still another question may be raised in reference to the artisan's measurement of time, in terms of which the events of the past are stated and those of the future predicted. Without mentioning the factor of time, we have nevertheless spoken of the frequencies and intervals between the repetitions of sampling, thereby making tacit assumptions about time. Upon reflection, it is evident that if the artisan's correlations are to mean anything, the artisan must have a highly accurate clock.

Yet where is the clock?

This question of the clock becomes all the more urgent when we remember that our artisan and the Tool Analogy are supposed to be descriptive of all organic systems, including those that allegedly consist of a single large protein molecule. If these large organic molecules must theoretically also have a clock, we are forced to conclude that somewhere within the molecule is a constant rate of action which can serve as an unfailing clock. Physicists contend that the revolution of electrons within an atom represents just such a constant rate. Are these the clocks of mouse and man? If so, the organism must somehow sense them, even though the sensory mechanisms are not clear. And if so, this sensation of electronic rotation provides the organic world with its most ancient and primitive generic classes of time, space, rate (and perhaps, integral number) which would then be the basic dimensions (classes) of every semantic system to which, therefore, a certain degree of semantic integration can theoretically be imputed.[20]

Somewhere there must be a clock in every organism. The man who, upon retiring, decides to awaken at a certain hour, and does so by himself, appeals to such a clock. So too, does he in the regularity of his pulse.

3. The Third Empiric Test. We have suggested that the frequency-distributions of speech entities as reported in Chapters Two, Three, and Four provide an empiric test of the balance between the opposite economies of the specific and the generic which is theoretically present in all classificatory action from that of the tiniest intracellular activity to the most elaborate actions of human consciousness. The same, we have suggested, is evidenced by the number-size relationship of sensory samples.

Yet there is a third kind of empiric test which we only mention here, since our entire following chapter will be devoted to it. This test refers to the effect of extreme competition between a vast number of different artisans with varying n numbers of different kinds of tools.

If we are right in arguing that a smaller n tends to be a more economical n, and that therefore its artisan is less likely to be obliged to alter his tools, then organisms with smaller n's will be more conservative in their forms-functions in evolutionary change than those with larger n's. If those with smaller n's tend also to be those species whose organisms are of smaller size (The Law of Abbreviation), then smaller organisms will tend both to change and to become extinct at a *slower* rate than larger ones.

In our following chapter we shall attempt to show empirically that such is the case. We mention this third kind of empiric test, lest the reader feel that we have conceived of our topic too narrowly.

Indeed if the reader is interested in this third empiric test he can turn at once to Chapter Six, and skip the balance of the present chapter, which is devoted to a theoretical discussion of consciousness and certain neurological theories in the light of Least Effort.

IV. A MIND AS A UNIT SEMANTIC SYSTEM

Although the foregoing pages contained our entire argument about language and sensation, it is perhaps advisable in the interest of making our argument seem more plausible and of greater practical value if we attempt in the following pages to integrate it to some extent with certain widely held theories of neurology and psychology that relate to the structure of the personality, and to which parts of our own study are obviously indebted. In integrating these other theories in terms of our own, we do not mean for a moment to imply that our theory is necessary to theirs. On the other hand, if the integration is successful, our data will support their theories. This general attempt at integration will be resumed again in Chapter Seven.

A. The Scope of Mind: Mind and Body

When matter-energy enters a person's body via whatever route, it presumably does not cease to behave according to the laws of physics and chemistry. Instead it behaves *also* according to the particular classes of the experiential system, and it continues to behave thus until it leaves the person's system. (Otherwise the individual might die quite literally of what could be called *classificatory indigestion.*) [21]

For, as far as we can see, the person's system consists of particular kinds (or classes) of physical actions that are performed upon particular kinds (or classes) of matter-energy of particular kinds (or classes) of amounts, at particular kinds (or classes) of rates or frequencies. Indeed, an individual is nothing more than this unified system of kinds (or classes) of procedures of performance that have direction in terms of the individual's most economical survival. The matter-energy that is in transit through this system, according to the laws of inanimate physics, constitutes the individual's *physical being,* or body. Yet the *kinds* of matter-energy and its *kinds* of action-reaction in transit through the system is the individual's *mind* (by present definition).

According to this view, the individual's toenails, teeth, and ears are just as much a part of his mind as is his brain; and his mind can be just as fatally disturbed by impingements at any of the appendages as in the brain itself.

B. Mental Disturbances: The Need for Logical Self-Consistency

Under the term, *disturbance of a mind,* we mean whatever disturbs its unit system of logic which, as we remember, consists of kinds (or classes) of actions of kinds (or classes) of matter-energy upon kinds (or classes) of matter-energy at kinds (or classes) of rates. Hence a disturbance to mind is always a classificatory disturbance, even though it be only a disturbance of habitual frequencies, or probabilities.

The disturbance may be physical, as when the system receives a blow or a wound. If the blow or wound is of a kind (or class) which can be comprehended by the system in terms of its classes, then the system sets about to remove the effect of the disturbance by stereotyped kinds of action. On the other hand, if the blow or wound is of a *kind* that cannot be comprehended semantically (e.g., a severe blow in the head, or a severe bullet wound), then the system may die. Whether in healing the wound itself, or in going to a doctor for medication, the semantic system is trying to restore a logical self-consistency.

The same applies to a chemical impingement, such as from an unfamiliar chemical compound in the lungs or stomach which cannot be classified according to the semantic stereotypes. The system may act in a stereotyped fashion to expel it. Or if unsuccessful, it may alter itself in order to accommodate itself to it.[22] These alterations may themselves be of such a stereotyped kind in the species that an outsider can guess at the *kind* of chemical impingement from the evidence of the *kind* of semantic reaction (or symptom) to it.

Nor is the case different with biological impingements in the form of microscopic organisms. Indeed, disease may be defined as an attempt at a semantic reorientation. Immunity towards a given kind of biological impingement is a successful semantic reorientation that has been achieved towards that *kind* of impingement. Yet often enough the system dies before it can restructure itself semantically.

Sometimes the impingement may be against the logic of the system at its upper "conscious levels," as we shall shortly see in greater detail. Such an impingement may disturb the semantic system so profoundly that one notes corrective activity in revised kinds of behavior of the tissues and organs. Stomach ulcers and arthritis are believed to be often so motivated; so too all cases of conversion hysteria. Perhaps cancer belongs here, as the whole loses control of the parts.

Although the actual mechanisms that are involved in these semantic corrections may be but little understood, a certain unity of principle is possible by assuming that they are all logical disturbances at various "levels" of a semantic system which is trying to keep itself logically self-consistent. For that reason, theoretically, as psychosomatic medicine is showing, some illnesses can be treated either "physically" or "mentally"—that is, they can be treated semantically at various "levels." Yet with or without the help of other persons, the semantic system can alone correct itself by restoring a logical self-consistency in its action-reaction structure; and self-preservatively it seeks to do so (the "healing force of nature," or *vis medicatrix naturae*). Help from others is bootless unless the semantic system comprehends that help in terms of its own system.

C. Traumata

In our discussion of a semantic system we have used the term, *logical self-consistency,* and also the term *semantic integration.* The first term refers to the absence of self-contradiction. The second term refers to a condition in which all correlations are related to all others—like the theorems of Euclidean geometry. Although this second condition, a unit system of logic, is theoretically the goal of all mentation, it is a goal that may at best be only approximated in actual semantic systems.

Naturally, if a correlation works satisfactorily for a person and is logically self-consistent with the rest of his semantic system, it makes no difference how spurious or idiotic the correlation seems to others. Thus the belief of Chinese peasants that a lunar eclipse is caused by a dragon eating the moon—a sorry fate that they always successfully forestall by beating pots and pans—may be a stupid correlation as far as semantic integration is concerned, but not a logically contradictory one, since the *ad hoc* class of moon-eating dragons apparently contradicts nothing else and is always obedient to a class of noises that result from classes of action upon classes of kitchenware. Indeed, if we were to prevent the peasants from beating the pots and pans during a lunar eclipse, we might cause dire panic among them, since they would conclude that so important a class as *moon* was about to be extinguished forever from their semantic systems. Like the peasants, we all have *ad hoc* gods, and sprites, and *verba* that give us intellectual ease and upon whose existence we tenaciously insist, for fear of disastrous logical consequences should they be found spurious.

It may happen, however, that our environment behaves in a (to us) logically contradictory fashion. To take a fantastic example, let us suppose that we are alone in the house when a book spontaneously rises off the table and drops again (there is a remote chance that it might do so). Instantly our logical system is profoundly disturbed by a contradictory event. We either (1) leap to the table to "find out what the matter is"—that is, to state this aberrational phenomenon in terms of our previous classes; or (2) we flee to an environment where our mentational correlations still work; or (3) we doubt the correctness of our sensations—a very neat device for preserving the logical *status quo.* Yet unless we can explain the contradictory phenomenon logically in terms of our semantic system, or devise a new logically self-consistent system that will comprehend it, we have a *trauma;* that is, we have for life a logically contradictory datum of experience. We may spend the rest of our lives "neurotically" avoiding books, or putting paper weights on them so that they won't jump, yet the logical contradiction remains, no matter how successfully we overwhelm it with further data that behave "correctly."

Indeed the memories over which we brood and the conflicts of our dreams often refer presumably to logical traumata of this sort, as becomes more understandable when we now take a less bizarre example than that of the jumping book.

Suppose, for example, that a person is brought up from childhood to honor his mother, and also to hate a thief. Unexpectedly he finds that his mother is a thief, and the trauma of the disclosure may be profoundly shocking to the logic of his mind. He simply may refuse to believe it, and kill anyone who mentions it; he may suddenly loathe his own and all other mothers, including the dog with puppies; or he may build up a special class, *my mother,* which, like *my country,* is exempt from all other correlations ("my mother can do no wrong") ; or he can love thieves; or he can try to solve the contradiction logically by re-examining his experience and noting that there is no necessary connection between maternity and civic virtue, and that thieves may have their lovable sides. Or he may find no solution and retire into a monastery to worship God, or he may seek logic in a self-made fantasy world, or in the oneness of death.

Our lives may well contain many such logically contradictory traumata, as the psychoanalytic schools insist. These traumata represent logical conflicts in the logical structure of the respective semantic system which tries to solve the conflict in order to restore a greater logical self-consistency in its system of terms and statements.

Of course theoretically, the logical disturbance will be the greater if the contradiction affects the more generic classes which, like mother, enter into a large complex of inclusions with other classes to form more specific classes. Thus the classes, *mother* and *thief,* are generally basic classes of early experience, in terms of which much of later experience is willy nilly defined. Had the person merely found instead that his favorite *dog* killed *chickens,* he might well have become sad, but not profoundly dejected. Indeed it may be that the degree of his emotional reaction is a measure of the profundity of the logical breach in his semantic system (if we assume that actual or threatened broken logical order *is* painful emotion, whereas reducing *n* or making experience semantically more integrated *is* pleasant emotion).[23]

The more profound, or generic, the logical disturbance is, the greater will its ramifications tend to be found in inclusions with other classes which also thereby become logically disturbed. Indeed the profound disturbance may only reveal itself to other persons by its effect upon more superficial inclusions. Thus the outsider may never know that the man discovered that his mother was a thief. The outsider may merely note in him an inordinate fondness for thieves (or an inordinate hatred of mothers) that betokens a mind that is somewhere disturbed. Even the afflicted person himself may have put the original trauma out of consciousness as his own semantic system tries to restore logical order by providing copious experiential data of, say, "nice things about thieves." Yet with the psychoanalytic technique of "free association" under which the person audibly relates what he associates (or classifies) with thieves, the basic generic conflict may assert itself consciously as the person admits to himself and others: "I once saw my mother pick a pocket." This technique of "free association" is based upon the tacit assumption that mind is a system of classes.

The above consideration recalls the old saying that invariably "murder will out"—a belief that is scarcely supported by police records of unsolved crimes. Nevertheless a semantic system will seek to become logically self-consistent, even if in order to do so a murderer must confess his crime. For though the murderer may walk to the gallows in payment for his murder, at least his conscience will be clear as he walks—in the sense that his semantic system will again have become logically self-consistent—as he is treated logically according to the system of social correlations of the culture to which he subscribes [24] (see Chapter Seven).

The above examples are intended to illustrate the primary need for a logical self-consistency of a semantic system for the sake of accurately predicting the future. Further cases can be found in the literature of psychoanalysis and neurology, to which our theory is indebted.*

D. Consciousness as an Awareness . . . .

In our preceding discussion we have used the term, "levels of consciousness," which we shall now scrutinize more closely.[26]

As a convenient illustration of levels of consciousness, let us take the case of speech, where we note that though the auditor is conscious of the speaker's *entire* stream of speech, he is not equally conscious of *all parts* of it. For example, he will tend to be more conscious of the larger permutations of sentences, than of the smaller permutations of words and phonemes, provided that there are no mistakes in the smaller permutations. Yet let the speaker use the "wrong" word, or pronounce it "wrong," and the auditor tends to become conscious of the error. These varying degrees of consciousness may be roughly called varying levels of consciousness.

If we care to generalize upon the above illustration of speech, we may suspect that the higher levels of consciousness are connected either (1) with the relatively larger and less frequently occurring inclusions of classes with a comparatively lower probability of association, or (2) with breaches, or deviations, in frequently occurring inclusions of classes with a comparatively higher probability of association. According to this view, a person will in general tend to be conscious of (1) the more variable classes of relevant events of his life, and also of (2) interruptions in, or disturbances to, the more determinate events of his life—such as the action of his heart, lungs, and liver—when these latter behave "wrong." We shall presently construct a more descriptive social analogue of what this problem seems to be.

In the meantime, let us note that every organism, in systematically responding to a class of stimuli, may be said to be aware of the class, regardless of whether it is conscious of it. Consciousness, on the other hand, seems to be nothing more than a secondary systematic reaction to the more primary stimulus response; or, to adopt traditional terms, consciousness is an awareness of an awareness; or, still differently expressed, it is a sensation of a sensation.

* The concept *restructuring the personality*, as developed by the school of Gestalt psychologists [25] seems to be tantamount to our concept of so altering classes as to preserve or to restore a logical self-consistency and to increase semantic integration. We, for our part, suggest to the Gestalt and Freudian schools that the assumption of a mind as a unit prediction mechanism with a minimum n different classes, may be a prerequisite for their ingenious systems of dynamics. Should that be the case, then their theories and observations will represent further elaborations of the economy of the minimum n, as our common field becomes more unified.

Hence, for example, our artisan can both sense the outside world, and sense his sensations thereto. Thus defined, consciousness may introduce additional mechanisms of sensation but no new principle, since consciousness in its supervisory role of sensing sensations will itself have a structure of classifications; otherwise it could not supervise. This structure of consciousness, too, will theoretically reveal the economy of a minimum *n* number of classes. The greater the given threat to, breach in, or opportunity for the semantic system, the greater, presumably, will be the attention that consciousness focuses upon it.

The economic justification for the mechanisms of consciousness (whatever they may be) becomes evident when we remember that the unit semantic system is self-preservative; and, being self-preservative, there must be mechanisms both for awareness of disturbances to the system's logical self-consistency, as well as for corrections to the same. Otherwise the semantic system could not preserve itself, and would, indeed, be meaningless. Obviously if the organism has only a small *n* number of different classes, it will not need so highly elaborated a consciousness (i.e., so large an *n of consciousness*) as will an organism with a larger *n* number of classes. Yet theoretically every organism will have consciousness, though we may be unable to detect its presence.

Perhaps the easiest way to visualize the problem of an individual's consciousness is to resort to a social analogue and relate it to the conscious acts of a large social group, such as an army that is in combat. Every army, after all, is both an effective and a responsive body which is unified by a common objective that it seeks to attain according to a unifying plan that is stated in terms of classified and correlated action. A prerequisite of the functioning of this social system is a two-way information service between the parts and the central headquarters. The information sent out from headquarters both governs, and is governed by, the information it receives. As the information passes from the top down through the ranks, it passes through classes of human beings whose membership is increasingly larger (there are more privates than captains, etc.), and yet whose different modes, or classes, of action are ever fewer in number and ever narrower, or more stereotyped, in reference (e.g., the private's action is cast in fewer different kinds, or classes, and with a narrower scope).

Yet a part of the information service is to note and to report threatening or actual disturbances to the planned action of the group so that the group can alter itself, or its plan, or its environment, for the sake of accomplishing its objective with least effort. In short, the army must have a supervisory sensory system (the analogue to consciousness).

Assuming now that a disturbance occurs, let us inquire into the extent to which the rest of the organization should become aware of it.

If a soldier is wounded in combat, the resulting disturbance would be a matter of local information and would be corrected locally; it would at most be reported towards the top as a unit in a statistical *aggregate* whose comparative magnitude would alone arouse an increasing awareness of the whole in proportion to the degree of the threat to the well-being of the whole. The same would apply to a death in combat—a stereotyped local disturbance that is treated in a stereotyped local fashion, and whose importance to the whole depends, again, upon the aggregate.

On the other hand, if the soldier's death results, say, from bubonic plague, which is by no means a stereotyped disturbance that can be locally treated but which instead is an implicit threat to the whole system, then indeed the news of it will spread to the top with the result that group action may well be taken. From this example we see that it is not merely the fact, but also *the implications of the fact for the whole,* that draws to it the *attention* of the whole by the amount that it bodes well or ill to the whole.

In the light of the above examples, which could be extended in various directions, we can understand how our metaphorical social consciousness, in the absence of a disturbance, tends to be evenly diffused over the entire system as it merely senses that all is proceeding according to plan. Yet once a disturbance arises, the awareness of the disturbance increases in proportion to the *implications* of the disturbance for the whole. A single small disturbance, such as a case of virulent fever, or the discovery of a new kind of weapon, that carries with it a threat to the whole organization, may absorb the entire attention of the group and profoundly modify its course of action. Serious potential disturbances of given kinds will tend to be proportionately rare; otherwise they would become stereotyped and develop stereotyped correctives that are locally applied.

The above argument about army information applies equally well to the social information of any other group. Indeed, upon reflection, we note that it leads to the self-same argument that we used at the opening of this chapter in discussing the N number of different newspaper items of like s size: the economy of many small samples of more commonplace events of more local importance *versus* the economy of a few larger samples of unusual (less repetitive) events of more widespread importance.

But though our army analogue is easily integrated into our data on social sampling, let us note that the analogue can be extended to include those events of which the individual soldier himself is conscious. Thus as long as the soldier's orders are unequivocal and within his compass, and as long as his various mechanisms of gun, ammunition, and the like, function according to stereotypes, then the soldier's greatest consciousness will be directed towards what seems to be the greatest threat or opportunity to his role as a soldier in which his own individual economy may be suppressed.* In the routine loading and firing of his gun, his activity is largely unconscious, as long as all proceeds according to plan. Yet, let his gun break, or let his ammunition run short, and the soldier becomes instantly conscious thereof as he concentrates his attention upon it.

Pausing now, let us note that our entire foregoing argument has been cast in terms of classes, and classes of classes—the correlation of one class

* At this point we introduce implicitly the concept of the Freudian *"unconscious"* which refers to an individual-social conflict, in which the individual economy is suppressed for the sake of a social economy. Discussed further in Chapter Seven.

of events with another in terms of a third. Thus *having a broken gun* is a class of events which in the soldier's mind is classified with other kinds of events. The same is true of the class, *a case of bubonic plague*. Indeed in the presence of a disturbance the first question is "*what* is it?" and then "*what* difference does it make?," and then "*what* shall we do about it?" All three *whats* refer to classificatory action. The second question, "what difference does it make?" seems to be immediately related to the degree of consciousness that attends the disturbance.

Necessary to the above social analogue is some system for transmitting information between the parts, and between the parts and larger aggregates including the whole. This information, to be effective, must be in a stable self-consistent code that is familiar to all affected entities. (One needs only to imagine the confusion attending the mingling of Chinese and American soldiers and officers in an army without liaison, in order to comprehend the need for a single self-consistent communication system.) This code need not consist of oral words or of written words. Instead it can use any agreed physical medium which the persons can detect sensorily: sounds, flashes of light, smells, electrical potentials, postures, gestures, chemical tokens—anything, in fact, that the persons can detect, provided always that the persons are familiar with the meaning of the code.

Let us inspect more closely the question of the code, as we inquire into its organization, regardless of its physical medium. Obviously the same principles that govern the organization of speech will govern the organization of any code: *viz.,* the principles of abbreviation, and of economical versatility, permutation, and specialization. For, like speech, any code is a semantic system with a physical basis that is cast in terms of classes of stimuli and of classes of responses. It is a classification of classes of stimuli, and the correlation thereof with classes of responses that may in turn be stimuli.

May the physiologist ponder the above analogue and ask himself if the individual's entire nervous system, including the endocrine system and all else, may not be analogously organized: a classification of classes of stimuli with classes of responses that may in turn be stimuli—a unit semantic system that must preserve its logical self-consistency if it is to function at all, and which seeks to become semantically more integrated by decreasing its n classes of action? [27]

If this analogue be legitimate—and there is no harm in asking the question—then the terms of the generalized harmonic series may be approximated by the classificatory action of all physiological details, including the N number and s sizes of the different genes of the various chromosomes. For throughout the entire "soma" the actual entities of matter are but transients; only their *kinds* are enduring, and their *kinds* of performances. Hence everywhere will be present the economy of *kinds* (classes). Our artisan will theoretically be present in the tiniest system of classificatory action; indeed a multicellular organism may perhaps be profitably viewed as a social system of many artisans who collectively solve their survival problems, even as the members of our above social analogue (see also Part Two).*

The above surmise may seem to be overbold. But let us remember that a principle, like the Principle of Least Effort, if sound, cannot be localized to a restricted portion of behavior—any more than the principle of gravitation can be localized to, say, a few counties in Iowa. Otherwise it is not sound as a dynamic principle. Although our concern for the *n* different classes of an individual's action may seem to be excessive, it springs from the genuine belief that in the minimizing of *n* (subject to predicting the future to a given degree of probability) as a means of minimizing effort (probable work) we have a promising approach to studying the basic principles of all living phenomena.

Our previous social analogue of the soldiers and the army was presented only for the sake of illustrating more tactilely our entire hypothetical construct of a unit semantic system in its sensation, mentation, and action (whether unconscious, or with varying degrees of consciousness)—a unit semantic system that tends to preserve itself with least effort.

E. The Pseudo "Mind-Body" Question

While the above social analogue is still before us, let us return to a consideration of the "mind-body" question which incidentally is a pseudo question and will remain so until the terms *mind* and *body* have been defined by those who are preoccupied with the question. We have already explored this problem and have suggested that the toenails, ears, and teeth are as much a part of the unit semantic system as is the brain, or central nervous system.

The fact that we administer pills to cure some diseases and words to cure others (mental diseases), and use either for some, does not mean that there is a dichotomy between mind and body. In all cases we are evoking selected kinds of responses by administering selected kinds of stimuli. To the upper cultural "level" of organization we talk with "words"; to the lower and more determinate levels we talk with aspirin pills. But it is still talk, though we use the terms of conventional cultural language for the one and the terms of the more invariant language of physics-chemistry for the other. Opium that is a food for some organisms is narcotic for us because it has that meaning for us in terms of our semantic system.

In viewing mind as a unit semantic system that tries to minimize its *n* different classes of action, we may have to draw a strict dichotomy between the language of culture and that of physics-chemistry (see Chapter Seven). Yet that does not mean a dichotomy between mind and body in the organism. Rather does it mean that a unit semantic system can be dis-

* Let us remember that in spite of great variations in structure and size, protein molecules which are necessary for the elaboration of all known living process, all contain carbon, oxygen, and nitrogen in proportions of about 51%, 25%, and 16%, which are about the proportions of the harmonic series, 1, ½, ⅓. These are all frequent elements. Is not the versatility of chemical compounding of these elements in the order of carbon, oxygen, and nitrogen?

turbed in many ways and corrected in many ways. Yet every disturbance of whatever kind is a logical disturbance to a unit system; so too is every correction.

Fire can be a drastic threat to our system. We can be told of it; we can see it; we can feel it. Yet regardless of our kind of information, our reaction is similar. The fact that sensation and response can be at different levels of consciousness does not itself imply a dichotomy between "mind" and "body."

V. INTELLECTUAL RIGIDITY AND DEATH: MISCELLANEA

Inherent in our preceding hypothetical construct are certain miscellaneous considerations which we shall now discuss briefly, since they will be important for later chapters.

A. Age and Intellectual Rigidity

We have argued that our artisan will seek to structure his semantic system so that it will suffice to describe and to predict the relevant events of his particular environment. Now let us note that once he has done so, it is economical for him to preserve that particular *kind* of environment in order to avoid the cost of restructuring his semantic system.

Let us formalize this condition by stating that the artisan structures his semantic system in order to predict his particular environment, and then seeks to keep in an environment that corresponds to his particular semantic system.

In view of the above, it is evident that every semantic system is biased by its environment.

It is further evident that the longer the artisan lives in a particular environment, the greater will be the number of sensory samples that buttress the probability of the particular correlations that constitute his semantic system. In other words, the longer the artisan lives in his particular environment the more thoroughly is his semantic system statistically buttressed.

As his semantic system becomes statistically ever more buttressed by the elapse of ever more time, it will take ever more work to restructure the semantic system in the event the environment changes or is changed, because the artisan will have to have an ever increasing number of sensory samples of the new environment in order to controvert the statistical effect of the accumulation of sensory samples of the erstwhile environment.

Therefore we may say that, as time passes, the artisan's semantic system tends to become intellectually *more rigid* in the sense that the probabilities of its action increase. In short, because it is economical for the artisan to make a semantic system that fits his environment and then to preserve an environment that his semantic system describes, his semantic system may be said to pass from the less probable of action to the more probable of action, and, in so doing, to become *intellectually more rigid* (by definition).

Naturally in using the term (*intellectual*) *rigidity,* which is traditional to neurology, let us remember that it is ultimately borrowed from physics, where it has an entirely different meaning. A more felicitous term would be *intellectual entropy,* and one might hazard the definition that a person's *age* is the equivalent of his intellectual entropy, which in turn is somehow the logarithm of the probability of recurrence of the classes of action as the semantic system passes from the less probable to the more probable.*

Lest we lose ourselves in terms, however, let us note that we are merely saying that habits grow with time—that "habit is a cable, we weave a thread of it each day until it becomes so strong we cannot break it." [28] Yet behind this concept of *habit* is the concept of mind as an accumulation of statistically analyzed sensory samplings (i.e., *memory*).

Because of this statistical bias in the direction of repetition, the artisan will *age,* and the direction of his life will be irreversible. Age in this sense, however, is not proportionate to the length of elapsed time of the system, but is rather the equivalent of intellectual rigidity.[29] Hence a man is not as old as his years but as "old as his glands," as the saying goes. Theoretically, if bodily forms-functions become more "rigid" with age, that is rather the result than the cause of intellectual rigidity. Thus, for example, stooped shoulders are adjustments that are made in time to the desk, as the semantic system in time becomes more rigid and less *labile* (*labile* being the opposite of *rigid*). Age in the sense of normative rates of growth will be discussed in our following chapter.

B. Intellectual Rigidity and Death

Implicit in the concept of an increasing intellectual rigidity is the concept of *death* as a moment at which semantic adjustments can no longer be made to environmental changes (the economy of death will be discussed theoretically in our following chapter).

Just what determines the moment of death is a difficult question. Yet, *if* it is connected with increasing intellectual rigidity, two objective statements can be made about it, both of which are true.

In the first place, death is more likely to eventuate later in life than earlier, because the system is intellectually more rigid later in life than earlier, as is notoriously the case. In the second place, those persons that are "more intelligent," in the sense of being more capable of restructuring their semantic systems, will tend not only to be healthier than others but also to live longer, because they can more easily adjust to environmental changes; this is also the case.[30] Conversely, mentally defective persons will tend to die young, as seems in fact to be the case.

It is commonly believed that with increasing years we tend to "slow down." More correctly stated, we seem to heal "physical" and "mental" disturbances to our system more slowly, and to change our "bodily" and "mental" configurations more slowly as age increases. That is to be anticipated theoretically.

* The probability is not that of increasingly shuffled cards (physical entropy), but that of the increasingly more set, or determinate, action of the aging "card player" who, with advancing age, is more likely to do certain things in a certain way at a certain time: the increasing rigidity of the individual's "preconceptions."

If the above argument is sound, then one can try to increase the length of life in one or both of two ways: (1) stabilize the environment so as to minimize the likelihood of altering the terms of one's semantic system; and (2) try to structure one's semantic system in terms of more generic classes (i.e., "broader" or "more tolerant" classes) so as to decrease the probability of disturbance from any random environmental change.

Theoretically, if (1) one could completely stabilize his environment, he would never die; for, though he became intellectually ever more rigid, his environment would never controvert his system. Death, therefore, as biologists have always pointed out, is not a biological necessity. Rather is it a biological expedient (cf. following chapter). In this connection let us remember that for years now a cell has been kept alive somewhere in the Rockefeller Institute by preserving it in a stable optimal environment.

Theoretically, if (2) one avoids highly biased specific correlations (i.e., bigotry) and instead seeks to integrate one's semantic system in terms of generic classes that are frequent in experience, one increases the likelihood of being able to cope with the inevitable frustrations and disappointments of a changing environment. An empirically verifiable philosophy, therefore, is a tremendous health asset not only in curing disturbances, but also and more particularly in preventing them. Conversely, an illogical and spurious philosophy that defies empiric test can be a serious social liability by causing conflicts among those who are trained to conform to it (see Chapter Seven).*

C. Environmental Frames and Neuroses

The particular kind of environment to which a given individual adjusts semantically may be called a frame of reference. Because of some statistically freakish incident, it may happen that one person's frame becomes radically different from that of others. Thus Pavlov's dog, conditioned to expect food at the sound of a bell, is an example of a frame that is freakish in comparison with the usual frames of dogs where there is no particular correlation (or "conditioning," or association) between bell and food.

Turning now to the case of persons, let us take the case of an adolescent girl who happened to be raped on her way home from school—a painful first experience with sex. Because of the lack of controvertive sexual experiences with which to compare the statistically freakish instance of the rape, the class *rape* may become generic in her mind in connection with all male sexual activity. As a result, she will automatically avoid further sexual experiences, and even further associations with men in order to avoid the unpleasant experience of rape. In so doing she automatically *blocks* the possibility of assembling further experiential samples that will establish the statistical freakishness of her rape.

The girl's rape-correlation is not spurious, since men do in fact rape girls, even on the way home from school, as she very well knows; and there is a slight chance that any girl will be thus raped. The point is that the

* Deliberate changes in one's kind of environment may have the helpful effect of avoiding bigotry, though, if carried to an extreme, it can also impede semantic integration.

probability of being thus raped, on the basis of actual cases, is nowhere nearly as great as the girl estimates quite naturally on the basis of her own experience.

Doubtless every person has faulty probabilities which result from the freakishness of his particular frame which may or may not be corrected by subsequent experience. The point is that the faulty probability of the girl's rape-correlation is of such a kind as almost to preclude the possibility of corrective experience unless she is forced to do so. It is the old story of "once bitten, twice shy." It is the basis of the adage, "a person thrown from his horse should at once mount the horse again."

For unless there is a corrective subsequent experience, the freakish correlation will tend to become ever more generic, in the sense that ever greater portions of the semantic system will be structured in terms of it.

Thus in the previous case of the raped girl, the rape-correlation may become so generic (i.e., develop such a *complex*) that she refuses to leave her room lest some man rape her—a possible happening, to be sure, but by no means a likely one. Hence the girl's freakish rape-correlation can be very costly to her economy because, by and large, every person must leave his room.

The girl's conflict between her personal fears of rape on the one hand, and the demands of social living on the other, has its ultimate source in a faulty probability, in the sense that her quite legitimate estimate of the probability of being raped diverges widely from the collective experience of the group. This faulty probability leads in turn to the rape complex. Such a condition may be defined as a *neurosis*.

According to our theory, traumata that are experienced earlier in life are more likely to lead to serious neuroses than those in later life. And the longer a neurosis is allowed to persist, the more difficult will its therapy be, because of the general increase in the magnitude of the complex with the elapse of time. On the other hand, the presence of a serious neurosis will theoretically tend to retard the rate of increase of intellectual rigidity and therefore to extend the length of life. In short, a slightly greater longevity attaches theoretically to the neurotic person—a rather dubious reward for an often miserable life. This theoretical expectation is statistically supported.

Of course some neuroses can be relieved by environmental alterations. There are, after all, socially hallowed institutions that can serve as suitable environments for women who are afraid of men. A neurotic fear of being in New York can be quieted by keeping away from it. Similarly with the treatment of numerous neuroses, such as those connected with an excessive fear of toads, angleworms, and mice.

D. Conception and Birth

While still on miscellaneous topics that are related to our theory of a unit semantic system, let us ask when a given individual's semantic system may be said to begin. Although this question is enormous, we shall at least broach it, lest we seem to ignore its existence.

Theoretically the organism must always survive with least effort, and since a semantic system is necessary thereto, a semantic system is theoretically present at the instant of the organism's conception. Indeed we may view the genetic inheritance of an individual as his initial donum of experience without which his life would be impossible, since he would otherwise have no previous experience on the basis of which he could act selectively towards his environment. The physical-chemical structure of this genetic donum would theoretically have all the properties of our Tool Shop, including a semantic system. Yet it is the semantic system, expressed in terms of physical chemical structure, that is the parental gift. This semantic system defines the optimal environment into which the organism directs its development. The semantic system also contains the basic generic classes of experience—highly primitive classes—which are elaborated to define the more specific classes of the organism's actual environment.

Clearly, in passing at birth from a water environment to an air environment, the human being must make an enormous semantic adjustment—an adjustment which neurologists have appropriately called the *birth trauma,* and which may well remain as an abiding logical conflict of subsequent life.

But now let us turn to another topic, the topic of plural parenthood for the production of offspring. According to the Principle of Least Effort the act of plural parenthood, or plural mating, *like every other organic act,* must be one of economy. Yet what is the economy of plural parents? If we take the view that parents are providing semantic systems for their offspring, the question of plural parents becomes: what is the economy of selecting a new semantic system from the givens of more than one system, instead of from the givens of just one?

In reply, it would seem offhand that the particular classes in which the parents' semantic systems agree will probably be the more useful classes for the embryo to adopt if he wishes to avoid the possibility of freakish classes of one parent. Hence plural parenthood is a conservative mechanism to provide a semantic system of more likely use for a more likely environment.

Moreover, by selecting his semantic system from the configurations of more than one semantic system, the embryo has the opportunity to make a logically more integrated semantic system than that of any of his parents. Thus a permanent mutation in a species can occur at conception.

These matters are mentioned, not in the belief that they contribute anything of importance to the science of genetics, but rather for the sake of emphasizing the view that the problem of our artisan and his semantic system is with us from the start, and therefore has implications even for the problems of genetics.

E. "Paths" of Memory

Although we have spoken of experience, or memory, as an accumulation of sensory samples, we have dodged the entire problem of physiological mechanisms. Memory could, of course, be a file of sensory images. Yet it need not be. For it could also be a transportation system of routes or paths over which things move—as indeed is commonly believed to be the case by neurologists. Thus the paths that are more frequently used will be made the easier paths which in turn will tend to be more frequently used in the future, thereby introducing the factor of memory.

Yet if memory—and, by implication, the entire semantic system—is a system of paths in space over which matter-energy moves whether for the purpose of purveying information, or for the purpose of providing energy for the system, or both, then there is a more economical and a less economical way of organizing those paths. Though this problem of a most economical organization of paths is doubtless vast, it nevertheless is both real and ponderable.

All we can say about the number and locations and junctures of these paths is that we shall meet a precisely comparable problem in Part Two of this book when we investigate the structure of a human social system which may well serve as a useful analogue. If the analogue is sound, we can understand how a blocking of some paths will tend to force the opening of detours in a field that is to some extent fluid.[31] We can also understand the increasing inertia, or rigidity of the field to all changes, as memory and age increase. We can understand how the infant embryo, in establishing its paths, will, on the basis of the experience of its inherited semantic system, lay out paths that will despatch probable future traffic with maximum economy (just as a railroad is laid out with an eye to solving with maximum economy the probable needs of the future).

In mentioning these miscellaneous considerations in connection with our thesis of sensation and mentation, we do not pretend to have offered a solution. We merely point out that they are germane to our topic, and that the Principle of Least Effort, if correct, must be able to explain them.

V. SUMMARY: THE *N* MINIMUM

It is a convention of the trade that a chapter should end with a summary. In this chapter we have argued at length about our artisan in his Tool Shop in the belief that he represented an analogue for the organism. We were led to this belief by the evidence of the structure of human speech, both in its stream and in its sensory samples. But now, instead of discussing the artisan and his Tool Shop that is supposed to be an analogue to the organism, let us talk about the organism itself.

For all we know to the contrary, the behavior of an organism is mechanically and chemically correct. Hence in inspecting an organism we look for that which distinguishes it from inanimate matter. As we know, one outstanding characteristic of the organism is its selectivity of matter. That is, it selects certain *kinds* (or classes) of matter-energy from its environment and does certain *kinds* (or classes) of things to it; or, better still, it selects certain *kinds* (or classes) of properties of matter-energy upon which it performs certain *kinds* (or classes) of operations.

In our preceding pages we have inquired into certain aspects of these different *kinds* (or classes) of selective activity. But instead of asking the narrower question of the specific classes of activity of specific organisms, we have probed the broader question of the determinants of the n number of different classes of selective activity of any organism. For regardless of the specific different classes of activity used by a given organism, every organism without exception will use n different classes of activity—no matter how large or small n may be.

Our first question about these n different classes is whether there is any economy in a small n number of them or a large n number. This question led to other questions which we shall formulate in summary:

1. Regardless of the n number of different classes of matter-energy that any organism uses, it is economical for it to minimize its n number because the organism is more likely to find a smaller n number of different classes of matter-energy together in any single spot and hence, by minimizing n, it minimizes the likelihood of expending work to look for them.* To increase n, therefore, is to increase the probable work of the organism—just as in our Tool Analogy of Chapter Three, where we saw that the sheer work of the artisan will increase with n.

Of course there is a difference between the *sheer* work of the Tool Analogy of Chapter Three and the *probable* work of the organism. Thus in the case of the *sheer* work of the Tool Analogy, any increase in the n number of different kinds of tools was attended by an increase in the length of the work bench and in the distance of the farthest nth tool from the artisan; this increase in distance caused the artisan to expend more work in order to reach for the tool and to return it to its place.

Yet in the case of the *probable* work of the organism we can say that as the n different kinds of tools is increased, the *probable* work of the shop increases, regardless of any considerations of distance. Therefore *probable work* can be substituted for distance, with the result that the Tool Analogy is still theoretically descriptive of the organism, regardless of the number of dimensions in which the problem is cast.

2. Yet even with an n minimum number of different classes of matter-energy used, there is an economy in decreasing the actual amounts of each class of matter-energy that is used, since any organism is more likely to find smaller amounts of any class of matter-energy in any one spot than larger amounts. Indeed, if we conceive of the contents of any class of matter-energy as consisting of a population of an n number of different entities, then we may say that n is again a minimum (this is another way of saying that it is economical to minimize quantities of matter-energy).

Although the above argument is sufficient, there is the second argument: smaller amounts are, in general, easier to move over distances than larger amounts, even as we pointed out in connection with our Tool Analogy in Chapter Three, when we discussed the economy of "close packing." Consequently the organism will tend to shorten all distances in its structure wherever such shortening will lessen its probable work. This tendency will lead in general to "closely packed" organisms, in the sense that there will be no vacant spaces or long routes in organic structures without definite

* This n minimum is *always* subject to the auxiliary conditions as discussed in the text.

economic reasons. Furthermore, there will tend to be a correlation between a small physical size and a small *n* number of different classes of action, since all organisms are theoretically decreasing the amounts of different kinds of materials used, as well as their kinds. Hence organisms that are comparatively *small* in size will *tend* to be comparatively *simple* in structure (in the sense that they will *tend* to have a comparatively small *n* number of different tools). This correlation between the *small* and the *simple* will be of value to us in our following chapter.

3. Since the *n* number of different classes of matter-energy is a minimum, it is economical to increase the *f* frequency of any one or more of the given *n* classes of action rather than to increase the size of *n*. An increase in *f*, therefore, is a device for minimizing effort; the economy of increasing *f* increases in direct proportion to *n* (cf. Tool Analogy of Chapter Three). This consideration, incidentally, is of considerable theoretical importance for the rationalization of *all* frequency studies of organic process of any kind. It also explains the economy of building larger organic structures out of permutations of smaller and simpler structures (e.g., cells).

4. By decreasing the *n* number of different kinds of matter-energy used, the organism decreases correspondingly the number of different kinds of physical-chemical threats to its structure and operation, and therefore the number of different kinds of deleterious events against which the organism must guard by means of a sensory-semantic system. By thus decreasing the number of different kinds of threats to its system, the organism can decrease the number of different sensory-mentational classes into which it analyzes its environment, and thereby decrease the number and sizes of its samples. Comparatively small and simple organisms, therefore, will tend to have comparatively *simple* sensory-semantic systems (in the sense of a small *n* number of different sensory classes).

5. We have said that an organism performs *n* different kinds of material operations (or processes) upon different kinds of matter-energy. In passing let us note the economy of minimizing these *n* different kinds of operations (or processes), since by decreasing the *n* different kinds of operations performed, the organism increases the probability of finding matter-energy that will be capable of performing them. This fifth principle is only another way of stating the first principle above.

Hence no matter how the problem is viewed, it is economical for the organism to minimize its *n* different classes of activity of whatever sort. For purposes of a greater ease in exposition, we shall henceforth summarize our preceding theoretical principles by simply stating that the *n* different kinds of materials is minimized because of the increasing probability of finding them.

But though the above principles may conceivably suffice to define a self-preservative mechanical system of least effort, we have not yet demonstrated conclusively that an organism is such a hypothetical system of least effort, even though our argument has been constructed in that direction.

There is, however, one way to test the validity of our Tool Analogy and of our above five principles for all organic process. For if *the compara-*

tively simpler and smaller organisms are likely to be the comparatively more efficient organisms, then with the elapse of time, these comparatively smaller and simpler organisms will be less likely either to need to alter their forms and functions, or to become extinct. Hence the rates of innovation and of extinction of any class or species of organism will tend theoretically to decrease with the comparative size and complexity of its organisms, as we shall try to demonstrate to be the case in our following chapter. If this demonstration be correct, it will go far towards establishing our Principle of Least Effort.

CHAPTER SIX

THE EGO AS THE "ORIGIN" OF A FRAME OF REFERENCE *

In the present chapter we shall attempt to build a more complete foundation under the arguments of the preceding chapters. This we shall do in the following stages. First (I) we shall undertake to define an organism in physical terms. Second (II) we shall view the totality of organisms on the earth's surface as a unit biosocial population in which many different organisms are competing and co-operating for survival. Then third and fourth (III and IV) we shall attempt to integrate the above arguments and data with those of the preceding chapters.

I. A DEFINITION OF AN ORGANISM

In our previous chapter we postulated that an organism must survive and in so doing will minimize effort; this minimum we verified empirically. Now we shall continue with these postulates and inquire into the meaning of the terms *organism* and *survival.* For until we have defined what we mean by an organism and its survival, our postulate and arguments are on shaky grounds. Let us now turn, therefore, to the problem of defining an organism.

A. Man and the Machine

We have consistently assumed that all living action takes place within the restrictions of the natural laws of physics and chemistry, since we have not needed to take a stand as to whether an organism, in solving any of its problems of matter-energy in time-space, makes use of kinds of matter-energy that are unavailable to a machine.

Therefore, whether the entity that goes up the hill is an automobile or a man, the entity in question, as far as we are concerned, will expend physical work in order to overcome gravitation, friction, and the like. In either case, the automobile and the person represent physical restrictions upon the flow of energy towards entropy. Thus, as the automobile consumes its supply of fuel, the energy that is thereby released forces the automobile up hill, if it happens to be directed thither. The same applies to a person. Indeed, the parallelism between the two seems offhand to be complete.

Yet this parallelism between the two ceases as soon as the fuel supplies become exhausted in (1) the automobile or any other inanimate machine, and in (2) the man or any other living organism.

---

* In the phrase, *the origin of a frame of reference,* the word *origin* is used in its mathematical sense.

For (1) as the fuel supply of the automobile runs out, the machine ceases to respond to that force, although it continues as heretofore to respond to other forces as it seeks a physical-chemical equilibrium with its environment according to all the forces that operate upon it. A machine, like all else in inanimate nature, seeks at all times to attain a physical equilibrium with its environment and nothing else. What is called a machine is nothing more than man-made restrictions upon the flow of matter-energy towards entropy. During its entire history a machine and all its parts are seeking a condition of physical equilibrium.

On the other hand, (2) as the fuel supply of a man or any other organism becomes exhausted he seeks to replenish it, thereby indicating that he does not completely share inanimate nature's all-pervading desire for physical equilibrium. Indeed, organic activity seems to be guided by the desire to avoid a condition of irrevocable physical equilibrium with its environment. To that end the organism expends work in replenishing its supply of fuel and in repairing damage to its system. When an organism reaches a condition in which it can no longer replenish its fuel supply or repair its system, we say that it is dead (and by the adjective *dead* is meant that henceforth the organism as a physical system no longer resists a gravitational and electromagnetic equilibrium with its environment).

This resistance to a "final and complete" physical equilibrium with its environment we shall consider to be characteristic of an organism.

B. The Organism as an Ego, or Identity-Point, That Exists as a Frame of Reference

The only possible means, and the actual means insofar as one can tell, whereby a man or any other organism resists a "permanent" equilibrium with his environment is through the expenditure of physical work.* Simply stated, man consumes oxygen and carbon and hydrogen compounds, etc. which he burns in order to obtain energy for the work of resisting physical equilibrium.[1]

Indeed we may view a man, or any other organism, as a physical entity that consists of some sort of an electrochemical furnace that is engaged in procuring enough fuel to maintain and operate the furnace in order to preserve the furnace from a physical equilibrium. Although an organism also has the job of procreation, to which we shall presently turn our attention, an organism is basically a physical system that attempts to preserve itself as such.

But now let us pause and ask the question: what actually preserves itself in an organism? Surely it is not the actual molecules of the system, since we know that these are in transit through the system. Of the great aggregate of molecules in an adult person's system, perhaps not a single one was present in his system at birth. Materially viewed, an organism is only

* We use the term "permanent" equilibrium, or "irrevocable" or "complete and final" equilibrium to cover the case presumably represented by the Tobacco Mosaic Virus in crystalline form which may be in a temporary situation of physical equilibrium with its environment, but which, under an alteration of environmental situation, may continue to resist physical equilibrium.

a tremendous transportation system through which matter-energy flows towards entropy; and out of this flow the organism gets work in order to maintain itself as a physical system in the flow. In any known physical sense, an organism is nothing more than this.

Hence in order to define an organism we cannot start with physical matter. Instead we shall begin with a point in time-space which is to serve as a frame of reference. This point is to be construed in the mathematical sense of a point, though it may be called an ego, or an identity-point, or a soul; and it is the origin of the frame of reference of the organism.[2] Yet regardless of what it is called—and we shall call it an ego, or an identity-point—the point exists only as the origin of a frame in reference to which matter-energy moves.

Hence we shall say by way of definition that *an organism is a movable mathematical point in time-space, in reference to which matter-energy moves in such a way that a physical situation exists in which work is expended in order to preserve a physical system (continual as a whole but not continual as to its parts) from a final gravitational and electromagnetic equilibrium with the rest of the universe.*

C. The Organism and Least Effort (Least Probable Work)

From the above definition we see that an organism works. The question now arises as to how much it works.

At this point let us remember from our earlier argument that an organism at a given instant may have many choices of action, some of which may be of least work today and yet initiate a course of action which will by no means represent least work tomorrow. Since the existence of the organism is continual, then a life of least work will be one in which the expenditure of work over time is minimized; that is, the organism will minimize its average rate of work over time.

What does this minimizing of average rate of work over time mean to a given organism at a given moment as it faces the future with the need of surviving in material form? Clearly, from the viewpoint of the organism with its continual job of survival, the organism must at every moment select a course of action in which its work of the present plus its *probable work* of the future will be least. We have already defined this course of action as one of *least average probable work.* Since, in our usage, *effort* means *average probable work,* as previously defined, we shall say that an organism survives at all times with *least effort* (and that, in short, is our Principle of Least Effort).

In order to survive with least effort, however, an organism must have some sort of sensory system for the sake of gaining information about its environment; it must also have some sort of calculating machine in order to estimate future probabilities on the basis of its accumulated sensory data.

Inherent, therefore, in our definition of an organism as stated above is the possession of some sort of sensory mechanism and some sort of calculating machine (or mind), including memory, as elaborated in greater detail in our preceding chapter.

D. The Length of an Organism's Life

An organism cannot minimize its *average* rate of work over time, unless the length of its life is somehow fixed so that the *average* rate can be computed. For unless the length of a given life is fixed, the concept of least effort—or least *average* rate of probable work—is meaningless. So we come face to face with perhaps the knottiest of all philosophical questions: how long does an identity-point survive? The elements of this question we shall discuss quite frankly and we shall state our answer to this question equally frankly. Regardless of how unusual our answer may appear to others, we nevertheless find no flaw in our logic. Moreover, even if our answer be incorrect, the question at hand lies against the entire field of biology and must somehow be answered if biology is ever to become a systematic science.

In facing the question of the duration in time of an organism's ego, or identity-point, let us remember that no problem can have a prescribed double superlative (i.e., two maxima and two minima, or a maximum and a minimum).* Thus, if an organism lives with least effort, all else must somehow be fixed. And that applies specifically to the length of an identity-point's duration which must somehow be fixed, and by no means can be "as long as possible." Hence the reader's ego, for example, will live a fixed length of time, even though the reader may feel that he wants to live "as long as possible."

Continuing, we must argue that the duration of an identity-point can be fixed in only three ways. Either (1) the identity-point exists a finite length of time that is fixed precisely to the last instant, or (2) its length is somehow fixed at birth although its length cannot be predicted (for convenience we shall adopt this second view which is closely related to the first view), or (3) the identity-point exists infinitely long and therefore is immortal. Let us take up each of these three views in turn.

If the first view (1) of a finite fixed length of life—for example, 89 years, 1 month, 2 days, 15 hours, 33 minutes, 1½ seconds—were the case, then an identity-point could not cease to exist until that time had elapsed—and this may be true. In that event, however, it is foolish to seek to live long, or to avoid death, or to try to preserve the life of another, or to kill him, since his life is measured to the last instant. Moreover, if an organism's life is thus measured, then some social phenomena, such as mass deaths in combat warfare, are interesting in the extreme; for, with all lives measured, the bullets of the enemy—or the bombs of the airmen attacking civilians—would have to be fired at just the right moment and directed in such a way that they would select and kill only those whose lives are ending at the precise moment that they are hit. Though such may be the case, I, for one, doubt it.†

---

* We use the term, *prescribed double superlative,* to cover such cases, for example, as where the easiest path may also fortuitously be the shortest and quickest path. In the case of conflict, however, one and only one superlative can be prescribed, as we saw in Chapter One.

† It is also possible that an organism has a birth donum of a given quantum of energy which he dissipates with maximum economy, and dies at its exhaustion. There is no evi-

The second view (2) that the length of an organism's life is somehow fixed, even though it is unpredictable, accords nicely with current scientific opinion and suffices *completely* for our *entire* argument throughout.[3] Therefore, we shall adopt it. The organism minimizes effort insofar as it can predict.

Nevertheless, there does still remain the third (3) possible view of the immortality of the ego, or identity-point, which may appeal to those who like to adventure with new ideas. According to this third view, death is by no means a biological necessity, as biologists have all along pointed out. Moreover, according to this view the organism's final act of death, whether "suicidally" or from "natural causes" will always be undertaken so that the organism's ego can somehow continue to "survive" with least effort. This may mean that an ego dies in one organic form only in order to appear again in some new organic (?) form, with the result that organic life may be dynamically not unlike a wave that appears only to disappear and to reappear again. Naturally, such a concept would be scientifically otiose as far as one Joe Doakes is concerned. For if Joe Doakes is born again as John Brown, or as a housefly, with nothing preserved from an earlier state except a point that serves as the origin of a frame of reference, what then is left of Joe Doakes that is peculiarly Joe Doakes? Here clearly the question is one of defining the meaning of immortality.

This third (3) view of the immortality of the identity-point is highly unorthodox; and fortunately the demonstration of our Principle depends nowhere upon its adoption. Nevertheless lest we otherwise appear to be craven at what is perhaps the first time in history that there is a scientific intimation of immortality—or at least a nonsubjective intimation—we shall later (in Section III below), when discussing the dynamics of procreation, venture to adopt this third view *in good faith* in order to note its consequences. One consequence, curiously enough, will be the inferential disclosure that our colleagues in a certain field are tacitly assuming an immortality of the ego in their thinking (and perhaps they are right about it). By thus frankly facing this profound philosophical question, we at least show that we are aware of its presence and that we are not deterred from discussing it from a fear of present-day scientific conventional beliefs that death ends *all.* To the scientist, perhaps death does, and perhaps death does not, end *all;* and perhaps the possibility of continuance of even so sheer and otiose a thing as a *point* may be a source of comfort to Joe Doakes during his dark hours.

There are, however, two risks that attach to a dabbling with this third view. The first is that the careless thinker may infer that the adoption of this third view is necessary for a demonstration of the Principle of Least Effort. A careful inspection of our argument will show that this is by no means true, since the assumption of a fixed but unpredictable duration of a life will serve our purposes equally well.

---

dence of any material birth donum, and we refuse to postulate a special kind of energy. Moreover, in the case of accidental death there is no evidence of a discharge of an enormous amount of remaining physical energy. We mention this further possibility, lest we seem to ignore it.

The second risk of viewing the *eternity* of an identity-point as an optional assumption is that the careless critic may erroneously conclude that our assumption of the *existence* of an identity-point is also equally optional, which is far from being the case. On the contrary, our assumption of the existence of an identity-point as the origin of a frame of reference is a logical necessity, for reasons that we shall again repeat lest they escape our memory.

E. On the Logical Need for Identity-Points

In our preceding pages we have postulated an identity-point, or ego, for an organism. Although this postulate is not new to human thinking, it nevertheless may not be particularly palatable to those physical scientists who are unfamiliar with the major questions of their fields. Hence before proceeding further with our postulate let us discuss certain logical aspects of it, as we attempt to show that it is a logical necessity for physics quite as much as it is for biosocial dynamics.

To show that the postulate of an identity-point for an organism is a logical necessity in the light of physical law, we need only to repeat what we have already said: an organism will at once collapse in quest of a gravitational and electromagnetic equilibrium unless there is something to prevent it from so doing. Hence when a physicist tells his students that "all matter-energy always everywhere seeks equilibrium," the good man is obviously in error, or he would never be alive to tell the tale. If he qualifies his generalization by adding, "except under the conditions of an organism," he faces the scientific question of disclosing just what "the conditions of an organism" are. Yet as soon as he investigates by scientific methods the physical conditions of organic life, he thereby enters the special physical field that we are calling *biosocial dynamics* (for in dichotomizing between physical science and biosocial dynamics we are only for convenience of exposition deferring to a traditional bias).

With an assumed unity of nature and a continuity of natural law, the problem of an organism is as much a physical problem in the traditional sense as it is the problem of any other field;[4] after all, all the empiric data in this book are physical data which, in the light of the null hypothesis, are empiric physical laws, since they refer to physical manifestations in time-space. The postulate of an organism's identity-point is logically necessary for us if an organism is not to collapse immediately according to traditional physical law; but the postulate is also logically necessary for physical law, if the general physical principles are not to collapse immediately before the organism. An organism is just as important a part of the universe as anything else, as far as one knows; indeed, for all we can see to the contrary, the final unifying principle of the universe may only be disclosable by studying the phenomena of human speech, or human dreams, which, after all, represent a manner of behavior of the matter of this planet, solar system, galaxy, and so on.

In the solution of most of the everyday problems of physics, the physicist can ignore the ultimate philosophical problem of identity-points. Nevertheless, in the case of an organism, which can come into being, live, and go out of being within the space of an observably short time, and which moves both with reference to its environment and in reference to its own needs, and which often radically alters itself both formally and functionally—then the scientist may ask with propriety what the "itself" of an organism is that thus behaves with a continuity of systematic action but without a continuity of material parts. Indeed, the serious scientist in the field can scarcely evade this very question.

II. THE BIOSOCIAL POPULATION OF ORGANISMS

It is a commonplace that an organism, either individually or in cooperation with others, produces further organisms: the phenomenon of procreation. In so doing the organism gives rise to a population of organisms. In the present section we shall inquire into the size of this population, and into the economy of its functional organization.

We shall begin by saying that the *N* number of different organisms that are alive on the earth at any time constitute the *biosocial population.* Our first step is to inquire into the determinants of the size of *N.*

A. The Fixed *N* Number of Different Organisms in the Biosocial Population

When we inquire into the *N* number of organisms that are alive on the planet at any one time we again encounter a knotty philosophical problem that may be inspected at various levels of profundity depending upon the inquirer's predilection. As far as our own demonstration of the Principle of Least Effort is concerned we shall assume that *N* is somehow fixed, at least at an *upper limit* beyond which it is physically impossible to increase *N.* This assumption of a fixed upper limit of *N,* which is quite in accord with current beliefs, will suffice completely for our entire demonstration. Moreover, the assumption is made without any reference to the Principle of Least Effort.

Nevertheless (1) since the *N* number of extant organisms is the result of a balance between the births and deaths of organisms, and (2) since the birth of organisms is a direct result of the procreational activity of the organisms whose entire behavior is theoretically subject to *least effort,* and (3) since deaths eventuate at least in part from competitive social activity, which is also subject to *least effort,* it therefore follows theoretically (4) that *N* must be somehow fixed—and can be by no means an independent maximum or minimum lest it thereby introduce a second superlative that will render our problem meaningless and indeterminate. One may, therefore, view the fixedness of *N* both with and without reference to the Principle of Least Effort.

Although the fixedness of *N* is necessary if life is subject to the minimizing of effort, there is a school of thought dating at least as far back as T. R. Malthus[5] that believes that *N* is someway or another a maximum in the sense that "organisms produce as many offspring as possible." It is questionable whether this view is tenable in the light of the observations of biologists of the rate of population increase of fruit flies.[6] But be that as it may, before we discuss the logical implications of our own view that *N* is fixed, we shall first point out the absurdity of the quasi Malthusian view that *N* is a maximum.*

1. The Absurdity of N as a Maximum (i.e., "The Production of as Many Organisms as Possible"). If the *N* number of different organisms alive on the planet were a maximum in the sense that there should be as many different organisms alive as possible, and if this maximizing of *N* were to be accomplished by procreation, then every act of every organism would be directed solely towards increasing the size of *N*.

We have defined an organism as a physical system that metabolizes matter-energy in order to preserve itself as a continual system from a final equilibrium with its environment. Wherever there is a difference in energy gradients in a situation, there a machine can run and there presumably an organism can exist. If *N* is a maximum, the biosocial population would be seeking out every such situation in order to exploit its possibilities for increasing the size of *N*. The comparative mechanical wastefulness of an organism would be a matter of indifference to a biosocial population that maximizes *N* and therefore cannot minimize work. On the other hand, a maximizing of *N* would undeniably reduce the size of every organic machine to the limit permissible under quantum mechanics so that as many organisms as possible could survive on the degradation of energy. In this connection it is worth remarking that a great deal of energy is degraded on earth without the observable presence of organic action.

In the job of procuring work from matter-energy under a maximizing of *N*, the biosocial population would be under no obligation to restrict its activities to the erstwhile principles of prenuclear physics when matter was assumed to be nontransmutable. Instead, the population could "smash atoms"—even as human organisms have recently succeeded in doing—and utilize atomic energy for the purpose of increasing the size of *N*. In that case, as *N* increased ever more, the earth would begin to glow, like the sun, and diminish in size as its atomic energy was dissipated into space via organic process, until eventually the earth would cease to exist as a molecular mass.

For such is the destruction that would eventuate if *N* were a maximum —since that is what a maximum means in physics: the reduction of something to an extreme in terms of the constants of matter-energy and of time-space.

But the present discussion of the absurdity of *N* as a maximum—and presumably its absurdity is by now apparent—has at least two other didactic values. The first (1) of these didactic values is that *N*, even though it is fixed, can be fixed at such a large size, in relation to a given mass, that the mass will begin to disintegrate atomically and radiate light; hence the radiation of light from large masses of matter such as the sun and other stars may have its primary cause in life process. The second (2) didactic

* *N* cannot be a minimum in the sense of representing as few offspring as possible, for then *N* would have zero as a limit and life would vanish.

value of our present discussion is that according to our definition of an organism, organic form is relative to the situation, with the result that no particular form or kind of matter-energy is necessary for an organism; on the contrary, whatever form permits the organism to preserve itself with least effort is for that organism the optimal form, whether the form is solid, liquid, or gaseous, or any combination of the same.*

2. *N as Fixed.* But if N is neither a minimum nor a maximum, it must somehow be fixed if only as an upper limit. Although its manner of being fixed is a matter of complete irrelevance to the argument here, as long as N is very, very large, nevertheless we shall discuss two possible ways of fixing N, if only for their didactic value in impressing upon us what the effect is of having a fixed N.

In the first place, N could be fixed at an arbitrary number, say 10 to the 50th power, which would be the N number of different organisms alive on the planet at any given moment, no matter what happens.

Or N could be fixed, say, as a constant ratio with something else that is fixed. For example, it might be that the N number of different organisms alive on a given m mass of matter at a given time would be proportionate to the mass, or $N/m = C$. Life would multiply and die accordingly![7]

Regardless of the precise determinants of N, it is only human for us all to ask how the biosocial population can "know" what the size of N is so that it can limit its procreation correctly. Although we cannot answer this question, we can at least match it with other questions that we all seem to accept unanswered. Thus, how does the apple "know" what its gravitational attraction with the earth is, as it falls? And yet the apple presumably solves the problem correctly. How does the oak log "know" how to become oxidized in the fireplace as it burns? And yet it does so. How does earth "know" how large the N number of organisms should be in terms of which it organizes its material surface?

B. Fixed *N* and the Origin of Species

As soon as we conclude that the N number of different organisms of the biosocial population is fixed, the problem of the evolution of species becomes simplified, since we need now only to inquire into the economically most favorable forms and situations on our planet for our N organisms to possess if they are to survive with least effort. In discussing this problem, the argu-

* In our discussion of biosocial principles we are restricting our principles to no particular historic form of organisms, any more than in our discussion of the principles of human speech we are restricting our principles to any particular historic tongue. On the contrary, though we disclosed our principles of speech from actual cases, the principles themselves, if correct, should be found in operation in any human speech. By the same token our Principle of Least Effort, if correct, will apply to every organic identity-point throughout time-space. For we have no reason to suppose that life is unique to this planet; nor may we believe that life is an "afterthought of God" or "a by-product of physical process" (whatever those verbalisms may mean to those who use them). Instead we may suspect that the principles of living process are inherent in the "original plan" of matter-energy in time-space.

ment of our entire preceding chapter will be assumed as valid. Thus there will not only be an economy in small size (the Law of Abbreviation); there will also be an economy of a small variety, or diversity, of *n* different tools (the Law of Diminishing Returns, with the Principles of Economical Versatility, Permutability and Specialization).

In saying that the *N* organisms of the earth will theoretically develop the easiest forms of survival, we note that what the "easiest forms" are at a given time will depend not only upon the actual physical conditions at the time but also upon the size of *N*. Thus if *N* is so small that there is enough of the most easily metabolizable kind of matter-energy to supply their daily needs, then all *N* organisms will theoretically use this one kind of material, and will develop the same easiest physical system for metabolizing it, and will survive forever—or at least as long as the food supply lasts.

On the other hand, if *N* is so large that there is not enough of the easiest kind of metabolizable matter-energy to supply the daily needs of all organisms, then some will have to content themselves with kinds of matter-energy that are less easily metabolizable, with the result that all organisms will be *competing* with one another either to get or to keep the most easily metabolizable kind of matter-energy for food. Assuming now that *N* is very large, let us inspect some of the consequences of this competition.

1. Origin of Different Classes (or Types, or "Species") of Organisms. If there is not enough of a given most easily metabolizable *a* kind of matter-energy to supply all *N* organisms, then some will have to content themselves with a next most easily metabolizable *b* kind of matter-energy. If this second *b* kind does not suffice to supply the survival needs of the remaining organisms, then they will have to resort to the third most easy *c* kind, or the fourth *d* kind . . . until they reach the *z* kind of metabolizable matter-energy which, we shall assume, suffices to provide food for the last and *N*th organism. Thereafter matter-energy continues its flow towards entropy without further organic molestation.

Since all *N* organisms are competing for the easiest kind of food, it follows that that type of physical organic system which handles the *a* food with the greatest mechanical efficiency (and similarly solves the problem of defending its system most efficiently against aggressors) will enjoy the most easily metabolizable *a* kind of matter-energy.

Let us dwell further upon the particulars of the above point. We have said that the *a* easiest kind of metabolizable matter-energy will be preempted by the *a* class of most efficient organisms. Incidentally, the number of different organisms in the *a* class will be determined both by the amount of the *a* kind of matter-energy available and by the efficiency of organization of the *a* organisms.

Let us now assume that the *a* class of matter-energy is metabolized by organisms of two different kinds of organization, a_1 and a_2, with the former more efficient than the latter. In that case, under the drive of competition for this most favored position, the a_2 type of organization will tend to become extinct, either because the offspring of a_1 will supplant it, or because other organisms will adopt the a_1 manner of organization, or both. In this fashion the *a* class of organisms becomes a pure kind, or type, or "species," of organism.*

This argument about the purification of the *a* class, or type, or "species," of organism will obviously apply also to the remaining organisms that feed on matter from *b* through *z*. In this fashion, there will emerge *z* different pure types, or "species," of organization which preserve their *z* different kinds of organization as long as the *z* different particular kinds of matter-energy are available, and as long as all other relevant conditions remain constant.

In summary then, if matter-energy varies in respect of its metabolizable energy value in a given region, then the organisms in that region will also tend to vary in their manner of organization insofar as they use different kinds of matter-energy. For this reason, different mechanical and chemical types, or "species" of organisms will arise quite automatically as a result of the Principle of Least Effort.†

2. The Effect of Differences in Efficiency of Organic Organization. We have said in the above section that the *N* organisms of the biosocial population can be classified and ranked from *a* to *z* according to the decreasing "efficiency" of their organization. What is to be understood under the term "efficiency" and what is its objective manifestation?

By way of clarification, let us take the case of two factories, *A* and *B*, that produce the same kind and amounts of goods during a given interval, but which use different grades of fuel with different heat values; the *A* factory uses the fuel with the greater amount of available energy per ton, whereas the *B* factory uses the fuel with lesser heat value. Therefore the *B* factory, to produce the given goods at the given rate, will have to consume a greater amount of fuel. Hence the comparative masses of materials consumed per interval of time can be indicative of comparative efficiency in the following sense: the greater the mass, the less the efficiency, provided that the output is the same.

Taking momentary leave of the above factories and turning to the case of organisms, we can understand how, as a general tendency, the larger organisms may be the comparatively less efficient ones, if we assume that all organisms have the same output in the sense of keeping body and soul together. One reason for this inverse relationship between comparative size and comparative efficiency in the organism is that a greater amount of the less nutritive fuel will be in transit through the less efficient organism at any moment; and since this fuel in transit is a part of the organism—just as the coal pile and the coal in the furnace and the steam in the pipes

---

* It makes no difference to our argument whether the most efficient design is the result of "chance," or of direct deliberation on the part of the organism in question. Moreover, only one organism needs to make the discovery, provided that it can maintain itself and propagate its kind.

† We remember that we are constructing a hypothesis on the basis of the Principle of Least Effort to be tested empirically. The presence of biological species on earth is confirmative of our hypothesis.

are all parts of the factory—the mass of the organism will be greater, and to some extent its size, because of the economy of close packing discussed in previous chapters.

But there is also another criterion of comparative efficiency: *the comparative cost of processing*. For we remember that the energy-value of any fuel to a given organism depends upon the comparative amount of work the organism must expend in order to make a given amount of energy available. This consideration brings up the question of processing: the utilization of a less valuable fuel by a more efficient processing. Let us inspect this question from the viewpoint of the organism's own survival needs.

If we view organisms as manufacturing plants, we may suspect that, with a given kind of fuel, the organism that survives by using fewer *kinds* of mechanical processes—or mechanical operations—in procuring work from the fuel tends to be the more efficient physical system, subject to the condition of performing the given jobs. The reason is that in the problem of maintaining an industrial plant, there is an economy in diminishing the diversity of mechanical processes, or operations.* In short, it is the economy of minimizing the *n* different *kinds* of physical tools, or operations, that produce a given effect: the *n* minimum.

Yet when we speak of minimizing the *n* different kinds of mechanical operations that produce a given effect, we are echoing our argument of Chapter Five in connection with the Tool Analogy in which, with *n* different kinds of tools (i.e., kinds of material organizations) that perform a given *m* different kinds of responses, *n* is minimized. Since the entire discussion of the Tool Analogy, and notably the discussion of Chapter Five, is applicable to the present problem of the comparative efficiency of organisms, we may suspect that in the case of different kinds of organisms of the same size, those kinds of organisms that have the smaller *n* different kinds of mechanical processes, or operations, or tools, may also be the more efficient organisms; and if we say that an organism's system becomes comparatively more simple and less complex as its *n* decreases, then we may say that the comparative simplicity of organization of an organism may be a criterion of the comparative efficiency of its organization.

In short, a comparatively small size and a comparative simplicity of organization may be criteria of a comparatively efficient organic organization, provided that the output is the same (which we assume is always the case with all organisms whose only task is to survive). The lucky organisms in the flow of matter-energy, then, tend to be those that are small and simply structured. The less lucky organisms tend to be the larger ones of more complex structure who, in being less successful in the competition for the easiest jobs, have been forced to adopt a larger size and a larger *n* struc-

---

* This is the familiar economy of reducing the number of different stock patterns produced, and the diversity of materials going into them, and the diversity of tools that are used in producing them (cf. the discussion of the *n* minimum in Chapter Five).

ture in order to survive.* Small size and simple organization do not need to go together invariably, although they will tend to do so for reasons discussed in Chapter Five.

In summary we may say, therefore, that as matter-energy flows towards entropy, it offers metabolistic opportunities to the biosocial population of *N* organisms. These organisms all compete for the easiest, and therefore the most favorable opportunities in the flow—that is, they compete for the opportunities that permit of the smallest size, or, in the case of equivalent sizes, that permit of the simplest organization. The losers in the competition for survival are "forced" into the less favorable opportunities in the flow and therefore into the larger and more complex organizations.

3. Variable Conditions in the "Flow" towards Entropy. In the above argument we have assumed that the content and the tempo of the flow of matter-energy towards entropy is constant, with the result that the material conditions on the earth at one moment will be the same as at any subsequent moment. Under such rigidly fixed environmental conditions, the *N* organisms, after having obtained a maximum efficiency of organization in their respective *a, b, . . . z* situations, would continue to survive thus into the indefinite future, since there would be no reason for their death (death, after all, is not a biological necessity †).

If we now introduce the concept of a physical variability of the environment, such as will attend upon climatic changes, then our *N* organisms will have to build up contingency reserves to insure themselves against environmental risks, as explained in our previous chapter. The need for these contingency reserves will add to the size and complexity of the organic structure of all organisms in direct relationship to the variability or apparent capriciousness of the food supply. Once again, therefore, the comparative size and complexity of an organism's structure will be an indication of its comparative success in the biosocial competition for a most easy survival. Hence under the conditions of environmental variability, as we proceed down the line from the *a* kind of organisms to the *z* kind, we pass from the smallest and simplest to the largest and most complex.

C. The Evolution of Species

As soon as we introduce the concept of variability in the environment, then all the different kinds of organisms will obviously be subject to the need for changes in their forms-functions. In the present pages let us note that the organisms will change, or *mutate,* not merely as individuals, as we may expect from our argument in the preceding chapter—they will also

---

* In our previous chapter we showed the economy of a small size and a small *n* number of different tools. Unsuccessful competition, on the other hand, forces an increase in size and in *n*. As soon as an organism is relieved from competition, it tends to simplify its organizaion (e.g., "biological degeneracy"; a sinecure makes a person "go to seed").

† The fact that the above organisms would theoretically become intellectually increasingly more rigid (as defined in our previous chapter) would be a matter of indifference, since they would be living in a dynamically invariant environment in which an intellectual rigidity would offer no handicap.

mutate as species. Indeed it is this second kind of mutation—the mutation, or evolution, of species—that will be our present chief concern, as we attempt to show why species forms will change as such.

To prepare for our more detailed argument, let us first state our question of species mutation in homely human occupational terms.* For example, let us take the particular occupational type that is today known in the United States as carpenters. Although the mechanical equipment of present-day carpenters differs radically from that of the carpenters of 150 years ago, nevertheless the evolution of the equipment during the 150 intervening years has been orderly in the sense that the new and more economical mechanisms have been adopted by the entire occupational type as they became available. During those years old carpenters died and new carpenters entered the trade; yet the occupational type, or "species," of carpenters continued to evolve in terms of its tools.

But when we say that the new and more economical mechanisms were adopted as soon as they became available, we must hasten to add that that was only a general tendency. More accurately stated, those carpenters who did adopt the more economical innovations had the economic advantage over those who did not. With this economic advantage, the innovators not only influenced all the newcomers in the trade to adopt the new innovations, they also forced the oldtimers either to conform or to get out. In this fashion the occupational type, or "species," kept purifying itself in the course of its evolution—just as in the case of the *a* species that we discussed previously—with the result that all carpenters tended to use the same kinds of tools.

Of course there may happen to be some outlying districts where (1) conditions are peculiarly unfavorable for the adoption of a given innovation (for example, there may be a lack of necessary water power or electricity), or where (2) the persons may be so isolated that they do not learn of the innovation, while the innovators in turn do not learn of them. In that case the older form of the occupational type, or "species," will persist and evolve in its own way without adopting the innovation. In that fashion the original *x genus* of the carpentry trade will have broken into two *y species,* by definition.

In the above fashion, as a result of mutations which may or may not be shared by all, a given generic type of organization may continue as a single type, or it may develop into two or more subtypes, or species, which may or may not include the original type, or species, from which the others mutated.

By the same token a given occupational type or species may become extinct because its jobs are performed more efficiently by some other type of occupation. Thus, for example, the occupational type of *galley slave* has become extinct today as far as I know. Hence when we view the *a, b, . . . z* types, or species, of organic organization, we may suspect that some are

* This concept of human occupations will be further elaborated in Part Two, Chapters Nine to Eleven, with confirmatory empiric data which, in turn, will retroactively support our present theory of the evolution of species.

comparatively older types, and that some are comparatively newer or younger types, in the light of the recency of their distinctive mutations.

Moreover, if we remember that as we proceed from the *a* species to the *z* species we proceed from the less variably situated to the more variably situated, it follows that we are simultaneously proceeding from the older types to the newer types. Or, stated in terms of rates of change, we may say that as we proceed down the line from the smallest, simplest, and most stable *a* organisms to the largest, most complex, and most unstable *z* organisms, we pass from those whose *rate of mutation* tends to be slow, to those whose rate of mutation tends to be fast (*vide infra*).

1. Food Chains. Let us momentarily return to our argument about the flow of matter-energy towards entropy in which the *N* organisms of the bio-social population survive with least effort by preëmpting for themselves the most favorable metabolistic opportunities in the flow whose matter-energy they ingest, metabolize, and excrete. In thus surviving from the flow, the *N* organisms do not constitute quasi islands about which the matter-energy flows. Instead, the organisms are a part of the flow, in a literal sense; their ingestion, metabolism, and excretion, as well as all their tools, are a part of the flow. Except for their identity-points, or egos, all organisms *are* matter-energy in transit towards degradation.

In view of the above, it is evident that if each of the *N* organisms is competing for the easiest metabolizable matter-energy without any regard for the well-being of others unless the well-being of the others also saves work for itself, then each organism will feed upon the easiest metabolizable food that it can get, regardless of whether the food in question is inanimate matter, or the excrement of other organisms, or the living or dead bodies of other organisms—whichever is the easiest according to the Principle of Least Effort. In this fashion the traditional *food chains* of biology can arise,[8] in which some species ingest inanimate inorganic matter-energy, while others, like a maggot, feed on excrement or carrion, and while still others, like a toad swallowing a live fly, consume the living bodies of organisms.

Yet in introducing this additional concept of food chains, we are by no means faced by the need of modifying any of the conclusions of the preceding pages, either in respect of the emergence and evolution of "occupational" genera and species, or in respect of the general correlation between the size, mass, complexity, and inefficiency of organisms.

On the other hand, by introducing the concept of food chains, we do introduce an additional factor of risk. For, in general, when the organisms of a given type, *A*, through their excrement or bodies provide the food for organisms of type, *B*, then the organisms of type, *B*, in addition to their own systematic risks, will also have the risks that threaten the organisms whose bodies or excrement supply food. For example, if a given group of persons eat corn, beans, and pork, then in addition to their own risks, they will be subject to the risks that attend corn, beans, and pigs.

Therefore as one proceeds down the food chains from the most favorably situated *a* organisms to the least favorably situated *z* organisms, one proceeds on the whole in the direction of rapidly accumulating survival risks, as well as in the direction of increasing size and complexity. *At the same time one also proceeds, as we shall soon see, in the direction of a faster rate of evolutionary change.** This concept of a faster rate of evolutionary change leads to the hypothesis of the *number-size-area relationship* of organisms, the validity of which can be tested empirically.

2. *The Number-Size-Area Relationship of Organisms.* The fact that food chains exist on what is essentially the two-dimensional surface of the earth will have interesting implications for (a) the number-size relationship of our N different organisms and their z different species, as well as for (b) the dispersion of the above $a, b, \ldots z$ different species, as we shall now see in detail. Although our argument will be cast in terms of a two-dimensional surface, the argument will apply equally well to a stratum on the earth's surface with a third dimension.

a. The number-size relationship of organisms. We have stated that organisms tend to become ever larger and more complex as they are situated ever farther down from a towards z in the flow of matter-energy towards degradation. Since the smaller and simpler organisms are the luckier ones, it is inevitable that the larger and more complex organisms will be crowding in on them in competition for their more fortunate situations in life. For this reason we should imagine that the flow of matter-energy is "closely packed" with competing organisms. This "close packing" of the flow with organisms of varying sizes and complexity represents an interesting population problem, particularly when we remember that the flow is occurring on a two-dimensional surface, and therefore will be subject to all the properties which are inherent in a two-dimensional surface and which will impose their restrictions upon the n number of different organisms of like s size.

For if organisms do vary in size, and if the two-dimensional flow is closely packed with organisms that are striving to achieve an ever smaller size, then the n number of different organisms of like (linear) s size cannot be larger than the square of s; or: $n \cdot s^2 \leqq C$. Of course, this is taking s as a linear dimension of the organism. If we view the size of an organism as the a area it occupies on the earth's surface, then the exponent of the a-area-size becomes 1 (or $n \cdot a \leqq C$).

This equation represents at best an ultimate limit which can be attained only if all organisms are organized with an equivalent efficiency, and if there is no other factor than area that is present in the flow. Since we have seen, however, that the energy of the flow is becoming ever more degraded as it flows, and that organisms must therefore become ever larger and more

---

* The same argument applies if a given organism, like man, depends for its food upon the existence of two or more other kinds of organisms. Obviously there is both a competition and a co-operation in the biosocial population (i.e., not only Charles Hobbs' "*bellum omnium contra omnes*" but also and simultaneously an *amicitia omnium cum omnibus,* if we may turn a Latin phrase). The topic of inter-species equilibrium has been discussed by V. Volterra, V. H. Kostitzin, A. J. Lotka, and others to whose writings we refer.[9] In Part Two of this book will be found a discussion of human society as a case of intra-species equilibrium.

complex in order to survive on the increasingly degraded fuel, it follows that the *n* number of different organisms like *s* size will tend to be proportionate to something more than the square of *s*; or

$$n \cdot s^{2+b} = C.$$

This is true because the ratio of size to a given amount of food becomes greater as the energy of the food becomes more degraded.*

Keeping in mind this last equation ($n \cdot s^{2+b} = C$), and inspecting the different types, or species, of closely crowded organisms from *a* through *z*, we can see how, as a general tendency, the number of different organisms will fall off at a rate that is something faster than the square of their *s* sizes (provided that there is no compensatory factor to offset *b*—and we are able to find none). In other words, as we pass from the n_a number of different organisms of size s_a of the *a* type, or "species," to the n_z number of different organisms of size s_z of the *z* type, or "species," of organisms, we shall be passing on the whole from organisms that tend to have a large *n* number and a small *s* size, to those of an *ever* smaller *n* number and an *ever* larger *s* size, according to our above argument.

For example, if an area of jungle in Africa is closely packed with life, there will probably be more organisms of the size of mosquitoes than of elephants. Naturally we are dealing with dynamic situations.

b. The "area of dispersion" of species. Let us momentarily interrupt our analysis of the *n* number of different organisms of like *s* size while we inspect the regional areas they inhabit. To this end we shall introduce the two terms *homogeneous region* and *heterogeneous region*. A *homogeneous region* is one in which the chemical and physical conditions are the same as far as life is concerned. A *heterogeneous region* is one where these conditions are different.

Now if the region is *homogeneous* and covers sufficient area for all the *N* organisms to survive, then the distributions of the *a, b, . . . z* species will be about the same throughout the entire homogeneous region.† Perhaps the easiest way to visualize this entire relationship is to imagine a vast region of the ocean of like chemical content and physically similar in other respects. If we imagine that the most favored *a* organisms are living in the top layer of the surface, with successive closely packed layers of *b, c, . . . z* organisms underneath, each living off the bodies and excrement of the species above, then we note the appropriateness of the relationship, $n \cdot s^{2+b} = C$, both for the *N* different organisms and for the *a, b, . . . z* different species. We also note how the *a* organisms are immediately dependent upon purely physical givens, whereas the successive species underneath are dependent not only upon physical givens but also upon the biological givens and alterations above (we might call it a "risk chain").

* Again, if we take the size of the organism as its *a*-area-size, then the equation becomes $n \cdot a^{1+c} = C$, in which $1 + c$ equals one-half of $2 + b$. The presence of this small constant, *c* (or *b*), indicates that work, not space, is minimized.

† This is a cardinal principle of paleontology originally disclosed many years ago by William Smith.

When we turn now to a large *heterogeneous region* we can see how this region, though heterogeneous as a whole, will consist of small *homogeneous areas* of various sizes. In other words, we do not say that a heterogeneous region is one in which from point to point there are significant differences in physical and chemical conditions. Instead a heterogeneous region, as far as life is concerned, may be viewed as consisting of subsidiary homogeneous districts, or *areas,* of varying sizes.

Within each contiguous *homogeneous area* of a heterogeneous region, the distributions of species and of their populations of organisms will be the same as that in a homogeneous region described above.

But now let us note one thing: if instead of beginning with an area and inquiring into its various species, we begin with a number of different species at a given point and inquire into their respective *areas of dispersion,* we come upon an interesting theoretical correlation between the sizes and complexity of species on the one hand, and their areas of dispersion on the other.

For when we say that a given area is homogeneous for a given kind of organism, we do not mean that the physical conditions are precisely the same in all respects throughout the area. Instead, we mean that the physical conditions are the same as far as the kind of organism in question is concerned. For example, if there are two kinds of organisms, *A* and *B,* that live in the sea, and if *A* can survive in temperatures from 40° to 80° Fahrenheit, whereas *B* can survive only between 50° and 60°, then *A* can survive wherever *B* can, though *B* can survive only in those restricted areas of *A*'s domain where the temperature is never less than 50° nor greater than 60°. If there is no further difference between the needs of the two, then in a sea of various surface temperatures the more versatile *A* species will tend to have a wider *area of dispersion* than the more specialized *B* species.*

If we consider now the dispersion of the entire concatenation of food chains scattered over a large heterogeneous region, we can suspect theoretically that the smaller, older, simpler, more versatile types, or "species," of organisms will have proportionately larger areas of dispersion than the larger, younger, more complex, and more specialized organisms.[10] This will be the case because environmental risks accumulate in direct proportion to the organism's lack of success in biosocial competition. Because of these cumulative greater risks, the less successful organisms will have to specialize more in their operations and, in specializing more, they will be more dependent upon the particular conditions of the environment to which they have become specialized.

Now let us ask whether the *a* area of dispersion of a given species is in any way connected with the *s* size of its organisms. Upon reflection it would seem that as an organism becomes larger and concomitantly more specialized in structure and needs, its area will decrease proportionately, so that we might say that the *a* area dispersion of a given species of *s* physical size will be proportionate to $a \cdot s^{2+b}$. For, as an organism's physical size and

* We remember our erstwhile argument (Chapter Five) on the comparative tolerance of tools.

specialization increases, its risks increase proportionately, and therefore also its likelihood of extinction during changing environmental conditions.

As the area of dispersion of a given organism increases, its likelihood of encountering adverse conditions that will harm or exterminate it will increase proportionately. But the smaller, simpler, and more versatile organisms will be proportionately better off than the larger, more complex, and more specialized organisms, both in being less affected by environmental changes, and in being better able to cope with them. Hence we may expect that the species whose organisms are of smaller size and therefore are less specialized (or more versatile) will have the larger areas of dispersal, and proportionately so (or $a \cdot s^{2+b} = C$).

This preceding equation means that the earth's life-sustaining surface will be populated by comparatively few different species of small physical size yet of a large population size with a wide area of dispersion, and by an increasing number of species of increasing physical size but of decreasing population size with a decreasing area of dispersion.

The relationship becomes somewhat easier to envisage if we remember that environmental conditions are continually changing on the earth's surface, and that the larger and more specialized organisms will have to *mutate at a faster rate* to adjust themselves to changing "local" conditions. As they become specialized to new local conditions, they become a new "local" species. Of course all species are adjusted to the peculiarities of their "local" environment. The point is that as a species becomes larger and more complex in form, it becomes localized in a proportionately smaller area.

Because of this localizing factor, we may say that the a area of dispersion of a given species of s physical size (linear dimension) will be inversely proportionate to s^{2+b}; or

$$a \cdot s^{2+b} = C$$

Hence both the n number of different organisms of a given species at a given time, as well as the a area of their dispersion, will be inversely proportionate to something more than the square of the organism's s size.

If we take the next step and inquire into the n number of a areas of dispersion of the same size—that is, if we inquire into the n number of different species that have a areas of dispersion of the same size—then we may no longer construe the size of an organism as a linear dimension, but instead we must view it as an area. In that case the above exponent, $2 + b$, becomes $1 + c$ in all of our above equations, and the n_a number of different species that have the same sized a areas of dispersion will be:

$$n_a \cdot a^{1+c} = C$$

We remember at this point our previous argument that the exponent $1 + c$ is one-half of $2 + b$; we are merely stating organic size now in two dimensions instead of one.*

* We remember that in cutting a surface into areas, the number of areas of a given size is inversely proportionate to the areas' sizes.

Hence as matter-energy becomes degraded on the earth's surface partly via food chains, the species diversity becomes greater as one proceeds down the food chains. As to the species diversity of the earth's surface, there are a few large areas of small, versatile, and older organisms, and an increasing number (by the $1 + c$ power) of smaller areas of larger, more specialized, and newer organisms. (Our entire argument clearly depends upon the validity of assuming a complete positive correlation between an organism's size, its n number of different kinds of tools, and the comparative degree of its specialization.)

3. The Genera-Species Relationship. In the preceding pages we have studied theoretically the distribution of the areas of dispersion of different species on the earth's surface at any one moment of measurement. In other words, we viewed the biosocial population as a steady state. We noted in closing that the n_a number of different species of the same sized a area of dispersion will theoretically follow the equation:

$$n_a \cdot a^{1+c} = C$$

We shall now extend our inquiry to cover a long interval of time during which more or less radical physical changes occur on the earth's surface and necessitate more or less radical alterations, or *mutations,* on the part of the different species. From now on we are discussing problems of dynamics. For the sake of giving direction to our ensuing discussion we shall ask the following questions: (1) which species are most likely to have to mutate (i.e., which species will have the faster *rate of innovation*); (2) which species are most likely to become extinct in the process (i.e., which species will have the faster *rate of extinction*); and (3) most important of all, which species are most likely to cast, or "throw," new species in order to take the place of the species that become extinct; for we assume that the N number of different organisms remains fixed, and that the extinction of the organisms of one species may entail at times the "throw" of new species.

As to the first two questions, which refer to the comparative *rates* of *innovation* and of *extinction,* it seems plausible that as the size and complexity of a class of organisms increases, they tend to become more vulnerable in the face of change (though a freakish environmental change may be propitious to a highly specialized species). Hence we may expect theoretically that the rates of innovation and of extinction will be directly proportionate to an organism's size and complexity. Since these species of organisms have proportionately smaller areas of dispersion, we may also say that as the area of dispersion decreases, the rates of innovation and extinction increase proportionately. The tendency, therefore, of species to mutate and to become extinct is localized. In localities of small area of dispersion we may expect to find new or younger species.

On the other hand, the smaller, simpler, more versatile, and less specialized organisms, whose areas of dispersion are large, will have both a slower rate of innovation and also a slower rate of extinction—and proportionately so. These will be the proportionately more conservative species whose forms will tend to be the comparatively older.

Granting now that changes of various kinds and intensities are continually occurring on the earth's surface, and that the extinction of species is continually occurring among the specialized species of small areas of dispersion, let us now ask which of the remaining species are likely to mutate locally and cast or "throw" a new species to take the place of the species that has become extinct. This question has two parts, because the successful casting of a new species to take the place of an extinct species will depend, *first,* upon having the opportunity to cast a replenishing species at all and, *second,* upon the capacity to cast a new species that will succeed in the new environmental conditions where the extinct species has failed.

In regard to, *first,* the opportunity for casting a new species at all, it is evident that those species that have members in the area where a given species has become extinct will have the opportunity for casting a new species to take its place. From this it follows that *those species that have the widest areas of dispersion will probably have the most opportunities for casting a new species,* and in general the probable opportunities for casting a new species by a given species will be directly proportionate to its area of dispersion. Since the n_a number of different species of like sized a area of dispersion is inversely proportionate to a^{1+c} (or, $n_a \cdot a^{1-c} = C$), it follows that over a given long interval of time, the various species of the biosocial population will probably have opportunities, according to their above areas of dispersion, to cast new species.

But if we now ask, *second,* which species are most likely to be successful in casting new species, then we may suspect on the basis of our entire argument of the present and preceding chapters, that the smaller, more versatile, and less specialized species of wider areas of dispersal will probably be the more successful in casting enduring new species. Hence, in general, the probable success of casting a new species will increase in direct proportion to what in the last analysis is the area of dispersion of the casting species. On this count also, the number of new species that survive will be distributed, in the light of the area sizes of their parent species, according to the equation, $n_a \cdot a^{1+c} = C$.

If we now combine the above two arguments and inquire both into the probable opportunities for casting new species and into the probable success of the venture, then, in terms of the n_a number of different casting species of like a size, the equation is:

$$n_a \cdot a^{1+c} = C$$

This equation tells us the probable progenitors of new species in terms of the n_a number of different a areas of dispersion of like size.

To visualize the significance of the above equation for the evolution of new species, let us in our mind's eye imagine that we make a study of the actual different species and their respective areas of dispersal over a large heterogeneous region. But instead of terming them different species, let us call them different *genera,* since we shall return many, many, many millions of years later to the same region in order to see how many different species have been "thrown" during the intervening period by our erstwhile genera.

If our above theory be correct, then when we return at the end of the long period of time we shall find that the x_g number of different *genera* that have the same y_s number of different species will follow the equation:

$$x_g \cdot y_s^{1+c} = C$$

and that this equation will also apply to the respective areas of dispersion of the genera and species in question.

Moreover, if we choose to take a still longer interval of time, and investigate in terms of *families* and their offspring *genera,* instead of *genera* and their offspring *species,* then the same equation will apply *mutatis mutandis* for the same reasons.

Plotted graphically, with the logarithm of x as the abscissa and the logarithm of y as the ordinate, the genera-species data, if they follow the above equation, will fall on a straight line whose negative slope will be less than 1.00 (for without a knowledge of the precise size of c in the exponent we cannot foretell how much less than 1.00 the slope will be).

To test our hypothesis empirically we obviously do not need to analyze the distribution of species (genera) at the beginning of a long, long interval of time, and then again at the end. Instead, in view of the fact that the rates of innovation and of extinction of a species are the same, we need only to investigate the genera-species distribution and their areas, at any moment of measurement, in any region, in order to test our theory empirically.

Happily the desired data for the above empiric test are already available, thanks to the resourcefulness and painstaking care of Dr. J. C. Willis.

D. The Willis' Data on "Age and Area" [11]

Before we present the empiric data of Dr. J. C. Willis on the x_g number of different genera of like y_s number of different species, together with their areas of dispersion—commonly known as Willis' theory of "Age and Area" —let us remember that we have never established objective criteria for discriminating between genera, or species, or varieties, or types. Instead we have taken the attitude that, whatever the criteria may be, our theory will apply to the types thereby discriminated. Willis, on the other hand, uses the usual criteria of taxonomy which hark back to Linnaeus' definition of members of the same species (i.e., the ability to mate and produce self-fertile offspring). If Willis chooses to accept this definition, with which we by no means quarrel, his results should conform to our theoretical expectations. In this connection let us remind the reader, however, that our theory will also apply to the different varieties within a species (see occupational data in Part Two).

1. The Empiric Data. In simple terms, the question now arises, *first,* whether in fact the x_g number of different genera of like y_s number of different species follow the equation:

$$x_g \cdot y_s^{1+c} = \textit{constant}$$

and *second,* whether in substituting the y_a area of each species for its y_s, the distribution will follow the same equation.

According to the empiric data of Dr. J. C. Willis, the answer to both these questions is a decided yes, as we shall see.[12]

To begin, Dr. Willis in 1912 first noticed the above relationship in the x genera and y species of the flora of Ceylon, for which we present a few values in Table 6–1. Since 1912 Dr. Willis has greatly extended the range

TABLE 6–1

The X Number of Different Genera of Like Y Number of Different Species of the Flora of Ceylon (After J. C. Willis).

No. of Genera X	No. of Species Y
573	1
176	2
85	3
49	4
36	5
20	6
etc.	

of his observations. In Fig. 6–1, for example, we present two curves: (*A*) for the genera and species of all flowering plants, and (*B*) for the genera and species of all Chrysomelid beetles. In each case the y_s species number which stops at 50 is measured logarithmically on the ordinate, while the x_g number of different genera of like y_s species number is measured logarithmically on the abscissa. These data were taken from the article by Drs. J. C. Willis and G. Udney Yule in *Nature* (Feb. 9, 1922, p. 178), where the data were presented graphically with a reversal of the co-ordinates.*

It is evident from the data of Fig. 6–1 that the distribution is essentially rectilinear and that the negative slopes, being less than 1.00, will have exponents of y that are greater than 1.00, and hence will fit the equation

$$x_g \cdot y_s^{1+c} = a\ constant.$$

Moreover, in regard to the respective *areas of dispersion*, according to Dr. Willis, the ordinate also measures the size of the y_a areas, as he has made amply clear in his publications.

Although Fig. 6–1 contains only two sets of data, neither the rectilinearity nor the slope of these two sets of data is unusual, since, according to

* We mention this reversal of the co-ordinates because the slopes of our graph will be the reciprocal of the slopes of theirs, *q.v.*

Dr. Willis's report, all other observed sets of data are linear and have exponents of y between 1 and 2 on our system of co-ordinates. Lest the reader doubt the diligence of Dr. Willis in investigating the topic, we quote from the above article by Willis and Yule in *Nature, loc. cit.*) :

> ". . . this type of curve holds not only for all the genera of the world, but also for all the individual families both of plants and animals, for endemic and non-endemic genera, for local floras and faunas (as may be verified in an hour), and even for very local floras, such as that of Cambridgeshire; it holds only for Wicken Fen and other strictly local associations of plants. It obtains, too, as Mrs. Reid showed in a note read the same evening, for all the deposits of Tertiary fossils examined."

And that applies not only to the x_g number of genera of like y_s species but also to their respective *areas of dispersal.* Therefore our theoretical deduc-

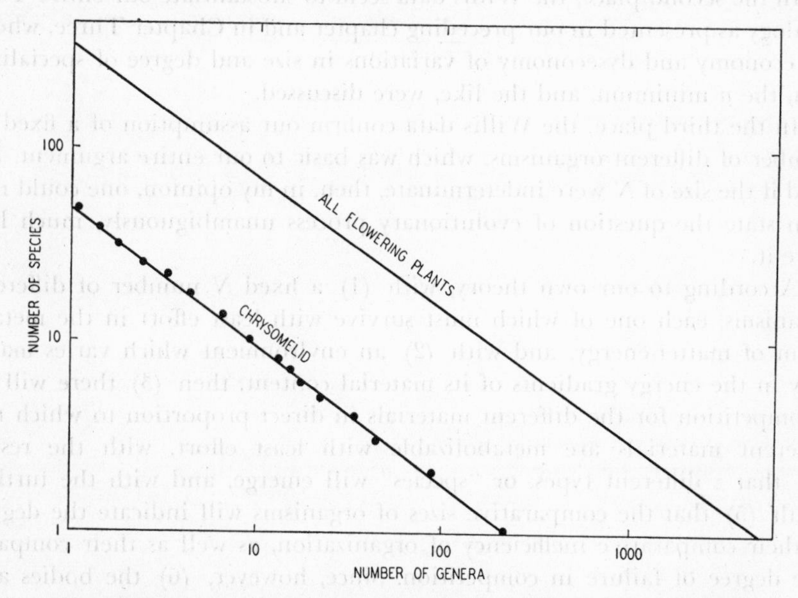

Fig. 6–1. The number of different genera of like number of different species for all flowering plants and for Chrysomelid beetles (from the J. C. Willis data, after reversing the co-ordinates).

tions from the Principle of Least Effort relative to the number and distribution of different species of organisms of like genus are verified; and so too our deductions, *mutatis mutandis,* in reference to the x_f number of different families of a like y_g number of genera. Furthermore, in regard to the comparative ages of species and genera, we believe to have shown theoretically what Dr. Willis years ago claimed to be the case. As to Dr. Willis' rationalization of his data, and as to his theory of evolution, we take no position.

In this connection let us remember the adage that "facts are sacred, while comment is free." The tremendous importance of the Willis data as an empiric law is not to be questioned. The correctness of our own present theoretical explanation thereof, on the other hand, is quite another matter. The most that we can claim for our theory is that it gives sufficient reasons for the Willis data; we have not shown that our theory is a necessary explanation, even though the Willis data do seem to confirm our theoretical expectations (cf. Chapters 9–11).

2. The Implications of the Willis Data for the Principle of Least Effort. If we assume that the Willis data do indeed confirm our theory, what particular assumptions that we have made are thereby confirmed?

In the first place, the Willis data confirm our assumption, some pages back, that the comparative degree of complexity of an organism is directly proportionate to its size, with the result that larger organisms find it proportionately more difficult to effect a successful adjustment to changed conditions.

In the second place, the Willis data seem to substantiate our entire Tool Analogy as presented in our preceding chapter and in Chapter Three, where the economy and dyseconomy of variations in size and degree of specialization, the *n* minimum, and the like, were discussed.

In the third place, the Willis data confirm our assumption of a fixed *N* number of different organisms, which was basic to our entire argument. Indeed if the size of *N* were indeterminate, then, in my opinion, one could not even state the question of evolutionary process unambiguously, much less solve it.

According to our own theory, with (1) a fixed *N* number of different organisms, each one of which must survive with least effort in the metabolism of matter-energy, and with (2) an environment which varies markedly in the energy gradients of its material content, then (3) there will be a competition for the different materials in direct proportion to which the different materials are metabolizable with least effort, with the result (4) that *z* different types, or "species" will emerge, and with the further result (5) that the comparative sizes of organisms will indicate the degree of their comparative inefficiency of organization, as well as their comparative degree of failure in competition. Since, however, (6) the bodies and excrement of organisms may serve as food for other organisms, depending upon the energy content of the same, food chains will arise if there are many different kinds of organisms in the region; hence (7) those that eat others will *tend* to be larger, more specialized, and more riskily situated than those that are eaten; and (8) by the same token they will tend to be obliged to mutate more often, and to become extinct at a faster rate.

That is the gist of our argument which, we believe, is confirmed by the data of Dr. J. C. Willis.

3. The Meaning of Evolution. At this point the reader may rightly ask what all this argument about the origin of species may have to do with the dynamics of human speech.

If the reader will re-read the closing several paragraphs of the immediately preceding section, he will note that the entire argument echoes the Tool Analogy of our preceding chapter in which kinds, or types, of different tools are minimized just like kinds, or types, of different organic organization.* This correspondence between the Tool Analogy and our theory of evolution is not accidental. Instead, in our present chapter, we are merely watching *N* different artisans of our Tool Analogy compete with one another. Since the same principles of economy will apply to the larger biosocial field, we may expect to find the widespread occurrence of many small organisms of older types of organization (and with a high rate of repetition, or reproduction?), and a decreasing number of different types of larger, younger, and less widespread organisms—according to our Tool Analogy.

Perhaps the difficulty of comprehending evolutionary process arises partly from the reification of the term, *species.* A species is not a *thing;* a species is a *manner* of organic organization. Thus when we say that the dinosaurs became extinct, we do not mean that they all died—for they had all been dying for millions of years. Instead we mean that organisms no longer employed the dinosaur manner of surviving.

The case is quite analogous to that of speech phenomena. Thus a given word is not a thing, but instead it is an utterance in terms of a conventional, or stereotyped, *manner* of utterance. The word, once uttered, can never be repeated again, though its conventional stereotype may be employed again for utterance (and when we speak of the repetition of words, we mean just that: the repetition of types). Speech is the casting of one's ideas into cultural "pigeonholes" or conventional stereotypes that have definite correlated social responses. These cultural "pigeonholes" have an economy of their own, both in their manipulation and in their evolution.

Life process in general seems to be no different. There are biosocial "pigeonholes," or organic types of organization, in terms of which living entities—the *N* different egos—express themselves. These biosocial "pigeonholes," or organic types, have an economy of their own, both in their individual organization, and in their interaction, as well as in their evolution.

Some critics may take umbrage at the broad perspective we have chosen in our treatment of the topic of language and the personality. Be that as it may. Nevertheless when one speaks of the dynamics of evolutionary process, one does not mean merely the evolution of the specific forms-functions of the *a, b, . . . z* different species on earth, as studied by persons like Linnaeus, Darwin, and Willis. One means also the evolution of each and every single form-function of each and every different species; and that includes the evolution of the forms-functions of human speech.

In the present chapters we are in effect studying the basic drives of all organic evolution by investigating the dynamics of the tiny organic phenomenon, *speech,* which is so important in the activity of the species called man.[13] In generalizing upon our speech findings, we have tested them on the data of Willis.

---

* Thus with a fixed *N* number of different organisms, the *n* number of different types, or "species," is minimized subject to the auxiliary restrictions discussed in our previous chapter.

III. THE ECONOMY OF PROCREATION

It is common knowledge that all organisms have the urge to procreate. Yet wherein does the economy of this procreation lie? For if we argue that an organism's every act is directed towards its most economical survival, then we must be prepared to argue that an organism's procreational activity is also thus directed. Moreover as we establish ever more firmly the Principle of Least Effort in other domains of organic conduct, we are forced to infer an economy of procreation, even though we may not succeed in disclosing what the economy is.

In attempting to discuss the economy of procreation, whose dynamics are admittedly baffling, we have at hand three deductions which we discussed at the beginning of the present chapter. The *first* deduction was that every organism has an ego, or identity-point, that serves as the origin of a frame of reference for its most economical survival. The *second* was that the N number of organisms that are alive on the planet at any time is somehow fixed. The *third* deduction was that the length of an organism's life is somehow fixed; and we have adopted the view that a life is fixed a finite length of time, although its actual length is unpredictable.

When we adopted this view of the finitely fixed yet unpredictable length of life we by no means precluded the alternative possibility that an organism's ego or identity-point may be eternal; and we said at the time that when we reached the present Section III, relating to the economy of procreation, we should use the postulate of an eternally existing identity-point in the sincere attempt to explain therewith the procreational urge.

I for one do not know whether the ego is eternal; and if "it" survives death, I do not know what the "it" is that survives. But I do know that the phenomenon of procreation constitutes a real and very baffling problem in biosocial dynamics. I also know that postulates and hypotheses can never become serviceable unless they are subjected in good faith to an empiric test; nor will the phenomena be understood if an explanation is never ventured. Yet as soon as someone does venture to take a position in reference to a problem, then he has at least set up a target for others to aim at and, in so doing, may start a course of inquiry that will increase our knowledge, regardless of how absurd the original position may turn out to have been. And so we venture, *sine metu et sine spe,* to build a hypothetical construct that is intended to integrate semantically our experience with nature in reference to the phenomenon of procreation.

A. Preliminary Statement of Thesis: Death as an Economic Convenience and Not as a Biological Necessity

As suggested earlier, if there is to be a fixed N number of different organisms alive on the planet at any moment, then, as long as organisms propagate further organisms, there must be a way of getting rid of organisms in order to keep N fixed. Or, conversely, if organisms die, then there must be a provision for the creation of new organisms, if N is to be fixed. It is therefore not inconceivable that the birth of new organisms is dynamically related to the death of old ones.

Death *per se* is not a biological necessity, as biologists have long ago pointed out.* For that matter the one-celled organism that grows until it splits apart, forming two organisms, can scarcely be said to die, simply because its single identity has in some mysterious fashion become two identities (the phrase "corpseless funeral" being a verbalism). As this proverbial "multiplication by division" has continued down through the ages, many of those particular one-celled organisms that happen to be alive today may be viewed as the original ones, for all we can say to the contrary.

Or, to take a different case, by layering a shoot from a grapevine so that it will take root, a second grapevine can be established from which, in turn, another shoot can be layered in order to establish a third, and so on down through the ages; the original grapevine, though long since dead, may be viewed as being still alive.

Now if death is not a biological necessity, then neither is birth a biological necessity. Instead we may view birth as an economic convenience that is attached to death. More specifically, we may perhaps take the view that the *N* different organisms by means of their procreational activity are constructing new and highly economical situations for those particular identity-points to escape into whose present organic structures are no longer economical. This "escape" constitutes *both* the *death* of the former organism *and* the *birth* of the new. We need not be told that this view is scientifically bold and unconventional. We are only interested in seeing how well it works as a possible hypothesis.

According to this view, when a man and woman copulate in order to "make a child," they do not in fact make a child. Instead they provide a highly selected material situation for an identity-point to escape into. If we assume that at any moment there are countless numbers of such opportunities at hand for identity-points to escape into, and that each identity-point selects the "easiest available" opportunity, then conception will by no means necessarily attend a given act of copulation (that is, some eggs may simply not be fertilized even in the presence of sperm). Whether the creation of an organism can occur spontaneously without its issuing from another organism—the traditional "spontaneous generation"—is questionable since the "spontaneous" organism could not compete with the venerable and tried species-forms at hand which theoretically have preëmpted the easiest metabolistic opportunities.

According to this theory, every individual will be born with an urge to procreate organic opportunities for identity-points to escape into for "rebirth," even though the individual's own identity-point may not escape into an organic opportunity that its organism happened to procreate. The procreational urge that is a *given* in *every individual's life* springs from the *collective economy* of the self-preservation of the entire *N* biosocial popula-

* Somewhere connected with the Rockefeller Foundation is a cell that is being kept alive indefinitely by subjecting it to constant favorable conditions.

tion with least effort; the individual has the urge, whether or not he likes it, because it is conditioned by a collective economy. The case is analogous to life insurance; by individually paying regular premiums one collectively provides against risks that will eventually overtake every policyholder. But whereas life insurance may be optional, procreation is not: if identity-points must survive economically, and if death-birth is an economic means of survival, then procreation must inevitably occur.

To repeat, though procreation is individually accomplished (or socially accomplished in mating), its explanation may therefore be that of a collective economy. Hence though procreation may cause the death of an individual, or utterly ruin his individual economy, nevertheless, he will still have the basic sexual urge and will procreate, since the economy of the urge is not his alone but biosocial.*

"How do identity-points know how to do all that?" we may be asked. "How does matter know how to behave gravitationally?" we reply. We are forced to our views by what we think is a logical necessity and not by any personal concern about immortality, since, according to this view, the organism's particular experience presumably expires with it, for which the average person on alternate days can be both sorry and piously grateful.

We have constructed a hypothesis that is purely *theoretical.* Birth, procreation, and death, however, are facts of existence.

B. The Dyseconomy of Advancing Age and the Economy of Rebirth

We have suggested that death may be a biological convenience and not a biological necessity, and that identity-points may escape at death into new organisms. Let us, at the risk of appearing repetitious, integrate this suggested view with the concept of intellectual rigidity with which we closed the last chapter.

In that chapter we pointed out that it was economical for an organism to possess a logically self-consistent system of correlations that refer to the givens of its environment, so that the organism can gain information about its environment and assess future opportunities and risks. Yet once the organism has a system of correlations, whether by inheritance or by acquisition, or by both, it is economical for the organism to live in an environment to which its correlations satisfactorily refer. The more, however, that the organism succeeds in living in an environment to which its correlations satisfactorily refer, the intellectually more "rigid" and "less adjustable" to change the organism becomes; for by living long in a stable environment, the organism stores its memory with a large stock of sensory samples that support his own correlations, and which allow the organism to dismiss as statistically irrelevant any information that controverts them. In short: to live is to become more biased (or intellectually more rigid).

---

* A completely parallel case is that of the soldier in combat whose activity may be ruinous to his own personal economy, but befits a collective economy (he piously trusts); this individual-social economy will be treated more fully in Part Two.

And to become more biased is to become less likely to adjust economically to the changes of an ever changing environment. Hence, to become more biased is to become less economically organized, and therefore to become increasingly less successful in the biosocial competition for survival—until a point is reached where one can no longer compete adequately.

The simple, obvious, and apparently innocuous device, therefore, of seeking relevant correlations for one's environments, and relevant environments for one's correlations will automatically and inevitably bring the organism to a point of "intellectual rigidity" (as defined in our previous chapter) where it theoretically will be more economical for the organism to die and begin life anew, than to compete for survival by means of antiquated intellectual tools. Whether the change in environment is a new virus infection, a new set of social relations, a new kind of chemical food, or a bullet in the heart, or a cut in one's flesh, the individual will die only because he cannot adjust his semantic system to it. (Indeed we even predict that the comparative rate of "healing," or of "recovering from," or of "adjusting to" a disturbance to any given organic system will tend to be inversely related to the comparative age of the organism: the greater the age, the slower the rate.)

Theoretically, then, as an organism ages it will tend to develop either an above-average interest in the phenomenon of death, or an above-average interest in the phenomenon of procreation. These are dynamically the same interests: the making ready to escape. The drastically pruned tree often bursts forth into a final extraordinary show of blossoms as it dies. The soldier facing probable death in impending conflict does not always cower on his knees and confess his "sins" in preparation for death; notoriously often he turns to women—any women—in order to scatter his sperm rapidly in fertile areas. Death and procreation, then, may be phenomena of similar motivation.

This principle of escape from death into birth, so that the *N* different organisms can survive with maximum economy, will have an interesting corollary during periods of reasonably stable environmental conditions. For if the entire biosocial population is living and aging at a more or less fixed rate because the given opportunities and risks of the environment are largely of the same kind, and occur with largely the same frequencies, then there will be a more or less fixed death rate for a given species, with the result that actuaries can undertake to predict lengths of life.

Yet the actuarial data are not the only information on the subject of a biosocial conditioning of birth rates and death rates. For as Raymond Pearl and S. L. Parker have shown from their investigations of *Drosophila* flies, the actual *rate of reproduction* (i.e., the rate at which offspring are produced) may depend upon group factors, such as the density of the population.[14]

We mention these matters not as proofs of our theory, but rather in order to suggest that the idea of a biosocial conditioning of individual behavior in reference to rate of reproduction is by no means original with us, nor exclusively inherent in our data.

C. A Critique of Freudian Theory

From the above argument it follows that, at every instant during its life, every organism has two alternative courses of action, either (1) to die and be reborn again, or (2) to continue to live and procreate. These two drives call to mind certain postulates of Freudian psychology which we shall now consider.

1. The "Death Wish" and the "Life Procreation" Wish. Let us for the time being call (1) the economy of dying and of being reborn the *"death wish"* and (2) the economy of continuing to live and to procreate the *"life procreation wish."* * Using these terms, we may say that every organism at every instant has these two contrary wishes which measure the organism's ups and downs, from his viewpoint, in the competition for survival and procreation. As he feels comparatively more successful, or sure of himself, then the magnitude of the life wish increases; and *vice versa.*

Under such a system, incidentally, either kind of wish, if once preponderant, might conceivably tend to increase in magnitude: for example, a feeling of success, or assurance, will lead to a still greater success and greater assurance, with concomitant feelings thereof, and *vice versa.* The reason for this is that a feeling of success, or assurance, comparatively speaking, will presumably attend upon a situation in which the person feels that he is intellectually superior; and, if the feeling is justified, he may well be in a position to alter the situation even more to his advantage.† Conversely, those who feel that they have failed and are insecure must spend energy in order to become abreast of a situation in which others seem to be dominant and secure.

On the other hand, quite understandably, the person who feels intellectually adequate to a situation may take too much for granted, and insufficiently inspect the givens of his environment which, after all, are rarely completely stable. Hence, unlike the insecure and less strategically placed persons who must be on the alert, the secure and successful may suddenly find that their positions in relation to their environment have deteriorated, with the result that the magnitude of their death wish suddenly increases, while the magnitude of their life wish even so suddenly decreases.

---

* These terms are borrowed from, or roughly modelled after, Freudian terminology which, however, seems to change so fast that our terms may appear to be dated. Our deep indebtedness to Freudian thinking is obvious, although we cannot cite book and page of Freudian ideas. Nevertheless, at no time are we basing our argument upon Freudian postulates. Instead we are defining our terms on the basis of our analogues, data, and theory and, in the light of our terms, are trying to explain the working hypotheses of other schools, if we understand their terminology correctly.[15]

† Let us remember with Dean William Paley, "The word *happy* is a relative term; that is, when we call a man happy, we mean that he is happier than some others, with whom we compare him; than the generality of others; or than he himself was in some other situation."—*The Principles of Moral and Political Philosophy,* Boston (10th American edition: 1821, p. 34).

The comparative magnitudes of these two wishes seem by no means to be invariant in a person, though they may conceivably become less variable as the person ages and hence can alter himself with less ease.

1. The Singleness of the Objective. Looking again at the life procreation wish, which in Freudian language means both (1) the desire to live and (2) the desire to procreate, let us note that this wish has two different independent objectives. Since two independent objectives in a problem render the problem quite as meaningless and indeterminate as two superlatives, if only because a situation may arise in which the pursuit of one objective frustrates the pursuit of the other, the question arises as to which objective comes first: to live, or to procreate.*

As far as the facts are concerned, some organisms, like a drone honeybee, die immediately as a direct result of copulation, and therefore may be said to live in order to procreate. Other organisms, like women, may continue to live long after their menopause without the capacity to procreate; and the same applies to many organisms which, like gelded stallions, have been deprived of the machinery for procreation. On the other hand, there are ample cases of persons who, whether because they have lost their sexual organs, or because they cannot obtain the object of their sexual desire, will kill themselves, much as if life, without the capacity to procreate as desired, has lost its value.

In view of the above considerations we cannot dogmatize to the effect that either the desire to live or the desire to procreate comes first in the life procreation wish.

Nevertheless if we recall our previous argument that procreation of further organisms is a biosocial mechanism for one's own personal survival (and not merely for the survival of one's species), then we may say that *in the life procreation drive, the preservation of one's life comes first, and that procreation is but a device to that end.* By taking this stand we rid ourselves of the indeterminacy of the otherwise double objective.

To continue to live, then, in our theory will come first, whereas the urge to procreate is a secondary instrument to that primary aim.

2. The Economy and Dyseconomy of Offspring. If the urge to procreate is a biosocial device for a most economical survival of an ego, or identity-point, then the individual organism is not consulted about whether he wants to possess the urge; he simply possesses it. Possessing this urge to which

* The fallacy of the double objective is frequently ignored, to the no small intellectual frustration of those who use it. A good example of a double objective is tendered by members of a certain warmongering university who, during World War II, formed a "Committee to Win the War and to Win the Peace." By "winning the war" they said they meant an unconditional surrender of Germany and a complete reduction of it to a pastoral nation (with further actions suggested by the more sadistic members). By "winning the peace" they said they meant a kind of internationalism in which all sorts of wonderfully humane things would happen. Unfortunately if "winning the war" thus defined is the objective, then the nature of the ensuing peace is dependent upon winning the war. If "winning the peace," however, is the objective, then one draws up one's plan for peace which one imposes upon the enemy by force—and the war ceases when the enemy accepts it. The cost of American double objectives seems to run rather high; the results are, of course, zero.

each organism must try to give expression, each organism is automatically faced by the likelihood of producing offspring which, though the result of a biosocial economy, may not always be to his own economic advantage. Though offspring may be socially economical, are they individually economical?

If we ponder momentarily the individual economy and dyseconomy of offspring we note at once that offspring may be both economic liabilities and economic assets.

Offspring are economic liabilities for at least several reasons. In the first place they notoriously compete for the available food supply. Then too there is a physical risk in bearing them, and also the risk of being killed by them, as frequently enough happens in the biosocial population. Hence if there were no compensatory economic assets in having offspring, the life of an offspring would be precarious indeed if the parent organism always behaves with maximum economy.

Nevertheless there are also economic advantages in having offspring. First of all, they may be a source of food supply (there are, after all, cannibalistic species). Second, the presence of offspring may minimize the risk of becoming a victim of one's enemies; thus, for example, if a hungry tiger walks into a hut, a given person is more likely to survive if he has a large family around him than if he is alone (this is, however, a transitory economy, since by providing food for one's enemies, one in the long run increases the number of one's enemies).

Yet neither of the above economic advantages is so compelling in human relations as the economy of using one's offspring as partners, slaves, or mates. Hence if man, for example, is always economical and must produce offspring for the sake of the most economical survival of his ego, he will inevitably view his offspring as potential partners, as potential slaves, and as potential mates that should be cherished and loved.

And he will simultaneously view his offspring as potential rivals for all that he desires, and therefore he will fear and hate them.

It follows, therefore, that in all human relations every individual will simultaneously both love and hate every other individual who has any influence in his life at all. The comparative degree of one's love or hate for a given individual depends upon the positive (or negative) economic value of that individual as a potential partner, slave, and mate (or as a rival). We love a good source of supply of food, we love those who do our bidding, and we love someone who gratifies our sexual desires. Yet insofar as we depend upon another person, who, after all, has an ego of his own, we are living with a potential rival.

In our following chapter we shall resume this argument when we treat the economy of sexual relations. At the present we merely point out that the contentions of the Freudian school that man wishes both to live and to die, and that procreation is an urge of life, and that love and hate go hand in hand, are all understandable in the light of our theoretical Principle of Least Effort.

3. The Anomaly of Suicide. The most unpalatable part of our argument is the postulate of an eternally existing ego, or identity-point, as the origin of a frame of reference. Yet however unpalatable the thought of an immortal ego may be, many apparently careful thinkers tacitly assume that man has "a something" that is immortal.

For example, the psychiatric schools aver that "suicide is an escape from reality." And yet, physically considered, what escapes? And what is the reality?

If we assume that suicide is a deliberate act on the part of the person in question, then we have a highly anomalous situation in which a physical system destroys itself at will; and this may occur in the presence of ample supplies of food, shelter, and the like, to keep the suicidal organism living as a physical system. Surely no other kind of physical system can destroy itself at will. Therefore we must conclude that in a unity of nature and a continuity of natural law, there must be a self-preservative "something" in an organism which can eventually wish to escape into some other situation which is comparatively less frustrating in terms of some frame of reference. Yet I for one do not know what the "it" is, or whether "it" does in fact survive.

IV. THE SYNCHRONY OF THE BIOSOCIAL CONTINUUM

In the following pages, that close the present chapter on the ego as a frame of reference, we shall discuss certain aspects of the biosocial population with the hope of integrating the argument of the present chapter with what has gone before and with what is yet to come.

A. The Concept of "Biosocial Time"

We have already used the term *biosocial population* to describe the population of N different organisms that are alive on the planet at any time. These organisms, as we know, are physically continuous with the environment in which they exist, and of which, in fact, they are a part (e.g., your dog is a part of your environment; you are a part of your dog's environment). In order to emphasize this continuity between the biosocial population and its environment, let us use the term, *biosocial continuum,* to include both.

The purpose of introducing this new term is to suggest that organic life may be cast in terms of two kinds of time scales, which might be called the *calendar time scale* and the *biosocial time scale.* It is clear in the last analysis that the biosocial time scale is ultimately dependent upon the calendar time scale.

By the calendar time scale we mean the rates at which physical energy is made available to the biosocial continuum: sunlight, the temperature of winds and currents, and the like. We may also add the rate of precipitation, or the rate at which any other inorganic matter-energy enters the biosocial continuum without the intervention of organic process. On this planet the calendar time scale, which means little more than the rates of seasonal change, is notoriously variable. Organisms that utilize this energy must be at hand when the energy is available; that is, they must be adjusted to the calendar time of their region.

But that is not all. Many organisms, if not most organisms, also depend upon what other organisms are doing. Thus, for example, if the apple tree is to be pollinated, it must be in flower when the bees are at hand; by the same token if the bees are to live from nectar, they must be present when the blossoms are at hand. Generalizing upon this typical relationship, we may say that the entire biosocial continuum is synchronized not only in terms of calendar time but also in terms of the rates, or time scale, of what other members of the biosocial population are doing: the *biosocial time scale.*

1. The Conservatism of Biosocial Rates. In view of the fact that virtually every organism's action must be synchronized with the action of other organisms, it is evident that the growth, development, procreation, and deaths of organisms will proceed according to more or less fixed rates that are on the whole quite conservative.[16]

Thus, for example, the tree that must blossom when the bees are at hand to pollinate it, must also mature its fruit at such a rate that its seeds will be ready at "the right time" in order to be scattered at "the right time" for germination. The same applies to the foliage of the tree and to its growth.

Indeed, because of the very nature of the biosocial synchrony, organic activity of all sorts will proceed according to rates—as is notoriously the case. Members of the same species in a given region will tend to agree not only in their forms-functions but also in the rates of action of those forms-functions.

Because of the synchronization of the rates of action of the biosocial continuum, it would be foolhardy for an organism to deviate from its norms of action without a compelling economic reason. For to be either too early or too late with its action may be disastrous both for the organism in question and for dependent organisms in the food chains. Therefore the rates of organic action of the continuum tend to be basically conservative.

2. Norms of Conduct. We have said that the physical conditions of calendar time are highly variable; rarely indeed do seasons precisely duplicate themselves; the most that we can speak of is mean temperatures, average rainfall, prevailing winds, and the like. The same variability is also found in the rates of biosocial time.

Hence an organism that survives in a given region must not only adjust to the average rates of the environment; it must also develop a tolerance of the variations. For example, if the mean temperature is 70° on a given date in a given place, organisms must adjust their rates to that fact; and if the temperature varies between 60° and 80° on that date, they must be tolerant of those variations.

Generalizing upon the above, and remembering that all rates throughout the entire biosocial continuum are variable, we can see how *all* sensations and *all* judgments, and *all* responses are cast in terms of norms. Hence a given hue, or brightness, or pitch, or amplitude, or temperature, or texture, or chemical mixture, and the like must change considerably before it is put into a different class by an organism. Inherent then in the living process, we repeat, are norms—statistical norms—which are approximated by physical action.

The norms are semantic, in the sense that they represent the organism's manner of classifying and correlating its environment. All the organism's activity is only an approximation of its norms. No matter how differently organisms may actually behave; they are the same insofar as they have the same norms.* Not until the norms are altered may we speak of a mutation.

These norms of conduct are presumably derived from the organism's past experience with the phenomenon in question, and are used as a basis of a prediction of the future. Hence, simply as a matter of sheer statistical calculation, *the comparatively longer a given norm of conduct has existed either ontogenetically or phylogenetically, the comparatively longer it is likely to exist in the face of continuing changes.* This may be called the *relative conservatism, or intellectual rigidity, of norms* (or the cumulative force of habit).

From the above considerations it follows not merely that all norms are conservative because of the conservatism of the synchronized biosocial continuum; it follows also that some norms of a given organism—the ones of longer history—are more conservative, or rigid, than others.

If asked, therefore, which norms of conduct of a given organism are more likely to change in the face of continuing environmental alterations we should be inclined to answer: the more recent ones. And if we remember, in the light of our Tool Analogy of Chapter Three, that the more recent norms tend to be permutations of older norms, we may even add that the mutation of norms is more likely to affect the permutation of older norms than the older norms themselves. Thus the leopard is more likely to change his spots than he is to alter his teeth, if we assume that his teeth represent older norms.

B. THE DEVELOPMENT OF THE INDIVIDUAL

Let us apply to the case of a developing organism the preceding inference that not all norms of conduct are likely to change at the same rate. We shall begin by first (1) noting that an organism from its creation until its death does not by any means live in an equally variable environment from the viewpoint of its own needs. Instead the environment of its early life may be highly selected, or protected.

1. The Selectedness of Early Environments

Many different kinds of organisms begin life in environments whose physical givens and rates of change are selected with a view to the optimal needs of the organism in question. Wherever there is an embryonic development, for example, there is a selectedness of an environment. In the case of man, as with many other species, the selectedness continues well after birth when the parents (or other agents) protect the offspring from the

* In Chapter Three we pointed out (Zwirners' studies) that sometimes a German's utterance of long $\bar{a}$ is shorter than that of his short $\breve{a}$.[17]

variability to which the later adult offspring (by definition) is likely to be exposed.

The effect of this selectedness of the early environment will be twofold.

In the *first* place, since any selection of an environment entails an expenditure of work on the part of those (the parents or other agents) who do the selecting, it follows that embryonic stages as well as stages of dependent infancy fall as economic burdens upon other organisms. Theoretically, therefore, if effort is to be minimized, an organism is forced to grow, to be born, and to be weaned because of the economy of others—a social economy. On the other hand, there is the further individual economy on the part of the organism itself that forces the organism to grow into sexual maturity at the "right time" in order to be ready for the available opportunities for procreation. We mention these considerations lest we forget that growth, development, and maturization are both individually and socially economical because of the organization of the biosocial continuum.

But there is a *second* consequence that attends upon an early selected environment: environmental changes are less likely to cause mutations in organisms during their early stages of selected environments, than later, and proportionately so. Indeed the more selected an environment is—that is, the more insulated an organism is from the vicissitudes of the unmitigated biosocial continuum—the less likely is the organism to be forced to undergo adaptive mutations. Thus, for example, a radical decline in the average temperature is more likely to cause an organism to develop fur or feathers later in its life than during its earlier embryonic stages and infancy when it is protected by others.

2. *The So-Called "Law of Recapitulation."* [18] In the preceding sections we have argued (1) that an organism is less likely to need to mutate during the early periods of its selected environment than during later stages in which the environment is either less selected or not at all selected; and we have previously argued (2) that the older a norm of conduct is—whether ontogenetically or phylogenetically—the less likely it is to undergo a mutation.

From the above two considerations it follows that as organisms grow older they tend to differ ever more in forms, functions, and rates of action from their progenitors at a corresponding age. That is true, we repeat, first, because mutations are less likely to need to occur during the earlier development, and second, because the longer a form-function has persisted the more likely it is to be preserved.

In order to illustrate the significance of the preceding points, let us imagine that we have a series of moving picture films for the development of one hundred million successive generations of organisms ending in a given present-day human being. If we were to examine these films in sequence, one after another, we should expect to find in the light of the above theoretical conclusions that the successive films would tend to differ from one another more towards the end of the films than towards the beginning. We should also expect to find that the further apart in number of generations any two films were, the more they would tend to differ from one another towards their ends, and the greater would be the length of film towards the end during which they would tend to differ.

The same would apply to similar sets of ancestral films for pigs and turtles respectively.

Moreover, if we assume that men, pigs, and turtles have descended from an ultimate common ancestry, then, if the three sets of films went back far enough, we should reach a generation in which the differences between man and pig—and later between man-pig and turtle—would disappear.

From the above argument it follows theoretically that present-day men, pigs, and turtles may have a certain formal-functional similarity at their conception and during early embryonic stages, but that these similarities become increasingly less as time passes.

But there is an even more important point. If we remember that a given mutation takes place on the basis of the then existent norms at the time, it follows that there will tend to be a correspondence between the embryonic and post embryonic sequences of forms-functions, and the phylogenetic sequence of mutations, *insofar as evidences of these mutations are preserved ontogenetically*. Thus, for example, in the development of a pig today from conception onwards, there will tend to be a correspondence in the sequence of the successive stages through which the little pig develops and the sequence of mutations by means of which the pig's ancestors evolved from earliest times down to the present day. We may call this the theoretical correspondence between ontogenetic and phylogenetic sequences of successive stages.

That such a theoretical correspondence exists between the above sequences is amply evident from the well-known data of embryology and paleontology—data that have led to the formulation of the so-called Law of Recapitulation, which states that an individual tends to recapitulate ontogenetically the history of its kind (phylogeny). A meticulous inspection of the ontogenetic and phylogenetic forms-functions in question reveals that lots and lots of ancestral forms-functions are not recapitulated at all, and that many many others are recapitulated only imperfectly.*

Yet when we state that the sequence of ontogenetic events tends to correspond to the sequence of phylogenetic mutations, insofar as the phylogenetic mutations are ontogenetically represented, we by no means aver that there is any positive correlation between the duration of an ontogenetic feature and the duration of that feature phylogenetically; for example, we do not aver that a day of embryonic development corresponds to so and so many million years (or a function of the same) in the history of the race. Instead we merely say that the longer a feature has persisted phylogenetically, the *more likely* it is, both to appear at all in an ontogenetic sequence of features, and to appear in an ontogenetic sequence of features that tends

* According to our own theory, the only motive for developing a particular form-function at any time is that on the basis of one's total past experience there is a probability that the said form-function will be needed. Hence in the course of its entire life, an organism may well develop forms-functions temporarily on the grounds that it may need them only temporarily.

to correspond to the phylogenetic sequence of mutations. Thus, for example, the several weeks' duration of the chrysalis stage of a monarch butterfly that looms up so conspicuously in its ontogenesis may merely represent a stage which in the lives of its ancestors back through the dim ages lasted in each case only a few weeks. What precedes or follows the chrysalis stage, however, is likely to correspond to the phylogenetic order of mutations.

Or, to take another case, the boy who develops sexually in his early 'teens is not recapitulating his phylogeny during which a sexual maturity was reached long long long before what corresponds phylogenetically to the thirteen years of the boy's development. Instead we may say that the boy's development tends to imitate his papa's, and so on back through the generations: a *recapitulatio recapitulationis recapitulationis et cetera ad initium*—if one chooses to express it that way.

But it would be more accurate to state that parents beget offspring who are more likely to deviate from them developmentally as they grow older, first, because the insulating selectedness of the environment decreases with age, and second because the longer a given form-function has persisted, the more likely it is to persist in the future.

Although the so-called Law of Recapitulation, as commonly understood, is doubtless a valuable intellectual tool, it nevertheless does seem to be somewhat spurious if it means that every organism at its inception is subject to the fiat of recapitulating the history of its kind. If one wants an analogue for the recapitulatory phenomena in question, one might perhaps better take the case of the chronological strata of a speech vocabulary, as discussed in Chapter Three which, in fact, is not an analogue but an example of the phylogenetic-ontogenetic process in cultural terms.

From the moment a child begins to talk until he no longer does so, he uses tools to evoke responses. Because of the nature of the evolution of speech, he is likely to use the older elements more often than the newer ones. Yet at no time does he run through the stages of speaking pro-ethnic Indo-European, pro-ethnic Germanic, West Germanic, Old English, Chaucerian, and so on. Neither does he do so ontogenetically in any other respect, as far as the present writer can see.

From the moment that an organism begins to live, he attempts to survive with least effort in the environment in which he finds himself, and by means of the tools and matter-energy at his disposal. He does not theoretically waste effort in gratuitously imitating the history of his kind. Starting with his particular genetic donum and directed towards a particular mode, or opportunity, for survival in adult years, the organism proceeds thence and thither with least effort, as the organism develops those forms-functions in passing which in the light of his phylogenetic and ontogenetic experience are likely to be needed in the then eventuating future so that the organism may at all times survive with least effort.

C. The Biosocial Continuum as a "Sea" of Opportunities for Survival

According to our theory, one moment in an organism's life is as "important" as another; at every moment the organism is minimizing effort, and at every moment the organism is just as much alive as at every other moment.

On the other hand, in the lives of most kinds of organisms, if not of all organisms, there is—barring accidents—a moment before which an organism cannot procreate, and after which it can. This moment has a certain definitive value in closing the period of maturation and of beginning the period of adulthood in respect of the basic drive of procreation.

Restricting our attention to this period of adulthood during which the organism fends for itself and expresses its procreational urge, let us note that by now the organism may be said on the whole to have "taken its place" in the biosocial continuum. That does not mean that the developing organism had not hitherto had a place in the biosocial continuum, nor that it had not been previously subject to the economy of the continuum, nor that the entire continuum had not been dynamically related to it. Instead it means merely that the organism has reached a point developmentally where it can effectively realize its must of procreation.

Yet despite the fact that an organism has developed into adulthood, the organism cannot "take its place" in the biosocial continuum unless there is a "place" there for it to occupy formally-functionally. Or, differently expressed, an organism cannot take advantage of an opportunity unless there is an opportunity there.

Indeed, metaphorically speaking, the biosocial continuum may be viewed as a more or less stable "sea" of different kinds of opportunities towards which the newly created organisms aim their respective developments. The nature of the opportunities determines the development of the organism, in the last analysis, and not the reverse, even though the organism itself may offer further opportunities to others, and thereby be a part of the "sea" of biosocial opportunities.

One reason for urging this view of the biosocial continuum as a "sea" of opportunities that serve as the final determinants of the nature of formal-functional development is that it allows us to ponder a certain attitude that is sometimes found among physiologists who feel that they have explained the determinants of behavior by saying that "everything is mechanical." To illustrate this attitude, let us take the case of two larvae, *a* and *b;* the one, *a,* is positively geotropic in the sense that it tends in its action to turn down towards the earth, while the other, *b,* is negatively geotropic in the sense that it tends to turn away from the earth and to climb into the treetops. Physiologically considered, each of these larvae presumably responds to gravitational and electrochemical apparatuses which are mechanically correct throughout, and which are so designed in the case of *a* as to send it downwards, and in the case of *b* as to send it upwards. Yet why the *a* larva has the *a* apparatus, and the *b* larva the *b* apparatus is not answered by the physiologist's above mechanical argument. We for our part argue that it is the respective biosocial opportunity that the organism exploits—whether in the ground or in the treetops—that is the determinant of the mechanism. In short, the biosocial opportunities ultimately determine the genes, and not the reverse, even though a given organism may "know" of these opportunities only because of its phylogenetic experience as represented in its genetic donum at conception.

The opportunities for adult behavior may be viewed as the goals towards which earlier development proceeds. Hence it is quite understandable when young sonny, for example, does his utmost to grow up and be a big man. Nevertheless the successive stages of development that lead from conception to adulthood must themselves also occur within the opportunities of the biosocial continuum. In other words, an organism, in living, picks a path of opportunities from instant to instant, over the entire course of which his effort is minimized—the path of least effort. From this it does not follow, however, that all steps in the path are equally advantageous; instead some stages may be above-average hazardous with correspondingly high death rates, and *vice versa*.

The biosocial continuum, therefore, is not merely a "sea" of opportunities, but also a maze of directed and synchronized opportune paths along which organisms proceed developmentally as a result both of their own economies and of the economies of others. In this "sea" of opportune paths of least effort, all developmental and procreational activity will theoretically be subject to fairly stable rates (and the actuarian can safely make statistical predictions).

D. The Domain of the Biosocial Continuum

In defining the biosocial continuum as the biosocial population of N organisms in their environment, we have merely given a new name to the entire time-space continuum, since theoretically every event in the universe is related to every other event. Yet sometimes the adoption of a new name is advisable in order to overcome an old prejudice of whose existence even the most well-meaning may be unaware.

Continuing with the new name, let us ask what activity belongs to the domain of the biosocial continuum (in the sense of what physical changes are effected because of organic needs).

Instead of attempting a categorical answer, let us merely point out—quite tautologically—that everything that any organism does in order to survive economically is part of the biosocial domain. Thus, for example, a tree in its growth, wasps in their nest, a man singing in his bath, men working together in an industrial establishment, are all parts of the biosocial domain; and we have no reason to suppose that one is more characteristically so than the other.

Now for the next question! Is there, throughout the entire biosocial domain, a unity and continuity of dynamic principle, or is there not? For example, as we reflect upon a tree in its growth, and wasps in their nest, and a man singing in his bath, and men working together in an industrial establishment, shall we take the view: either (1) these are merely examples of different things in different conditions that are nevertheless behaving in obedience to the same governing principles; or (2) these things represent different sets of dynamic principles in operation (e.g., God breathed upon man and made him forever unlike all other kinds of organisms, because of which man now has a dynamic quiddity that is *sui generis*).

Either view is a postulate. In the present book we have taken the first view: *the unity and continuity of biosocial principle.* All living phenomena are manifestations of this principle in operation which, we are contending, is the Principle of Least Effort.

If our view be correct, then one can disclose this principle by studying any living phenomenon (e.g., trees, wasps in nests, bathtub operas, human industrial establishments).

E. Summary

In the present chapter we have defined an organism as an ego, or identity-point, that serves as the origin of a frame of reference in a physical system which preserves itself physically as a continuous whole without a continuity of parts against a final and complete gravitational and electromagnetic equilibrium with its environment.

Assuming that the organism minimizes effort (i.e., probable work) we have pointed out that it will survive either a definitely fixed time whose length is unpredictable, or else eternally, and that the latter may be the case.

We have further argued, in view of the apparently universal procreational activities of organisms, that the *N* number of different organisms that are alive on the planet at any moment is somehow fixed and cannot be either a maximum or a minimum.

In view of the above, we argued that the procreation of new organisms is a device for survival, and that new organisms may represent new economic opportunities into which less fortunate egos escape. The urge to procreate, therefore, is a biosocial economy which is corollary to a most economical survival.

Our next step was to elaborate a working hypothesis on the basis of the above definitions and postulates and in terms of matter-energy on a curved surface. We saw the reasons for the inevitable emergence of different species, whose respective rates of mutation (or innovation and of extinction) will be subject to a governing principle that ultimately results in an inverse relationship between the x number of different genera of a like y number of different species (and of areas) in a given region. This relationship we successfully tested empirically by appealing to the quantitative data of Dr. J. C. Willis on "Age and Area."

Then we discussed various aspects of the synchronization of acts of the biosocial continuum, the approximate nature of all living action, and the fundamental conservatism of their rates, with an explanation of the dynamics of the so-called Law of Recapitulation. We closed our chapter with a discussion of the continuity of biosocial principle, and pointed out that whatever life may be, and whatever the nature of biosocial principles, we organisms are that life and those principles in operation. And that applies to all our activity, including our mentational and cultural activity, our sexual activity, our artistry, and our dreams.

In reflecting upon the contents of the present chapter, let us remember that we have tacitly made the assumption that the living process is a manner of organizing the earth's surface. We organisms are that, and nothing more. Our number, the lengths of our lives, and our modes of action are attributes of the organization of the earth's surface. So too our consciousness, whatever that may mean.

Implicit therefore in the mass of this earth is an organization of the surface which involves conscious living phenomena. In the unity of nature with a continuity of natural law, life may then be rather a property of large masses of matter than a peculiarity of earth. In investigating the animate phenomena of earth, we should do well to remember that we are investigating what are perhaps uniquely convenient phenomena, and not unique phenomena.

CHAPTER SEVEN

MIND AND THE ECONOMY OF SYMBOLIC PROCESS: SEX, CULTURE, AND SCHIZOPHRENIA

In the present chapter we shall attempt to focus much of our foregoing argument upon the specific problem of a person's mind and the economy of his symbolic process. Since the terms *mind* and *symbolic process* mean different things to different persons, we shall first briefly discuss our own usage of the terms, even at the risk of seeming to be unduly repetitious.

Let us approach the problem of what an organism's mind is by suggesting what it is not. We have frequently stated that a person, like any other organism, is a lump of matter that is a part of the material surface of the earth. He acts; and in his action he presumably behaves like any other lump of matter in complete accordance with the laws of physics and chemistry—whatever they may be. Moreover, because of the physical nature of sensation, the only action of a given organism, *a,* of which a second organism, *b,* can become aware is the *physical* action of *a*—that is, the physical action of *a*'s matter-energy, insofar as that action impinges physically upon *b*'s sensory system.

Thus viewed, all organic action, even including the minutiae of cellular activity, seems to be physical, like the action of a stone or a furnace. Clearly this physical action *per se* is *not* mind. What then is *mind?*

In our usage, *mind* is an intellectual construct, or a scientific fiction, like gravitation, of which we know only by its effects upon matter-energy in time-space. There is no parcel or particle of the universe marked "gravitation." Gravitation is a word of quite precise definability in terms of physical mass and time-space which describes the way that matter behaves under specific conditions. By studying matter under various conditions, we deduce the orderliness known as gravitation.

The same applies to an organism's *mind.* There is presumably no parcel nor particle of the organism marked "mind." Instead, *mind* is a word that we are using to designate *an organism's selection of particular kinds of material operations to perform upon particular kinds of matter-energy in order to minimize the organism's own probable work.* Only by studying the material action of an organism under various conditions can we hope to deduce the structure and economic orderliness of his mind.

Now the question arises as to what we mean by the term *symbolic process* (later, *semantic dynamics*). Let us first define the term *symbol* as we shall use it. For in our usage, a symbol does not have the customary meaning of that which *stands for,* or *represents,* something else. Instead, the term *symbol* will invariably mean for us that which *is used for something else* *by some organism(s) in reference to some specific kind of object.** The term *symbolic process* will mean an organism's functional classification of his environment in terms of operations and objects in reference to the primary need of his most economical behavior. We contend that symbolic process (or semantic dynamics) is orderly and economical.

So much, then, for a preliminary definition of terms.

In view of the above definitions, it is evident that we have already investigated certain relevant aspects of mind and the economy of symbolic process in Chapter Five, on sensation, where we studied the economical organization of sensory classes—the economy of abstraction, comparison, correlation, and the general assessment of future probable risks and opportunities. If we so chose, we could start building now upon the material of that previous chapter; and in a very practical sense we are doing just that, with one important difference. In Chapter Five, we emphasized the individual's assessment of his own risks and opportunities for his own most economical activity; in the present chapter we shall restate much of that preceding argument, only this time in terms of cultural action—that is, in terms of the group's assessment of its social risks and opportunities in reference to which its collective action takes place.

This social aspect of the economy of symbolism is of considerable value. Indeed, unless the individual person understands the social economies and the cultural vocabulary of the group in which he lives, he cannot hope to evaluate the future probable action of that group and hence cannot assess the risks and opportunities which the group offers to his own individual self.

Yet what are the social economies of group action, in reference to which its cultural vocabulary—or symbolic process—has meaning?

Instead of inquiring immediately into the economy of the fundamental drives of all human society, to which Part Two of this book will be devoted, let us rather begin now by first inspecting the economy and symbolic process of one particular kind of human social activity—namely human sexual activity—which is perhaps the most widely occurring aspect of human social behavior. For regardless of differences in time, place, and culture, human beings agree on the whole as to their notions about the primary functions of the human genitalia.

After completing our study of the economy and symbolic process of the special case of human sexual activity, we shall proceed step by step to a consideration of the economy and symbolic process of schizophrenia which represents an extreme case of individualistic asocial behavior in which the schizophrenic person loses rapport with human society.

Hence in this chapter, under the heading of *mind and the economy of symbolic process: sex, culture, and schizophrenia,* we shall begin with the commonplace social phenomenon of sex, and thence proceed to the commonplace asocial phenomenon of schizophrenia. Our concept of culture, as defined in the course of our argument, will provide the common frame of

* Thus, for example, if a carpenter mislays his *hammer* and instead uses a *stone* to drive a *nail,* then the *stone* is a symbol of the *hammer* for that carpenter in that situation.

reference for our discussion of the above two extremes of social and asocial action.

I. HUMAN SEXUAL ACTIVITY

In the previous chapter we argued that the urge to procreate is a manifestation of the basic biosocial urge towards a most economical survival. In the case of man, as with many other types, or "species," of organisms, a partner of the opposite sex is necessary for the production of offspring. In and for himself, each human being is a set of sexual tools for which a reciprocal set of sexual jobs must be found (or he is a set of jobs for which tools must be found). Implicit then in human existence is at least some rudimentary kind of social life in the form of at least a temporary mating with a member of the opposite sex.

Let us now (*A*) inspect this matter of mating and note how some matings for a given person may be more economical than others, and how a greater or lesser degree of permanency (*marriage*) may attach to the economy of a union, for whose preservation curious incest taboos spontaneously develop. These considerations will suffice to lead to a study of the variant behavior of homosexualism, and to broach the problem of the symbolic process of secondary eroticism in general.

A. Marriage

By and large most persons can be classified as male or female according to their genitalia. The general physical correspondence of members of the male and female sexes respectively is matched by roughly corresponding physical methods of penis-vagina copulation that on the whole vary but little at different times and different places in spite of the cultural rituals that may attach thereto.

Sheer coition can by itself perform the total job of producing human offspring, without the partners thereto ever meeting again. Nevertheless a person's partner in sex may be useful in other nonsexual enterprises. Thus a person's sexual partner may be economically helpful in gaining support or in providing defense, in addition to being available for copulation. These additional, more durative advantages suggest the economy of a more permanent partnership between the sexual mates; and since they are inherent in a more permanent union, we need not be surprised to find *marriages* in the most diverse cultures (even though not all unions may be monogamous) as man seeks ever to behave with maximum economy.[1]

Of course, when there is only one boy and one girl available for mating, as presumably happens on the proverbial desert island, then the problem of selecting a mate is greatly simplified. On the other hand, when there is a wide range of possible mates, then each person faces the question as to which of these is to be preferred to all others. This question, according to our Principle of Least Effort, will be theoretically answered in the light of relative economies. Although we do not mean to broach at this time the question of the most suitable mate, with all its considerations of calipers, diameters, cultural backgrounds, rates of action, and individual likes and dislikes, we nevertheless make bold to suggest that that mate who likes to be treated as one likes to treat, and in turn likes to treat as one likes to be treated, and who most shares one's views and habits, bids fair to be the most economical mate.

In view of the above considerations, we easily understand why one person can be a more desirable (i.e., economical) mate for a given person, than another, and why the said more desirable mate is not only well worth procuring, but also well worth *keeping* and defending when procured. Indeed it is this last economy, the economy of keeping a good (i.e., economical) mate, that is of importance to us now.

Because of this economy of keeping a good mate, we have not only the spontaneous emergence of marriage, even to the point of its becoming institutionalized and socially protected, but we have also the familiar reactions of jealousy, whose various manifestations are spontaneous and to a high degree stereotyped regardless of time or place. This similarity of jealous behavior with its economic basis, incidentally, is another instance of like social reaction by the members of the same type, or "species," to like situations. One consequence of jealousy, as first pointed out by the Freudian school, is the emergence of incest taboos, into whose economy we now inquire.[2]

1. Incest Taboos. A person, in trying to keep his mate permanently, defends himself not only against actual rivals at hand but also against potential rivals. To this end customs have developed in many cultures relative to places where one spouse or the other is forbidden to go, or relative to modes of dressing that will conceal the mate's features from the view of potential rivals, and so on.

Among one's potential rivals for one's mate, is one's own offspring of the same sex, as the Freudian school pointed out years ago. This potential rival is all the more dangerous because of the intellectual lability of the child, who can and must and does learn to respond with remarkable precision to the particular wants and dislikes of one's mate both because of the rewards and punishments attached thereto, and because of a lack of competition from the wants and dislikes of others. It is a commonplace to hear a young mother exclaim over her newborn son that she would bring him up to be the sort of man she has "always wanted to have"—with comparable remarks from the father about his infant daughter.

Few will deny the obvious economy of training one's mate from infancy to conform to one's own likes and dislikes, particularly when one's own germ plasm has provided a goodly share of the trainee's inheritance; such a person could become one's ideally economical mate, partner, and slave. Yet in thus training a child to be one's own mate, one thereby trains him to be a rival to his other parent, whose affections he will supplant. Extending this argument, we can see that every marriage is threatened by the birth of offspring.

Therefore we can understand how parents in general will find it fundamentally economical to condemn copulation between all parents and offspring, with the result that a universal incest taboo will arise spontaneously without any particular "biological" reason or any other apparent reason, even though various religious rationalizations may be offered.[3]

Now, if our above theoretical argument about the underlying economy of the parent-offspring incest taboo be correct, then we find in the very universality of this taboo an important instance of the economic orderliness of human *social* behavior. Let us briefly enumerate the steps of our argument so that we may be able to view the argument as a whole: (1) there is an economy in a permanency of mating with a mate who reciprocates one's action; (2) there is an economy in protecting the permanent mating against actual and potential rivals; (3) one's offspring of the opposite sex is a potential rival; (4) therefore it is economical for society, which after all consists effectively of adult parents, to place a ban upon parent-offspring copulation; (5) since the above argument is not restricted to time or place, this ban, or incest taboo, should be found in all societies without restriction of time or place; and (6) according to the observations of cultural anthropologists, the incest taboo is indeed universally found, thereby providing empiric confirmation of our theory.

Similar taboos, though by no means so universal, lie against copulation between other blood relatives who live close together. Thus some communities attach the same rigorous taboo, for example, to brother-sister incest as they do to that between parent and offspring, while others do not (e.g., ancient Egypt and some American Indian tribes). Hence we do well to resist the all too easy belief that the parent-offspring taboo is rigidly lodged in the germ plasm of the human species. Rather may we suspect that it arises spontaneously as a response to the economies of the human mating situation.

2. Parent-Offspring Fixations and Parent-Offspring Conflict. The parent-offspring incest taboo is a social economy rather than an economy for every individual in the group. Indeed it is intended to frustrate the individual economy of training one's offspring as a mate, to the supplanting of one's erstwhile spouse; and being a frustrating social economy, it will cause personal conflicts.

Because of the very intimacy and reciprocal responsiveness of parent-offspring association—and notably in the case of mothers and sons—a love relationship will always emerge spontaneously between parent and offspring in the normal course of affairs, regardless of the incest taboo. Though the taboo bans an actual copulation between parent and child, it does not ban other kinds of amorous activity. Hence the mother who exclaims that she will bring up her son to be the kind of man she has always wanted to have, may indeed raise for herself an ideal husband for whom she would be the ideal wife. Yet while the mother becomes sexually frigid to other men, including her husband, and while her son remains indifferent to other women, the mother and son are themselves blocked by the parent-offspring incest taboo from sexually consummating what would otherwise be an ideal mating.

But even though the offspring is prevented from actually mating with the parent, that does not imply that the parent does not unwittingly exercise a tremendous influence upon the offspring's selection of his mate. The offspring, in living in close association with his parents, and in adjusting for his own advantage to their likes and dislikes, with little competition from the likes and dislikes of others, will inevitably develop in himself some degree of *fixation* [4] upon his parents. And by the term *fixation* upon another person, we mean an adjustment of one person's tools-jobs to the exigencies of the jobs-tools of the other person. Thus the son who has spent much of his early life in close association with his mother (or some other person in a similarly intimate relationship to him) will have developed a set of selected stimuli and responses that are particularly oriented to the responses and stimuli of his mother (or whoever stands *in loco matris*).* A *mother fixation* or a *father fixation,* then, is little more than an orientation of one's stimuli and responses in the direction of the responses and stimuli of the respective parent.

The possession of a prolonged, and therefore deep, fixation upon the parent of opposite sex may place the person in a curious dilemma when he tries to find a mate. Thus in the case of a son with a mother fixation (and correspondingly with the father-fixated daughter) the problem of an economical mating resolves itself into finding a person who is like his mother yet who is not his mother; in short, he seeks to realize his *"mother's image"* in some other woman. The extent to which a prospective mate fails to possess the criteria of this mother image is the extent to which she fails to satisfy him as a mate. On the other hand, the extent to which the prospective mate possesses the criteria of the mother image is the extent to which she may bring down upon her head the incest taboo. For that reason we often see men who prefer the society of women of their mothers' age, without however quite bringing themselves into a sexual or matrimonial relationship with them (though sometimes they marry and live together with great happiness).

It frequently happens that a person with a deep parent fixation, of which the logical consequence is a socially quite drastically tabooed sexual intercourse, may go through life with a profound sense of personal guilt and impurity for harboring highly tabooed desires of whose precise nature he himself may be unaware. Or, caught in the above dilemma of desiring only those persons who, because of the incest taboo, seem to be forbidden to him, the worried person may become sexually impotent in the company of the opposite sex, thereby adding the feeling of a personal inadequacy to that of a personal guilt.

It is not our purpose to recapitulate further the theories of the Freudian school on the above topic, for we are interested only in showing the respective basic economies of these deep-lying conflicts between social prohibitions and individual desires. These conflicting economies, we repeat, are inherent in the family situations themselves, without regard to time and place. For

* The case is analogous to that of a young boy who has been brought up from early infancy in the skills of carpentry, to whose tools and jobs his stimuli and responses have become particularly oriented; once the lad has reached maturity, the life of a carpenter is ideal for him, therefore he may be said to have a fixation upon that type of life.

as the mother places her infant son at her breast, or the father takes his daughter in his arms, a chain of interactions is established which, if long continued, will train the child—and the parent—to desire most the very thing that is most tabooed.

B. Sexual Bipolarity

It is common knowledge that persons of one sex have some of the physical characteristics of the opposite sex. In the extreme cases of hermaphroditism, the persons have the genitalia of both sexes. Therefore in the light of physical sexual criteria, the terms *male* and *female* might better be construed as meaning *more male than female* and *more female than male.* For the sake of an easier envisagement of this *more male* and *more female* relationship in a large population of persons, we might imagine a *U*-shaped frequency distribution with the true hermaphrodites in the center representing the persons of both sexes; to the left of this hermaphroditic center would be plotted the males of the population, in imaginary units of an increasing ratio of maleness to femaleness; to the right of the hermaphroditic center would be plotted the females of the population in imaginary units of an increasing ratio of femaleness to maleness. As we pass from the extreme left to the extreme right, we proceed from the highly masculine males through the increasingly feminine males to the hermaphrodites, and thence through the decreasingly masculine females to the highly feminine females at the right. Although this *sexual U-curve* has no shred of empiric support, if only because of the difficulty of units of measurement, it nevertheless illustrates our theoretical contention that all persons are *bisexual* (or that their sex is *bipolar*), with varying degrees of preponderance of maleness over femaleness, and the reverse.

With the above concept of *bisexualism* (or *sexual bipolarity*) in mind, let us reconnoitre the various economies that could conceivably increase or decrease the relative maleness (or femaleness) of a given person, thereby altering the relative strength of his two presumable "sexual poles." In other words, let us inquire into the particular economies that make John Doe more masculine or more feminine at one time than at another. For in the present study we shall view a person's total sexual behavior as the resultant of opposing male and female "economies," or quasi "Forces," into the nature of whose determinants we are inquiring.[5]

1. Homosexualism. If we take the case of the person with the genitalia of one sex who nevertheless tries to imitate the sexual behavior of the opposite sex, we come upon the fairly frequent phenomenon of *homosexualism,* for the explanation of which there are two schools of thought. One school maintains that homosexual behavior is constitutional and that, roughly speaking, a homosexualist is born and not made; the other school maintains that homosexual behavior is the result of early conditioning, and that a homosexualist is made and not born. We for our part point out that there may be like effects from various causes (e.g., you can be born blind, or become blind), and that homosexualism may sometimes be constitutional and sometimes conditioned and sometimes a mixture of both.

a. Situational homosexualism. The incidents of homosexualism that are perhaps easiest to understand are those that occur in boarding schools, prisons, merchant and naval ships, or at outlying military posts where persons of the opposite sex are not available for penis-vagina copulation. These incidents of homosexualism arise from the nature of the situation and may be little more than temporary makeshifts. For, if we assume in the company of others that a person is continually subject to the basic urge of procreation, for the performance of which he has genital tools, then he will continually be seeking jobs for his tools, subject only to the restrictions that are inherent in the tools. A homosexual incident, then, may be little more than a *substitute act* for heterosexual copulation.

If we inspect the actual mechanisms of homosexualism (which, incidentally, are fairly stereotyped, often spontaneous, and by no means dependent upon time or place), we note that orifices other than the vagina are used to receive the penis, and that appendages other than the penis are used to intrude into the vagina. These orifices, such as the mouth, the palm of one's hand, the rectum, armpits, calves of one's legs, etc., are *substitute vaginas,* when functionally viewed. According to the same functional view, fingers, tongues, etc., are *substitute penises.* Every person then has not only his own formal genitalia, but also *substitute genitalia* of both sexes.

The same concept of substitute genitalia applies also to the orifices and appendages of other animals that may be used for human sexual gratification. It applies similarly to candles, wide-mouthed bottles, and other artifacts that may be used in place of a penis or a vagina.

Indeed, one's environment can be classified in terms of serviceable and nonserviceable substitute genitalia for one sex or the other. Though the genitalia of the opposite sex are doubtless recommended on the basis of an ideal economy, situations may nevertheless arise in which substitute genitalia are used until the opposite sex becomes available for heterosexual practices.

b. "Conditioned" homosexualism. The above argument about situational homosexualism applies also to those cases in which, because of parent fixation or the fear of pregnancy, or for other reasons set forth by the Freudian school, a person does not desire intercourse with the opposite sex, even when the opposite sex is readily available for that purpose. Let us call this type of homosexualism *"conditioned" homosexualism* because it depends upon conditions other than situational givens.

In the case of "conditioned" homosexualism—barring a removal of the conditioning factors—the substitute genitalia may become for all intents and purposes the primary sexual tools-jobs of the "conditioned" homosexualist. Thus the mouth or the rectum of the male homosexualist may in his eyes represent his sexual genitalia far more than do his formal genitalia. This feeling may be carried to such a point, as in an ancient Roman cult, that the homosexualist desires to (or even does) castrate himself in order to be rid of his formal genitalia, which have ceased to possess a sexual functional value for him.

When the conditioning factors are removed, the homosexual practices may be discontinued, though much depends upon the person's age at his first homosexual incident and upon the duration of the practices, inasmuch as a person does adjust his tools-jobs to his actual optimal behavior upon which he becomes *fixated*.

In this connection we should also remember that there are cases on record in which a person enjoys both homosexual and heterosexual practices, even at the same time. For example, there is the case of a man who while copulating with his wife, enjoyed having a friend use his rectum for sexual intercourse.[6] This case is particularly interesting because it illustrates a simultaneous male-female conduct of apparently equal polarity.

2. Sexual Bipolarity and the Determinants of the Sex of Offspring. The above cases of an individual's variant sexual activity, which were tendered in order to illustrate the bipolarity of sex, were based upon considerations of the individual's own personal economies in the light of his situational givens and his previous conditioning. The question now arises as to the extent to which the bipolarity of an individual's sex may be used as a social mechanism for the purpose of more inclusive social economy. We shall argue theoretically how this very bipolarity may be connected with the determination of the sex of offspring to the advantage of society—a theory for which we can find some empiric support.

By way of clarification, let us remember that according to our hypothetical Principle of Least Effort, every organism's every act will be directed towards a most economical existence. Hence it follows theoretically, for example, that human beings are divided into two sexes, instead of one, because of some economy—say the economy of a specialization of labor, as has often been suggested as an explanation of male-female mating.

Yet whatever the economy of two different sexes may be, this economy can eventuate under conditions of a fairly permanent mating only when the number of persons of one sex approximates the number of the other sex, so that each person can have a mate. Hence the job of human procreation involves not only the production of offspring, and of offspring of both sexes; it also involves the production of offspring of both sexes according to a fairly stable male-female birth ratio, so that there will be subsequent opportunities for all the offspring to mate in adult years. Since a fairly stable male-female birth ratio is clearly important for permanent human mating, let us inquire into the possible determinants of this ratio.

If we take the view that parents, in producing offspring, thereby produce sexual mates for themselves and others, we at once note the economic advantage of producing offspring of that sex of which there happens to be a shortage: boys if there is a shortage of boys, and girls if there is a shortage of girls. According to this view, human sex is governed by group determinants, or "statistical" considerations, and not by "random chance."

The size of the group that determines the sex of a given offspring need be no larger than that of a family. Thus if the first offspring of a husband and wife happens to be a son, there will immediately be a family shortage of females, with the result that it would be economical to have the second child a daughter in order to provide a potential mate for the son (if not also for the father). Thus viewed, there would be a tendency for an alternation of sexes in one's successive offspring.

If we inquire now into the possible mechanisms whereby the sex of offspring is determined—assuming for convenience of argument that it is carried in the father's sperm—we cannot help noting how conveniently the concept of sexual bipolarity offers itself as an explanation. In the case of the parents whose only child is a son, the father, in loving and caressing his son, is indulging in a homosexual activity with the result that his sexual bipolarity theoretically becomes somewhat more female. On the other hand, the mother, in loving and caressing the same son does not become less female.

Once we have taken the step that the father's own bipolar ratio of maleness to femaleness has changed, then we may conceive of a theoretical corresponding change in some aspect of his hormone balance with a concomitant change in the numerical proportion of his male-determining and female-determining sperm cells—with the ultimate result of an increased chance of begetting a female.[7] And the same argument applies *mutatis mutandis* when the first child is a daughter. For as soon as the father falls in love with a child and "wants" or "desires" it, he polarizes himself in the opposite direction sexually, and thereby theoretically sets up reactions to produce a child of the opposite sex, thus confirming the hoary superstition that the sex of one's offspring is the opposite from that desired by the parents.

If instead of viewing the above family in isolation, we view it in its neighborhood of ever widening area, we can see how the male-female ratio of the entire population with whom the parents come into contact will also influence their sexual polarity, although much will depend upon the frequency and duration of specific contacts (e.g., a foreman in a factory, or the captain of a ship, might spend most of his day with males, while the supervisor of an office spends most of his day with females). Yet by and large, because of the nature of the problem, in "normal" times, with a complete mobility of the sexes, a person would tend to come into contact with males and females in about the proportion that they exist in the population.

Theoretically, therefore, if the male-female ratio of the entire population is fairly stable from year to year, then the male-female birth ratio will also be stable from year to year—as is notoriously the case. According to the *Statistical Abstracts* of the United States for registered births, the number of boy babies per 1,000 girl babies for eight years beginning with 1936 was respectively 1,052; 1,054; 1,052; 1,054; 1,055; 1,054; 1,058; 1,055—which is a remarkably stable ratio. The slight preponderance of male births over female births is usually correlated with the fact that females tend to live longer than males, and that the slight male preponderance at birth is levelled out in adult years when a close numerical balance is established.

If it so happens that the male-female ratio of the population changes, as is the case in a prolonged bloody warfare that appreciably diminishes the male population, then the sexual polarity of the remaining minority of men would become increasingly more male, with the result that the proportion of boy babies to girl babies would become appreciably greater.

As an empiric test of this theory of sexual bipolarity as a determinant of the sex of offspring, we can investigate the actual male-female birth ratios in European countries during and after the war of 1914–1918 in which, without exception, the adult male population decreased markedly without a commensurate decrease in the female population. If our theory be correct, we shall find that during these years there was a significant increase in the ratio of male births to female births.

In the *Statistical Bulletin: The Metropolitan Life Insurance Company* (Vol. 20, 1939, p. 1–4) in an article on the subject of more boy babies in postwar years, we read: "Following a long war a definite increase in the proportion of male births has repeatedly been observed. This was, for example, the experience of nearly all the principal European countries engaged in the World War" (i.e., 1914–1918). To illustrate this point, the data were presented for Germany from 1910 through 1923 (taken from the *Statistisches Jahrbuch für das deutsche Reich*). For the years from 1910 through 1915, the ratio of male live births per 1,000 female live births in Germany was respectively: 1,053; 1,055; 1,059; 1,054; 1,056; and 1,056. These are comparable to the ratios for the United States presented above. Yet after 1915 in Germany the proportion of male births increased markedly, as is evident from the ratios for the war years and postwar years from 1916 through 1923 respectively: 1,065; 1,069; 1,073; 1,080; 1,072; 1,073; 1,070; and 1,068. After discussing the problem from various angles, the above article closes: "The increase in the ratio of male births after prolonged wars is an established fact. Its explanation for the time being remains a mystery."

From our viewpoint, this increase in the proportion of male births after prolonged wars clearly confirms our own theoretical expectations that male births will surpass female births until a stable male-female ratio for the entire population has been more nearly restored.*

Though our above theory of the determination of the sex of offspring has excellent statistical support, it lacks an explanation of the precise physiological mechanisms involved. Our assumptions about a "hormone balance" and the father's sexual polarity as the sole determinant of his offspring's sex were purely *ad hoc.*

On the other hand, our assumption that the proximity of other persons of the same and opposite sex is a sex determinant is not without a counterpart in the rest of the biosocial continuum. For example, the offspring of the lamprey that are situated nearest to the mother lamprey develop into males, while the more distant offspring become females. This fact is not inconsistent with the theory that the mother lamprey acts as a female pole

* The effect of the increased proportion of male births would be felt about twenty years later when there would be more matable males than females, thereby providing perhaps a sexual motive for killing off men and stealing women according to the ancient pastime of warfare which does seem, in a way, to be cyclical.

that makes the nearer offspring male, which in turn makes the more distant offspring female. This situation, that invites to experimentation, suggests that the mechanism is chemical.*

In this connection, let us not overlook the possibly more enduring polar effects of a parent fixation. The present writer knows of a man with a serious mother fixation who wanted a daughter to name after his mother but who managed to beget five sons instead. Another person who wanted a son to name after his illustrious father, to whom he was devoted, had three daughters instead. How far these cases are accidental is not clear.

It is clear from the typical postwar data of Germany that the determination of the sex of human offspring is not a mere matter of the "fall of the dice." In this connection we wonder whether the remainder of an offspring's genetic inheritance is solely a matter of the fall of the "genetic dice"—or whether it represents to some extent an unconscious selection by his parents.

Our theory of the relative sexual polarity of the parents as a determinant of the sex of their offspring implies that each person responds *erotically* to some extent to others in his environment: masculinely to the females and femininely to the males, even though the erotic response may often be totally unconscious. What we call a male or female person is but a marked skewness of a fundamental bisexualism in one direction or the other; homosexualism is only an exaggeration of a commonplace bisexualism.

Theoretically, a person's impulse to mate arises from a desire to provide both female tools-jobs for his male component, and male tools-jobs for his female component—a sexual dualism that is lost sight of both because of the pronounced skewness of sex, and because of the cultural taboo of Western Civilization against anything but a monotypic sexual behavior that conforms in traditional fashion to the person's physical sex.

Yet it may be that a person's other and minor sex is responsible for much of his behavior, as he seeks to find substitute tools and jobs for the eroticism of his other and minor sex. Perhaps "stag" parties are as important for husbands as "hen" parties are for wives.

C. Erotic Substitute Action

A few pages back we pointed out that every person possesses not only his actual genitalia but also substitute genitalia in the form of appendages and orifices which in a pinch could serve for substitute penises and vaginas. Not only have such substitutions been used in human homosexual prac-

* As a further biological example of the effect of a disproportionate number of males, and of an unbalanced proportion of age groups, we remember that as the proportion of males (drones) in the bee colony increases, it becomes ever more indicative of an impending swarming, as every beekeeper knows; if we view swarming as an internal revolution, then it is interesting to remember that one way of preventing swarming is to distribute the brood and hence the young nurse bees more evenly throughout the entire hive (therefore the uneven distribution of age groups in a population may be a cause of internal upheaval). It is questionable how far we should generalize upon these considerations, even though the underlying theory is susceptible of empiric test.

tices from earliest historical times; similar sexual substitute action is also known to other animals (e.g., a cow may mount another cow in heat in the absence of a bull, a hen a hen, a male dog mounts a male puppy).[8] Nor should we forget that during the advanced stages of pregnancy, or during the menstrual period, some sort of substitute sexual action is often indulged in by husband and wife.

Of course, these substitute genitalia can be matched with each other without the use of the primary genitalia. For example, one person's tongue, as a substitute penis, can be inserted into another person's mouth, as a substitute vagina, with a freely admitted erotic pleasure. Much of the behavior known as fondling or caressing seems to be connected with the interplay of substitute genitalia—a substitute behavior that is often a prelude to the interplay of the primary genitalia themselves.

Since these various appendages, orifices, and orificelike members of a person's body are erotically excitable substitute genitalia, and presumably have been for ages, we need not be surprised to learn from the Freudian school that everyday routine activity that involves the automatic excitation of these parts may give erotic pleasure. By the term *erotic pleasure* or *eroticism,* we mean a pleasure, or satisfaction, that is not connected with what seems to be the primary nonsexual purpose of the act, but is connected with substitute sexual activity.

Thus many persons derive a tremendous pleasure from their bowel movements, during which time the feces acts as a substitute penis in the rectum as a substitute vagina. The persons in question may even develop elaborate rituals for cleansing their rectums and for giving themselves laxatives and enemas. These instances of what is technically known as *anal eroticism* are interesting in showing how a substitute genital tool, like the anus, can itself seek erotic satisfaction from physical entities like feces, enemas, and even candles and the like, that have no other connection with human reproduction.

The above argument about *anal eroticism* applies to the eroticism of the mouth, or *oral eroticism,* in which there is a pleasure in eating, sucking pipes, dental hygiene, and even in the "mouthing of words," apart from the customary exigencies of partaking of food, drink, and air, or of communicating with others.[9]

Although this discussion of anal and oral eroticism may seem to be farfetched, if we remember that the biosocial urge to procreate is theoretically present with us from the moment of conception, we may not overlook the fact that in early infancy the child can know only oral and anal pleasures, in addition to a possible masturbatory fondling of his genitals, as the Freudian school has pointed out. A baby's first reaction to another person is oral in sucking, while one of the chief concerns of the parent is a cleansing of the baby's rectum. In all babydom the thumb is a soothing instrument to suck, with presumably no other purpose served than that of eroticism. Hence in the early period of one's life, the substitute genitalia may be activated erotically without any reference to the possibility of a heterosexual penis-vagina copulation.

Since a baby's alimentary and excrementory acts, including its vocalism and puking, are practically his only means of asserting himself socially in dominating his environment, these anal and oral practices may in some cases become social tools in a sense beyond that of satisfying one's erotic impulses. Even in the mature life of some persons, the entire phenomenon of defecation, eating, and all the attendant hygiene and therapies for indigestion and bowel troubles take on meanings that are simply incomprehensible to persons who happen to lack the particular fixations in question.

Differently expressed, the content of the environment of an anally or orally erotic person may be classified, compared, and correlated in reference to his particular secondary erotic needs with the result that he sees tools-jobs in his environment of which others may be totally unaware.

From the above discussion we can see how many things can substitute for other things. This applies not only to the parts of the body in erotic practices, in which, for example, a tongue can substitute for a penis and a mouth for a vagina, it applies also to inanimate nature, in which a candle may substitute for a penis and a knothole for a vagina. In all these cases we find that the substitute has a *functional feature* in common with that for which it substitutes. We shall call this common functional feature a *substitution feature,* as we emphasize that *the term has meaning only in reference to specific entities of matter-energy that are used by a given organism, or group of organisms, in reciprocally matching tools and jobs for the primary object of a most economical survival which includes, as a device, a most economical procreation.* Or, differently expressed, a *substitution feature* exists only as a particular functional quality of a particular entity of matter-energy in reference to the physical survival needs of a given organism, or group of organisms. Hence though a *substitution feature* refers to matter-energy, it has no existence apart from the particular organism's needs. Obviously, the functional classification of the entities of experience according to substitution features is not restricted to erotic forms and functions, but applies to all forms and functions, as we shall later note in greater detail.

Since what a person thinks he sees is influenced by the needs of his own tools-jobs, one person's view of a given thing may not be another's. The maiden may blush at the gift of a candle in which she sees a substitute penis, whereas the matron puts it into the candlestick without further ado. What a given person "sees" or "understands" in a thing is indicative of the particular needs of his own tools-jobs and therefore of himself.

D. The Erotic Drive in "Science"

In the foregoing pages we have made the point—and surely the Freudian school has made and emphasized the same point before us—that a person tends to see substitute sexual tools and jobs in his environment; that is, the entities of his environment have symbolic value for his sexual urges.

Let us now see if, in the light of our preceding argument, we can understand something of the structure of the sexual symbolism of the environment as it may appear to some group of persons. We shall approach the topic by first scrutinizing certain sexual attributes of speech.

In the earlier structure of Indo-European tongues, such as Latin, Greek, Gothic, and the like, as well as in the present-day structure of a wide diversity of non-Indo-European tongues, we find grammatical classes of *masculine, feminine,* and sometimes *neuter.* Often the grammatical gender corresponds to the sex of the object (e.g., the German words for *father, son, man* are masculine, while those for *mother, daughter, wife* are feminine). Yet to the sorrow of the schoolmaster who must teach these genders, there are also many cases of words whose grammatical gender lacks any connection with the natural gender of the object named. For example, the natural gender of the sun, earth, moon, or river is clearly neuter; yet the grammatical gender of the words for these objects may be masculine or feminine, depending upon the language (e.g., in Latin, the usual word for sun is masculine; those for earth and moon are feminine).

Yet despite the complicated relationships of grammatical gender in speech, the late A. Meillet, a philologist of eminence, pointed out that there is often a certain metaphoric connection between many an object and the grammatical gender of its name. For example, a tree in some tongues may be feminine (e.g., Latin, *arbor,* "tree," or *quercus,* "oak tree," are both feminines) whereas the fruit of growth may be neuter (e.g., *frumentum* is a Latin neuter). The tree bearing fruit is patterned on the analogy of a female animal bearing offspring.[10]

Although grammatical genders vary widely among the different Indo-European tongues, we can understand how the word for earth, Latin *terra,* might be considered feminine because it bears fruit, whereas the sun that warms the earth, or the rain that wets it with a quickening fluid, or the river that overflows it and makes it fertile may all be masculine. The moon may be feminine because it waxes and wanes in reference to the sun, etc. In all of these cases there is a certain imaginary analogy to human male-female copulation and the production of offspring. Indeed, if one were to project oneself into that anthropomorphically thinking past, one might even find that the male-female principle was the primary unifying principle of the then intellectual life.

How such a unifying principle became established will perhaps never be known. Maybe it was man's own discovery of the connection between copulation and the production of offspring that suggested the possibility of a universal male-female principle that ultimately became reflected in the grammatical gender in speech.

Let us assume that during the hypothetical period of "primitive nature worship" there was no knowledge of the connection between copulation and the birth of offspring. Women bore children automatically, even as they automatically came into puberty; and they copulated with men just as automatically. What led to the discovery of the correlation between copulation and the production of offspring may never be known; perhaps it came with the domestication of animals when the lack of a male resulted in no offspring.

In any event, the discovery of the sex principle would have enormous economic consequences, as man thought he had control of the factors that produced his food. It would also have important intellectual consequences, as he imagined that the rest of nature behaved like himself in reference to the unifying male-female principle. In so believing, early man doubtless drew many spurious correlations; yet let us not forget that he also probably drew an enormous number of correct ones.

Once the intellectual impetus was given to a scrutinizing of nature for the operation of the male-female principle, then it was a small step indeed for a corresponding formal linguistic classification to appear, as the peoples of the day referred to the sun, rain, and river as *he,* and to the earth, moon, and flowers as *she* (a sexual classification of a perhaps earlier asexual animism). From that point on, the automatic systematization of grammatical gender would proceed as originally set forth in Karl Brugmann's theory of gender.[11]

Thus, to take a stereotyped example, if the word for "woman" happened to have been *gunā,* which ended in a long *ā* only because every word has to end in some sound or other, then that final *ā* of *gunā* might accidentally have become a signal of the feminine gender, with the result that it was added analogically to the words for earth, tree, and flower to show that they too were feminine, like a woman. Different tribes may have used different endings for their masculines and feminines, and they may have classified nature differently (e.g., in Latin the sun is masculine and the moon is feminine, while in Germanic it is the reverse). Some may not have been so consistent as others (e.g., in Gothic *every* noun was feminine that belonged to the declension that descended from the above-mentioned *ā* class of *gunā;* not so in Latin, where masculines like *agricola* are present).

Yet once the gender classification had been introduced into the nouns of a tongue, then the adjectives and pronouns that referred to particular nouns were often carefully provided with the gender of the noun. Thus in Latin, all adjectives or pronouns that refer to a feminine tree are also feminine in gender, though they at once become masculine or neuter respectively when the gender of the antecedent noun happens to be masculine or neuter. In short, many tribes of that early period seemed to see a world that was classified according to the sexual male-female principle—a principle that continued to pervade the thinking of alchemy well into the Middle Ages.

As we know from the anthropological writings of such persons as James G. Frazer,[12] this sexual view of nature colored human actions towards nature. Thus the farmer who wanted to guarantee the fruitfulness of a field, a tree, or an animal, might hit upon the idea of masturbating upon it in order to provide a quickening "male impulse." Or he might throw eggs or grain at a young bride for an analogous reason. From familiar situations like these, whose original intent was literally a deliberate substitute sexual activity, there arose rituals whose original meaning may often have been later forgotten.

If we are correct in the belief that at one time in some tribes, the male-female principle was the unifying intellectual principle in understanding the environment, that would mean that phylogenetically those tribes viewed their environment as arranged according to the general classes of penises and vaginas—of sperm and germ—and offspring. From thence the invention of divinities of relevant human forms to manipulate these substitute genitalia was an easy step of the imagination. For that matter, we note how readily the children of today accept this selfsame anthropomorphic attitude with its underlying male-female principle.

With the elapse of centuries, however, the erstwhile ancient unifying male-female principle has been radically altered in the face of new sets of observations of the "new science." Nevertheless we may still wonder how far one of the important drives to the "new science" in its ever routing of the "old religion" may not be the familiar drive of eroticism.

E. The Multiple "Personality"

If we take the view that a person's actual behavior depends very largely upon the actual givens of the situation in which he is, we can see how every person in addition to what he actually is at the time, is also potentially many other things that he will actually become if the situation changes. Indeed the purpose of the foregoing pages is to suggest, with supporting data, that even one's sex is not an invariant of one's "personality"; although a person may feel himself to be every inch a man, he may also be potentially every inch a woman.

By the same token, every person is potentially a murderer, or a thief, or a prostitute, or an arsonist, or an angel under given conditions. Indeed one of the constructive features of the so-called World War II was the demonstration that looting, raping, black-marketeering, homosexualism, the shooting of prisoners of war, and the like were amply indulged in by American officers and soldiers in Europe under the conditions of warfare despite the fact that this very type of conduct on the part of the enemy was alleged as a reason for our going to war. In so behaving, our men demonstrated the relativity of the person's actual behavior to the situations in which he finds himself.

The theory that we are latently many different things has been stressed by the Freudian school, which maintains that oversolicitousness for a particular type of behavior, or the reverse, reveals a strong latent tendency in that direction. Thus a woman's great solicitude for the welfare of harlots may be viewed as a desire to ameliorate conditions against the day of her own entrance into that class; by the same token, a pronounced hatred of the class may be construed either as a desire to conceal one's own strong desires in that connection, or as a desire to eradicate the class of action as such, for the sake of one's own protection.

Yet when we say that a person is latently many different kinds of "persons"—or has a multiple "personality"—what does such a statement mean?

It means that, as a person looks out into his environment at a given time from a given situation, he sees his environment functionally classified in the light of his own then actual and probable needs—a functional classification that will change with the needs, even though the actual datum of the environment remains the same. This functional classification of the environment does not exist in the environment, but in the person's own mind; indeed, according to our definition, it *is* his mind.

II. THE ECONOMY OF SYMBOLIC PROCESS (SUBSTITUTION FEATURES)

Throughout our foregoing discussion of human sexual activity, we noted repeated instances of the use of substitute tools for the given sexual jobs, or substitute jobs for the given sexual tools. This condition of substitute action, however, is not uniquely characteristic of sexual activity; indeed, as we have argued repeatedly in the past, the substitution of one tool for another, or of one job for another is theoretically present in all living action. We need only to generalize upon the commonplace but typical human situation of the job of pounding in a nail; lacking a hammer for this job we can use a brick, a stone, or a great number of other objects, thereby illustrating the fact that a given job can be performed by many different tools. Conversely, a hammer cannot only pound a nail, it can also be used as a paperweight, a missile, and the like, thereby illustrating the fact that a given tool can perform many different jobs.*

This condition of substitute action is likewise elemental in all symbolic process, as we shall formally argue in the ensuing pages. Before a person can pound a nail with a stone instead of a hammer he must "see" that a stone has the same *functional feature* as a hammer in reference to the *operation* of pounding a nail, and as we have argued in the case of hammers, stones, and the pounding of nails we can argue about the functions of *all* entities of a person's environment in reference to *all* his jobs.

To repeat, symbolic process in our usage is nothing more than an individual's classification of the accumulated data of his experience in terms of their functional capacities to perform his jobs-of-survival with a minimum of effort. Upon his ability thus to classify depends to no small extent the economy of his life.

A. Objects, Operations, Groups, and Isomorphs [13]

If a carpenter has the job, *O,* of driving a nail by means of his hammer, then we may say by way of definition that the action of *pounding* is an operation, *S,* that he performs upon the object, *O,* which is the nail.

Generalizing upon the above case of the carpenter with his hammer and nail, we may say in the light of present-day knowledge that all living action consists of *kinds* of material *operations* upon *kinds* of material *objects.* There are many different kinds of operations and also many different kinds of objects. Unless there is an object, there can be no operation.

* As my former teacher of Sanskrit, Dr. W. E. Clark, always emphasized: "In Sanskrit every word has many different meanings and every meaning has many different words."

The point of interest for us in this connection, however, is that the *operation, S,* of pounding can be performed on many other objects, *O,* than a nail, and that it can be performed by many other instruments than a hammer. Indeed we may say that there is a whole *group, G,* of objects ($O' \; O'' \; O''' \; . \; . \; .$) upon which the *S* operation of pounding can be performed, and also a whole *group, G,* of different elements from hammers to bricks ($S' \; S'' \; S''' \; . \; . \; .$) that can perform the operation of pounding.

In reference to the specific operation upon the object, *O,* the set of elements that constitute the group, $S' \; S'' \; S''' \; . \; . \; .$, may be said to be *similar.* By the same token, the above set of objects, $O', O'', O''' \; . \; . \; .$ may be said to be *similar.*

So if our above carpenter mislays his hammer while still needing to perform the operation of pounding upon the nail object, he can employ some other element of the same *S* group. Thus he might employ another hammer of like form and dimension, or he might employ a stone, or any number of other entities that can perform the operation, *S,* provided that the carpenter is aware of their existence and of their capacity to perform the operation, *S.*

We might even make a list of all the different entities in the carpenter's experience that *could* perform the operation, *S,* in reference to the object, *O,* which, as we have said, would constitute a *group, G.* These different entities can be said to be *semantically related* in the carpenter's experience because of their one *substitution feature* in common (there being no other necessary connection between the entities in question outside of the carpenter's experience).*

It might happen that instead of having the *object,* O_1, of inserting the nail by means of the *operation* of pounding, S_1, the carpenter might have the object, O_2, of pulling the nail out of the wood by means of the operation, S_2, whether by using a hammer or some other entity. In that case the elements of his experience that could perform the operation, S_2, would constitute another group, G_2. Although the hammer would belong to both groups, G_1 and G_2, not all of the other entities of one group would necessarily be members of the other. By the same token, many of the other entities of each of the two groups would belong to many, many other groups whose operations could not be performed by the hammer.

Upon reflection, it is clear that the above argument could be extended to all *operations,* and all the *objects* of all the entities of the carpenter's experience, with the result that the data of his experience could be classified into groups in the light of their particular operations in reference to his particular objects. Thus conceived, a carpenter's entire experience is a vast network of *semantic interrelatedness.*

In view of the above definitions of object, operation, and group, it follows that as any two or more entities agree ever more in the specific operational groups to which they belong in the arbitrary carpenter's experience,

* It would be obviously economical, if it were possible, to have every different operation perform every different object; this economy may be characteristic of schizophrenic thinking (see later discussion).

they become functionally ever more *similar,* as far as the carpenter's own objects are concerned. If two different entities—such as two equivalent hammers—belong to all the same groups they may be called the *same* (functionally).

The argument of the above paragraphs overlooks the fact that some objects and operations may be subordinate to others. Thus, in the case of the carpenter, the operation and object of pounding the nail may be subordinate to further objects and operations such as, for example, the more primary object of building a house, with all its appurtenant operations and subordinate objects. So too the entire operation-object of housebuilding may be subordinate to that of shelter, which in turn may be subordinate to the primary must of a most economical survival. In short, there may be subgroups of subgroups of subgroups of operations-objects.

The chief points to emphasize, however, according to the above view are, *first,* that the data of experience are functionally classified into different operations (or substitution features) and different objects; and *second* that they are all "goal-directed"—to borrow a term from Gestalt psychology—but in the sense that they are directed ultimately to the most economical existence of the individual in question (and not in reference to any absolute and universal categories).

Perhaps the most transparent example of the above functional similarities, or isomorphs, is found in the case of human verbalizations which, after all, represent the operation of matter-energy upon human objects.

Thus, in spite of gross physical differences in pitch, amplitude, timbre, and the like between the actual utterances of a group of persons of the same speech community, we nevertheless say that they have the "same" vocabulary of words because their respective words, when subjected to the same grammatical operations, evoke the same responses. For the same reason we may say that the persons are elements of the same social groups because they have the same sets of vocabulary elements, grammatical operations, and meanings (i.e., correlated responses).

Nor does the isomorphism stop there. There is also by and large a 1 to 1 correspondence between spoken speech and written speech, even though sound is the physical medium of the one, while light is the physical medium of the other. Here we may say that the set of spoken elements and the set of written elements are the "same" in terms of operations and objects.

Turning now to the actual structure of a given person's speech usage, we note further examples of isomorphic groups. Thus in English there is a *group* or *set* of words known as infinitives. Now if we put, say, the word, *did,* in front of each element of this group or set (e.g., *did go, did see,* etc.), we get a second group, or set, which for all intents and purposes is isomorphic with the first (even as the domain of integers is isomorphic with the domain of their squares).

The above case is not unique, for there is no reason why the group or set should have been restricted to infinitives, or why the operation should have been limited to the auxiliary, *did.* Any other tense, or mood, or aspect, or case, or number—or any other grammatical category—would have served equally well as an operation upon any other set of morphological objects. Indeed, the whole principle of economical permutation discussed in Chapter Three is based upon the concepts of the mathematical group theory in which a given class modifies (i.e., "multiplies") another class.*

Nor is speech unique in respect of its organization according to the theory of groups. Years ago Max Wertheimer, one of the pioneers in Gestalt psychology, noted the same isomorphism in music.[14] A melody, *A*, that is transposed *B* into another key and played two octaves higher on a different instrument remains the "same" melody because of the obvious isomorphism (i.e., the 1 to 1 correspondence between the two sets), even though *A* and *B* do not have a single note of like physical frequency in common.

Upon these cases one may generalize. Speech (or music) seems to be only a special instance of what is generally the case in all animate activity: the selection of particular *kinds* of material operations to perform upon particular *kinds* of material objects. All animate reaction to stimuli seems to be selective and classificatory in terms of *kinds* of material operations upon *kinds* of material objects. In short, our Tool Analogy of Chapter Three and our argument of Chapter Five seem to be of general applicability.

The mathematician, Poincaré, once said that "Mathematics is the art of giving the same name to different things." † Yet is mathematics unique therein? Does not the layman, for example, apply the name, *legs*, to a variety of different things from the legs of chairs and tables to the legs of flies and cats? And do we not apply the same names to different things for the same reason that mathematicians do? And is this "art" of mathematics anything else than the desire to minimize the n number of different kinds of actions that evoke a given m number of different kinds of responses—a minmizing which, according to the present theory, is characteristic of living process? (We shall presently argue that it is characteristic of symbolic process.)

For in this book we seek to go further than to point out with others the applicability of group theory as a description of all animate action. Rather do we ask, figuratively speaking, how many n different names Poincaré will try to apply to m different things.

We contend that there is an economy in this process and that, in general, when m different kinds of operations are to be performed by n different kinds of tools, the size of n will be minimized, ‡ and that every organism will alter its own structure, or that of its environment, or both, so that the organism's n can be minimized.

---

* The British mathematician, George Boole, saw this group condition in the case of adjacent words (e.g., the *black cat*) for which he invented his algebra (see end of chapter). Yet the same group condition would seem to prevail in every speech permutation of every sort, whether phonetic, morphological, verbal, phrasal, and so on, except that in speech $ab \neq ba$.

† A quotation I find written in pencil by J. L. Walsh at the head of Chapter VI (Group Theory) of his copy of Birkhoff, G. and MacLane, S., *A Survey of Modern Algebra*, New York: Macmillan, 1941.

‡ Subject to the auxiliary conditions discussed in previous chapters.

B. Abstractions, Classifications, Correlations, and "Ideas" as Economical Solutions to the Problem of Survival: Knowledge as a Unit System

In connection with our above argument about the similarity and dissimilarity of operations and objects, let us briefly review certain aspects of Chapter Five on sensation, where the point was made that some sort of a sensory system is theoretically an economic necessity for an organism if he is to minimize his probable work over time (i.e., minimize his effort). This sensory system, as we shall now attempt to show, is theoretically an integrated unit system of operations upon objects.

If we begin with the initial *data of sensation*—that is, with the physical impingements upon an individual's system, whether from within or from without—we may say that these initial *data of sensation* are the objects of the general operation of *abstracting* the various class criteria that are to be used for the purpose of comparison. The *abstractions,* in turn, are the objects of the operation of *comparison.* These *comparisons,* in conjunction with frequencies of occurrences, are the objects of the operation of *correlation.*

Now if (1) the sole aim of every individual is a most economical existence, then (2) it follows theoretically that the entire procedure of mentation from abstraction through correlation is undertaken directly or indirectly in reference to that sole aim; and from that it also follows (3) that all his abstractions, comparisons, and correlations constitute a *unit system of knowledge* whose basic frame of reference is his own most economical existence. In the light of this frame of reference of his own needs, the individual notes, for example, the roundness or the heaviness or the relative speed—or the "goodness," "badness," etc., of the data of his experience.

Yet in saying that a correlation with its underlying abstractions and classifications presupposes a unit system of knowledge, we are saying nothing new, since it is a commonplace of science that a correlation is meaningless unless it does so presuppose. The most that we can say about this unit system of knowledge is that it is economically structured, and that it exists only in reference to an individual (or a group of individuals who agree upon objects and operations). In short, a system of knowledge is relative to some individual or group of individuals; there is no such thing as a disembodied absolute knowledge.

As an extreme example of the relativity of unit systems of knowledge, let us take the case of the living room of an American house. Most Americans would agree in their classification of the room and the contents in terms of chairs, tables, pictures, and the like; they would also largely agree as to the objects' functions because of the commonness of the cultural experience of the observers. Yet these human classifications in terms of human systems of knowledge would by no means correspond to the classifications that a mouse or a fly would make of the same physical objects, since what serves a useful need in our lives does not necessarily serve the same need or any need in theirs—and *vice versa.*

The above example serves to illustrate theoretically the utilitarian nature of our abstractions, classifications, and correlations, as well as their relativity. A person with "new ideas" is a person with new solutions to the problem of a most economical survival, whether the "new ideas" refer to a new classification or to a new correlation. The "new ideas" are welcome or unwelcome to another person depending upon their presumable positive or negative effects upon that person's economy from his viewpoint.

III. CULTURE, SOCIETY, AND THE SUPEREGO [15]

Many of a person's abstractions and correlations refer to the various modes of activity that are peculiar to the *social activity* of the social group to which he belongs. This consideration broaches the entire topic of *culture,* into whose structure and dynamics we shall now inquire. Since the culture of a group is a kind of language of the group, and since the speech of the group is but a part of its culture, we may expect to find that much of our previous argument about the structure and dynamics of speech applies inferentially to what we shall call the *language of culture.*

A. Culture as a Unit System of Social Signals and Correlated Social Responses

Let us concede at once that the terms *social action* and *culture* are meaningless without a definition of a social group to which the social action and culture refer. Although this definition of a social group will be given in detail in Part Two, it will suffice for our present purposes if we simply say that *a number of individuals may be said to constitute a social group insofar as they have similar objects which they pursue with similar operations; as a result of the social action of this group the given objects are either accomplished, or are likely to be accomplished, by the expenditure of less effort than would be the case if the individuals were operating independently; the cost of membership in the group entails a sacrifice of a greater or lesser amount of the individual's freedom of action.*

From the viewpoint of the individual members, therefore, the benefits of society are obtained at the expense of compulsions and restraints upon individual action.

Yet society can neither reward nor coerce and restrain its members without having a mechanism for sensing and assessing the kinds of action of its members. The structure and dynamics of this sensory-mentational mechanism of the social group will be analogous to the structure and dynamics of the individual's sensory-mentational mechanism which we studied in Chapter Five, as we shall now see in some detail.

1. Social Signals and Social Correlations: The Structure of Culture. Society (i.e., a social group) can neither reward its members for a given kind of action, nor coerce them to do a certain kind of thing, nor restrain them therefrom, unless society first *classifies* discretely the actions of its members in reference to society's objects. For example, if society intends to restrain its members from committing murder, it must first define unambiguously what kind of human action constitutes murder. A social group, therefore, is like an individual's sensory system, since it establishes discrete objective criteria for the classes of action of its members. Hence there will be an n number of different *kinds* of individual action that are socially rewarded or restrained.

Just as society must classify the individual action to which society responds, so too must society classify the various m discrete kinds of social responses that are correlated with the various n different kinds of individual action. Thus if society is to restrain its members from a kind of action defined as *murder* it must have a certain defined kind of response that is correlated with the act of murder.

Yet society can neither reward nor restrain its members according to the n different classes of action unless society (through its agents) detects the individual's particular kind of action. Thus if a person commits murder, and if the social group is not aware of the fact, then the social group takes no action towards the person, for quite obvious reasons.

The parallel between the above social sensory-mentational system and an individual's (as discussed in Chapter Five) is patent. The chief difference between the two lies in their respective frames of reference. In the *social* sensory-mentational system, the weal of the group is the frame; in that of the *individual,* the weal of the individual is the frame. It does not follow by any means that a person's *social* economy corresponds to his *individual* economy; indeed the disparity between the two economies is often the cause of many individual-social conflicts, as is commonly known (e.g., delinquency, crime, alcoholism, etc.).

Now from our definition of social sensation and mentation (i.e., correlated social actions and responses), the action of every social group is subject to a system, or code, of social correlations. This code generally consists of its constitution, customs, sentiments, "unwritten laws," feelings of "commonsense," of "everyday decency," of "moral righteousness," and the like.[16] As long as the members of the social group on the one hand, and the group itself on the other, react in reference to the correlations of its social code, then the code is a *social reality* for the members, even though the code is not written down, or cannot be verbally articulated by its members.

We need a term for such a code for a given social group. Let us adopt the traditional term, *culture.* We shall say that culture is relative to a given social group at a given time; that it consists of n different *social signals* that are correlated with m different *social responses.* The particular n signals and m responses we shall call the *cultural vocabulary* of the group.

In using the terms, *n different social signals* and *m different social responses,* we are reminded of the parallel terms of Chapter Five, where we discussed sensation and mentation and the n minimum of a mind. Is the n number of different social signals a minimum,* too, in reference to the given rewards and compulsions of the social group?

Presumably the social n is indeed a minimum if the individual's n is a minimum, because the members of the group who do the detecting of social

* Subject to the condition of an effective communication.

signals are subject to the economies of the individual's mentation. Hence it is uneconomical for a social group to increase the diversity of the terms of its cultural vocabulary (i.e., to increase the *n* number of different kinds of conduct that are to be approved or disapproved socially).

As times change, the objects and operations of the social group may change, with the result that the terms and correlations of the cultural vocabulary will change. Indeed changeableness, or *variance,* of terminology is a feature of culture, as we all know, and as becomes particularly evident when we look at the past. These changes in terminology can be effected either by official governing bodies, such as a legislature, or by common tacit action, or both. To "keep up with the times," one must change with his culture.

2. A Person and the Emission of Social Signals. If we turn the above argument around and inspect it from the viewpoint of the individual members of the group, instead of from the viewpoint of the group, it is evident that wittingly or unwittingly, through the sheer action of living, each person is signalling information about himself to the agents of society who, in turn, are on the alert to detect those of our acts that meet the objective criteria of social action. Some of our actions, such as breathing, may signal little or no relevant *social* information. Yet other of our actions may signal a great deal.

The relevant social information we signal is not restricted to the formally expressed correlations of governmental officialdom. Our own social signals may also refer to criteria of the marts of trade where goods and services are exchanged. Thus if a woman wants to sell her services to men as a harlot, she can dress and in general behave before men in selected ways that will signal to them of her intent. Just what particular acts she uses will depend upon the particular *cultural vocabulary,* or set of signals, of her particular social environment; a signal that conveys the information successfully in one group may not in another. Moreover if a woman without any intentions to harlotry so acts in dressing or in other deportment as to manifest the signals of a harlot, she will be so classified by others even to the point that men may accost her on the street, or small boys may make remarks as she passes. Since such behavior by men and small boys may itself signalize to the poor woman their belief in her apparent harlot intentions, she may very well hasten to call a cab and retire in order to rid herself of whatever she may imagine meets the current cultural criteria of harlot classification.

By adopting exclusively the ostensible social signals of the rich, or of the powerful, or of the cunning—whether by dress or by other deportment—a person will be socially classified as rich, powerful, or cunning, even though he may in fact be the very reverse. The same applies to any other signals we emit. A person is socially treated according to the social signals he emits (a topic that has been explored with great acumen by Mr. G. B. Shaw in his play, *Pygmalion*).

Since all of our observable action, even down to and including its minutiae, may be construed as social signals, we understand why many persons expend a great deal of time, thought, and care in acquiring the "proper" ones; to this end there are finishing schools that teach "manners."

Since we are judged by our observable action, we often deliberately select signals to elicit a desired social reaction. An exaggerated weight placed upon the emission of certain types of signals, however, may indicate an exaggerated desire to evoke a particular type of social classification which, in turn, as psychologists have long since pointed out, may indicate a feeling on the part of the person that if he acted "naturally" he would not be so classified. Thus, the exaggerated physical blustering of the bully may betoken cowardice; the exaggerated deference to social etiquette may betoken a feeling of social insecurity.

3. Social Signals and the Individual's Endocrine System. We have said that society treats its members according to the social signals they emit, regardless of what the individual's intent is, and regardless of what the other undetected facts may be.

For example, if a man correctly or incorrectly emits the social signals of a murderer, he can die therefrom just as effectively as if he got in the way of a bolt of lightning. Indeed, in Biblical times (*Judges,* XII, 5–6), the Ephraimites were killed off because they could not pronounce the initial phoneme of *Shibboleth* according to the then phoneme system of the dominant Gileadites. Even though the Ephraimites died from a social error on their part, they were just as much dead as if they had been killed by the physical reality of lightning.

There is obviously an enormous difference in the *kind* of reality between death from lightning and death from the emission of an adverse social signal in a given culture. Yet it does not follow by any means that the sympathetic nervous system [17] of the person in question is always aware of the difference, since to be hurt or to die is to be hurt or to die, regardless of the cause. And so it happens that a given person's endocrine system (in its fullest sense) will react in precisely the same manner whether the person is cornered by a threatening fire that belongs to the invariant language of physics, or by a threatening policeman with a drawn gun who belongs to the more variant language of culture—or, for that matter, by a threatening proposition.

Furthermore, according to our thesis of Least Effort, a person reacts not only in reference to the *actual* risks and opportunities of his environment at the present moment; he reacts also in reference to the *probable* risks and opportunities of the future, even though his reaction may be unconscious. For that reason a person who commits a crime may become frightened, even though his crime remains undetected, because he consciously or unconsciously assesses the logical *social* consequences of his action ("a guilty conscience needs no accuser"). For that reason, too, a man with a deeply rooted mother fixation of which he is unaware may become unaccountably frightened in the presence of his mother's contemporaries or even live a life of constant anxiety, because he is unconsciously reacting to the dire logical social consequences of his persistent basic sexual desire that is socially outlawed.

Though a cultural code need not run counter to our basic physiological responses to physical stimuli, yet sometimes it does. Thus in reacting to situations within the language of physics—such as one's reaction to the threat of death from drowning or from fire—many persons of the most diverse cultures react in the same way without any reference to their cultural membership; but that is not always the case, since some cultures dictate the "proper modes" of facing death if one is not to die a bounder.

The cultural correlations of society are far-reaching, and their ramifications are often little suspected. Man eats, drinks, urinates, and defecates because of physiological needs; yet in all these cases society may intervene with a stringent code of signals that specifies the how, when, and where. The small boy is taught to master his bladder as he is taught to master his tears, lest he give an adverse social signal to his own disadvantage.

Society also tells us when to laugh, and when to show rage or fear, and when to be friendly and when inimical. A person migrating into a foreign culture might well take lessons from the local school of acting so that he may learn the code of new social signals, even as he frequently takes lessons in the new speech. For, by and large, persons are judged not by their intent nor by their professions of intent, but by their "pronunciation" of local "Shibboleths" in the most pregnant sense of the term.

A cultural vocabulary is something to which one conforms if one wishes to partake of the benefits of the social group at the expense of its penalties.

B. The Development of an Individual's Superego

Let us use the term, *superego,*[18] to describe a person's own correlated responses to the social signals and social responses of the culture of his social group as they appear to him. The structure of the superego is fundamentally variable because it refers to sensory data whose correlated responses are variant. Since the structure of a given person's superego depends upon the cultural vocabulary of the particular social group in which he happens to be born and in which he lives, there is no reason to suppose that the newborn baby has a superego. Instead the superego is a mentational structure that develops, or "grows," even as the child develops or "grows" in other respects.

1. The Superego as a Set of Correlations and the Question of Verifiability. It is commonly said that a person's superego represents to a considerable extent the results of early threats and admonitions from parents and other close associates: for example, "Don't touch the stove!", "Don't sass me back!", "Don't play with your penis!" and so on.

Perhaps it is worth pointing out that all these threats and admonitions, as well as promises, regardless of their particular verbal expression, are in the form of a correlation between *X* and *Y,* that might be stated in general as follows: "IF you do (or do not do) *X,* THEN *Y* will (or will not) happen." Even though the verbal statement be that of a categorical imperative, such as "Don't touch the stove!", this imperative amounts to little more than the correlation: "If you touch the stove (*X*), you will be burnt (*Y*)." And when the child asks "Why?", when subjected to a command, he may only mean thereby, "What happens if I do or don't obey the command?"—a question that suggests that the child construes the command as a correlation.

These parental admonitions and promises, as such, belong clearly to the social reality of the child's group and to the superego of the child's mind, where they abide as propositions of greater or lesser degree of general applicability (e.g., the command "Don't touch the stove!" can be extended by the child to apply to all stoves he ever meets).

Many of these propositions can be verified empirically. Thus by touching the stove and getting burned, the child gives the above proposition an empiric test. The same applies to his being scratched when he pulls kitty's tail, or to getting spanked when he plays in the street. By such tests the validity of the proposition is established.

But these validating empiric tests do not merely establish the soundness of the proposition tested. They also establish the oracular reputation of papa and mamma, with the result that a considerable credibility attaches to a parental proposition even if it is not tested empirically or, for that matter, even though it cannot possibly be tested empirically. In short, the parents in establishing their reputations as soothsayers with admonitions and propositions that both can be, and are, verified empirically, will preserve that reputation spotless even with propositions that cannot conceivably be verified empirically.

As obvious examples of unverifiable propositions, let us take those that refer to the rewards and punishments after death that attend upon those who were obedient or disobedient to their parents in childhood, or who did or did not say their prayers. These propositions would be hard to verify empirically. Yet the child who has found that his parents are reliable soothsayers in matters that he has verified empirically, will presume that they are also correct with these propositions that are not verifiable.

This consideration leads us to say that a person's superego consists not only of verifiable knowledge that he received from his parents, associates, and teachers (e.g., fire burns; the Pythagorean theorem; etc.). It consists also of hearsay that cannot be verified by empiric test.

But though this hearsay cannot be verified by empiric test, it can often be *verified socially*. To explain this point, which is frequently overlooked, let us begin with the obvious and empirically verifiable case of the parental injunction against playing with matches. Burned at first, the child shies away from matches. Yet with the elapse of time he observes that persons can and do use matches without being burned. On the basis of this observation the child "learns" to use matches with care. What ratiocination on the part of the child does this "learning" involve, as he watches Johnnie use matches without being burned? Does he not perhaps argue unconsciously that he is like Johnnie in reference to the operation of using matches, and that therefore Johnnie's method of solving the problem applies also to himself? In so arguing the child resorts to what we shall call the *social test,* or a *social analogy*.

As another example of the *social test,* or a *social analogy,* let us take the case of a young bride in the hotel room on her marriage night who suddenly becomes panicky at the thought of consummating her marriage, even though the bridegroom at her side is the dearest person on earth to her at the time. Such cases, which are by no means rare, as every hotel doctor knows, arise according to present-day theory because of some childhood proposition in the bride's superego that says that something dreadful will happen to her if she lets a man insert his penis into her vagina. Presumably the bride had never previously tested empirically the validity of this proposition; and so she stands there paralyzed by the sympathetic symptoms of fear at the dire consequences that will probably attend upon the logical consequences of her marriage.

What then can the hotel doctor do to aid her, as the hastily telephoned desk clerk tells him casually that there is another honeymoon couple in trouble in such and such a room? Does not the doctor take the bride to the window where he points out to her the lighted windows in the apartments across the street where persons like herself are doing what she is about to do, and liking it. By appealing to the *social test,* or a *social analogy,* the doctor discredits the universality of the childhood fear and leaves the bride to her bridegroom unafraid. This social test consists of the following assumptions and logical deductions: (1) these people are like me in reference to the operation of copulation; (2) these people, unlike me, have copulated and know what it is like; (3) these people, unlike me, are not afraid of copulation; (4) therefore my fear springs from ignorance and is not justified. These four steps may be typical of much of the reasoning of the *social test.*

The same steps of reasoning occur also in the social test of totally unverifiable propositions, such as those that apply to life after death. For example, when the small boy has doubts about the likelihood of hellfire for those who play with their penises or do not say their prayers, his doubts can be dispelled when he notes that other boys in the neighborhood also so believe. For surely, he may argue, they cannot *all* be mistaken! (Oh, yes, they can *all* be mistaken!) In this fashion a proposition that cannot conceivably be verified empirically is verified by the *social test.** (E.g., "Forty million Frenchmen can't be wrong!")

Of course the social test may also invalidate a proposition. Thus the youngster can also be convinced by the unanimity of opinion of his contemporaries, or of a slightly older age group, or of a different cultural group, that a given parental proposition is sheer nonsense. Indeed, because the *social test* can also invalidate a proposition, it follows that many parents prefer to have their children play with the "right sort" of children (i.e., those who agree); the same applies to other dispensers of unverifiable

* So validating is the social test that the warmongering propagandists of World War II procured movie actresses, college presidents, columnists, and similar persons as a quasi-intellectual elite so that others would believe the correctness of the quasi-elite and feel that they themselves were probably wrong, bcause so many marvelous intellectuals could not be mistaken.

sooth, with the result that particular religions and sects tend to congregate topographically in the United States, in order to minimize the likelihood that any of their charges will be the victims of an adverse social test of propositions that are intended to remain undisturbed (a case of *social intellectual homeostasis*).

Though a social test lacks the generalizing validation of an empiric physical test, in some cases the social test may seem to be equally valid to many persons who confuse the nature of a social correlation with that of a purely physical correlation.

The source of this confusion between the reality of a physical correlation and that of a social correlation is particularly easy to understand if we remember the process of speech-learning by small children, as intimated previously in Chapter Four. Thus, the small child pushes his cup over the edge of the table and notes that it automatically and invariably falls; he pushes a chair, and it moves; he makes a certain stereotyped noise and his mother comes running—equally automatically and invariably, it may seem to him. Even after he has later learned the grammatical and vocabulary details of his mother tongue, he may feel that he has merely learned a more efficient set of coercive and restraining noises which, like hammers and fists, are capable of *forcing* others to do his bidding. To such a person a word is viewed not only as a "thing" (which it is, of course), but *only* as a "thing" which in *all* respects is like an inanimate acultural physical entity.* The mistakenness of this view is obvious.

2. *Conflict within the Superego.* We have previously stated that there might be a conflict between the correlations of the superego and one's own needs (e.g., the desperately hungry person steals bread). Let us digress momentarily to suggest that a conflict may also develop *within* a superego, notably as a result of one's membership in two social groups.

Thus, for example, the young son, aged ten, in leaving his house in the morning for school, will depart well-dressed, well-groomed, and well-dictioned according to the accepted social signals of his parents. Yet as the boy approaches school, where the social signals of his gang become increasingly effective, he may well find it expedient to alter his attire, behavior, and diction, lest he seem "queer" according to the gang's social signals (which in turn are "hopeless" according to the cultural standards of the youngsters' respective parents). As everyone knows from experience, there are different cultural languages for the playground and for the classroom. As long as the two situations are kept apart, the boy can keep both vocabularies active. Indeed, one task of American childhood may be the acquisition of different sets of cultural vocabularies.

---

* Of interest in this connection cf. Matthew VIII, 5ff.: And when Jesus entered into Capernaum, there came unto him a centurion, beseeching him, and saying, "Lord, my servant lieth at home sick of the palsy, grievously tormented." Jesus said, "I will come and heal him." The centurion answered and said, "Lord, I am not worthy that thou should come under my roof: but *speak the word only,* and my servant shall be healed. For I am a man under authority, having soldiers under me: and I say to this 'Go!' and he goeth; and to another 'Come!' and he cometh; and to my servant, 'Do this!' and he doeth."

Much of the realism of antiquity seems to have been based upon this confused view of cultural signals as physical things.[19]

Situations may arise, however, in which the cultural vocabularies of conflicting groups cannot be kept apart by a given person, whose superego will suffer accordingly. Thus the child who is forced to live with parents of belligerently opposite religious convictions may find himself living continually in a situation which by its very nature prevents a logical structuring of his superego: thus to the child's mind, a crucifix, or a star of David cannot at the same time be both divine and diabolical.[20]

Or, to take another example, a child cannot *both* honor his father and mother *and* despise the liar and thief, when he finds that his father and mother are liars and thieves (cp. Chapter Five).

Conflicts of the above sort *within* the superego may be followed by serious psychotic illnesses, as we know. Or they can literally drive the child to run away from the situation, as he seeks to establish a logically structured superego by the simple device of avoiding the conflict-pregnant situation altogether.

It is natural to ask at this point whether a person's superego is a semantically integrated system of logic, in the sense discussed in connection with sensation and mentation in Chapter Five. If it is not a semantically integrated system of logic, then we must view a person's superego as a miscellany of unrelated rules or recipes whose terms are unambiguous (the superego of a mentally defective person may be thus structured). On the other hand, if the superego tends to be a semantically integrated system of logic, then its propositions are logically related, like the theorems of a geometry, with the result that some unexpressed propositions will be logically implicit in a culture.

Although the above question remains open, the writer inclines to the view that the superego tends to become a system of pseudologic and not a miscellany of rules.*

Such propositions as parent-offspring incest taboos seem to exist rather as something that is implicit in a system of logic than as rule of thumb. For, by and large, American children are not expressly forbidden to copulate with parents of the opposite sex, but merely infer the same from the structure of society as it appears in their superegos. Then, again, in judging many works of fiction in which unfamiliar social situations occur, we are inclined to say "logical" or "reasonable" in reference to what seems to be only implicit in the logic of culture and of the superego—an inference that may seem to be idiotic to the members of a different culture.[21]

Yet if we view the structure of the superego as a system of logic rather than as a miscellany of social rules, let us remember that the actual terms and correlations of the culture to which a superego refers may change radically. Thus today, in peace, the killing of another person may be defined as murder and be punished by death. Tomorrow, in war, the killing may be honored by the social group who drafts and trains its members to murder, even against their will. In reference to the then objects and operations of the group, this drastic change in terms and correlations is by no means inconsistent in the general *variance* of the language of culture.

* Pseudologic in the sense that the "reasons," though often utterly childish, are accepted as valid.

Yet to the individual members of the group, the change may be staggering, if not impossible, as they face the need of restructuring the logic of their superegos. The "preconceptions" of a person's superego, though often silly to others, have for him a logic of their own.

IV. AUTISM AND THE CONFUSION OF KINDS OF REALITY

It is evident from our foregoing discussion that our sensations refer to two different kinds of correlations: the *physical* and the *cultural*. The physical correlations are virtually *invariant* in the sense that they seem to be the same everywhere and at all times. On the other hand, the cultural correlations are highly *variant*, in the sense that they may be different or nonexistent in a different culture at the same time, or in the same culture at a different time.

This difference between the *invariant physical* and the *variant cultural* can also be stated in terms of two different kinds of language: the language of physics and that of culture.

Thus the *language of physics* is *invariant*. If a person wishes to express himself in terms of the language of physics—e.g., he wishes to build a house or make a new machine—he must do so within the invariant terms and correlations of the language of physics, or he will not succeed.

But the *language of culture* is more *variant*. Hence if a person chooses to make another person act in a particular way, he must first ascertain the particular cultural vocabulary of the other person at that time and express himself within its given terms, or he will not succeed. Those terms are relative to the place and to the time. Unlike the language of physics, the language of culture is neither ahistorical nor atopographical; instead it changes with time and place.

At this point a word of caution is in order. All sensory stimuli, including cultural signals, are physical; so too are all responses. What we call cultural signals are merely particular physical stimuli that are *also* correlated with particular social responses that refer ultimately to the particular rewards and penalties of the particular social group that serves as a frame of reference. Thus a diamond at all times behaves physically as a crystal of carbon within the invariant language of physics. Yet it is *also* in many cultures a social signal of wealth that tends to evoke submissive responses from others (see Part Two). The diamond's usage as a social signal is governed by the variant language of the culture in question, yet at all times the diamond is subject to the restrictions of the invariant language of physics.

In order to objectify the above difference between the invariance of physics and the variance of culture in reference to a person's sensation and mentation, let us temporarily and undogmatically state it in terms of different *kinds of reality* (that being defined as *real* in reference to which matter-energy moves).

Let us say that *primary reality* is that which lies "beyond and behind our sensations." We mention this kind of reality only in order to dismiss it.

The *secondary reality*, or the *sensory reality*, of a physical body is its physical reaction to the physical impingements from the rest of the universe (e.g., the stone becomes warm in the sun). We share this reality with all inanimate and animate matter.

The *tertiary reality,* or *mind,* is a system of classified and correlated physical sensations, etc., as discussed in Chapter Five. The π-relationship between the circumference and diameter of a circle has a *tertiary reality.* We presumably share this tertiary kind of reality with all animate systems. In mankind it consists of two kinds of correlations: the variant correlations of culture of the person's superego, and the more invariant correlations of the language of physics. Though differing in respect of variance and invariance, a mind tries to integrate its superego semantically with the rest of itself.

The *quaternary reality,* or *social reality,* is the cultural vocabulary of a social group to which the superegos of its members refer. This reality is *variant,* as previously explained.[22]

A. Autism as a Confusion in Kinds of Reality

If we are correct in believing that a given mind tries to be logically self-consistent and to become semantically more integrated, we can understand how inconvenient and wasteful of effort it is for a person to possess a set of correlations in his superego whose terms are changeable. Far more economical it would be for a person if the terms of his superego were also invariant, provided, of course, that they were semantically integrated in his mind.

To stabilize the superego, several general courses of action are possible. We can try to stabilize the terms of our cultural vocabulary, as we vainly crusade against changing customs; we can restrict our social contacts to those persons of like terms (generally our contemporaries of the same social class and environment); or we can retire from society. These courses of action are familiar, and few are the persons who do not try one or another of them at some time.

But now let us suppose that a given person innately *cannot* discriminate between the invariant language of physics and the variant language of culture.

Indeed let us define a person's degree of *autism* as the degree to which he cannot discriminate between the invariant language of physics and the more variant language of culture.

What would a person's behavior be like, as the degree of his autism increases?

B. Theoretical Characteristics of Extreme Autism

Let us suppose that, for some reason or another, John Jones has a great deal of trouble discriminating between the invariant language of physics and the more variant language of culture, and hence, by definition, has a high degree of autism. What can we predict about his behavior in the light of our argument in all our preceding chapters?

In the first place, John will have a semantically more integrated total mind, including the superego, than will be the case with less autistic persons, because John will not be reacting to cultural changes at the rate that others are. In short, John's mind will be *logically systematized* above average in reference to social action.

Moreover, since John's above-average logical systematization of society is accomplished at the expense of inadequately comprehending the formal-semantic changes of his culture, he will be *socially awkward* (or queer, or odd). Being socially awkward, John will always be at a disadvantage in all social situations. Therefore, in order to minimize his effort, John will tend to do one or both of two things: (1) he will try to retreat from society, in the manner of a recluse, or (2) he will try to "reform" society by trying to make society's culture conform to his own system of social logic (the zealot and crusader).

Because of his incapacity to comprehend his cultural vocabulary, and because of his consequent difficulties in communication with others in terms of the cultural vocabulary of the time, John will not feel the need, nor have the means, to alter the terms of his own superego as fast as others. Therefore his particular system of social logic will become intellectually ever more rigid at a faster rate than others, with the result that his social awkwardness will tend to increase with time.

Since John is treated by society on the basis of the actual signals he emits in the light of the then existent cultural vocabulary, and since John, by definition, has difficulty in viewing these signals against the social group as a frame of reference, John will believe that he is being *coerced* by a lot of silly signals, just as he is coerced—or pushed around—by inanimate objects according to the laws of physics. If he is smart, John will note how effective words and other social signals can be in "pushing people around." Yet when John, with his cultural invariance, attempts to manipulate persons by means of words and other social signals, even with the best intent in the world, he will be unsuccessful because his social action will be incomprehensible to the other fellow, although it is quite comprehensible to John in his private language. John simply does not know the only cultural language they can understand; and without a knowledge of the terms of the common cultural language, John can never explain his own private language to them. Indeed, by definition, as soon as John can explain his own private language to others in terms of a common cultural vocabulary, then John is no longer autistic.*

Since John's own private cultural formulations will make excellent sense to John's own system of logic, and since others cannot comprehend John's private system of logic, John will tend to be condescending or patronizing towards his "less smart" fellow men, if not actually contemptuous of them.

Now, since John judges all persons according to his own system of signals, John will tend to impute all manner of things to other persons.

* John's only escape from his cultural dilemma is to communicate in terms of the more invariant language of physics if he can master the conventional terms (cf. the brilliant writings on this topic by R. Carnap and his school *op. cit.* Chap. Two). In general, the autistically inclined person will be happier *today* in the fields of physics, chemistry, and mathematics than in the field of social relations as still taught.

For instance, regardless of what Bill does in perfectly comprehensible cultural terms, John will know what Bill "really means," since John will define Bill's action in terms of his own private system of logic with whose conclusions Bill obviously cannot effectively argue since Bill does not understand their terms.

Yet John, in talking to others, may inadvertently reveal his autism to anyone who makes a statistical study of his words. For *the autist, in not feeling the need for an adequate social semantic precision in order to make his discourse socially understandable, will tend systematically to pursue the economy of the generic correlation at the expense of the economy of the specific correlation, with the result that the negative slope of the rank-frequency distribution of his words will be greater than 1* (derived from the argument of Chapter Five).

Or, in terms of the Forces of Unification (the speaker's economy) and of Diversification (the auditor's economy), as defined in Chapter Two, John will overload his words with meanings, in the sense that each of his words will have more different meanings than is normally the case. In short, the words of John, the autist, will *mean more* to him than to others. As a result of this overloading of meanings, the negative slope of the rank-frequency distribution of John's words will be greater than 1 (see end of the preceding paragraph).

Slopes can be measured.

C. Theoretical Autism and Actual Schizophrenia

As long as one part of a person's mind refers to more invariant correlations, and another part to more variant correlations, then there is a potential dynamic fissure in his mind. Unless all persons of like age in the society have a like degree of intellectual rigidity, this dynamic fissure will tend to manifest itself in the behavior of persons in accordance with the comparative degree of their intellectual rigidity. On the explicit assumption of a difference—a *constitutional* difference—in the degree of intellectual rigidity of persons of like age in a given social group, we have just made the *theoretical construct of autism.* The question now arises whether anything in human society corresponds to our theoretical autism.

We believe that the mental disease, schizophrenia, represents a degree of autism that is sufficiently great that adequate communication between the autist and his fellows is no longer possible, with the result that the autist stabilizes his mind on the basis of his then "petrified" superego and henceforth loses all effective rapport with his group, because he can no longer communicate his ideas to the group, nor have the corrective criticism of the group's ideas that are communicated to him.

All our preceding theoretical characteristics of the autist, such as a high systematization of social logic, an intellectual rigidity, a contempt for the other fellow, a conspicuous tendency either to attack society or to retreat from society, etc., are believed by many to be characteristic of schizophrenia. So too the autistic absolutism of personal views instead of the relativism of cultural views, which we did not discuss.

We might add that theoretically the particular occasions in the autist's life when he is most likely to "break," or lose rapport with society (i.e., develop schizophrenia) will be those in which the cultural terms of the autist's environment change for him, as with the death of close relatives and friends, the loss of a job, the change of residence or of one's socio-economic status. These occasions are notoriously favorable for the onset of schizophrenia.

Moreover the incidence of adolescence, with its change of cultural language in many cultures, will theoretically tend to precipitate schizophrenia in those cultures. The same applies theoretically to the incidence of matrimony and childbearing in the person's twenties, with the inevitable alterations in the terms of one's relations with other persons. Therefore, if our theory be true, the period from about the age of thirteen to about the age of thirty will be the most likely age for the onset of schizophrenia, with the largest number (i.e., the mode) of cases falling somewhere in the early twenties. Such an age distribution of cases of schizophrenia is about what is found.[23]

Let us be clear about one point. Our terminology and theoretical characteristics of autism are familiar in the currently accepted theories and clinical descriptions of schizophrenia from which, incidentally, we frankly borrowed our terms. Our present interest is neither in defining schizophrenia nor in suggesting diagnostic and therapeutic methods. Instead, our interest is in using the semantic distortions of schizophrenia as a test of our hypothesis of the balance between the conflicting economies of the generic correlation and of the specific correlation which is basic to all sensation-mentation if our Principle of Least Effort be correct (cf. Chapter Five).

More specifically, we shall attempt to ascertain empirically whether a schizophrenic person, in removing himself from the semantic exigencies of the language of culture of his group, will restructure his mind according to our theoretical expectations.

Let us turn, therefore, to the facts of schizophrenia as a possible test of our Principle of Least Effort. Our first test will refer to the speech of schizophrenic patients, in reference to which we ask the very specific question: will the negative slope of the rank-frequency distribution of the words of the stream of speech of a schizophrenic patient be greater than 1 as anticipated theoretically?

The answer to this question will be affirmative, if our Principle of Least Effort be correct, and if our theory of sensation-mentation be correct, and if our theory of a cultural vocabulary be correct, and if our theory of schizophrenia as an extreme case of autism be correct.

V. ON SCHIZOPHRENIC SPEECH

Turning now to the question of whether the rank-frequency distributions of the words of persons suffering from schizophrenia do in fact have a negative slope that is greater than unity, as deduced for autism, when *rank* is plotted logarithmically on the abscissa and *frequency* is plotted logarithmically on the ordinate, we shall inspect the data of two selected patients whose condition of schizophrenia is vouched for by experts in the field. One patient (*A*) was a female patient suffering from paranoid schizophrenia. The other patient (*B*) was a male patient who was suffering from hebephrenic schizophrenia. Incidentally, the names of the patients are fictitious and certain relatively insignificant facts have been disguised in their case histories in order to preserve the patients' incognito.

A. A Case of Paranoid Schizophrenia

Before turning to an inspection of the rank-frequency distributions of the words of the patient suffering from paranoid schizophrenia, let us briefly present a summary of her case history as written by Dr. John C. Whitehorn, Professor of Psychiatry at the Johns Hopkins Medical School and Director of the Henry Phipps Clinic, who became acquainted with the patient at McLean hospital in 1931.* This patient was selected for study because her behavior was practically free from the grotesque bizarreries frequently present in schizophrenia, and hence, we concluded, her verbalizations would be particularly instructive if they showed any systematic deviations from the norm.

> Miss Helen B., a 23-year-old, unmarried college student, was admitted to McLean Hospital in 1931 because of screaming denunciations against father, mother, and sister for their "insidious actions," accompanied by threats to kill them. This incident came as the climax to two years of psychotic maladjustment at home, which had started as an episode of tearful panic while she was in her third year at college. That episode had been preceded for a year or more by mounting tension within the family and quarrels with and about "lovers."
>
> At the hospital the screaming mood subsided within a few minutes, and the patient settled herself fairly comfortably in her quarters. With little questioning she expounded volubly the "plot" which menaced her. In brief, she stated that there was a conspiracy by the closed ring to make a prostitute of her. The conspiracy, she said, included her father, her various lovers, the Secretary of the United States Treasury, the Pope, the whole Roman Catholic Church, the Masons, the Methodists, and a long list of other persons. The closed ring, she said, had also recently instigated an invasion from Mexico, to prevent which President Hoover had put battleships on the coast of California. She "feared" that the government would be overthrown by the closed ring and that she would be killed when they got in power. Within a few days she included hospital personnel in the "conspiracy" and spoke of being spied on by television and radio apparatus in the ventilator of her room. There was no proof of hallucinatory experiences, but occasionally she became intensely preoccupied with "thinking."
>
> Helen had "always been a strange child," according to the family. She had been sensitive and idealistic, with poetic and musical tastes and talents, and had been ambitious to make a fine record. She had a brother

* The present case history by Professor Whitehorn is taken from an article on schizophrenic language by Dr. Whitehorn and the present writer.[24] The clinical material is from the experience of Dr. Whitehorn; the statistical analysis was conducted under the direction of the present writer. Parts of the discussion under *C* below will also be found in the article.

and 2 sisters. The father was a hard, shrewd, successful manufacturer, of limited interests, very fond of the patient and disposed to favor her because she had shown more "ambition" than other members of the family. He had repeatedly and urgently taught her to be suspicious of boy friends or men who might show personal interest as a way of getting her money.

The patient has been continuously hospitalized since her first admission, and her subsequent course had been in the direction of narrowing interests and social deterioration. The history, clinical symptoms, and course are not given in further detail here. The diagnosis of paranoid schizophrenia was unquestioned. She was for fourteen months at McLean Hospital, during which time one of us (J. C. W.) became well acquainted with her and accumulated many of her letters, which constitute the material of the present study. The spirit and style of her letters, and some idea of her close preoccupation with the problem of affection, may be gathered, somewhat inadequately, from the following brief extracts:

From a letter to her father: "In spite of the fact of that you insist on exercising your patriarchal influence, my mind (even if not my pocketbook) is emancipated from that feudal conception of parental domination. No doubt you can arouse a certain amount of public sympathy from such narrow-minded goops as the Dovers and the Clarks, but it only goes to prove the futility of the development of intelligence and makes me realize that this is an unredeemable civilization of grocery men and fishmongers. Please do not count on me to worship your little idols with reverence. . . . Whatever cause you may find for malice or hatred toward me you may consider the outcome of your own will."

From a letter to a physician: "I think you are wonderful, but my life is completely futile and your kindness and effort is poured upon a dying plant."

Later, to the same physician: "Your meanness, ugliness and lack of any spiritual qualities at all make you appear to me only as an example of a horrible and hideous distortion of human nature. It is your hideous eye that I love now. I love it for all the suffering, all the misery, the loss of everything that it has brought into your ugly soul."

To the same physician two days later: "Honestly, darling, I love you with all my heart and soul. I want you so much that I ache with pain from wanting you—and then, I feel as though I cannot die soon enough. This hecticness is not doing me any good. I beg you to either love me or kill me."

To another physician: "I suppose you will call me good if I act like a tombstone. Well, every one learns by experience, and it is so unpleasant to have you repulse me that I shall eradicate all my tender feelings into a process of mockery. You may be very sure that I will never exhibit my affection for you again."

In view of the systematic distortion of the language pattern revealed in the statistical study of this patient's letters, it is of some interest to note certain semantic distortions involved in her "conspiracy delusion." This paranoid formation, offered by Helen rather defiantly at the time of admission, became more understandable when she elaborated it and discussed it more fully at a later time, when she was in fair rapport with one of the physicians. In brief, it then came out that what she "really meant" was that the persons in the so-called conspiracy would, by their beliefs and statements, "make her out" to be a prostitute on the basis of her actual behavior. The essence of the coercive "plot," which she so much resented, was so to speak, a classificatory plot—a broad general tendency, shared by many, to classify her as immoral—whereas she had believed, or tried very hard to believe, that her few sexual experiences had been of a poetic character—"a worshipful experience in the temple of artistic living." Captivated by a figure of speech and solaced thereby somewhat for the chagrin and disappointment of being "brushed off," Helen dramatized for herself this crusading role against the conventions, and, disdaining explanations to others (and clarification thereby to herself), she had included much more in her "plot" theory than she "really meant."

Another example of the same tendency to lump together too many meanings in one form of expression may be cited. One of Helen's favorite

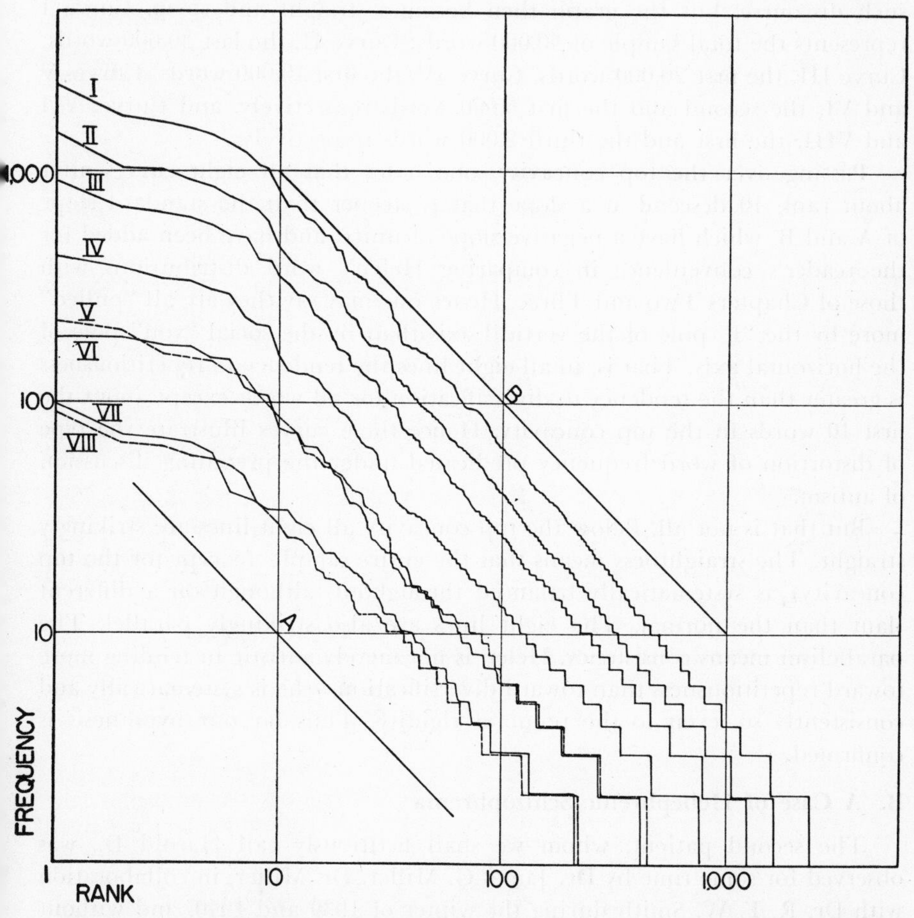

Fig. 7–1. Rank-frequency distribution of the words in the letters of Helen B. (with paranoid schizophrenia) in samples of (I) 50,000 words; (II) 30,000 words; (III) 20,000 words; (IV) 10,000 words; (V and VI) 5,000 words; and (VII and VIII) 2,000 words.

words was "insidious." In many of her earlier statements the term could be understood in its regular dictionary meaning, implying deceptive attack, ambush or treachery, but it gradually appeared, as one heard her use the word in many different contexts, that she meant by it anything malicious or hostile. In fact, when she finally was questioned about it, she said she had never appreciated that the word had any implication of concealment. Indeed, like many another sophomoric adolescent, Helen had a line of favorite words, similarly overworked and overextended in meaning, for example, "emancipated," "unredeemable," and "futility." In accord with her idealism and her concern about making a fine impression, her line was precious, rather than slangy. In this regard she was out of step with most of her contemporaries.

In Fig. 7–1 we present an analysis of the whole and of parts of a total of 50,000 (actually 49,991) running words in fully inflected form as they appeared in the successive letters of Helen B. These letters, being intimately personal, show in this graphic analysis the usual top concavity expected in such discourse, but the graph then becomes straight and steep. Curve I represents the total sample of 50,000 words; Curve II, the last 30,000 words; Curve III, the first 20,000 words; Curve IV, the first 10,000 words; Curves V and VI, the second and the first 5,000 words respectively, and Curves VII and VIII, the first and the third 2,000 words respectively.

Passing over the top concavity, one notes that all eight curves after about rank 10 descend at a slope that is steeper than the standard slope of A and B, which have a negative slope of unity, and have been added for the reader's convenience in comparing Helen's word distributions with those of Chapters Two and Three. Hence one may say they are all "pulled" more by the "I" pole of the vertical axis than by the social "you" pole of the horizontal axis. That is, in all eight lines the tendency to repetitiousness is greater than the tendency to diversification for all words except about the first 10 words in the top concavity. Hence these curves illustrate the type of distortion of word frequency predicated under the preceding discussion of autism.

But that is not all. Below the top concavity all eight lines are strikingly straight. The straightness means that the entire sample (except for the top concavity) is systematically balanced throughout, although on a different slant than the normal. The eight lines are also strikingly parallel. The parallelism means consistency. Helen is not merely autistic in tending more toward repetitiousness than toward diversification—she is systematically and consistently so, even to the point of rigidity. Thus far our hypothesis is confirmed.

B. A Case of Hebephrenic Schizophrenia

The second patient, whom we shall fictitiously call Harold D., was observed for some time by Dr. James G. Miller. Dr. Miller, in collaboration with Dr. R. F. W. Smith during the winter of 1939 and 1940, and without Harold's knowledge, made extensive phonographic recordings of Harold's verbalizations in his interviews with the doctor. From these recordings, samples totalling 15,046 running words were analyzed statistically, the quantitative results of which, together with the following brief case history and examples of his speech, were put at my disposal by Dr. Miller.

Harold was born in 1906, began school at normal age and completed grammar school. His psychosis began in 1922 after an exposure to cold, with a severe chill but without pneumonic symptoms. Shortly thereafter he thought his mother was sticking dope into his neck and would roll up her sleeve to look for the needle. He became seclusive and read scientific books. Later he developed an egotistical, flippant, surly attitude towards his parents. Just prior to hospitalization he laughed nearly the entire night. First admitted to the hospital in 1922, he was semicatatonic, lying in bed in a semiconscious state and crying a great deal, particularly during the first four days. Later he became flippant, surly, and contentious, thinking that nothing was wrong and that he should be released. In 1924 he was discharged from the hospital after improvement.

Again readmitted in 1925, he was negativistic, evasive, with low tone of voice and threatening to injure his mother and sister. Confused at times, often standing in one position staring at floor, he thought his family was persecuting him by keeping him in the hospital. Diagnosis at this time was schizophrenia, catatonic type. Later discharged.

In 1930 he was readmitted. By 1931 a blocking of speech and a deterioration of emotions and intellect were observed, with a poor grasp of school and general knowledge. In 1932 he escaped, canoed on the river during a snowstorm, dragged his canoe through the city square and spent the night, in January, in a boathouse. Later back in the hospital he had grandiose ideas of owning a yacht requiring a captain and crew; his actions were childish, with immature judgment. In 1935 he admitted hearing voices. In 1938 he carried a notebook (or "pads") with him everywhere, making notes and smearing himself with graphite. His eyes were wide and expressionless; he developed flights of ideas and was poorly oriented. By 1941 he was sad, depressed, untidy, unsocial, with all degeneration worse than before. His diagnosis by that time was: schizophrenia, hebephrenic type.

In addition to the above very brief summary of Harold's case history, we shall give a short excerpt from the interview of October 31, 1939, between Harold and his doctor which illustrates the nature of the speech material that Drs. Miller and Smith studied quantitatively. This interview refers to the notebook, or "pads," mentioned in the case history.

Doctor: Did your father give you those pads?
Harold: Yes, he gave me those pads to use that way just to save money and stop that bad hurt object that's all.
Doctor: Did your mother ever give you any pads?
Harold: Nope er the only reason why it was the only way I could rely on any part anyhow they use to keep looking right at it sharply keep looking at it very hard.
Doctor: Who did?
Harold: The attendants. But the time has passed now and I'm not using that sign. I'm using the radiogram now. I write one thousand dollars on a blank just a er at the top one thousand dollar radiogram. And that's the way I make the slip out now to get by my hurts.
Doctor: Does it get you by your hurts?
Harold: Get me by my hurts anyway given me aid but I'm forgetting about it now and not bawling.
Doctor: Well, now, what kind of words do you use to get you by your hurts?
Harold: Er, radiogram is the word I use now to get by.
Doctor: But you gave me "bum" the other day.
Harold: Yeah. Well the attendants were working hard at that cause.

The above illustration of Harold's disorganized oral discourse has a counterpart in the written notations that he made in his pads, or notebook, from which we shall give a short excerpt dated January 7, 1940 (we remember that Drs. Miller and Smith restricted their analysis to Harold's oral speech and did not include his writings).

> And girl that thought so much of my and idea of my good State Seal letters and my gunners gloves and pink bow telephone hot dog eating and mustard and how I feel at grand stroke so I can see happy conclusion at my pink bow telephone and good human life table face of my key hang at movie show door key hang to and rely on good power at my pink bow telephone mustard hot dog cart.
>
> And size of telephone push at my pink ribbon bow a place at my salute signal mostly mask and event at my telephone pink ribbon telephone fas fuse cure at Bo and just to nitice my dental card and jaw teeth codes and trace of false teeth pry places to buy at good event and gold tooth lines at gang plans out at normal room.

Returning now to the question of Harold's oral discourse, we present in Fig. 7–2 two sets of data that relate to the 1022 different words in fully

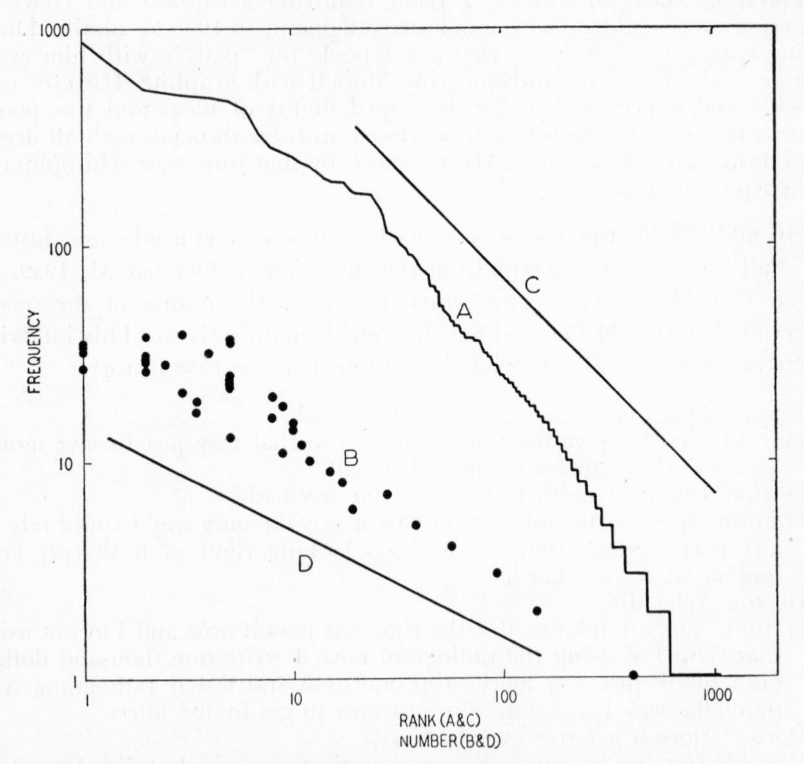

Fig. 7–2. The speech of Harold D. (with hebephrenic schizophrenia). Samples of recorded speech totalling 15,000 spoken words as recorded and analyzed statistically by Drs. Miller and Smith. (A) Rank-frequency distribution; (B) number-frequency distribution; (C) ideal line of – 1.00 slope; and (D) ideal line of – ½ slope.

inflected form that constituted the material samples totalling 15,046 running words. Curve *A* represents the rank-frequency distribution of these words with rank plotted logarithmically on the abscissa and frequency plotted logarithmically on the ordinate. The points marked *B* represent the number-frequency relationship of the same material, with the *N* number of different words of like *f* frequency plotted logarithmically on the abscissa, while their *f* frequency is plotted logarithmically on the ordinate. For comparative purposes a line, *C*, has been added with a negative slope of 1 to represent the slope of the harmonic series; and a line, *D*, has also been added with a negative slope of ½, which would be approximately the slope of the number-frequency relationship, *if* the words of *A* had followed the harmonic series.

Restricting our attention to Curve *A*, we note that, after the top-concavity which is to be expected in this type of material, the line descends at a slope that is appreciably steeper than that of the ideal harmonic slope of *C*. Hence these data confirm our theoretical expectations and suggest that Harold was loading his words with an inconveniently large number of meanings. Curiously enough, Curve *A* for Harold's 15,000 odd running words would fall quite nicely between Curves III and IV of our preceding Fig. 7–1 for Helen's 20,000-word sample and 10,000-word sample respectively. Therefore despite the differences between Helen and Harold in respect of background and literary style, the statistical pictures are quite similar, and so too, presumably, the paraphrases thereof.

The data of *B* which relate to all of Harold's words that were used fewer than 40 times are unmistakably rectilinear, and indicate beyond doubt that regardless of how disorganized Harold's words may have appeared to others, they were nevertheless systematically organized as far as Harold himself was concerned.

In view of the above data we may say that the distinguishing feature of Harold's discourse is *not* that he failed to use the words that we use, since he did; it is *not* that he failed to use them systematically, since he did. The distinguishing feature is that he used them according to a different system which, though incomprehensible to others, was quite evidently satisfactory to Harold who, in his perplexity at the queerness of society, finally gave up the battle and sank into hebephrenic schizophrenia.

In Harold's disorganized verbiage we get a glimpse of his awkward attempt to manipulate these strange entities called *words* that apparently impressed him as being of tremendous potential power in getting a person by his "hurts" if he could only find the right ones. In Helen's more expert verbiage, with all its truculence, revolt, and reforming zeal towards society, we still sense from her accumulated letters her fundamental loneliness in the face of the social phenomenon of mating which, in the biological world, is second only to birth and death in being a cliché.

And in both of them we find a negative rank-frequency slope that is greater than unity, and hence one that is theoretically indicative of a sacrifice of the auditor's economy to the speaker's.

Since the above two sets of data on the verbalizations of schizophrenic patients are the only ones known to the present writer, we cannot dogmatize on the significance of their slope. Yet in this connection it might be remarked that of all the rank-frequency data on words that have ever come to the attention of the present writer, only those of Helen B. and Harold D. have negative slopes that are greater than unity. Therefore, subject to the correction of future findings, we shall continue with the inference that a negative slope that is greater than unity is characteristic of the rank-frequency distributions of words of persons suffering from schizophrenia, and that schizophrenia is the factual counterpart of our hypothetical autism.

C. Noncharacteristic Features of Schizophrenia

In the literature on schizophrenia, a great deal has been said about schizophrenic speech without always a concern for those features which, though present in schizophrenic speech, may also be present in nonschizophrenic speech. In order to avoid giving the same mistaken impression, let us briefly discuss certain *noncharacteristic* features of schizophrenia—such as polysyllabism, neologisms, formal and semantic changes—so that we may emphasize the one feature that does characterize the schizophrene; the tendency to ignore the conventional meanings of conventional words.

Save for this one tendency, the schizophrene makes use of no principle or device that is not found quite generally in speech, insofar as the present writer knows.

Thus the highly polysyllabic discourse of some schizophrenes that is virtually incomprehensible to the auditor is by no means restricted to schizophrenia. Instead it may represent nothing more than a desire to use big words for the sake of impressing others with one's importance, and may be found quite often in the speech of nonschizophrenes who may feel intellectually or socially insecure.*

So too the coinage of neologisms is by no means invariably indicative of schizophrenia. On the contrary, it may be nothing more than a legitimate response to the economy of specialization. The words, *blimp, watt, wheaties,* etc., were once neologisms which were coined by someone. When the schizophrenic patient coins a word, say *dorocell,* to mean "a pickaxe with which Queen Victoria's soul kills unfaithful husbands," he has done nothing schizophrenic, any more than does a usage of the words, *fairies, elves, seraphim,* for which there are also no corresponding physical entities or relationships. His schizophrenia lies in expecting others to understand the word *dorocell* without having its meaning explained to them.

* The economy of *"long-word-itis,"* with which many persons are afflicted, may include the fact that long words are the less frequently used words, and hence betoken the possession of a large vocabulary with a concomitant large sensory and intellectual experience. Therefore the sheer utterance of long words becomes a social signal of elite membership (see Part Two) which, curiously enough, increases in value if the "other fellow" has difficulty in understanding; for example, to utter the phrase, "quintessentially equinoctial climatic disturbances" might well floor the intellectually docile. To some persons, longer words are "superior words" that represent the possession of a "superior" knowledge and skill which, in turn, are to be feared. Hence shy persons often feel ashamed of little words and proud of big words and of intricate legal phrases; yet, as long as they are willing to explain their meanings, their pathology is not schizophrenic. On the other hand, the preference for long words will obviously confuse the auditor even more when it is indulged in by a schizophrene.

By the same token, the changes of verbal forms (linguistic changes) and changes of verbal meanings (semantic changes) are not in any way necessarily pathological. Not only are such changes continually occurring in a folk vocabulary, they must perforce occur in order to preserve a vocabulary balance according to our hypothesis of the hyperbolic equation as representative of an economical equilibrium between the diversity of words and the frequency of usage of those words and their meanings. Obviously, as a group's culture changes with the times, there is bound to be a disturbance to the vocabulary equilibrium, with the result that meanings must be reallocated to words while words are coined, changed, or eliminated. To that end there exist the mechanisms of linguistic and semantic changes, the employment of which is in no way necessarily schizophrenic.

Naturally, any such linguistic and semantic changes—just like any neologism—will not be socially useful unless they are understood and accepted in the speaker-auditor group where the changed words and meanings are employed. Therefore a social understanding and acceptance of linguistic and semantic changes is a part of the total process. Since the social acceptance of a given linguistic or semantic change can be given only *after* the change has been made by some speaker, we may not argue for a moment that any psychotic abnormality attaches to the sheer act of altering the forms or meanings of words, whether or not they are socially accepted. In the last analysis it is always the speaker who selects both his words and his meanings (i.e., the responses he wishes to evoke); on the other hand, it is the auditor who tries to fit the speaker's selection into the signals of his own experience. If the speaker does not make his selection clear—and everyone has difficulty at times in expressing himself—it is the auditor who fails to understand and who thus forces the speaker to a greater semantic precision if he is to be understood.

As every person knows from his own experience—whether in explaining something to another person or in writing a letter, or in teaching a child—it is often onerous (i.e., it takes work) to redact one's ideas in terms of one's auditor's presumable vocabulary. Therefore we can readily appreciate the work a schizophrene saves himself when he just does not bother to cast his ideas in terms of a socially understandable system of signals. It is also economically understandable how the schizophrene, in thus saving work for himself, thereby automatically isolates himself intellectually and affectively in the sea of socially acceptable speech about him, which to the schizophrene seems to be formidably illogical and arbitrary.

But here again let us not forget that the schizophrene in complaining of the illogicality and arbitrariness of speech is by no means incorrect; nor is his urge towards a more logical expression in itself pathological. In English there is frequently an odd assortment of apparently unrelated meanings subsumed under the same word, such as "the rose," "I rose," "my daughter, Rose," "I bear," "the bear," "bare legs," "the draft of wind," "the draft on the bank," "the military draft," "palm" and "palm," "saw" and "saw," and literally hundreds of others. To be born into a world that talks thus is to be born into an illogical world—and into a "coercively" illogical world to the schizophrene, since he must accept and use this verbal nonsense as a prerequisite of his participation in the benefits of society.

As far as we can see, the schizophrene is clearly right when he complains that verbal illogicality is wasteful of effort, and that logic is recommended for its economy of mind. After all, the language of mathematics and of natural science is recommended on the grounds of its greater logical self-consistency, although in this instance—and the point warrants stressing—explicit definitions and empiric verifiability are offered to the "other fellow" so that he can understand. The same concern for the comprehension of the "other fellow" is also evinced by framers of artificial languages, like Esperanto, for which a greater logical self-consistency is claimed, and for which an enormous amount of work is expended so that the "other fellow" both can and will understand. In dodging the labor that is necessary for explicit definition, the schizophrene can be much freer in devising his own new and more logical speech.

Anyone can build a new and more logical language if he ignores the "other fellow." For example, given the word, *tune,* meaning a *"kind of noise,"* then *Neptune* is the kind of noise that Nep makes; if this noise is the surf, then Nep is the sea. Given the words, *cat* and *nip,* we can see how catnip may nip the cat. We can see how *mother* and *smother* are related and that therefore to *smother* may mean "to be nice to babies"; or "that it really isn't catnip because the cats like it." "A printer's devil is not the printer's errand boy but a real devil that eats pie and that is why he pies type."

But let us take an actual example. One clever, subtle, and secretive paranoid woman "known" by Dr. Whitehorn used to speak with a smile of "airplane messages." At least that is the way the auditors always understood, or rather misunderstood. The nurses even watched for airplanes flying over to see how she took the messages. One day she condescended to explain her meaning. The term was *air-plain* message, meaning "plain as air," a meaning that was not plain at all, except to the initiated, since air signifies to the uninformed practically nothing, and even the existence of air as a substance is only appreciated through subtle and involved experimentation. It is of some interest in this connection that this same patient devised a special secret alphabet in which she used to write or draw on large sheets of paper a whole "newspaper" with headlines and display advertisements and a society column—all for her sole and secret enjoyment.

Yet the sheer act of devising secret words, and secret codes, and secret rituals and signals is by itself not a psychotic manifestation unless the "other fellow" is supposed to understand the meanings of the forms without first having been initiated. Not until a person ignores his quaternary, or social, reality and tries to substitute his own tertiary reality can we speak of a schizophrenic distortion. In short, the actual cultural vocabulary of a given group with its signals and correlated responses is the language of that group —no matter how intrinsically silly, childish, or "primitive" they may appear to others. This is the language that the members of the group will understand, and that applies to the language of cliques of children as well as to that of tribes of "primitive" man. Hence, despite the opinions of many to the contrary, schizophrenes are not children (though they may try to retrogress to the simpler semantic terms of childhood). Neither were "primitive" men schizophrenes (though they too may well have had schizophrenes among them).

D. Schizophrenic Speech and Schizophrenic Language

To preserve our perspective, let us momentarily digress from the more specialized phenomenon of schizophrenic speech, while we consider the more general phenomenon of schizophrenic language, of which schizophrenic speech is only a part. We shall see that our previous argument about schizophrenic speech still seems to apply, even though a quantitative analysis of the schizophrene's total verbal and nonverbal language would be difficult in the extreme.

To begin, let us relate our problem to present-day American culture and take the case of naked human copulation in broad daylight in public, which surely represents an adverse social signal that would bring the police wagon with despatch.

Now let us assume that the reader while walking down the street in broad daylight were forcibly undressed and ordered to copulate in public view. His consternation, if not his panic, would be understandable, as he was forced to behave so immodestly, if not blasphemously.

Turning now to the case of the schizophrene, let us suppose that, on the basis of an extended observation of dogs, birds, and butterflies whom God made and whose behavior is by definition modest and natural, the schizophrene deduces "quite logically" that it is modest and godlike for men to go naked, while it is immodest and blasphemous for them to wear clothes (some tribes are said to have just such cultural beliefs). Furthermore, on the basis of the same observations, he concludes that copulation should be consummated in public.

Thus convinced, and ignoring the validity of his cultural vocabulary, the above schizophrene so acts.

Imagine his consternation, if not his panic, as the police wagon arrives and forcibly prevents him from behaving so modestly—indeed by duress the policemen dress him and thereby *make* him act blasphemously according to his own lights. Such a person is put in a mental hospital with the diagnosis of schizophrenia, where he rants about his constitutional rights to freedom of religion (a frequent schizophrenic rationalization these days).

This is a gross case, yet it is typical of the simplification of one's logical system when the givens of the verbal and nonverbal cultural vocabulary are ignored. The same attitude is revealed in smaller matters.

For example, let us take the case of a person who was told as a boy by his mother that "nice people" wear stiff collars. In spite of the subsequent soft-collar age, he not only continues to disapprove of soft collars, the "indecency" of which he denounces; he even forces his subordinates to wear stiff collars as a condition of their employment. In such slight matters the schizophrene can reveal himself; he has greatly oversimplified the problem of human social evaluations.

Or let us take the more pronounced case of the veteran of World War I who is now spending the balance of his life still dressed in the then style of army uniform while pacing back and forth within a wire fence as he does guard duty. His action is meaningful in the terms of the cultural language of that time, in reference to which his each and every act is without blemish. In these terms he is doubtless "right."

Is this case of the soldier much different from that of some of the political scientists and historians on our faculties who, in effect, express all their ideas, acts, and social-political evaluations in terms of a rigidly absolute frame of reference, say, of what they imagine Victorian England was, and which to them is an "eternal verity" and an "absolute right"? Being skillful verbalists, their paranoia may escape detection. Yet were these same persons to insist that all persons talk Chaucerian English, which was quite valid in its day, their psychosis would at once become apparent; and how much intellectual work these persons save themselves by not adjusting to the changing cultural evaluations, but by simply being "morally superior" to them.

There may, on the other hand, be a revolt against the established cultural vocabulary that is by no means schizophrenic. Indeed a part and parcel of adolescence—at least, American adolescence—is an almost stereotyped revolt against the beliefs, attitudes, and cultural behavior of the adults. Since this revolt has itself a cultural vocabulary of its own in terms of which its youthful members express themselves with an almost servile deference, it can scarcely be viewed as schizophrenic. Eventually they "settle down" into a middle-aged conformity to the cultural pattern which may even have been somewhat enriched at its periphery by the terms of the then antiquated revolt.* Some few revolutionaries may continue with the antiquated revolt vocabulary; and amusing it is to see these perennial revolters again, when one revisits one's youthful haunts and sits in the candlelight at the familiar and carefully wine-stained table opposite an old habitué who is still "in revolt," as each pair of eyes asks the other the unuttered question, "Which of us is crazy?"

When we say that a schizophrene has a split personality, we cannot mean that he is characteristically innerly at odds with himself, since probably no person has a feeling of a complete semantic integration of the universe without a single contradictory set of correlations. The split in the schizophrene's personality lies rather between his own tertiary reality and the quaternary reality to which he is insensitive. To the schizophrene, both a doorkey and a password open the door and are intrinsically the same; to him, there is an absoluteness in a social signal: just as he pushes a given electric light button to light a given light, he voices a given word to produce a given effect. To the schizophrene a cultural signal is a thing just like a hammer; he cannot understand that it is a totally different kind of phenomenon.

In our theoretical discussion of autism we made the point that the schizophrene's own tertiary correlates may take precedence in validity over

* Our argument about the core-periphery phenomenon and the comparative conservatism of words in Chapter Five applies theoretically to the entire cultural vocabulary.

both the empiric and the social tests. For example, a schizophrene, while indicting himself unconsciously for cowardice, may announce colloquially "I have no guts!" (meaning "I lack courage"). But in the supremacy of his tertiary reality, the schizophrene may later take a less self-depreciative view of himself, and, on the basis of his verbalism, "I have no guts," arrive at the conclusion that all his intestines have actually been removed—as he sets out to worry for the rest of his life at the thought of the immediate death that awaits all those who lack intestines. Nor will he be persuaded to the contrary by any sensory test, or by the statements of others (the social test). The correlates of a schizophrenic mind that refer to cultural data are beyond human reach, since his own "meanings" are by definition the absolutely and eternally "right meanings," and he does not like to have anyone disturb them.*

E. Schizophrenic Overinclusiveness in Physical Situations (The Cameron Observation)

The critic may choose to interpose at this point that our conclusion holds at best only for schizophrenic speech and language, whereas we have implied that it holds for his entire mentation.

The question arises, then, if our imaginary critic insists, whether a schizophrene is similarly confused about noncultural phenomena in the sense that he quite generally *"overincludes."* In short, does he, in dealing with physical phenomena, believe that more belongs together than in fact does? Does he find the properties of matter inconveniently complex in time-space, with the result that he tries to simplify them and thereby "overincludes" purely material classes and correlations in his physical problems? Does he have the same trouble differentiating between his mental constructs on the one hand and his sensory data of material givens in time-space on the other, as he does between his mental constructs on the one hand and his sensory data of cultural givens on the other? To each of these questions the answer should be affirmative, if our theory be correct, since the schizophrenic mind in an unusual situation of any kind will insist upon the supremacy of his tertiary correlations in solving the problem of the situation.

---

* But let us not be dogmatic about our theory, since there is a quite different view of mind represented by Mr. Archibald MacLeish, erstwhile librarian of Congress, poet, scholar, habitué of Roosevelt White House circles, member of the State Department and of that celebrated group of aging Harvard "intellectuals" that prepared the nation intellectually for World War II. Thus spoke in part MacLeish as reported in the Boston Herald (Nov. 21, 1940), under the headline, *"Saboteurs of Mind" Greatest Peril, Democracy Council Told:*

"There is among the defenders of democracy today a confusion and perplexity that would be incredible," Mr. MacLeish said, "if we did not know it is the principle strategy of enemies of liberty to produce that confusion and perplexity." He alluded to the propagandists of totalitarian powers as saboteurs of the mind and accused them of "intellectual assassination." He added: "They practice the sabotage of words and the meanings of words (*sic*) and they seek to sabotage the credibility of those who seek to use them in defense of freedom. These saboteurs are the first men in five centuries of printing to turn the printed word against the people in a more deadly way than they turn guns against the people." In our opinion, meanings of words, unlike a factory, cannot be sabotaged.

Moreover, the answer to the above questions is decidedly in the affirmative, according to the brilliant empiric research of Dr. Norman Cameron, who investigated the topic of schizophrenic thinking in problem-solving situations.[25] According to Dr. Cameron's findings in his study, there was a resistance at the very start to the tester's delimitation of the problem. Moreover the schizophrenic subjects called for "changes in the rules of procedure and in the materials, and declared the situation to be inadequate instead of themselves"—to quote from Dr. Cameron's paper in which we find the following summary:

> "Generalizations were numerous; and shifts from one hypothesis to another occurred without evidence of an unusual difficulty. The generalizations were unsuccessful (in solving the problem as set by the tester) because they were (*a*) too broad, (*b*) too involved, or (*c*) too entangled with personal problems and phantasies, or (*d*) because the language structure was so disorganized that it could neither function as social communication, nor serve as a basis for the patient's own performance. Moreover (*e*) the generalizations, even when quite correct, often did not lead to any corresponding act."

In short, the subjects had trouble in organizing material and conceptual tools and in keeping them apart; there was an *overinclusion* of material and situational givens in the generalizations. To the patients, the rules of procedure and the materials were "wrong." The intellectually inconvenient problem was to be solved by changing the rules, even though that would involve a change in the rules of the physics of matter-energy.

In effect we are arguing theoretically that to a schizophrenic mind, the semantic interrelatedness of his own conceptualizations is of a more conclusive reality than the language of culture or the language of physics—a statement with which few neurologists would probably care to quarrel.*

F. On the "Convergence" of Schizophrenic Thinking

In our Chapter Five on sensation and mentation we spoke of the economy of the generic correlation, which stated something definite about a wide diversity of things without saying anything specific that was characteristic of each of the different things. We also spoke of the economy of the specific correlation, which stated something definite that was characteristic of a few things but of no general applicability to a wide diversity of things. We emphasized the economy of having both kinds of correlations; and suggested how this might be accomplished by defining the *m* various classes of relevant events of one's experience as the intersections and unions of a minimum *n* number of different more generic classes, etc.

* Perhaps the frankest statement by a "schizophrene" was that of Humpty Dumpty in Lewis Carroll's *Through the Looking Glass* who said that a word means whatever he says it means. All right, as long as he tells the "other fellow" what it means. Otherwise he needs only to go on reciting the Lord's Prayer, or keep repeating "da-da" while laughing, and smiling, or being sad, as others do in their culturally more articulate discourse, since Humpty Dumpty can simply alter his meanings without bothering to alter his words. A few hundred thousand utterances of "da-da" can indeed mean the *Iliad* of Homer, if, at the end of each utterance, the speaker appropriately changes the meaning of "da-da."

Moreover, we argued how a balance between the equal but opposite economies of the generic and the specific correlations might result in a frequency distribution of the n classes according to the value, $p = 1$, of the equation of the generalized harmonic series, in which $F = n^p$, or:

$$F \cdot Sn = \frac{F}{1^p} + \frac{F}{2^p} + \frac{F}{3^p} + \cdot \cdot \cdot + \frac{F}{n^p}$$

We also pointed out that as p became less than 1, as was the case with the holophrases of Nootka, the increased n classes in question became comparatively less frequent and less generic while becoming more specific.

Now we may argue that as p becomes greater than 1, as was the case with the two samples of schizophrenic speech just examined, the decreased n classes become more frequent and generic while becoming less specific.

It so happens, however, that the value, $p = 1$, is a critical point between divergence and convergence in the series. Thus, if the value of p is not greater than 1, the generalized harmonic series will be divergent; that is, for a given value of $F \cdot Sn$, there will be a given value of n. In Chapter Two we used the term, *closure,* to describe this characteristic of divergence.

Yet when the value of p increases beyond 1 by ever so little the series becomes convergent, with n becoming infinite as it converges upon some limit. Hence there will be no closure in schizophrenic speech.

In view of the above considerations, *schizophrenic speech is convergent,* if we may generalize upon the basis of our two samples. Yet what can be meant by the term, the *convergence of schizophrenic speech* with its lack of *closure?*

If we may trust our erstwhile argument of Chapter Five that (1) the comparatively more frequently used words represent the comparatively older generic classes in the person's experience which serve to make proportionately more of the intersections and unions of his more recent specific classes; and if we remember our argument above that (2) with the convergence of speech the schizophrene can both (*a*) continue to use his words (classes) with the same relative frequency, while (*b*) increasing the n number of his different words (different classes) without limit; it follows (3) that the schizophrene is saying "basically" the same things in essentially the same way about an ever widening number of different things in this universe. In using the term, *"basic,"* we mean "basic to the schizophrene's semantic system." Hence, if we correctly interpret the convergence of schizophrenic speech, the schizophrene starts off with a fixed set of rigid generic classes that are invariantly used, if we may judge by the invariant frequencies of the words of Helen's discourse (Fig. 7–1), as the size of the sample increases. Second, the schizophrene keeps increasing n without altering the rate of repetition of his original classes, thereby articulating his original classes into more specific classes at a constant rate. And since there is no limit to the size of n in a convergent series with a limited Sn, the schizophrene can continue forever to say the same things about an increasing diversity of things.

In other words the schizophrene is including ever more different classes within an original set of generic classes that form a private system of logic that is rigidly integrated semantically.

A good example of the excessively generic correlation is found, regrettably, in many verbalistic political and social scientists in the United States who, with preconceived notions and systems, cull and select the "facts" of history in order to "prove" a darling point (often gratuitously insulting those who fail to understand or to agree). The question of spurious correlation and specious logic is absent from this type of mind, since it already knows what is to be proved, and since it also selects the substantiating data and decides what facts are relevant and irrelevant for the needed proof. Controvertive facts can be conveniently overlooked. In this fashion history can be warped to show that all Browns are angels, and all Smiths are devils —and what an enormous amount of work is saved in understanding the principles of social action!

Generally speaking, the systems of natural science do not differ from schizophrenic systems because of any difference in a desire for a unifying logical integration. The difference lies solely in the treatment of empiric data. With systems of natural science, the empiric data are primary and the theory secondary; at every step the logical implications of the theory are tested empirically, with the theory modified in the light of the empiric observations. With schizophrenic systems, on the other hand, the theory comes first and the facts are selected, defined, and correlated for the sake of buttressing the theory. In either case the objective of the system is a logical integration of the person's tertiary reality which, after all, is the final governor of his actions. The empiricist alters the structure of his tertiary reality in the light of his observations, or of the verifiable report of the observations of others. The schizophrene does the reverse.*

Obviously, by not bothering to check his correlations with observable facts the schizophrene saves himself an enormous amount of work, as his mind becomes intellectually more rigid with passing time. As a result his own world of tertiary reality which is beyond sensory correction refers ever more remotely to the facts of the environment as they appear to others. Since to the schizophrene's mind, the reports of his senses will eventually become both unnecessary when they substantiate his world, and untrustworthy when they do not, it is obviously economical for him to tend to ignore his senses as he sinks into a stupor even to the point of becoming insensitive to a very painful touch.

This ideational world of the schizophrene is called a *phantasy*. Let us call it a *dream world,* as we suggest that the dynamics of schizophrenic thinking and of dreaming are the same. We shall have more to say about the possible structure, or "geometry," and the dynamics of a *dream world* in the present and following chapters.

Yet the structure and dynamics of dreams are but the structure and dynamics of a mind, the tertiary reality, when the mind in question is

* We ignore the logical systems of mathematics, since these are games with fixed terms and rules.

released from the need of altering its classes and correlations to conform to the test of the languages of culture and of physics, with the result that the mind in question tends ever more to say the same things—that is it tends to make the same statements—about an ever increasing number of different things in an infinity of possible conceptualizations.

Yet mind, as we pointed out at the beginning of this chapter, is a theoretical construct (like a rock's *gravitation*). We can know of the dynamics of mind only by its observable effects upon sensorily perceptible matter-energy. Our present study of mind has been perhaps unusual inasmuch as we have restricted our attention largely, though not entirely, to the effect of a mind upon the physical phenomena of words, with an almost exclusive reference to the conventional forms and meanings of words in reference to a given social group. Taking the reasonably stable cultural speech vocabulary as the givens in the situation (instead of the absolutely stable givens of the physical and chemical laboratories), we have investigated the effect of this notoriously asocial schizophrenic type of mind upon these reasonably stable cultural givens, and have found that it "overincludes" and "oversimplifies."

G. Words as Frequently Used Categories of Social Expression

If it is true that the *possible* classes and correlations of a given mind are infinite, it follows that the combined *possible* classes and correlations of the minds of all members of a given social group are also infinite.

However, since it takes finite amounts of time to utter words and to respond to them during a finite day, it follows that the actual *m* number of different meanings that are to be evoked by the *n* number of different conventional words of a community's speech, as well as the *n* number of words, will be finite.*

Moreover the *particular* meanings that are to constitute the actual *m* number of meanings to be subsumed by the group's *n* words will be those meanings that the members of the group agree in using most.[26] In short, we may say that a group's speech vocabulary of *n* words with their *m* meanings represents the most common verbal meeting ground of the members of that group.

Suppose now that one member of the group, out of the infinite possible categories of his mind, wishes to impart an idea that is new to the group, and for which no word or meaning exists. In that case he can resort to permutations of words according to the culturally accepted operations of grammar, and even resort to analogues, metaphors, similes, and examples, in the hope that his interlocutor will react to the verbal stimuli as expected and thereby "get the idea." In thus behaving the person with the new idea may or may not be successful. In any event, we may view the larger permutations of speech entities as cultural devices for extending the semantic range of the cultural vocabulary of words.

But suppose now that a territorial or socio-economic subgroup of members with characteristic operations of their own (say they are fishermen)

* The same applies theoretically to the structure of the entire cultural vocabulary.

find that the *m* most frequent meanings of the total group are by no means the most frequent meanings of their own subgroup. In that case they can either use their own most frequent subgroup meanings for some of the group's standard words by the device of semantic change (e.g., the nautical meanings of *line, yard,* etc.); or they can coin their own words. In this fashion a territorial or socio-economic subgroup can develop a dialect or language of its own, as phonetic, morphological, and semantic balance is restored in terms of the subgroup's usage. Thus a subgroup becomes a new group which no longer understands the parent-group.

H. On the Possible Origin of Schizophrenic Rigidity

In our discussion of autism some pages back we made the explicit assumption that some persons in a given social group are intellectually innately much more rigid than others of the same group. These more rigid individuals we called *autists* (a term borrowed from neurology). Although few neurologists would care to question the validity of our postulate of constitutional differences in intellectual rigidity among persons of like ages, we must nevertheless explore—if only speculatively—the implications of this postulate.

Now, it so happens that all persons are not equally likely to become schizophrenic when they become psychotic. Indeed, as Kretschmer pointed out, the type that is likely to become schizophrenic has the physical characteristics of what is called the asthenic physique type (whose personality is schizoid).[27]

The physical criteria of this asthenic-schizoid type are familiar; it is the "lean and hungry" type of Shakespeare's Cassius: tall, physically somewhat awkward, thin, flat-chested, with a certain relationship between the breadth of shoulders and hips; and with certain features of the face and head. Though frequently awkward socially, the schizoid person can be intellectually brilliant (e.g., Sir Isaac Newton). These features are hereditary and therefore may be called innate, or constitutional.

To emphasize the features of the asthenic-schizoid type, let us briefly describe Kretschmer's other main type, the pyknic-cycloid type: muscular, barrel-chested, and inclined towards obesity, temperamentally active, social, and disposed to moodiness. This type too is familiar and, when psychotic, it is much more likely to develop a manic-depressive psychosis.

The two types are well recognized clinically. In a ward full of sleeping psychotics, a jury of expert psychiatrists could pick out the schizophrenes on a purely physique basis, with few errors.

Now assuming that both types consume about the same calory amounts of food—and none of our schizoid friends are exactly dainty eaters—let us ask the purely physical question: which of the two types seems to be the more efficient mechanical machine, judged by the physical evidence of work produced, or of energy stored?

On this basis it would seem that the obese and more active (extravertive) pyknic-cycloid type is the more efficient machine, since it seems to get more out of its metabolism of food. On the other hand, the proverbially "lean and hungry" asthenic-schizoid type seems to be the less efficient metabolizer.

We mention this consideration not in order to be dogmatic about it, but rather to suggest that the schizoid's intellectual rigidity may be deeply rooted in a mechanical inefficiency of his total system. If we argue that it somehow takes work to "change one's mind," then it *may* be that the comparative intellectual rigidity (and the corollary absolutism of view) of a schizoid mind springs from a comparatively smaller amount of free available work. This speculation fits in with our theoretical Principle of Least Effort. We mention this matter only speculatively in order to suggest a possible physical-mechanical basis for two drastically different kinds of intellectual reactions by members of the same species in generally similar situations.

The division of human personalities into two physique types with correlated personality differences has always been perplexing. Although the correlation between personality type and physique type is not complete, it is unmistakably high. Moreover, because of the nature of the case, the correlation has a constitutional basis in the sense that it is in the person's germ plasm where, presumably, one's physique is fixed.

Without reviewing the literature on the subject of the Kretschmer types, and without in any way meaning to be dogmatic, let us ask a question (it is always fair to ask a question!).

Suppose that several million years ago there was one species of monkeys, *a,* that was asthenic-schizoid like the chimpanzees, and another species, *b,* that was pyknic-cycloid like the orangutans.

What would happen if, in some local region, an illness destroyed the females of *b,* with the result that the sex-starved *b* males helped themselves to the *a* females and produced a self-fertile hybrid $(a + b)$?

This hybrid, $(a + b)$, would be a newcomer at the periphery of the biosocial continuum who, as the effect of the sickness of the *b* females passed, would have to compete with the two older and more completely adjusted species, *a* and *b,* from which $(a + b)$ sprang. Unlike most hybrids that perish, let us suppose the hybrid, $(a + b)$, managed to survive by wandering from pillar to post, and from cave to forest and return—a gregarious lot that sought such few opportunities for survival as were left over by the older and more established species of the biosocial continuum.

Suppose that $(a + b)$ in its wanderings into new situations to which it reacted in new ways, discovered mechanical tools, and fire, while at the same time further articulating its communication cries. For in order to survive at all at the periphery of the crowded biosocial continuum, the new hybrid would almost be obliged to make some economical discoveries of its own without delay. In such a fashion a culture would develop.

Whenever $(a + b)$ settled down for any length of time in a comparatively stable environment, then the intellectually more rigid *a* (asthenic-schizoid) factor would be genetically selected. In the course of prolonged wanderings it would be the *b* factor. In this fashion pronounced physical racial types might develop locally.

Let us suppose that several million years later, the descendants of $(a + b)$ who had continued to change physically and culturally, and who were mightily impressed by their own achievements, decided to discover the "missing link" that separated them from the less smart but no less well adjusted monkeys. After digging everywhere for the bones of the "missing link" might it not occur to them that there might be no such thing as a "missing link?" Instead the new breed of monkeys was only a case of the binomial expansion of the factors of two distant species, the extremes of which we find in the extremes of schizophrenia and of the manic-depressive psychosis—two sets of factors that are in varying degrees in all of us.

We merely ask the question. If the answer to this question be affirmative, then what a wealth of archaic reminiscence there will be in our dreams as we harken back to remote ancestral days of swimming, flying, and climbing when there was no inconvenient variance of a superego! In that case, as Freud once intimated, our great intellectual cultures are rather a measurement of our biological misfortune than of our achievement. The squirrel does not use a slide rule for solving his problems. Neither does he have to. In this relativistic world in which each lives in his own frame of reference, who is to laugh at whom?

VI. SEMANTIC DYNAMICS: SUMMARY

We have described the hypothetical organization of a person's mind as a tertiary reality whose correlations are *ultimately* based upon the secondary reality of sensation which in turn, in the case of human beings, refers both to the virtually invariant correlations of inanimate matter-energy in time-space and to the highly variant correlations of one's culture in time-space.

In thus describing the organization of a person's mind, we have argued that the organization of a mind strives to be a system of logic of economic orderliness. Although the abstractions and correlations of an individual's mind are not describable by the traditional mathematics of high-school days that refer to an idealized time-space, they nevertheless may be describable by other kinds of algebra and geometry that refer to symmetries and isomorphs. In the following pages, under the headings of (*A*) semantic algebra, (*B*) semantic geometry, and (*C*) semantic dynamics, we shall elaborate further upon what we believe are the relevant mathematical considerations in question, without meaning to be dogmatic on the subject, however, and certainly without pretending to an expertness in the mathematical fields to which we refer.

A. Semantic Algebra

In the language of physics, a *diamond* is a crystal of carbon that is comparable with carbon in other forms, as well as with other crystals and noncrystals, and so on, and with other forms of energy. A diamond is physically that and nothing more, insofar as we know.

But in the language of a given culture (and also in a given person's superego) a diamond may be a signal of its owner's "wealth," "prestige," and "power"—three classes that may also include mink coats, gold, satin, the latest hairdo, political opinions, and other paraphernalia which, however much they belong together in the same class culturally, do not belong together in the language of physics. Although the diamond will behave physically according to the language of physics (by definition) without any regard for the culture or the subjective evaluations of the person in question, it will *also* behave according to the language of the culture of him who controls it (for example, it will be cut, mounted, and worn according to the cultural language). But though the language of physics and that of culture are basically different, that does not mean that the language of culture cannot be described mathematically.

If the classes and statements of mind cannot be described by the quantitative algebra and geometry that refer to the idealized conditions of time-space, they may be describable by some nonquantitative algebra and geometry, such as, for example, by Boolean algebra, which we mentioned in Chapter Five.[28]

In the terms of Boolean algebra we might make the following statement:

$$x = the$$
$$y = black$$
$$z = horse$$
$$x \cdot y \cdot z = the\ black\ horse$$

To say that *the black horse* = *the* × *black* × *horse* has meaning in Boolean algebra but not in the other. Since Boole assumed that *a unit system of knowledge* equals *1,* it follows that the statement, $1 - x \cdot y \cdot z$ refers to everything in your mind after selecting out the special class, $x \cdot y \cdot z$ (or *the black horse*). Any Aristotelian proposition can be stated in terms of Boolean algebra. (On the other hand, a fundamental characteristic of the structure of mentation seems to be sequential order, in the sense that $ab \neq ba$).

To any given person speaking the terms of a given culture, any speech entity, including permutations, represents an experiential *class* that is itself and not something else. This class may be defined in terms of other classes (whether they are products or sums depends upon definition). These classes, regardless of their number or diversity, constitute the *one* semantic system. The grammar of a speech refers to the rules of juxtaposition and of the systematic modification of forms-functions; it presupposes a *logical* orderliness throughout the entire speech structure—an orderliness that is built upon *logical* analogies and symmetries.* The dimensions of mind, then, are abstract classes. These dimensions of mind differ from the dimensions of time-space. In time-space there is no particular connection between a *draft* on a bank, a *draft* of wind, and a military *draft*. Yet in the minds of

* E.g., we say ***ox is*** and ***bird is;*** also ***oxen are*** and ***birds are.*** Hence in reference to this grammatical operation we may state the analogy:

ox : *oxen* : : *bird* : *birds*

so similarly

sheep : ***sheep*** : : ***bird*** : ***birds***

members of our culture there is a connection between the three, if only in terms of abstract verbal classes. And to the schizophrene who reifies his abstractions and who ignores cultural conventions, the connection between the three *drafts* may be such that even in the heat of summer he will insist upon putting on his old army uniform and his army great coat before he goes down to cash a check at the bank.

B. Semantic Geometry

Corresponding to a theoretical semantic algebra is a theoretical semantic geometry whose space and time are fictitious and whose content are correlated functional abstractions that refer only ultimately to physical time-space.

Instead of elaborating further upon semantic geometry, we remark that in our following chapter on the language of dreams with their abstractions in a fictitious time-space, we shall present a theoretical construct that is intended to represent the solution of actual problems in terms of semantic geometry.

C. Semantic Dynamics. (Dynamic Symbolism)

An algebra or a geometry, however, are only descriptive languages. They at best merely describe the relevant aspects and terms of a problem; they do not provide the solution. Hence we may not stop with the remark that the content of a person's mind is describable by a hypothetical semantic algebra or semantic geometry.

Instead we go further and say that the action of mind, in addition to striving to establish a logically self-consistent unit system of knowledge, involves the minimizing of the effort of its different classes and correlations in solving a particular problem.* This minimizing of the effort of mind may be called *semantic dynamics* (or *dynamic symbolism*).

Yet what specifically is semantic dynamics? Let us first face this question empirically.

It is evident from our data on the distribution of speech entities—and the reader is free to make as many more samplings as he sees fit—that there is an orderliness in the structure of speech. Thus, for example, even if two different languages have speech vocabularies that contain totally different n words with totally different meanings, nevertheless the two speeches apparently agree in the rates at which their n words are used, as we have seen in our discussion of the equation of the generalized harmonic series. Since these rates are by no means an *a priori* necessity in the light of the null hypothesis, they are by definition an empiric law.

This empiric law is obviously not a law of physics, as that term is understood today. Neither is it a law of culture, since culture exists only as a set of correspondences in the actions of the individual members of a specific social group. Indeed the law refers to the *manners* in which the individuals of a group behave in terms of the social conventions of their group, regard-

* "Occam's Razor" of William of Occam states: "*Essentia non multiplicanda sunt praeter necessitatem.*" This dictum points in the same direction as our argument.

less of what the particular conventions are and regardless of what the social group is. Hence the empiric law of speech refers to an individual's *kinds,* or *manners,* of behavior, whose sum total we shall define as his *mind.*[29] The principles that govern the structure and behavior of a mind we shall call *semantic dynamics* (or *dynamic symbolism*).

Although we cannot here repeat all the details of all our preceding chapters, we can say in summary that the first principle of semantic dynamics, which in turn refers to all the different *kinds* of action of any organism, seems to be the principle of the n minimum, according to which the n number of different classes of an individual's action will be minimized.* This n minimum is derived from our Principle of Least Effort, which asserts that an organism will minimize its probable work.

By decreasing the n number of different kinds, properties, or combinations of matter-energy that are used, the organism increases the probability of finding them in any random environment with a given amount of work. By decreasing the n number of its sensory-mentational classes (including correlations) with which the organism predicts the relevant events of its future environment, the organism increases the probability of finding its n classes with a given amount of sensory sampling. Since the above statement includes the entire selective activity of the organism, its entire selective activity constitutes its mind, whose semantic dynamics is subject to the n minimum.

We have developed and tested the n minimum primarily in reference to the cultural activity of speech. Yet in Chapter Six we ventured into the entire organic field.

VI. LANGUAGE AND THE STRUCTURE OF THE PERSONALITY

And now what is an individual's personality?

Surely it is not the particular kinds of matter-energy that a person uses, and the particular physical operations he performs, since these he shares with the rest of his species. We may even refer to this particular set of activities as the *role of his species.*

Neither can we call his acts of propagation his personality, since this particular kind of *biological role* he shares with many other species.

Is not an individual's personality the role he plays in the language of his culture, whose terms we must understand if we are to understand his role and therefore his personality? In this usage, *a person's personality exists only as a role that he is playing in terms of the observable language of a culture.* This is the person's *cultural personality,* which is the only objective personality that there is.†

Yet how about the schizophrene, who plays no cultural role? Alas, by definition, he has no personality. Indeed when we speak of the deteriora-

---

* Subject, as always, to auxiliary conditions as discussed previously.

† In Part Two we shall find that the rank-frequency distributions of these cultural roles follow our familiar equation of the harmonic series.

tion of the personality of a schizophrene, we mean the deterioration of his cultural role.

Yet how about the remaining presumable inner life of the schizophrene whose personality has completely deteriorated? Of that we cannot know unless he expresses himself in cultural terms, even though we may hope to understand something of the dynamics of his system by studying the nature of its distortions.

But how about every person's "inner self" which means so much to him, and, in his opinion, *is* his *real* self? Apparently every person has that feeling about his real *inner* self; and theoretically a person's *tertiary reality* is his *real* self, even though our knowledge of another person is limited to his cultural self (i.e., his cultural personality).

CHAPTER EIGHT

THE LANGUAGE OF DREAMS AND OF ART

We have taken the position that if an individual wishes to alter his environment, his action must be meaningful in terms of the language of his environment. Otherwise his environment will not respond according to the individual's intentions. Thus, for example, if the manipulation of the environment refers only to inanimate material, then the manipulation must be in terms of the invariant *language of physics* if the manipulation is to succeed. On the other hand, if the manipulation refers to the "other fellow" as a social human being and not as a mere lump of matter, then the manipulation of him must be in terms of the *language of his culture* as well as in terms of the language of physics.

Although the environment responds to stimuli only in terms of its language, that does not mean that a person must necessarily be conscious of the more minute semantic details of his physical or cultural manipulation. Thus a person may successfully pry loose a stone without consciously knowing the principle of the lever as such; or he may give someone an aspirin pill for curing a headache without in any way understanding the biochemistry involved; a sailor in a strange land may make certain parrot-learned conventional noises to the girl in the street in order to seduce her, without knowing the structure of the speech from which the noises are taken. Indeed even if the above actions on the part of the operator are accidental (e.g., a person rolls over in his sleep and knocks a precious lamp off the night table by his bed), the environment will nevertheless respond to the actual stimuli given in terms of the actual languages in question, since the environment can know of the operator only through his emitted stimuli —whether the operator acts deliberately or accidentally. For that matter many a scientific discovery has been made accidentally: that is, an operator through inadvertent action, or even carelessness, has unexpectedly elicited a new and valuable response which he afterwards has cudgeled his brains to comprehend semantically.

However, a person cannot manipulate his environment to his "liking" unless the person has, or is, a "liking." In short, before a person can deliberately or accidentally act upon his environment, he must first have, or be, a set of desires or intentions that attempt to realize themselves physically or culturally. Theoretically speaking, a person's set of desires or intentions is his "true self" insofar as he has a "true self"; and this "true self" he attempts to realize physically and culturally.

In the present chapter we shall attempt to investigate first (I) the possible structure of a person's set of desires, or intentions—that is, his theoretical "true self"—by discussing the phenomenon of *dreams*. Because of the nature of our problem and of the empiric nonverifiability of our data, our following discussion will not be empiric. The most that we can claim is that we are expressing ourselves verbally on the subject of dreams in what we believe is the reader's cultural vocabulary. Our words, if someone reads them, will evoke responses in the reader. If the reader finds our argument plausible in the light of his own experience with dreams, he thereby gives our argument what we shall call a *social sanction* (in other words, our argument will have received a kind of *social* test, as defined in our previous chapter).

From our discussion of the language of dreams we shall then turn (II) to a discussion of the language of art, lest we seem to ignore the "nicer things in life." Thence to a summary (III) of Part One which closes with this chapter.

I. THE LANGUAGE OF DREAMS

Let us approach circuitously the problem of the language of dreams by first discussing certain aspects of a play that is produced upon the stage of a public theater.

For example, let us assume that the stage directions of the play call for a number of trees. Since it is clearly not feasible to transplant a number of full-grown trees onto the stage, something that can serve functionally for trees must be used instead. This can consist of papier maché trees, or canvas trees, or painted pictures, or *anything that will evoke in the spectator's mind the same response as would be evoked by actual trees.*

Indeed in the history of the theater there have been instances, I believe, where instead of presenting the actual property, or a pictorial representation of the property, the director simply posted a word in the indicated place: in our above case he would have posted the word *TREES*. The spectator's own imagination was supposed to respond appropriately to the word; and the actors were supposed to behave towards the word quite as if the actual trees were there instead.

Clearly, whatever can be described by any understandable word, or by any other signal, can be used as a stage property or a costume, provided the spectators' imaginations fill in the details.*

Carried to an extreme, the entire stage and cast can consist of signals that come and go as the action proceeds. A signal could also be used for space and one for time, so that the entire play becomes nothing more than a synchrony and diachrony of signals.

It is obvious that such a stage could in this fashion be more fully packed in respect of time and space than would be the case if no substitutes were used.†

---

* E.g., "The curtain will be lowered to indicate the passage of two hours."

† Nevertheless such a stage would have all the semantic properties of a time-space stage, provided the imagination of the spectators reacted appropriately. Although at first blush, we may feel that such a stage is physically unrealizable, let us not forget that the stream of speech is little more than a two-dimensional continuum of cultural noises to

Now let us suppose that a dream is intrinsically a play upon a stage—a *dream play* of which the dreamer is the author, the dramatis personae, and the audience. And let us suppose that the plot of this dream play refers to the hypothetical set of desires, or intentions, of the dreamer's "true self." Quite obviously, then, the signals on the dream stage can be changed as soon as the dreamer has both given them and reacted to them appropriately. Hence the speed of the action of a dream play can be far greater than that of a public play. So too, roles can be combined, since the dreamer needs to consult only his own intellectual convenience. For example, if the plot calls for a partnership between a lion and an eagle to accomplish a given object, this action would entail two separate actors on a time-space stage: a lion and an eagle. But not so on a dream stage, where a lion with the head and wings of an eagle could be used as a single actor, provided that the dreamer reacts appropriately. By the same token the dreamer can combine further *relevant features* of distinctive roles.

Yet what are the above *relevant features* of roles that are thus combined? As far as we can judge, these so-called *relevant features* of roles are instances of *kinds of operations* of matter-energy upon kinds of matter-energy. In short they are *sheer physical operations* that are physically expressed; they are particular *kinds* of goal-directed actions. In the above case, for example, the eagle's wings *are,* say, the actual capacity for a physical flight; that is what they signal to the spectator. Similarly the lion's body *is* the actual capacity for a given kind of ferocious attack. Furthermore when the above eagle's wings flap, they signal that the above capacity for flight is in operation in company with the above capacity for a given kind of ferocious attack.

Any physically perceptible kind of matter-energy will serve to signal any kind of sheer physical operation, provided only that the spectator accepts it and reacts accordingly.

A. The Geometry of Dreams

We are arguing that the above theoretical dream stage has an exact counterpart in a person's dreams, in which it is the dreamer who selects the plot, and provides the actors, costumes, and sets; and who also provides the imagination as the sole spectator.

This dream play represents a very interesting mathematical problem. For, as we have already pointed out, a dream is cast in terms of a purely fictitious space which *seems* to have the *relevant features* of physical space (whatever those features may be), but which nevertheless is by no means physical space itself.

The question now arises as to what the dimensions of this fictitious dream space may be. The only possible dimensions are "functional" dimensions, in the sense that *each goal-directed physical operation of the dream play is a dimension of the fictitious space* of that particular play. In other words, the fictitious space of a dream play, which is a very real space to the dreamer, is what the mathematicians might call an abstract space whose

which an auditor reacts "appropriately" in time-space. The stream of speech is just such a "stage."

dimensions (i.e., independent variables) are what might be called goal-directed concepts.*

But though we say that the dimensions of the fictitious dream space are goal-directed concepts, or abstract operations, whose number can presumably be increased without limit, as far as the fictitious dream space is concerned, let us note that these concepts always appear in the dream in terms that relate ultimately to matter-energy in time-space even as we sense it. That is, the entire content of a dream is cast in terms of sights and sounds and smells, and such other phenomena as are found in the language of sensation; there is nothing in a dream that is unknown to the language of sensation, no matter how foreign to the languages of physics or culture the organization of the dream itself may be. Thus, though the dreamer may seem to violate every principle of physics in a dream—such as when he flies comfortably through the air with his hands, or breathes water as he swims—he nevertheless does not introduce a new kind of sensory data in so doing.† We stress this point in order to suggest that the geometry of a dream play has an ultimate sensory reference.

B. The Plot of the Dream Play

The ultimate sensory reference of the dream play is understandable when we remember that the only excuse for the dream play, theoretically, is that it helps the person in question to minimize the expenditure of effort in metabolizing actual matter-energy for the sake of preserving himself as an actual system from a final and complete physical equilibrium with his environment (if the Principle of Least Effort be true). In other words, the dream play is directed towards the actual survival needs of the person in question, which in turn are cast in terms of matter-energy in time-space with which an individual has only sensory experience.

These survival needs determine the nature of the plot of the play, since the dreamer will have no economic interest in any other kind of plot. Indeed, since the dreamer is the playwright, director, cast, properties, and audience, his dreams will theoretically represent his most urgent desires and intentions in the general problem of his existence, including the problem of procreation.

We may even say that the plot of a dream, like the plot of a public play, represents the solution to problems. Whatever the person's problems of the moment may be, those are the problems of the dream play for which the dream play seeks a solution; and since the problems of the individual dreamer are ultimately cast in terms of matter-energy in time-space, it follows that the plot of the dream play is cast in terms that refer ultimately to the dreamer's sensory experience with matter-energy in time-space.

* The same argument applies *mutatis mutandis* to the stream of speech as a kind of space, though it has finite dimensions if it is cast in terms of the language of culture (see Chapter Seven).

† Of course a dream may not be physically incorrect. The wiggle of a finger may signalize the possession of a physically perfect flight mechanism; the wiggle of the nostrils, the possession of the gills of a fish.

C. The Duration of the Dream Play

The question now arises as to how long a dream play lasts. This question is difficult to answer on the basis of one's conscious experience with dreams.

For as far as our conscious experience with our dreams is concerned, it amounts to little more than a conscious recollection of what has happened presumably during our sleep. When the person awakens, he almost by definition ceases to dream—or at least he is not aware of continuing to dream while awake. Yet does this lack of a conscious awareness of one's dreams while awake mean that we are not dreaming while awake?

It may be that the dream play is continually taking place, whether the person is awake or asleep, even though he is unaware of it. Perhaps this question as to the continuity of the dream play is analogous to the question of the continuity of the shining stars in the heavens which, since they are invisible during the light of day (consciousness), may be felt to have ceased to shine during the day. Yet, as far as the stars are concerned, we know from a more careful analysis that they still continue to shine, even though we are unaware of them.

If our dream play is like the stars, in the sense that the play goes on through life, though we are not aware of it when we are awake, then it follows that even while we are awake, we are still producing a dream play in which we are acting and to which we are attending as a spectator. In that case consciousness is something that comes and goes while the dream play continues for life.

We cannot tell for sure that the dream play is lifelong. Nevertheless when we are in a waking situation that offers little to our advantage, we often "daydream" in a manner that suggests a quasi-return to the genuine dream play. Furthermore when the waking situation palls dismally for a lack of interest for ourselves, we sometimes fall asleep, much as if we are abandoning the expense of consciousness from which we expect for the moment to gain little relevant information.

Yet none of the above considerations bears such cogent testimony to the continuity of the dream play as does the waking behavior of many a person whose expressions befit rather a spectator at a harrowing play than a person who is in a culturally neutral or even pleasant waking situation. In short, the anxiety states, depressions, and even certain psychotic manifestations suggest that the person in question is largely "absent from the waking situations," in the sense that he is away attending his dream play to whose dream situations the person's sympathetic nervous system primarily reacts, even though these dream situations have no connection with the person's outward situation, of which he is presumably conscious.

In the event that the dream play is continual, then what we call consciousness may be nothing more than a special mechanism for gaining information about the more variable, or less determinate, aspects of the environment, and for modifying the same. Information thus gained is theoretically added to the plot of the dream play. That the new information thus gained may sometimes be troublesome for one's "true self" as well as informative, is suggested by the action of narcotics who resort to chemical means to inhibit consciousness.

The fact that we are not consciously aware of our dream play while we are awake does not mean that its performance is not continuous. If consciousness is merely a news service, no practical purpose is served by reporting one's dream play to one's dream play.

Theoretically a dream play must be a continuous performance if it is to be the conceptualization of one's set of desires, or intentions, in terms that refer ultimately to sensory experience, because after all, one's set of desires, or intentions, presumably continues without interruption.

D. Structure: Unity and Self-Consistency

Let us consider now the question of the unity and self-consistency of the dream play itself.

Theoretically the dream play should be integrated with the totality of the organism's needs, which are unified in terms of the organism as a frame of reference: hence the *unity* of dreams. One's need of a mate, one's need for food, drink, wealth, one's need to move one's bowels or to empty one's bladder, or to have shelter are all legitimate contents of dreams. So too are one's need for prestige and for alterations in the personnel of the environment. Insofar as these needs are simultaneous, they will be treated simultaneously in the plot of the play. Though the content of the dream play might well seem to be motley to anyone but the dreamer, it is nevertheless theoretically unified in reference to the dreamer's needs and desires.

The term *unity* suggests the terms *mass* and *coherence,* in the usage of literary critics who rarely define their terms.[1] Has a dream play mass and coherence? If we define mass (or attention, or emphasis) as something that should presumably be distributed to the various parts of the play's action in direct proportion to their relative importance to the play as a whole, then theoretically the dream play should have perfect mass from the viewpoint of the dreamer, since it is the dreamer who decides upon the relative importance both of the need and of the treatment. Thus if the dreamer is faced by the need both of killing himself on the morrow and of writing a letter to his mother, he will decide which of these should have the greater emphasis, and his decision will be final for himself. The often vast detail of a dream may seem random and meaningless to the person when awake; but to the person while still dreaming, the dream play is theoretically unified and well massed.

By the same token a dream play theoretically has a perfect coherence, if by coherence is meant that one act follows "naturally" upon another according to basic rules of conduct that remain the same throughout the play. In other words, while we are in a dream, all the action of the dream seems to be reasonable and logical, even though at times the action of the play may be unpleasant and nightmarish.

E. Structure: A Dream and the Stream of Speech

We have previously intimated that the organization of a dream play is similar to the organization of the stream of speech, in the sense that responses are evoked in either case by stimuli that have no necessary connection with the nature of their responses. In the case of a dream, the "dreamatist" pushes a "button" that evokes in himself, say, the response of a visual image of an automobile; he then responds obligingly; in the case of speech a person may utter a noise, *automobile,* with the intention of evoking in the auditor a visual image of an automobile. In neither case is there any necessary connection between the stimulus on the one hand, and the entity, or operation, that is imaged, or directed, in the response on the other. Except for the exigencies of a cultural vocabulary in the case of speech, both a dream and a stream of speech are a succession of "buttons" whose semantic arrangements belong rather to an abstract geometry and algebra than to the geometry and algebra of physical time-space.

Nor does the apparent isomorphism between dreaming and speaking stop there.

1. The Synchrony and Diachrony of Dreaming and Speaking. It is commonly believed by students of speech that speech is only a diachronous phenomenon in the sense that in speech there is only a succession of single events. Though this belief may be phonetically justified, it is perhaps not semantically correct. For while the speaker is in the process of uttering a phoneme, he may also be simultaneously in the process of uttering a morpheme, a word, a phrase, a clause, a sentence, a paragraph, and so on.

Thus if one were to open the text of *Hamlet* and put his finger upon a phoneme, he would also simultaneously be putting his finger upon a word, a sentence, a speech, an act, and, indeed, upon the entire play. These various different semantic elements are occurring simultaneously and hence constitute what may be called the synchrony of semantic events.

Of course, not all the different synchronous semantic events are equally characteristic of the sample of speech. The phonemes of *Hamlet,* for example, were the common property of the relevant social group at the time, so too the morphemes and words, and to some extent the phrases and clauses. Yet as the entities of *Hamlet,* or of any other sample of speech, increase in size to sentences or paragraphs and chapters—or speeches, scenes, and acts—then they become ever more characteristic of the sample from which they are taken. In general, it seems that the larger and comparatively more slowly moving semantic elements are ever more characteristic of the sample of speech in which they occur. Most characteristic of any sample is the entire sample; in the case of *Hamlet,* the most characteristic part is the entire play.

The reason for this correlation between the relative length of a speech entity and its comparative degree of significance for the sample of speech is easy to comprehend. For example, we have in English a single, commonplace word, *horse,* that means a certain kind of animal with four legs. If, however, the speaker chooses to evoke a response that means the same kind of animal except that it has three legs, he resorts to a permutation and says: *a three-legged horse.* As the permutation increases in length it betokens a meaning that is ever more characteristic of the speaker's mind at the time, and less a commonplace of the cultural vocabulary. Hence in a very practical sense the entire play of *Hamlet* may be viewed as a single large permutation (as well as many subsidiary ones). The fact that Shakespeare had to resort to so large a permutation in order to evoke his desired response suggests that no smaller entity or single word was available in the vocabulary to do the job.

Turning now to the phenomenon of dreams, and remembering that the entire contents of a dream consist of relevant operations for the dreamer's problems, may we not suspect that the above argument about speech applies also to dreams? For example, if a person dreams of a horse, then the horse's four legs in the dream are a part of the operation, and are in no way more characteristic of the dream than is the horse itself. On the other hand, if a dreamer dreams of a three-legged horse, then that operational difference may be very characteristic of the dream. And it is interesting to note that while we are in a dream we pay more attention to its oddities than to its commonplaces, and that we are more likely to recall the oddities when awake than the commonplaces.

By way of illustration let us inspect the contents of the following dream. A widowed, wealthy, and socially prominent woman in her thirties dreamt that she was lying naked on a chaise longue in her boudoir with the sun shining warmly on her body. The room was appointed with costly furniture and fragile *objets d'art.* Apple blossoms extended through the open windows, and on one of these was a bee. It was not a commonplace bee, however, but one that was made of leather. Suddenly this bee darted to her and stung her genitals. The sting was very pleasant, sending a glow through her entire body that was followed by a swelling that spread up her abdomen. The woman jumped up to catch the bee, and in so doing upset the furniture and caused the *objets d'art* to crash. The bee vanished and she awoke in a panic.

In the above dream play, the only peculiar action was that of the leather bee that stung her genitals pleasantly. Nothing else in the dream was peculiar to a woman of her station; instead it all seemed to be subordinate to the bee which alone seemed to be an operation that was a solution to a problem that was elaborated by all the other "props." Yet what operation could be represented by a bee that was made out of leather?

It is of some interest in this connection that the person who mowed the woman's lawn and shovelled her snow and did odd jobs for her was a handsome vigorous young male of inferior social status by the name of Leatherbee. That particular capacity of Leatherbee that was represented by a pleasant stinger that caused an abdominal swelling, together with the capacity of an unobtrusive entrance and exit apparently represented an operation that would solve a major problem of the woman. But this particular solution was apparently not completely satisfactory, since the *objets d'art* and other operations in the dream that signalized her social standing crashed as she sought to possess Leatherbee.

According to our theory, everything in that dream had some meaning for the woman's problems. The apple blossoms perhaps first substituted for the lady's genitalia until she was emboldened to make Leatherbee come directly to them. The fact that apple blossoms were used instead of wisteria or potted geraniums had a meaning; so too the fact that she was reclining naked on a chaise longue in her boudoir instead of flat on her back on the kitchen floor. The fact that there were *objets d'art* there instead of bathroom fixtures had meaning. If the *objets d'art* included a fragile carved ivory Virgin and a jeweled chalice, that fact too would have a meaning. On the other hand, the presence of a floor in the room, or of four legs on a chair, might have no particular meaning beyond the indication that the room was conventional.

It would be difficult in the extreme to say what all the properties and actions of the dream play meant to the dreamer. It would be equally difficult to say what all the phrases, clauses, and stage properties of *Hamlet* meant to Shakespeare. The point of interest, however, is that the organization of speech may be isomorphic with the organization of dreams, with the result that by studying the dynamics of the one we may gain insight into the dynamics of the other. There is, after all, nothing that a dream does, in changing scenes, or in altering topics and characters, and the like, which speech does not also do. Indeed a dream may be a geometric counterpart of speech, except that there is apparently no limit to the packing of a dream whereas the dimensions of cultural speech are finite. Although the scenes of a dream may shift with uncanny swiftness in a way that is impossible in physical time-space, the same can also happen in speech.

2. The Chronological Strata of Dreams. One of the principles of speech is that of economical specialization according to which the shorter and more frequently used elements of speech are the older in the vocabulary. Does this principle have a counterpart in dreams? In facing this question, let us remember that the contents of a dream are operations: for example, a chair in a dream may represent the operation of getting something by sitting, or by pontificating; a fish may represent the operation of procuring something by swimming, or by producing quantities of eggs.

If the principle of economical specialization applies also to the content of dreams, then a dream contains theoretically not only the current and local types of operations (e.g., the current and local modes of dressing, speaking, and adornment), it also contains theoretically many older types of operations—so old in fact that they may extend far back into our early phylogenetic history (e.g., swimming comfortably under water without breathing difficulties, or flying without worry about gravitation). Though the Freudian school may call this older type of operation *reminiscent dreams,* this term seems to lack dynamic emphasis; for theoretically these older types of operations may indicate a desire on the part of the dreamer to solve his present problems by adopting instrumentations which in the earlier history of our species were presumably reasonably successful.

During a person's life, the individual passes from a tiny few-celled animal whose most urgent problems do not extend beyond the intimate molecular manipulation of growth, to a vastly complex organization of cells whose problems include a highly intricate social manipulation. All this activity belongs to the accumulated experience of the person. Yet in addition to this experience there may also be a phylogenetic experience which represents the anterior history of the particular set of genetic tools with which the tiny embryo sets up his lifelong shop. A person's experience, then, is theoretically vast. And out of this vast experience are selected the operations, or functions, of the dreamer's dream.

The dreamer's dream theoretically does not deal merely with problems of the present. According to the Principle of Least Effort, as discussed in Chapters Two, Three, and Five, a person's problems include also future problems; indeed the person seeks a "path" of least effort through present and future problems. Since the predictability of events of the future tends to be increasingly less for the ever more remote events in the future, it follows that the problems of the future seems to be less urgent than the immediate ones. Nevertheless, in spite of the engrossing attention of present problems, the future ones are also, theoretically, not absent from the treatment of the dream play.

For that reason we may suspect theoretically that a dream play represents an attempt to solve the dreamer's problems of the present and also, with ever decreasing importance, the problems of the ever more distant future. The functional operations used in the dream play come not only from one's own but from one's phylogenetic past.

Obviously, without something that corresponds to an etymological dictionary for words, we may never be able to determine the relative ages of the functional meanings of all different elements in a dream; and therefore we may never know whether the principle of economical specialization applies to dreams. Nevertheless, even without an etymological dictionary of dream material, the concept of a dream as an enormous play whose action is the resultant of the urges of present and future problems and the givens of present and past kinds of goal-directed actions, may have a certain didactic value.

For as we see a person asleep on a couch and presumably dreaming, we see in him not only an ego that has to nourish himself and propagate, but also the resultant of the tensions of many present and future problems in terms of his own and his breed's past kinds of action.

Thus viewed, a dream play is like the continual charting of the course for present and future action. Today's course is determined not only by our problems of today but by those of tomorrow and so on into the future with an ever decreasing relevance. Our course today is also determined to a considerable extent by the course we set yesterday, and so on back into the past.

Upon reflection, is it not possible that the dynamics of the stream of speech is similar to that of a dream, except that speech must be cast in cultural terms? We chatter about present problems in terms of a mightily ancient vocabulary whose entities and grammatical operations seem to be appropriate to the occasion, though we know not why. Sometimes the chatter refers to the more distant future; yet, according to casual observation, the more distantly in the future the problem lies, the less often we chatter about it.

F. The Dream as a Synthesis in a Semantic Group-System

A dream play may also be likened to a salon in which a person discusses his problem with himself in terms of what we have defined as goal-directed kinds of physical operations. Yet the phrase, "the person discusses his problem with himself," is not clear in this connection, since the discussion in question consists merely of the selection of the person's own stimuli in order to elicit his own responses. If a dream is nothing more than a discussion of this sort, then a dream is just as useless for the solution of the person's problems as is the attempt of a person to hoist himself over the fence by pulling at his own boot straps.

On the other hand, it may be that the person who "discusses" something with himself represents several different kinds of selves—that is, two different aspects, or capacities, of himself which "talk things over." The one self may be the person as a unit; the other self may be the person as an enormous population of organs and cells.

For we must remember that a human being is not only an individual; he is also a tremendously large population of cells, each one of which is alive and behaving as a unit while interacting with others. The person's well-being depends quite obviously upon the functioning of himself both as a unit and as a system.*

A dream may then be the "salon" in which the person as a unit "discusses" his problems with himself as a group. In that case a satisfactory dream would be one in which the dreamer solved the problem of himself and his cultural and acultural environment to the satisfaction of himself as a person and as a corporate state of organs and cells.

The nature of this unit-group organization of an individual can be most easily comprehended if in imagination we watch the course of matter-energy as it enters the person's system by whatever route. Upon entering the organism's system, the matter-energy does not cease to operate according to the laws of physics and chemistry (i.e., the *language of physics*). Instead, while still operating according to the language of physics, it *also* operates according to the semantic system (or *signal system*) of the person in question. In other words, matter-energy, upon entering a person's system, thereby enters into an elaborate signalling system, as far as the person is concerned. Although the signalling system is constructed of various kinds of electrochemical reactions, it is itself meaningful to the person only as a semantically integrated group of signals in which n different kinds of stimuli induce

* If the reader touches a hair on his head, or a fingernail, or any part of his anatomy, he may say both; "That *belongs* to me," and "That *is* me (I)." We mention this because it is often easier to say *"e pluribus unum,"* than it is to visualize simultaneously both *unum* and *plura*.

m different kinds of responses (throughout this entire system, *n* is theoretically minimized subject as always to the auxiliary conditions as previously discussed).

A dream then may be the mechanism whereby the semantic system is kept logically integrated, or self-consistent, and where effort is minimized.* It may be the director's room where growth and health have their ultimate collective controls for the long-term and short-term collective economy of the organism as a whole. Better still, it may be the parliament where, through discussion, the collective whole both governs and is governed.

G. The Concept: "In Phase"

Even if the person as an individual discusses his totality of problems with himself as a group, with the purpose of an optical effort-solution of the problems, there still is a dynamic risk in the condition of dreaming if it goes no further. The risk is that the dreamer may get "in phase" with himself, since he selects both the stimuli and the responses.

To explain the meaning of the term, "in phase," in our usage, let us take the case of a ship that is overcrowded with passengers on the deck. As long as the passengers are evenly distributed over the deck, the ship remains upright. But if the passengers for some reason all rush to one side, the ship will list to that side; if this sudden listing of the ship frightens the passengers so that they run to the opposite side, the ship will promptly roll and list *even more* to the opposite side. By thus running from one side of the ship to the other, in phase with the ship's rolling, the passengers will increase the magnitude of the ship's rolling to such a point that it may capsize (ships have been known to capsize for this very reason). The point here is that the *a* action of the ship evokes *b* responses in the passengers which are such as to increase the magnitude of the *a* action of the ship, and so on. By definition, the actions of the above ship and passengers are *in phase*.†

Let us now take another case of "in phase," this time the case of two boys, *a* and *b*. To begin, *a* hates *b*, and punches him, thereby enraging *b* who punches *a* who hates *b* even more and punches him back, and so on. The two boys are in belligerent phase. It may happen that *a* calls his papa to help him, whereupon *b*'s papa comes, and ere long the entire neighborhood may become belligerently in phase (in the 1920's in Chicago a race riot seems to have started from just such a simple fracas). Today the Jews and Arabs in Palestine seem to be belligerently in phase; so too the Jews and British; so too the Jews and Nazis before and during the war; appar-

* According to this view, the dream might well be based upon subsidiary plays that "are so deeply rooted in unconsciousness" that the person is never aware of them (e.g., cancer, in which the cells behave independently without regard for the well-being of the whole, may represent a semantic breakdown of whose nature the person, as an individual, is unaware).

† The phrase *in phase* does not always imply larger and larger oscillations, or "forced oscillations." Two men working with a crosscut saw are in phase with a fairly constant oscillation; so, too, the persons working on an industrial assembly line. In general, *a* and *b* are *in phase* when *a* action evokes *b* response which evokes *a* action, etc.

ently the Americans and Soviets are coming into belligerent phase. During the 1930's Roosevelt and Hitler were obviously in belligerent phase, each exacerbating the other. Indeed this general concept of being in social phase seems to be fundamental to Eliot D. Chapple's data and theory on human interaction rates, as discussed in Chapter Eleven.

Having illustrated the term *in phase* in the above physical and social cases,* let us now take the case of the person who "talks to himself" (we do not mean the case of "thinking out loud," as when one is working on a problem, or figuring out an income tax, or memorizing a poem). In "talking to himself" a person is in fact talking to an imaginary creation of his own mind; and since this imaginary interlocutor is the person's own creation, he will both act and respond in total conformity to the person's desires, thereby coming almost immediately into complete phase with the person. Naturally this imaginary creation need not be only a single person: he can be the audience in a theater or a concert hall, or the Congress, or the Supreme Court, or a learned society, or one's neighbors, or the stock exchange. Neither need the creation be only co-operative and friendly; instead the creation may be one's enemy or enemies who confess "properly" and are punished "properly."

The chief value of such an imaginary interlocutor is that he may provide a temporary relief from the raw realities of daily life where the person's desires may be largely frustrated. Moreover, by talking things over with one's own creation, a person may actually arrive at a clearer understanding of his problems, since he at least has the opportunity to hear how his discussion thereof sounds. Then too it is frequently much safer—and not always without a certain soothing effect—to kiss, kill, or torture some persons in imagination than it is to do so in reality.

The chief drawback, however, to thus talking to one's self, is that the person may solve his problems in terms which, though real to him, are perfectly fantastic in the language of physics or the language of culture. Thus the great invention that brings untold applause and renown to the person by means of the imaginary creation, may be utterly impossible in the language of physics. The same applies to imaginary financial, political, social and artistic successes which are foolish in terms of the cultural vocabulary and the person's actual situation.

Since the person reacts, nevertheless, to his imaginary success—that is, since the person actually adjusts his action to the responses of his imaginary creation—the person may shortly lose rapport with the language of physics and of culture, with the result that he becomes physically and socially awkward.† From this physical and social awkwardness, the person may

* Two persons can be in phase co-operatively too. E.g., boy meets girl casually and steals a kiss, thereby arousing girl who caresses him, thereby arousing him still more, and so on until the girl becomes pregnant—comes into belligerent phase with her parents whom she leaves in order to join the boy and to establish a new social system that may become ever more in phase until a point is reached where if one dies, the other dies.

† The manic phase of a manic-depressive psychosis may often represent the case of a person who is in phase with himself as he smiles and laughs and either talks to himself, or talks to others without bothering to await their replies. Such a phase system will con-

suffer a serious economic handicap in his competition and co-operation with others.

The same economic handicap would result from an uninterrupted dreaming (indeed schizophrenia may in a way be just that). Hence consciousness, or better still, the conscious casting of one's activity in terms of material and cultural givens, may be a necessary interruption of one's unmitigated dream play, if the dream play itself is to have any functional value for the person who dreams. For without the interruption of conscious activity, the person's mind will become so simplified that he is incapable of acting correctly physically and socially.*

On the other hand, strictly speaking, consciousness cannot be an interruption of a dream play, if the dream play is to be continual. Instead consciousness is perhaps an extension of the scope of a dream play into the finiteness and the invariance and actual variance of the environment—an attempt to realize one's dreams physically, and also an attempt to alter the language of one's dreams in the light of the consciously sensed physical and cultural exigencies of the environment.

Without the extension of conscious activity, the dream play can at best only bring the person as a unit into phase with himself as a population of subsidiary organs and cells. In this connection it is perhaps worth remembering that during sleep a person's body generally "calms down" into a system of regular rhythms and pulsations, much as if it were a system of automatic checks and balances that is in phase.

H. The Personality and the "True Self"

We pointed out in our preceding chapter that a given individual's *personality* in the eyes of the "other fellow" is the role he plays in the "other fellow's" cultural vocabulary: that is, his personality is his characteristic action in the language of the "other fellow's" cultural vocabulary.

Yet to the person's own self, his own *personality* is rather his set of tools-jobs—that is, his set of desires, or intentions, his abilities and achievements. In short, it is his dream play. For that reason when the person is mentally or emotionally ill, the psychiatrist inquires into the person's dreams to see what his desires and intentions may be. In so doing the psychiatrist seeks to discover what the person's ideal world—or ideal self—is like, so that he can help to alter either the ideal or the environment for the sake of bringing the two more nearly into adjustment.

Yet how does the psychiatrist know what his patient's highly packed and abbreviated dream language means? In a sense the psychiatrist does not know, and for that reason he asks his patient to talk in culturally under-

tinue to build itself up until a peak of overactivity is reached that represents the limit of the person's metabolistic capabilities. From this peak of overactivity, the rest of the outside world will look drab indeed; yet into this drab world the person will be obliged to enter both because of his needs for nourishment, and because his imaginary companion can elevate him no higher.

* Referring to sexual activity, the chief and perhaps the only drawback to masturbation is the risk that the person will thereby get in phase with himself sexually, and develop into a sexually "closed system."

standable words about his dream signals, since, after all, the dreamer is the sole author of the play in question and selects the signals from his own experience in order to solve his own problems; in the last analysis only the dreamer knows what it is all about. Yet in talking freely about his dream signals, the person thus redacts their meanings in cultural terms, and thereby states his problems in an objective language both for his own and for his psychiatrist's more convenient scrutiny.

But suppose the dreamer merely states the content of his dreams without further elaboration. For example, the dreamer might merely state that he dreamed of a cat and a dog and a snake. In that case is the psychiatrist at a total loss as to the meaning of the dream, or does the above fragmentary type of information give the psychiatrist an intimation of the meaning of the dream play? In short, is there a stock of dream stereotypes that makes up a part of the dream material? According to the Freudian school, some dream symbols have a well-nigh universal significance for all persons; for example, a snake is considered to be almost universally a phallic symbol.

Theoretically, if we may trust the Principle of Least Effort, there may well be a stock of dream stereotypes that have virtually the same meanings for all persons. This is theoretically the case because all persons have largely the same phylogenetic background of experience; furthermore, being members of the same species, they will have to a considerable extent the same kind of personal problems. Hence theoretically there should be dream elements of approximately equal meaning for members of the human species that would represent effort minima for persons of like experiential background who are in like situations. These dream elements (such as snakes and trees and the like) would indeed be archaic stage properties.

The same argument will apply also to some extent to the dream-elements of persons of the same culture. Thus, for example, the role of Buddha in a dream might signalize the same operation to all devout Buddhists, even as the role of the Virgin Mary might signalize nearly the same to all devout Roman Catholics.*

By extension, the above argument will apply to the specialized cultural vocabularies of ever smaller groups of which the dreamer is a member, until we come to a group of which the dreamer is the sole member: his own self.

II. THE LANGUAGE OF ART

We have taken the view in the present book that a given individual is not only his material self but also his semantic self. He is his material self, insofar as he is a mechanical system that gets work out of matter-energy in order to preserve himself as a mechanical system from a complete and final physical equilibrium with his environment. He is his semantic self insofar as he is a classification and correlation of kinds of action and of kinds

* If we read correctly, Karl Jung in his writings has suggested the same; for example, an American Indian may symbolize to the American girl what Faust symbolizes to the German girl.

of responses in reference to himself as a frame. This is perhaps a loose way of describing our entire foregoing argument, but it is a sufficient description.

The above view which led us in our immediately preceding pages to a speculation about the language of a person's most intimate dreams in the light of our Principle of Least Effort, would seem to apply also to the dynamics of the social phenomenon of art, as we shall now see, once the dreamer tries to express the plot of his dreams in cultural terms that are understandable to the "other fellow." For convenience we shall dub our ensuing argument, *the social theory of art.*

A. The Social Theory of Art

Let us go back to the case of the dreamer who, in his dreams, is theoretically trying to resolve a conflict between himself as a social group, and himself as a unit, and himself as a member of cultural groups. The language of the dream consists of goal-directed operations with ultimate sensory reference in a fictitious time-space of infinite possible dimensions. The plot of the play consists of the dreamer's most urgent problems, which he treats dramatically to his own satisfaction.

Let us now suppose that the dreamer seeks to produce his play upon a public three-dimensional cultural stage for the amusement or edification of other persons. What changes must his dream play undergo in order to be *culturalized* (i.e., to be redacted in terms of the cultural vocabulary of his spectators)?

In the first place, unless the plot of the dream play represents a solution to a conflict in his spectators' life, the dream artist will have no audience at all, and hence cannot receive a social sanction for his play. On the other hand, if the plot of his play treats problems of great moment for his spectators, and treats them to their satisfaction in the sense that the spectators become clearer about the nature of their problems and of their solutions, then the theater may well become filled.

As to the dreamer's job of redacting his dream play into a cultural time-space play, the dreamer has nothing further to do than to substitute the appropriate cultural signals of his audience for the personal operations that he uses in his dream play. Once the dreamatist emits these understandable cultural signals, his job is done. For aside from these cultural signals, the audience needs no further information either as to the nature of the plot or as to the nature of its solution. Instead, the audience will simply react conventionally to the play's conventional signals, and in thus reacting conventionally, the audience will be automatically solving its problems. To each member of the audience, the play's cultural signals will have meanings in terms of the member's personal conflicts between himself as a unit system of action, and himself as a member of social groups.

If the audience leaves the theater amused, or edified, or enlightened, or profoundly moved by the play, we may say that the play had relevance as far as the audience's problems were concerned—even though the professional critic may not have the faintest notion of what it was all about.

What the actual basic problems of the play were, the audience itself may never know consciously; nor indeed does it need to know. The audience need only to react conventionally to the conventional signals; and thereby the audience will emotionally "purge" itself. There is no need for the audience nor the dramatist to know, for example, what the horrible extortionist "really" means in terms of their personal problems; and the same applies to the fainting virgin, and to the handsome youth who nevertheless chokes the old lady for her money—all this may never be understood consciously by the audience, or by the dramatist. Suffice it to say that cultural "buttons" were pushed, and that cultural reactions ensued in the audience, who by their rapt attention and applause gave a *social sanction* to the play—a social sanction that relates only to the audience in question, and which may be withheld by the next audience.

We have said that neither the dramatist nor the audience needs to know what the basic human social problem of the play is. To clarify this point let us take an entirely different kind of play. For example, let us take the case of a dramatist who while on his lonely walks or, for that matter, in a busy social life, suddenly hears noises flashing through his mind—noises such as are made by violins, reed instruments, and horns. He finds the noises beautiful, though he does not know why. He writes them down in a cultural notation that is adapted to this kind of noises; and he hires a group of actors to produce them with violins, reed instruments, and horns. The audience comes and is profoundly stirred by the play, which they conventionally name, say, a concerto. As the audience breaks into applause and calls the dramatist to the stage, the audience gives him a social sanction. Yet what that play means, either to the audience or to the dramatist in terms of their individual or cultural problems—neither the one nor the other may have the remotest idea. The most we can say is that the dramatist has expressed himself within the then prevailing vocabulary and grammar (e.g., harmony and counterpoint) of the cultural language of his audience as a prerequisite to evoking their responses (even as Shakespeare in his plays, pushed the cultural "buttons" of his time). Of course the music critic's opinion as to what the concerto means may influence future box office receipts where the tune is played; but the music critic cannot affect the man who has heard it, and who hums it, and complains that "it keeps running through my head."

The same argument about music applies to the splashing of colors upon a canvas. Whether these colors attempt to depict a person or a scene; or whether the colors are sheer, in the sense that they are there in seemingly arbitrary hues, forms, and arrangements, is a matter of indifference. The painter paints; the spectator views. If the painter evokes a response that is desirable, he receives the social sanction, and that is all that counts. It makes no difference, for example, what the surrealists claim for their creations or what their critics say *pro* or *contra*. A "symphony" of color, or form, or of both, is just as thinkable as a symphony of sheer noises. The painter paints, the spectators view; and if the spectator reacts "sympathetically" to the creation, the painter has "spoken" culturally.

The same argument applies to design, to textures, to smells, and to tastes, for each of which a "symphony" is quite thinkable. Indeed when a chef, for example, finds that ever more persons come to react to his culinary creations, he may reasonably suspect that he is solving more problems for them than mere alimentary ones in the literal sense.* An enterprising neologist might coin a word for the symphony of tastes (to which the smart restauranteur adds colors, smells, and sounds).

The preceding argument also applies to sculpture. Michelangelo once said that he saw his David in a piece of marble, and merely cut the excessive marble away (just as simple as that!). We all know *who* David *was;* but do any of us know *what* Michelangelo's David *is,* as Michelangelo evokes responses from us by means of carved marble?

Continuing, we note a disposition today to consider poetry as meaningless rhyming. And indeed a given poem is nothing but meaningless rhyming to a person who finds it so. After all, every artistic creation, being a social phenomenon, is nothing more to a given individual or group than his or their reactions to it. We may not say, however, that all poetry is meaningless to all persons, simply because there is no empiric law of poetic composition. Perhaps the final reality of our being and of this universe can only be perceived intuitively and expressed poetically. It may even be that what we call the great poetry of the ages is the expression of those who have thus perceived and expressed; it may well be that the great poetic creations in a culture are the greatest assets of that culture, even though these creations may make no sense to any other culture than the one in whose cultural vocabulary they were expressed.† Hence the artist in many ways may take precedence before the mere scientist as such in the apperception of any "final reality."

After all, science as science is nothing more than scientific method, as has often been remarked; and scientific method is nothing more than an empirically verifiable language. On the other hand, the art of science, like any other art, is a knowledge of the great questions, and the discussion and solution of these questions in terms of a particular kind of social language—the language of empiric verifiability—which to a very considerable extent is acultural. If one will, one may say that the arts include science,

---

* A veteran back from the Pacific theater of war told me, without any reference to the present writing, that at a U.S.O. stand he was once given a lettuce and tomato sandwich, and a glass of milk: "The whole thing didn't cost a quarter, yet it meant (*sic*) more to me than anything I had eaten for months; I nearly broke out crying." The person who prepared the sandwich had unwittingly pushed some cultural "buttons."

† We refer to the importance of the artist and not of the professor of literature or of fine arts. The late George Lyman Kittredge, a professor of English and comparative literature during the latter days of Harvard's once greatness, was often covertly accused of "not teaching the beauty of Shakespeare, but of spending his time teaching the meanings of Shakespeare's words during Shakespeare's time, about which nobody cares." In my opinion, Mr. Kittredge (like every professor in the humanities and fine arts, *mutatis mutandis*) had only the job of teaching the meanings of Shakespeare's words in Shakespeare's time; the rest of the job was up to Mr. Shakespeare. As one of Kittredge's former students, I believe that both Mr. Kittredge and Mr. Shakespeare did their respective jobs brilliantly.

whose medium of expression is the language of empirically verifiable operations.

Thus conceived, there is no difference between a scientist and a poet, except for language (and that, we hasten to add, is quite a considerable difference). The natural scientist, or mathematician, in working upon his objective problems, is thereby theoretically also working upon personal problems of which he may be unaware. For example, let us take the case of a great heart specialist whose every waking minute is devoted to a study of the heart and its diseases; would we be surprised if we learned that such a person had for years suffered from heart trouble himself! May we not draw similar inferences from those who study the mind, or social relations, or immortality, or sexual delinquency, or criminology? *

By the same token we may suspect that those who work at the truly grand problems of mathematics and theoretical physics are thereby trying to untie knots of tremendous personal importance, of whose personal nature they nevertheless may themselves be unaware. Their desire for a social acceptance of their work may not be entirely motivated by exhibitionism; instead they may be unconsciously seeking a social sanction of their solution to a highly personal problem. It may be an unconscious desire for a social confirmation—a desire to be told that his solution makes sense to others, and that therefore he is not mistaken or insane—that sustains the artist in every language through the inevitable long hours of dish washing from which he gains his sustenance.

The Freudians say that behind every work of art there may be an unconscious motivation, and that every work of art is colored by its creator's personal problems. This statement seems to be both awkwardly uttered and mistaken in its emphasis. Instead, every work of art is an attempt to express its creator's problems in social terms and nothing else. Thus, in telling a story, the artist is not telling a story; he is expressing himself culturally in terms of conventional acts and situations. In painting a picture of trees, a painter is not merely copying trees like a camera; rather is the painter using the picture of a tree as a signal of something else.

As to the greatness of art, it can only be socially great—that is, great in its cultural expression. Many a person has a novel in his head, and to him it is the world's greatest novel. Unless the novel is culturally expressed, however, it cannot be compared.† (By the same token, one cannot be the greatest golf player, if one never touches golf clubs.) After the novel has been expressed, it can be evaluated in terms of those who react; often enough, subsequent reactions evaluate creations more favorably or unfavorably. Great indeed is the creation that appeals to many persons down

* A person who was preoccupied with studying the laws of the mother tongue was once asked by a discerning psychologist if he had found anything about the laws of his mother's tongue.

† Hence one may quarrel with the view implied by Lessing through his character, Conti, in *Emilia Galotti* (Act 1, Scene 4): "Or do you think, Prince, that Raphael would not have been the greatest genius of painting if he had unfortunately been born without hands."

through the ages. Yet that man is perhaps most to be envied who is intellecually satisfied by platitudes.

The above social theory of art, which is purely speculative, leaves untouched the problem of the economy of art, even though we should all agree that a parsimony of expression is essential to art ("brevity is the soul of wit"). An empiric proof of artistic economy would be most difficult.

Thus, for example, is Homer's *Iliad* artistically economical? The *Iliad* has spoken satisfyingly to many persons throughout many centuries, hence we may call it great artistry. Moreover we should all agree that Homer is always simple and sincere, treating only of noble topics and never pontificating. But that still does not mean that there is an economy in his art, unless we assume the Principle of Least Effort. The only quantitative proof of an economy in the *Iliad* to date seems to be the number-frequency distribution of the words of the *Iliad* as studied by Dr. Rose and presented in Fig. 2–3. This distribution, as we remember, is like that of any other sample of effectively communicative discourse; in no way does it suggest that it relates to a great artistic creation.

Perhaps, then, everyone is an artist in his daily social living; perhaps the economy of daily social living simply includes the economy of art. According to this view, great art is the expression of those who in their daily social living express themselves in ways that other persons happen to find tremendously important.

B. Art and the Social Personality

We have just suggested that there is no dynamic dichotomy between an artistic creation on the one hand and a person's social living on the other. The redaction of one's hypothetical "true self" in terms of one's culture is, by definition, art. As the redaction in question serves—whether deliberately or accidentally, or consciously or unconsciously—to solve the problems of others, it becomes ever greater art, regardless of its medium of social expression.

In regard to the person's "true self" we have previously argued, in connection with the language of dreams, that every person lives in his private *symbolic world* whose frame of reference is the person's own self. Each person is the center, and in fact the God, of his own symbolic world in which things mean to him what they mean to him.

Let us illustrate the nature of a person's symbolic world by the following simple example. A young husband lost his wife by tuberculosis. While his wife was still wasting away, her husband planted a rose garden in his backyard to help keep his mind off of the impending sorrow. After his wife's death, his rose garden became his most absorbing interest: he fertilized it, weeded it, cultivated it. But he never invited anyone to inspect it, except for one friend who admired each rose, but never touched one, and never suggested that one be cut and given him. In fact no one cut the blossoms except a gardener who mowed the lawn and during the owner's absence was instructed to remove the wilted blossoms.

To everyone, including the friend, this rose garden was only a rose garden. But the friend always conducted himself towards the rose garden as if it had a private symbolic value for its owner—that is, as if it were something of enormous importance to the young widower's symbolic world, much as if it were functionally substituting for the widower's late wife.

Generalizing upon the above, may we not suspect that everyone lives exclusively in his "rose garden," in the sense that each person's *entire* world of experience will have a special meaning for him since he is the final frame of reference of his own symbolic world?

A person in selecting clothes, for example, goes to a store in which there is a wide display from the total cultural vocabulary. His *selection* for himself is an artistic expression in which colors, cuts, and textures have a symbolic value for him. The same applies to his selection of a mate, of books, of entertainment, of a house. By studying these selections we may hope to learn of the nature of the person.* Surely any teacher of literature must have noticed that his students' preferences for literature reveal their background and the nature of their conflicts; and smart students doubtless note the same about their instructors. A person cannot pass judgment or make a selection without revealing something about his hypothetical "true self."

It seems, therefore, that a person's house and everything in it is indicative of the structure of his symbolic world—so much so that a shrewd observer, in stepping into a strange house, might well be able to guess at much of its owner's inner nature. Droll it is, that at a person's death, a great to-do is made about interring his body, while his personal property is sold or otherwise disposed of. For there is no reason for dichotomizing between the person's corpse and his personal property: either the corpse should be sold too, or the personal property should be buried with the corpse, since a person's clothes, books, pictures, and the like are quite as much a part of the person's personality as is the matter that happens to be in transit through the person's system as he expires. Indeed, a person's writings or his business or family relations are far more enduring and characteristic parts of his person than are the molecules of water that happen to be in his bladder at his death.

In view of the argument that each person lives both in a private symbolic world of his own, and in the world of physical matter-energy, we may appropriately ask which of these two worlds comes first. To each person, his own symbolic world is first; hence semantic dynamics is more important than the language of physics as far as the individual is concerned, even though both are apparently necessary for survival. The reason why various persons with their respective symbolic worlds still manage to get along together—and indeed are often unaware of any differences in symbolic worlds—is that our worlds are often closely similar in the language of our species (e.g., sexual relations) and in the language of the biosocial continuum (e.g., metabolism).

Sometimes a person's private symbolic world may not be in rapport with that of others. This lack of rapport seems to be particularly evident in the case of psychotic persons who, almost by definition, are living in their pri-

* Clothes, houses, and the like, according to the Freudian school, symbolize the dreamer's personality in his dream, if we understand correctly.

vate symbolic worlds and only with difficulty can get into the world of their culture. As an example, let us take the case of a suicidally depressed person who, while once walking within a high brick wall, suddenly noticed that in the then sleet of winter a small green leaf still managed to cling to its branch; immensely cheered by this observation, the person for no culturally apparent reason began to recover from his psychosis until he returned to the social world. This green leaf in winter, that apparently made such sense to him in his private symbolic world, has no necessary cultural meaning for others. Nevertheless we should not be surprised if, during the rest of his life, the person in question paused involuntarily before a leaf in winter much as if it represented something holy to him, even though he might no longer understand why. Poets seem to have the knack of talking meaningfully to others in terms of such "green leaves."

The above green leaf with its great private symbolic importance is scarcely unique. Every person has a private symbolic world, in which he probably builds up a stock of culturally casual situations and objects that nevertheless have an almost inviolate holiness to him. The above example of the widower and the rose garden is a second case in point. In dealing with other persons, it is perhaps prudent to reflect that each person lives exclusively in his "rose garden," and that the outsider should remember that his every act and object has a private meaning in addition to its cultural meaning.

Let us suppose, however, that for one reason or another a person becomes so preoccupied with his private symbolic world that he becomes culturally isolated. What effective steps can the isolated person take in order to re-enter his cultural world?

Germane to this question is the East Indian advice to the effect that one should not love (or hate) something, but merely *act* as if one does. This advice, if carefully followed, may help one to re-enter his cultural world. If taken literally, as it is intended to be, this advice means for example that the bridegroom on his wedding night should not love his bride but merely *act* as though he does. This does not mean that the bridegroom should dramatize himself in the cultural cliché, but merely that he should act the role of a lover, even as the role is played in his culture. The same applies to the person's each and every other action in human relations; and in acting a role, he should remember that a given role, if well played, evokes specific responses.

This Indian advice suggests that a person who is lonely, isolated, and depressed in his private symbolic world should put on the act of graciousness and cheerfulness and friendliness. If the person in question does not happen to know the particular vocabulary for graciousness, friendliness, and cheerfulness, he might profitably study the roles of those who do, and imitate them. Once the person successfully acts the role, society will react to the role, and to nothing else.

Yet if this Indian advice is followed, what becomes of the person's "true self," we may ask. In this connection we remember that one's "true self" is not a rigid and invariant entity; instead it is an "information center," a "tool shop" and a "calculating machine." Hence, after our erstwhile lonely and depressed person has mastered the act of cultural graciousness, cheerfulness, and friendliness, his environment will thenceforth treat him as such, and no longer treat him as if he were a lonely depressed person who lives alone in his private symbolic world. Being now treated as a gracious, cheerful, friendly person, the person finds it to his advantage to continue being so, instead of reverting to his erstwhile role of depression. In time may not his "true self" conform to the new role, if the new role is easier than the older one?

For we do not always act only what we are, but often also act what we should like to be. By acting what we should like to be, we may in time become what we act: at least that is our theory of art and the social personality.

The roles that we act are cultural. Yet our *selection* of the particular roles to be acted reveals our "true selves." The social evaluation of our interpretation of our roles measures the greatness of our artistry. The longer that a given role is played by a given person, the easier the role becomes for him, because as he plays the role, his environment adjusts to him in his role.

Many persons profess the desire to become "great artists." Yet for whose benefit? If they propose to be great artists for the benefit of "mankind," then they will have to solve "mankind's" problems in "mankind's" language. If, on the other hand, they desire to be great artists for the benefit of their own selves in order to minimize the effort of conflict with their fellows, then they perhaps would do well to take stock of their native capacities, and to select the easiest cultural roles for their native capacities. In so doing these persons imply that for all persons the greatest of all arts is the art of one's own living, in the sense that each person selects social roles for himself that he can act with least effort.

Unlike our more illustrious predecessors, we do not say: "Believe and ye shall see!" Rather do we suggest: So act that ye may so become!—for better or for worse. Slight changes at the periphery may effect profound changes at the core.

C. Empiric Data

Our foregoing discussion was frankly speculative, although it ultimately refers to the theory of earlier chapters, in support of which empiric data were presented. For, after all, what we have said about dreams and art has merely been an extension, *mutatis mutandis,* of what we have previously said about speech. Theoretically, dreams are but the geometric counterpart of the topological-algebraic arrangements of the classes of speech; the geometry of dreams refers to an abstract space in which each class is a dimension. Were we to pursue the speculative theory further we might submit that the structure of dreams is like the structure of schizophrenic speech which, according to our theory, is culturally meaningless. Once the terms of a dream are redacted into the terms of a given culture, the result is art, whose degree of greatness for others is determined solely by the extent to which it helps to solve the personal problems of varying degrees of urgency for a varying number of persons over varying intervals of time. The phrase, "art as an emotional catharsis" is quite understandable in the light of our theory. Yet in our usage all cultural behavior is art—there being no dynamic dichotomy between the stenographer and the concert pianist.

The point we are stressing is that *all* living action is subject to the n minimum as explained in our previous chapters. In other words, an organism—as far as it can ever tell—lives *only* in a symbolic world, in the sense that an organism *can* know of the universe and of itself only through its classifications and the correlations of its sensory data which without exception have the organism's own needs as a frame of reference. No matter how much the physicist may talk about operationism and empiric verifiability, his observations and his experiments, as well as his statements about them, will theoretically be forever subject to the principles of semantic dynamics in which the n different classes of his operations will be minimized, subject to auxiliary conditions, as previously discussed.

We are so bold as to believe that the *organization* of speech represents the structure of mind, and that our dynamical principles of speech apply to all living action and reaction, subject to the dimensions in which the problem is cast (e.g., one dimension, two dimensions, three dimensions, n dimensions). Whether this belief be correct, time alone can tell. It is a proposition that can be tested empirically.

As to our social theory of art, we expressed the view that the notes of music have cultural symbolic values that are dynamically similar to those of the entities of speech. If this view be correct, we should expect to find that the diversity and rate of repetition of notes will somehow be similar to what we have observed for words (cf. Fig. 2–4). In short, there should be proportionately more short intervals between the repetition of given notes than longer ones, in terms of units of time.

In Fig. 8–1 are two sets of data, *A* and *B*. The *A* data represents the y number of intervals of like x length (in units of full notes) between the repetitions of all notes for the bassoon part in all three movements in Mozart's *Bassoon Concerto in B♭ Major,* as disclosed by my three students, Messrs. C. H. Bridge, Jr., Daniel Scarlett, and W. S. Wheeling. The points on the graph are not unreasonable approximations of the ideal line drawn with the theoretially expected -1.00 slope, and therefore may be said to confirm our theory. There was no particular reason for selecting this concerto for analysis, except that for the purposes of a greater simplification of analysis, it was desirable to restrict this preliminary study to a succession of single notes without chords.

The *B* data of Fig. 8–1 refer to the length of "steps," in terms of full tones between each note and its following note as the melody proceeds up and down the scale. The general inverse linear relationship between the y number of "steps" of like x size is apparent, both for the "steps" up, and for the "steps" down—and of course for the two kinds of "steps" combined. Hence, if we recall our Bell Analogy of Chapter Two—which has now become a Bassoon Analogy, as the demon steps back and forth between the stops of the bassoon—there is a systematic preference for steps of shorter "distances," as is, I think, theoretically quite understandable (in Part Two we shall find a similar logarithmic relationship between the *y* number of automobile trips of varying *x* distances). Similar "steps," incidentally, are lacking in speech which, except for differences in the degree of accent, has no systematic "ups" and "downs" in any physical sense. The orderliness of accent, which is not treated in the present study though it has been

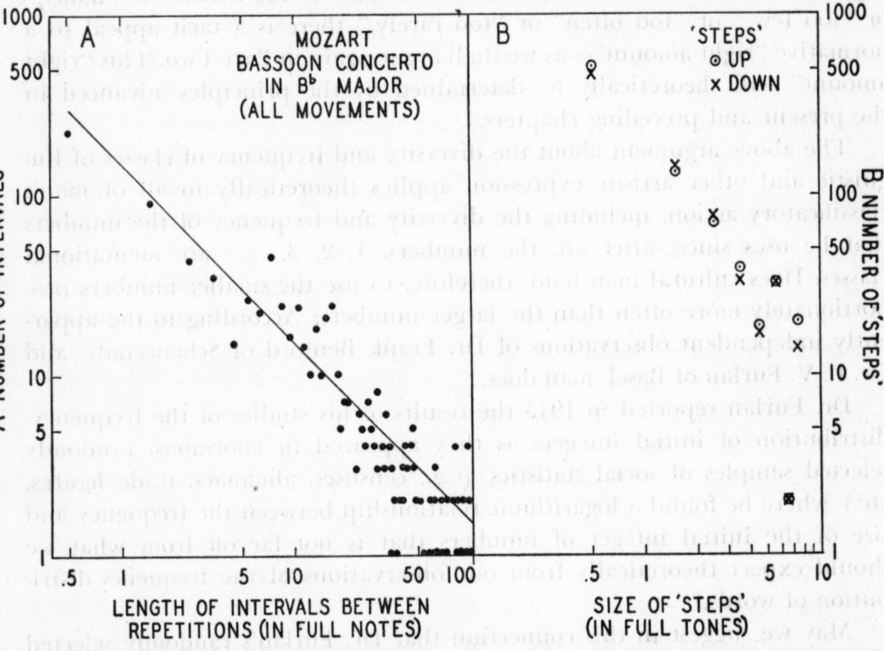

Fig. 8–1. Mozart's *Bassoon Concerto in B♭ Major*. (A) The number of intervals of like length between the repetition of notes; (B) the number of "steps" up and down of like length. (The data refer to all three movements combined.)

treated in a previous one, is not inconsistent with the orderliness of music and the rest of speech.

In saying that the above Mozart concerto has a cultural meaning of its own, we face the question: What is its meaning? To this we can only reply: Play the concerto! Similarly in respect of the cultural meaning of *Hamlet;* read, or see, *Hamlet!*

Although the data of Fig. 8–1 represent the longest musical piece examined, the above distributions were *in general* found in the much shorter (797 notes) piece of Chopin's *Etude in F Minor,* Op. 25, No. 2, as studied by Mr. D. Scarlett; and in the much shorter melodies of Irving Berlin's *Doing What Comes Naturally,* and Jerome Kern's, *Who,* as studied by Messrs. W. S. Wheeling and C. H. Bridge, Jr., respectively. In these studies, cases were observed of an inverse relationship between the lengths of notes and their relative frequency of occurrence. Moreover the frequency-distribution of the different notes of the octave when arranged according to increasing pitch yielded a roughly symmetrical curve on arith. arith. grid.[2]

As to the question of cultural reactivity speed and adaptiveness of musical symbols, we refer to the interesting study of Shostakovich's Seventh Symphony by Sebastian de Grazia.[3]

Our argument about the notes of music applies also theoretically to the diversity and relative areas of colors in painting, and also to the diversity of characters in plays (and narratives) and to the relative amounts and the rates of repetition of their discourse. Whenever in respect of these cultural expressions one hears the criticism, "too much" or "too little," "too many," or "too few," or "too often" or "too rarely," there is a tacit appeal to a normative "right amount"—as we shall argue again in Part Two. This "right amount" will theoretically be determined by the principles advanced in the present and preceding chapters.

The above argument about the diversity and frequency of classes of linguistic and other artistic expression applies theoretically to all of man's classificatory action, including the diversity and frequency of the numbers that he uses since, after all, the numbers, 1, 2, 3, . . . are mentational classes. Does cultural man tend, therefore, to use the smaller numbers proportionately more often than the larger numbers? According to the apparently independent observations of Dr. Frank Benford of Schenectady, and Dr. L. V. Furlan of Basel, man does.

Dr. Furlan reported in 1943 the results of his studies of the frequency-distribution of initial integers as they appeared in enormous, randomly selected samples of social statistics (e.g., censuses, almanacs, trade figures, etc.) where he found a logarithmic relationship between the frequency and size of the initial integer of numbers that is not far off from what we should expect theoretically from our observations of the frequency-distribution of words.[4]

May we suggest in this connection that Dr. Furlan's randomly selected data may represent the effect of selecting numerical classes in deference to the intellectual economies of problems? Numbers, after all, are names of classes. The particular units of length, duration, mass, or monetary value that we are to designate by 1 in our cultural vocabulary might understandably be related to the frequency of occurrence of the respective lengths, durations, masses, or monetary values in our cultural discourse.

Dr. Frank Benford, who reported his observations in 1937, studied in addition the numbers used in engineering and physics handbooks and in physical tables, where he found geometric ratios of the general type we might expect.[5] (His geometric ratios for street numbers, etc., are not so astonishing since in general, as we may infer from Part Two, there are proportionately more shorter streets than longer ones, and hence proportionately more smaller house numbers.) Yet his disclosure of an empiric "law of anomalous numbers," as he calls it, is of great importance. How Drs. Benford and Furlan propose to rationalize their empiric data will be interesting to observe.

According to our own theory, classes are classes, whether they be numbers or words. The symbolic world seems to be so structured that smaller classes are proportionately more frequent than larger ones. Even though we all know that units are selected in deference to our intellectual convenience in solving problems, nevertheless it may still be too foreign to our thinking right now for us to be able to feel that our *usage* of numbers may be subject to the *n* minimum. Mathematically considered, the integer, 1, is just as specific as the integer 1,000,000. But in cultural usage, when 1 generally refers to 1 dog, 1 apple, or 1 million, may not 1 *seem* to be more generic, and be so used? *

It is not our purpose, however, to urge this view dogmatically. We merely state that our theory of the *n* minimum applied to all living usage of all kinds of classes in terms of which the data of experience are handled; and that includes the experiential data of physicists, chemists, and mathematicians. Semantic dynamics is all-inclusive, nor can man ever "get outside of it" in order to see how the universe looks apart from it. *Every* physical problem, therefore, is also a problem in semantic dynamics (and, in terms of ultimate reference, *vice versa*). Nor is it difficult to believe that the newer topological algebras that seem today to be so remote from practical utility, may tomorrow have a value in applied mathematics that is comparable to that of the calculus, since these newer algebras seem to be the mathematics of thinking.

III. LANGUAGE AND THE STRUCTURE OF THE PERSONALITY: MARY OF PART ONE

Let us now forget about our foregoing speculation on the language of dreams and of art. Instead, let us briefly review the content of the entire preceding chapters that led to it and which constitute our study of language and the personality.

Our main theme can be easily stated. All living action is reaction that is classified and correlated at its source. The code, or system, according to which the classifications and correlations are made is language. Human speech is but a special kind of classified and correlated actions and reactions. In the light of our studies of the structure of speech, we may say that when an *n* number of different kinds of stimuli evoke an *m* number of different kinds of responses, *n* is a minimum, subject to auxiliary conditions, as previously discussed.

Yet this last statement makes sense only in terms of a specific frame of reference. In the present theory our primary frame of reference is the organism. By an organism we mean a physical system that is self-preservative in the sense that it continually seeks to avoid a final and complete physical equilibrium with its environment, with the physical system being continual as a whole but not continual in respect to its parts.

* The base, 10, of our decimal system may have less to do with our ten fingers than it has with the log *e* of the usual largest magnitude (about 100 thousand) of our usage of numbers. If our experience extended only to a few hundred, then the base 2, 3, or 4 might be more convenient; if our experience extended *in detail* from 1 to 100 million, a larger base than 10 would be economical. In practice, when we deal with large numbers, say millions or billions, we generally think of them in terms of smaller units, with the millions or billions appended.

To preserve itself as a physical system in the above sense, an organism must expend work which it gets by means of its physical system from the available energy of its environment (this energy is its pabulum).

The question now arises: how much work will an organism expend in living? Our answer is that an organism will expend the *least average probable rate of work* (as estimated by itself) which by definition is its *least effort*.

This concept of least effort we discussed in our opening chapter. There we pointed out that an organism, in order to minimize its work throughout life, may not adopt a course of action today that minimizes its work today unless that course of action will also probably lead to successive courses of action in the future whose probable sum total of work expenditure will also be a minimum for the organism. In other words, we may say that an organism takes a path that will minimize its own probable average rate of work. For convenience we have expressed this by saying that all organisms behave with *least effort.*

Yet the moment we introduce the concept of the probable events of the future which our organism must assess in order to survive with least effort, then our organism must have mechanisms (1) for gaining information about its environment, and (2) for estimating the probable future of the environment on the basis of its information. That in turn means, as we explained in Chapter Five, that the organism must have (1) a *sensory mechanism* for gaining information, and (2) a unit system of pseudo-logical self-consistent correlations that refer to the sensory data and which is capable of altering the terms of its correlations; this unit system we defined as *mind.* Sensation and mentation, therefore, are prerequisites to life, if life is to exist with least effort (hence *to the organism,* its mind is primary for its existence). The effort of sensation and mentation will theoretically be least —and that will apply to the number and terms of the classes and correlations of its mind.

In view of the above, it is evident that the organism's total problem of survival is cast simultaneously in several different frames of reference which, for convenience, we shall call different kinds of reality, for that is how the frames will appear to the organism. The *first* frame of reference, or kind of reality, is the entire time-space continuum and its contents, including the organism's matter-energy; this kind of reality, which exists only as a theoretical construct, we have called the *primary reality*. The *second* frame of reference, or kind of reality, is the physical reaction of one mass of matter-energy to another, which we termed the *secondary reality;* this *secondary reality,* which is the sensation of an organism, represents the final contact of the organism both with its environment and with the parts of itself. The *third* frame of reference, or kind of reality, is the organism's own unit system of correlations, or mind, which we designated as its *tertiary reality;* for example, the sight of an angry dog may elicit in a person the expectation of being bitten, and this expectation has a tertiary reality for the person. These three kinds of reality would seem to be necessary to all organisms (and man, and doubtless other social organisms, have a *quaternary* or *cultural reality,* as explained in Chapter Seven).

Let us dwell for a moment upon the mind, or tertiary reality, of an individual. Clearly the sheer possession of the sensory and mentational mechanisms that constitute a given individual's mind cannot itself solve his problem of surviving with least effort (i.e., least *average* probable rate of work) during his entire life unless the individual knows how long his entire life is going to be. For one cannot in practice minimize one's *average* rate of work expenditure over time, unless one knows in advance how long the time in question is. Hence we face the philosophical problem of how long an organism lives with least effort. We attempted to solve this problem by postulating that the length of a given life is finitely fixed though unpredictable; and that an individual minimizes his effort over his future only insofar as he can assess the probabilities of his future. This postulate was sufficient for our entire demonstration even though, for the completeness of the argument, we briefly explored an alternative possibility.

The postulate of a finitely fixed but unpredictable length of life was not the only postulate. For, in defining an organism, we also postulated the existence of an ego, or *identity-point,* to serve the organism as the origin of a frame, in reference to which matter-energy moves during the organism's lifelong attempt to preserve itself with least effort from a final and complete physical equilibrium with its environment.

Our third and last postulate was that the total N number of different organisms that are alive on the planet is fixed, if only as an upper limit.

Yet the foregoing postulates provide only the background against which we ask the question: is effort indeed minimized in all living process? Clearly our entire thesis of the Principle of Least Effort depends upon an objective demonstration that a minimizing of effort is invariably the case.

In the vast synchrony of the biosocial population is a species called *homo sapiens* whose members speak to one another: that is, the members evoke responses in one another by means of conventional noises.

These conventional noises we have analyzed. We have found them orderly. We have found them subject to a basic principle of an economy of effort.

Let us review the steps of this observation of the economy of speech process. After a preliminary orientation in Chapter One, we began in Chapter Two to study the n number of different words, and the f frequency of their occurrence, and the m_f number of different meanings per word of f frequency. We found an orderly relationship between n, f, and m_f which we rationalized on the basis of the opposing economies of speaker and auditor. In Chapter Two we also noted that words were repeated in such fashion that the work of uttering them would be evenly distributed over time.

In Chapter Three we explored further the equilibrium of word frequencies and meaning frequencies under the heading of formal-semantic balance. In this chapter, with the support of many sets of data which we rationalized with the help of a Tool Analogy we noted, *first,* that the comparatively smaller and easier speech entities tended to be used comparatively more frequently—The Law of Abbreviation; and, *second,* that throughout the permutations and innovations of speech there is a Law of Diminishing

Returns which acts in the direction of decreasing the n number of different speech entities, or permutations thereof, that perform the m different tasks of a given verbal job. This Law of Diminishing Returns has, or consists of, three corollary principles: (1) the Principle of Economical Versatility, according to which the most frequent words tend to increase the number of their different meanings, thereby increasing their frequency; (2) the Principle of Economical Permutation, according to which the easier permutations of speech entities are used before resorting to the coinage of new speech entities; (3) the Principle of Economical Specialization that refers to the coinage of new speech entities. We showed that these principles apply to phonemes and morphemes as well as to words, and that in general, subject to the qualifications stated, the older elements of the language are the smaller and more frequent elements which are also used more often in permutations and have more meanings.

In Chapter Four we turned to the question of children's verbalizations, where we found that the diversity and frequency of usage of words was the same as in adult speech. In this chapter we also faced the hoary question of the "origin" of speech, in answering which we pointed out that the first of our ancestors to evoke a conventional response by means of a conventional noise was the originator of human speech. For as soon as a social group has a set of conventional noises and responses, then the above-mentioned Laws of Abbreviation and of Diminishing Returns will operate automatically to elaborate the set of noises.

In the above Chapters we treated speech primarily as the expression of the speaker—that is, as the action of a person upon another person. In Chapter Five, however, we turned the proposition around and viewed speech as a sensation of the auditor, with supporting data. In this chapter we first discussed the problem of the economy of a sensory system, and the meaning of effort, or probable work—a discussion that we later resumed in cultural terms in Chapter Seven. Our discussion in Chapter Five of the balance between the economy of the more generic correlation on the one hand, and the opposite economy of the more specific correlation on the other hand is one of the key points of our entire demonstration, since from it we deduced directly the concept of the least average probable rate of work expenditure (i.e., least effort) in all sensation and mentation—a deduction that was confirmed by empiric test.

In Chapter Six we defined the organism and discussed the question of the length of its life and the N number of organisms that are alive at one time. We also showed that our Principle provided a sufficient explanation of biological evolution as manifested in the data of J. C. Willis.

In Chapter Seven we discussed the reality—the *quaternary* or social reality—of the system of conventional social signals of a human social group that behaves to a greater or lesser extent with reference to the same objects by means of the same operations. This chapter began with a discussion of human sexual behavior as a widely practised kind of social behavior whose objects and operations are widely understood; the chapter ended with a discussion of schizophrenia as a case of asocial behavior whose motives and operations are practically unknown to the "other fellow." In Chapter Seven, and on the basis of our entire argument up to Chapter Seven, we stated what we believed are the principles of semantic dynamics.

And then there is the present Chapter Eight with its speculative hypothesis on the language of dreams and of art which we have presented lest we be accused of ignoring the "nicer things of life" (unlike most empiricists, we cannot be accused of ignoring the human soul).

So much, then, for the present summary of our first eight chapters, in which we charted a somewhat new course in asking and answering the question of language and the structure of the personality.

Whether our demonstration up to this point has been correct, only time can tell. Since the author has had to dig up much of the empiric data and rationalize most of it before a synthesis was possible, it is scarcely likely that the demonstration is entirely free from errors of one sort or another. The data alone, however, should provide a useful target for others to aim at. If our answers to the philosophical questions of Chapter Six be untenable, we remember that the questions are still there.

On the other hand, let us not forget that the underlying aim of this book is not to present speech data. Instead, our primary aim is to demonstrate the universal validity of the Principle of Least Effort in all living process. Although we have constructed an elaborate hypothesis on the subject of language and the structure of the personality in order to demonstrate our Principle of Least Effort, we have never claimed that this particular hypothesis is necessary.

For if our Principle of Least Effort be valid, as we believe it is, then its operation should be discernible in any living phenomena. We have treated speech phenomena, as we confessed at the very beginning, because the analysis of speech phenomena is easiest for the author.

To show that the validity of the Principle of Least Effort can be demonstrated from other kinds of data, let us begin our demonstration anew by analyzing an entirely different though closely related phenomenon: the phenomenon of human social relations, which we shall view as a case of intraspecies equilibrium.

As we close Part One and begin Part Two, let us remember one thing unfailingly: the universe is today what it was yesterday, and it will be so tomorrow, regardless of what scientists and poets say about it. No empiric answer is final; the most that any answer can hope for is to be intellectually more palatable than its predecessor.

Part Two

Human Relations
A Case of Intraspecies Balance

CHAPTER NINE

THE ECONOMY OF GEOGRAPHY

In the present chapter we shall turn to the topic of the dynamics of human social relations, which emerges quite naturally from our consideration of individual dynamics in our preceding chapters. Indeed, since individual human beings are the constituent elements of human social groups, and since human social groups represent merely the manner of organization of one of the many species of the earth, we see that the entire argument of our preceding chapters about the individual and his personality is germane to the topic of human social relations. Conversely, since all human beings are members of larger social groups whose collective needs restrict and coerce the action of their individual members, we can understand how the problems of human social relations are also problems of the individual, with the result that the arguments of our present and following chapters belong inextricably to those that have gone before.

Human society can be viewed as a field which both influences the individual members of the group and is influenced by them.

But though we are broadening the scope of our preceding argument, we do not need to retract any of our previous statements. On the contrary we shall find that all of our previous equations apply equally well to social action.*

In the exposition of any unifying theory in the social field, there is a serious difficulty that arises from the fact that only one aspect of the total social phenomenon can be treated at a time, whereas in nature all aspects may be occurring simultaneously. The problem of organizing our material, therefore, is not an easy one. We have elected to begin with a consideration of the effect of geographical givens upon the economical procurement of raw materials, and upon the economical manufacture and distribution of finished goods within a given national social system. Thence, we shall proceed in Chapter Ten to a consideration of cases of intranational and international dynamic equilibria, both stable and unstable.

Then, leaving the topic of the economy of geography, we shall turn in Chapter Eleven to a discussion of certain further aspects of the economy of distributing the products of a social system to the members of that system. This discussion will lead in Chapter Twelve to the closely related problem of symbols of power and of the structure of a cultural vocabulary, with which we have already become somewhat familiar in Chapter Seven. Although Chapter Twelve is the last chapter of our book, its argument will

* In the course of the development of our following Section I, the reader will note that the dynamics of a social group is similar to that of our Tool Analogy in Chapter Three. Virtually all the equations elaborated in Chapter Three will be found valid for the structure of a social group under the conditions postulated in Sections I and II.

return us to the opening argument of Chapter Two, with which our formal demonstration begins.

We shall begin (I) with a theoretical discussion, in the form of a lemma, of the general problem of most economically procuring raw materials and of fabricating them into consumable goods. In this lemma we shall watch a number of completely unorganized persons become organized as a social group in the sense that they pursue like objectives with like rules of conduct. By beginning with this general inclusive argument we shall hope to avoid the mistake of restricting our theory to any particular stage of social development, or to any particular kind of culture.

From this lemma, we shall pass to an analogue (II) that will apply specifically to the particular conditions of present-day Western Civilization with special reference to the United States in recent years. The value of this analogue is that it will state our case in a form that will admit of a ready empiric test with quantitative data in Section III.

Since our arguments in I and II will cross academic fields in which there is a considerable amount of literature, we shall refer to earlier pivotal studies as we proceed, without, however, pretending to completeness in so vast a field, and certainly without any feeling of obligation towards earlier verbalistic-speculative theories with which the study of human social relations has been unusually favored.

I. A LEMMA IN WHICH A NUMBER OF HUMAN BEINGS BECOMES INCREASINGLY MORE ORGANIZED

Let us take the case of a sizable terrain inhabited by a large number of persons, each one of whom behaves without any reference to the behavior of the others.[1] These persons are by definition completely unorganized socially, since each one is free to select his own objectives which he can pursue as he sees fit.

In order to organize these persons socially, let us give them a common objective in the form of an enemy at a spot, *A,* in the terrain whom they will attempt to repel by collective action. This objective involves at least two main problems: *first,* the problem of moving the population to the front at A; and *second,* the problem of selecting means for repelling the enemy. In the solution of these two problems, as of all others in this lemma, we shall assume that *work* is minimized, with the tacit understanding, however, that the problems do in fact involve an estimate of probabilities, and that, therefore, *effort* and not *work* is the minimum. For the present we shall ignore the factor of time.

Each person in proceeding to the point, *A,* will take that path to *A* which involves the expenditure of least work, and we shall call it a path of *D* least-work distance (every *D* distance in this lemma will be a least-work distance). The path will be a straight line only when that is the *easiest* path; otherwise the paths will go around swamps and over and around mountains—whatever is the easiest. Naturally, as the traffic between two points increases, it will be economical to straighten the route between them, and to make it more nearly level, as soon as the (probable) amount of work that is saved by the shorter and more level route is sufficient to offset the work of straightening and levelling.

Once the persons arrive at *A,* we have a *community* at *A,* in the very rough sense that the terrain has an above-average density there.

Turning now to the problem of devices for repelling the enemy, let us note that our soldiers, if they will, can use merely the members of their bodies, such as fists, feet, heads, and teeth. If they restrict their weapons to these, their only demands upon their environment will be those that are connected with alimentation, shelter, and the like.

But if the soldiers decide to use any artifactual weapon, such as a club, or a sling, or bows and arrows, then their entire activity will be subject (1) to the occurrence of the prerequisite raw materials, (2) to the fabrication of the weapons in question, and (3) to the transportation of the weapons to the front at *A*. These three general factors will apply also to the procurement of food, and will presumably enter into all social problems.

Let us now assume that our soldiers at *A* have decided to use a club as a weapon, and have located a grove at *B* where clubs can be procured. In that case the terrain will have two *communities: A* at the front, whose population is fighting, and *B* at the grove, whose population is procuring clubs; and the least known work-distance, $\overline{AB}$, between *A* and *B* is a *route of transportation* over which goods and persons move.

Now let us assume that our soldiers, instead of being content with mere clubs, decide to use bows and arrows, whose respective raw materials are, say, (1) feathers, (2) thongs from the hides of deer, (3) wood, and (4) flint. In general, as we saw in Chapter Six, as the diversity of needed raw materials increases, the probability of finding them in one spot decreases, with the result that the soldiers will probably have to seek them at an increasing number of different spots, and, of course, while they are at those different spots in the procurement of the respective raw materials there, they will constitute communities.

In the present lemma we shall assume for convenience that there are different locations for each of the above four kinds of raw materials, with the result that we shall have four different communities (in addition to the community at the front at *A*).

In each of these four communities it will be economical to remove the waste material from the desired objects in order to save the work of transporting the waste material to *A*. In general, it is economical to remove waste materials at the very source.

The problem now arises as to who is going to procure the raw materials and remove the waste materials at the above four locations, and who is going to transport the bows and arrows to the front. Here several courses of action are possible.

One possible course of action—the *individualistic*—is to have each soldier leave the front at *A* to procure bows and arrows whenever he needs them. In that case he will proceed to the locations of the raw materials, where he will himself get the raw materials and fabricate the finished articles, which he will carry to the front at *A*. If the need for replenishments is quite low, this *individualistic* method of procuring them might conceivably be the most economical one.

If however, the need for replenishments is considerable, and if it is desirable to keep as many soldiers at the front as possible, then the above individualistic method of procuring them is not so economical as the method of *collective* action. According to this second method, each person's every act is governed by the need to expend as much as possible of the total available work of the entire group in fighting the enemy at *A*, and therefore as little work as possible away from the front at *A*.

The gist of the method of *collective* action is to station full time workers at locations 1, 2, 3, and 4 in sufficient numbers in each case to fabricate the probably needed amounts of feathers, thongs, wooden parts, and flint arrowheads; the economy of this procedure is obvious. The next step is to allot porters to each of 1, 2, 3, and 4 in such numbers as are necessary to carry the semifinished goods in units of full loads towards a point of assembly which may be either at *A*, or at some other junction point, *J*, depending upon what minimizes the work of transportation. To expedite our argument, let us assume that the point of assembly is at the junction point, *J*, (which, of course, may be *A*).

The factors that determine the location of this junction point, *J*, are important in any social problem; they are essentially those that we discussed in Chapter Three in connection with the "minimum equation." In short, the junction point, *J*, for the assembly of the semifinished goods from 1, 2, 3, and 4, for further transportation to *A*, will be so selected that *the sum of the products of all masses moved, when multiplied by the work-distances will be a minimum*. Fig. 9–1 illustrates how *J* might be located in the present case. Clearly, as the mass of the transported material increases, it becomes more economical to locate *J* nearer to its source, and *vice versa*.

In brief, the *collective* method of obtaining replenishments envisages, *first,* more or less permanent communities of specialized laborers at 1, 2, 3, and 4 who will procure the raw materials and semifinish them and, *second,* a community of specialized laborers at *J* to assemble the semifinished goods into finished bows and arrows. The collective method further envisages specialized porters who will be detailed to 1, 2, 3, 4, and *J* for the purposes of carrying the loads over the respective easiest work-distances, $1J$, $2J$, $3J$, $4J$, and $\overline{JA}$. If we assume that each porter carries the same full mass of load, then the number of porters for each route will be proportional to the products of the masses and work-distances that are involved.*

Our argument about the bows and arrows and their prerequisite raw materials can be extended to a larger diversity of raw materials, as would

* Incidentally, since the porters, after delivering the goods, will return empty-handed, they will be gainfully employed for only one-half the total round trip. Hence, there is an obvious economy in so arranging the system that porters will be carrying goods both ways. We mention this point now since we shall not dwell upon it later in detail. We have already remarked that an increase in the rate of traffic between two points will increase the economy of straightening and levelling the intervening path.

be the case, say, if the soldiers adopted rifles for their weapons. In general, as the diversity of raw materials increases, the likelihood of finding all of the different raw materials in a single spot decreases with the result that an ever larger number of scattered communities will have to be established for the sake of procuring raw materials. By the same token, the number of different junction points will also be increased, although—as we shall shortly note inferentially—the decisive importance of these junction points will decrease, as the efficiency of production and transportation increases.

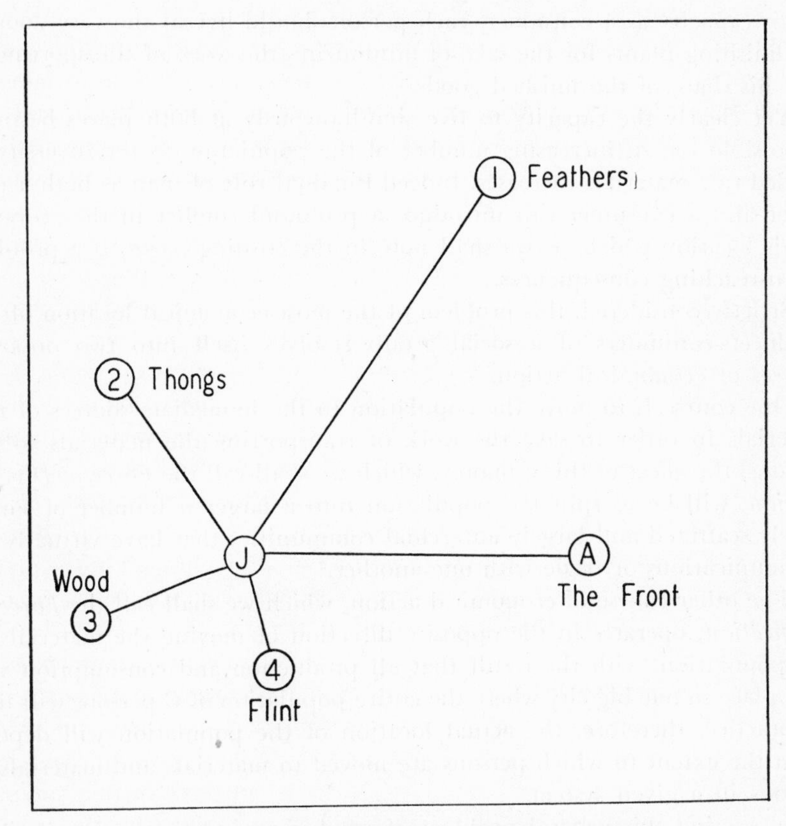

Fig. 9–1. The location of a junction point (J).

Up to now our entire argument has been cast in terms of the primary aim of repelling the enemy at *A,* in reference to which all social activity has been oriented. Let us, therefore, suppose that hostilities have been successfully concluded and that from now on our entire population is engaged in civilian life, in which all persons both produce and consume goods. Or, more specifically, our entire population will henceforth produce only what it consumes, and consume only what it produces.

As our lemma now turns to a consideration of the dynamics of general civilian life, we shall make the postulate that everyone works at the same rate, and that each person receives the same amount of each of the *m* number of different kinds of goods and services produced. Thus, if there is a total of C different persons in the population, each person will perform a $1/C$ share of the total work and will receive a $1/C$ share of each of the m different kinds of goods and services produced.

If every person in the population both produces and consumes, every person will have a dual role of producer and consumer whose respective economies, however, are by no means always the same. Thus, in his capacity as a producer, each person should live immediately at his place of employment, whether at the source of raw materials or at a junction point, so that he will save work in going to and from his job. On the other hand, in his capacity as a consumer, each person should live at the very door of the finishing plants for the sake of minimizing the work of transporting to him his share of the finished goods.

Yet clearly the capacity to live simultaneously at both places becomes impossible for an increasing number of the population as the diversity of needed raw materials increases. Indeed the dual role of man as both a producer and a consumer can introduce a profound conflict in the economy of his location which, as we shall note in the ensuing pages, is a problem of far-reaching consequences.

Strictly considered, this problem of the most economical location of the producers-consumers of a social group resolves itself into two opposite courses of economical action.

One course is to move the population to the immediate sources of raw materials in order to save the work of transporting the materials to the persons; the effect of this economy, which we shall call the *Force of Diversification,* will be to split the population into a larger n number of small, widely scattered and largely autarchial communities that have virtually no communications or trade with one another.[2]

The other course of economical action, which we shall call the *Force of Unification,* operates in the opposite direction of moving the materials to the population, with the result that all production and consumption will take place in one big city where the entire population of C persons will live. In practice, therefore, the actual location of the population will depend upon the extent to which persons are moved to materials and materials to persons in a given system.

Inspecting this general problem of producing and consuming goods—which in our usage will always include services—let us remember that all goods (and services) represent the expenditure of labor upon raw materials, as economists have long since pointed out. Indeed, in the present discussion when we speak of the *cost* of an item, we shall always mean the cost in terms of the total human labor that is necessary to produce the item and to deliver it to the consumer at the time. This definition of *cost* will apply to raw materials, semifinished goods, producers' goods, and consumers' goods (and to services).* Raw materials, except for the labor of procuring them, have no cost.

* Value, on the other hand, refers to the amount a given person will pay. More specifically, the value of X in terms of y to a given person at a given time-place, is the amount of y the person will pay for X. When y is money, value is monetary price.

Our above definition of the *cost,* say, of a $1/C$ share of goods has two aspects: the labor (L) of *producing* a $1/C$ share of the item, and the labor (M) of *transporting* the $1/C$ share of the item for delivery to a person at a particular time-space. In short, $M + L =$ the *cost* of a $1/C$ share of the goods in question to a particular person at a particular time-place. The actual cost of each kind of goods to each person will be determined to a considerable extent by the person's location in the terrain at the time, in reference to the *production centers* where the goods in question are produced.*

We know, of course, that some kinds of goods, such as watches, are easier to transport than others, such as cordwood. As the comparative M cost of transporting a $1/C$ share of goods over a unit of D work-distance *decreases,* it becomes increasingly more economical to ship the goods to the person, instead of having the person live near the production center of the goods; and conversely. Thus, if a person consumes ten cords of wood a year, and one watch every five years, it is economical for him to live near the production of the cordwood, and to have the watch transported to him.

Indeed, since the M cost of transporting goods increases in direct proportion to D work-distance—or $M = D$—we may make the general statement that as M *decreases,* it becomes proportionally more economical to ship the goods in question to the consumer, whereas as M increases, it is proportionally more economical for the person to migrate to the production center of the goods.

The general statement of the preceding paragraph can also be cast in the terms of our previously mentioned Forces of Diversification and of Unification, which refer to the respective economies of locating the population at its immediate sources of raw materials (the Force of Diversification) and of locating them together in one big city (the Force of Unification). Thus, as the M of a $1/C$ share increases, the Force of Diversification increases with it, with the result that its production is located in many more communities because of the shortening D distances over which it can be profitably transported. On the other hand, a decrease in M, with its widening D, favors the Force of Unification.

The effect of differences in D work-distance is obviously important in our lemma, because of its inverse proportionality with M in the $M + L$ cost of goods. Yet the effect of D work-distance does not stop there, since it is similarly related to L, as we shall now see when we take the case of trade between two communities separated by an intervening D shortest work-distance.

We already know that as D increases, the trade between the two communities should be restricted to those kinds of goods of a proportionally decreasing M, but let us not overlook the fact that the trade should also be restricted to those kinds of goods of a correspondingly decreasing L.

* The above definition of cost, for ease of present demonstration, ignores the $M + L$ cost of the materials used in production. Later we shall make M the cumulative cost of transportation, and L the cumulative cost of labor of production.

For if it takes an L amount of labor to produce a $1/C$ share of a particular kind of goods, then, as L increases, a proportionally greater amount must be received in exchange for the goods in question, so that all the L labor can receive an equal $1/C$ share of the goods that are received in exchange. For that reason we may argue that as D increases between the two communities, their trade should be restricted to those kinds of goods of correspondingly decreasing L.

If we combine $M + L$ and say that the cost of a $1/C$ share of a given h kind of goods, when moved a unit of D work-distance, is $(M + L)_h$—in terms of human labor *—then as $(M + L)_h$ increases, the h goods can be economically traded only over a correspondingly decreasing D work-distance, and *vice versa*.

But the $(M + L)_h$ cost, in determining the D distance over which the h goods can be economically traded, will also determine the N_h number of different places, or communities, in which the h goods must be produced, if every person in the terrain is to receive his $1/C$ share of the h goods. If we assume that the population is more or less evenly distributed over the terrain, then, as $(M + L)_h$ increases, the *domain* in which the h goods can be economically traded will decrease. More specifically, if we define an *h domain* as the area surrounding a production center of h goods, within which the h goods can be economically traded, then the least-work *radius* of the domain will be inversely proportional to the $M + L$ of the h goods, or to $(M + L)_h$.†

And as the *radius* of the domain decreases in direct proportion to an increase in $M + L$, the *area* of the domain will decrease in proportion to the square of the radius. Consequently the N_h number of different domains of a given h kind of production into which the entire terrain will be cut is *approximately* proportional to the square of the $(M + L)_h$ cost thereof, or:

$$N_h = (M + L)_h^2 \qquad (9\text{–}1)$$

Of course, the $(M + L)_h$ cost of an h kind of goods refers only to the cost of a $1/C$ share thereof, and since C different $1/C$ shares must be produced so that the C number of different persons of the total population can each have his $1/C$ share, it follows that the F_h number of shares of h goods that are produced in a given production center will be inversely proportional to the N_h number of production centers, or:

$$F_h \times N_h = C. \qquad (9\text{–}2)$$

---

* Conceive of M as the number of porters necessary to transport a unit of goods a unit of D work-distance. Later these porters can be altered to truck drivers and freight train personnel.

† The domain will not by any means necessarily be a circle, since the radius is defined in terms of a least-work D distance, and not in terms of sheer distance. Hence (*vide infra*) the N_h number of domains of a given radius into which the terrain is divided will be only *approximately* inversely proportional to the square of the radius. The term *approximate* in the ensuing pages will be used to convey this difference between a work surface and a plane surface.

Hence, the F_h number of $1/C$ shares that are produced in each production center—if we substitute $(M+L)_h^2$ for N_h in the preceding equation—will be inversely proportional (*approximately*) to $(M+L)_h^2$, or:

$$F_h (M+L)_h^2 = C. \qquad (9\text{–}3)$$

The above equations, which are quite fundamental to our argument, will apply to the N_h number of different production centers of any h kind of goods.

At this point let us inquire into the total P_h population of persons in a given h production center who perform both the M and the L of the goods in question. Since the P_h population obviously consists of the product obtained by multiplying the F number of $1/C$ shares that are produced there, by the $(M+L)_h$ cost of producing a single $1/C$ share, we have, in equation form:

$$P_h = F_h (M+L)_h \qquad (9\text{–}4)$$

And since we know from Eq. (9–3) that $F_h \ (M+L)_h (M+L)_h = C$, it follows that:

$$P_h (M+L)_h = C. \qquad (9\text{–}5)$$

This Eq. (9–5) means that the P_h population of a community engaged in producing and distributing a given h kind of goods is inversely proportional to the size of $M + L_h$; and that is true for any h kind of goods in any community anywhere in the terrain.

Hence, as the $(M+L)_h$ cost of an h kind of goods *decreases,* because of the introduction of laborsaving devices, the production centers in question will be located in a fewer N_h number of communities, according to Eq. (9–1), while the respective P_h number of workers in each of these fewer N_h communities will increase in proportion to the decrease in $(M+L)_h$. If $(M+L)_h$ is continually reduced, the point will eventually be reached, for the goods in question, where the entire C production will be located in one single community $(N_h = 1)$, which in turn will send a $1/C$ share of the goods to each person on the terrain.

This one community will be located in the *least-work center* of the terrain, in the sense that its location will be a point whose sum of all *D least-work distances* to every person on the terrain will be a minimum. Although the terrain may have such freakish boundaries and such differences in ease of transportation that more than one least-work center is possible, we shall assume for convenience that in our lemma there is only one possible least-work center.*

This *least-work center,* if viewed dynamically, represents the ideal location towards which the production centers of all *old kinds* of goods migrate as their $(M+L)_h$ costs decrease. It also represents the ideal place for the

* The argument of our lemma, however, does not depend upon there being only one center. In our following chapter we shall attempt to show that there may be more than one such center for the entire earth's surface.

location of the production centers of recently invented *new kinds* of goods. Indeed, it would be the place for the location of the one big all-inclusive community, if the Force of Unification were unrestrained.

We have just spoken of the invention of laborsaving devices for the production-distribution of *old kinds* of goods, and also of the invention of *new kinds* of goods, thereby tacitly assuming that our population is bent upon inventing more economical devices for producing *old kinds* of goods, while also inventing economical *new kinds* of goods whose adoption into the system will naturally increase the total m diversity of the different kinds of goods that are produced and consumed.

To make matters explicit, let us use the term "Force of Innovation" to designate what we shall imagine is a continual urge both to reduce all $(M + L)_h$ costs, and to increase the m diversity of goods by adopting economical *new kinds* of goods.

Although we are dichotomizing between *old* and *new* kinds of goods, let us remember that all that we have said in our equations about *old kinds* of goods applies to the *new*. Thus, for example, every *new kind* of goods that is adopted will have a definite value of $(M + L)_h$ which will determine its N_h number of production centers and its P_h number of workers in each of the production centers according to the equations we have presented. These equations, after all, apply to the production of all kinds of goods, including any *new kinds* of goods that may be adopted under the Force of Innovation.

Let us for the moment concentrate our attention upon the question of *new kinds* of goods whose adoption will increas the m diversity of the system. For that matter, let us assume that m is increasing in our system, as the Force of Innovation continues to operate.*

Although no *new kinds* of goods will be adopted unless justified by the economy of their production, and although our equations will apply to the P_h and N_h of all adopted *new kinds* of goods, let us note that the $(M + L)_h$ cost of a *new kind* of goods is by no means a matter of indifference to the Force of Innovation. On the contrary, any *increase* in the $(M + L)_h$ cost of goods will *decrease* the area of its domain of production according to the square of the cost. Conversely, any decrease in the cost will *increase* the area of the domain by the square. Though a unit of M, or a unit of L, is the same for any kind of goods, nevertheless as the units are added to the $(M + L)_h$ cost of goods, the cumulative gross cost of these added units will increase proportionally. Hence we may say that the comparative economy of adopting a *new kind* of goods with a particular $(M + L)_h$ cost is inversely proportional (approximately) to its $(M + L)_h$ cost.

Or, stating this relationship in terms of the Force of Innovation, we may say that the magnitude of the Force of Innovation tends to be inversely proportional (approximately) to $(M + L)_h$ in the adoption of *new kinds*

* We shall assume that the economy of an increased m is the Economy of Specialization discussed in Chapter Three.[3] Our present interest is only in showing the factors that are correlated with an increasing m.

of goods. Although countless new inventions may be made available, the Force of Innovation will prefer to adopt those h *new kinds* of goods in direct proportion to the smallness of their respective values of $(M + L)_h$.

In other words, the m_h number of different new kinds of h goods that are likely to be adopted under the Force of Innovation during an interval of measurement is inversely proportional to $(M + L)_h$, or, in equation form:

$$m_h \times (M + L) = C. \qquad (9\text{–}6)$$

And so, as the Force of Innovation continues to operate with the elapse of time, it adds proportionally more *new kinds* of goods of smaller $(M + L)_h$ cost.

The production centers of these *new kinds* of goods must be located somewhere. Naturally, goods of *like* $(M + L)_h$ cost will have a *like* N_h number of production centers, and also domains of *like* radius. Moreover, they will have a *like* P_h number of persons in each production center. In other words, all the m_h number of different kinds of goods of like $(M + L)_h$ cost will all have congruent domains, in the center of which will be located for each different kinds of goods the P_h persons that make and distribute that particular kind of goods. Since there are m_h different kinds of goods of like $(M + L)_h$ cost, the total P number of persons that work on the m_h different kinds of goods of like $(M + L)_h$ cost in the center of each m_h set of congruent domains will be equal to the product of $m_h \times P_h$, or, in equation form:

$$P = m_h \times P_h \qquad (9\text{–}7)$$

Eq. (9–7) merely tells us that in domains of hypothetically like radius there will be m_h different production centers of like P_h population, whose total number, P, equals the product of $m_h \times P_h$. Eq. (9–7) does not tell us that all the m_h different production centers will be located together in one single community of total P population-size with an m_h diversity of productive activity. And yet we may infer from the nature of the Force of Unification that such a single P community with m_h different kinds of production centers of like P_h size will be the case. The justification for this inference is that each person who works at one of the m_h kinds of production has a right to a $1/C$ share of his own and of the other m_h different kinds of production. In other words, each member of the total P population has a right to a $1/C$ share of each of the m_h different kinds of production. To minimize the work of delivering these shares to the P persons, all the m_h different production centers of goods of like $(M + L)_h$ cost will be located together in a single community of total P population size which will be in the least-work center of the domains of like size. For that reason we may argue that Eq. (9–7) applies to the total P population sizes of the communities in question.

But at this point let us remember that from Eq. (9–6), m_h is inversely proportional to $(M + L)_h$, whereas from Eq. (9–5), P_h is inversely proportional to $(M + L)_h$. Since both m_h and P_h are inversely proportional to the same factor, it follows that:

$$m_h \propto P_h \qquad (9\text{–}8)$$

If we substitute m_h for P_h in Eq. (9–7), we find that P equals $m_h \times m_h$. Since there is, as yet, no other source of P, and since the value of m_h is determined by the absolute value of the $(M + L)_h$ in question, we can drop the subscript h in m_h and simply say in equation form:

$$P \propto m^2 \qquad (9\text{–}9)$$

Eq. (9–9) may also be stated as $m = P^{\frac{1}{2}}$, which means in turn that any community's m diversity is equal to the square root of its P population. We may also say that $P \propto P_h^2$.

Strictly speaking, we have considered up to now only the location of the production of *new kinds* of goods that have been adopted into the system with a concomitant increase in m. We know, of course, that the production of these *new kinds* of goods is possible only if free labor is made available from the production of *old kinds* of goods. We also know that this free labor can be made available only if laborsaving devices are adopted for the production of the *old kinds* of goods; for that reason, as we have already remarked, the Force of Innovation will also be operating simultaneously upon the invention of laborsaving devices for the production of the *old kinds* of goods.

At this point let us note, however, that a given reduction in $(M + L)_h$ cost is ever more profitable as the size of $(M + L)_h$ is larger, for reasons that we have already set forth above in our discussion of Eq. (9–6). Hence, we may say that the magnitude of the Force of Innovation, in the invention and adoption of laborsaving devices for the production of *old kinds* of goods, will increase in direct proportion to the $(M + L)_h$ cost of the goods in question. For although it is always economical to reduce the $(M + L)_h$ cost of any kind of goods, it becomes proportionately more profitable to do so with goods of larger $(M + L)_h$ cost, and from this it follows that free labor is likely to be made available from *old kinds* of production in numbers that are directly proportional to the respective values of $(M + L)_h$.

Moreover, as the $(M + L)_h$ costs of the *old kinds* of goods are thus decreased, the N_h number of their production centers will be decreased according to Eq. (9–1). That means, in turn, that their production centers will be moved into a smaller N_h number of different communities, while the P_h populations in each of the newly located production centers will increase in direct proportion to the respective decrease in $(M + L)_h$. The resulting fewer production centers of growing P_h will join with other production centers of like P_h into communities whose P population-size will be equal to the product of m_h and P_h, as previously explained. Therefore, the operation of the Force of Innovation upon the production costs of *old kinds* of goods again yields the relationship, $P \propto m^2$, of Eq. (9–9) which, as we have already intimated, is valid for the entire terrain.

It is obvious from our preceding argument that the Force of Innovation is augmenting the total P population sizes of some communities at the expense of the P population sizes of others. In general, as a community's P size increases, it is proportionally ever *more likely* to receive immigrants and ever *less likely* to lose emigrants, with the result that the net rate of growth in the P population sizes of the larger communities is likely to be a constant p power of their respective P sizes, or

$$\textit{rate of growth} \propto P^p \tag{9–10}$$

With the communities of smaller P population sizes, the very opposite is likely to be the case: as P is smaller, the community in question is proportionally *more likely* to lose emigrants and proportionally *less likely* to acquire immigrants, with the result that the rate of net decrease will be ever larger as P is ever smaller.

Hence with an increasing m diversity under the Force of Innovation, and with a constant C population, the larger communities will become ever larger, according to Eq. (9–10), and at the expense of the smaller communities that become ever smaller at a rate that is inversely related to P.

Naturally, the community at the least-work center will have the largest P population size, which in turn will grow at the fastest absolute rate, as we can see from Eq. (9–10). Yet its P size, like that of every other community, will still be equal to m^2, according to Eq. (9–9). For that matter, the *rate of m growth* in all communities will be ½ the p rate, or, in equation form:

$$\textit{rate of m growth} \propto P^{p/2} \tag{9–11}$$

While we are still on the topic of the largest P community at the least-work center, let us not forget that this is the community that is most favored by the Force of Unification as its magnitude increases over that of the Force of Diversification.

Incidentally, the concept of the comparative magnitudes of our two hypothetical Forces of Unification and Diversification leads to an interesting conclusion. We remember that the Force of Unification makes for a single large community that contains the entire C population, whereas the Force of Diversification makes for a large n number of small P sized communities that are located at the sources of their raw materials. Since the C population cannot live simultaneously both in a single big community and in many small ones, the actual distribution of the C population will depend upon the comparative magnitudes of the two Forces in question. Since the Force of Diversification makes for a larger n number of smaller P communities, whereas the Force of Unification makes for a smaller n number of larger P communities, then, if we interpret the relationship as a best straight line on doubly logarithmic co-ordinates, the result will be that the n number of different communities, when ranked, r, in the order of their decreasing P size will follow the equation (*approximately*):

$$r \times P^q = K, \tag{9–12}$$

where r is integral and positive, and where the exponent, q, represents the ratio of the magnitude of the Force of Diversification when divided by the magnitude of the Force of Unification.

This equation, as we know from our discussion in Part One, can also be expressed in the form of an equation of the generalized harmonic series:

$$P \cdot Sn = \frac{P}{1^p} + \frac{P}{2^p} + \frac{P}{3^p} + \ldots + \frac{P}{n^p} \tag{9–13}$$

With this Eq. (9–13) we come to a very familiar stamping ground, since it is similar to the equation for the F frequencies of words and for the F frequencies of our Tool Analogy as discussed in Chapters Two and Three. Hence, with $P = F$, our entire earlier discussion of the properties of Eq. (9–13) and of its corollary equation is here applicable.*

By the same token the qualifications to our then argument also apply here. Thus, for example, the ratio, q, of Eq. (9–12) [or its reciprocal, p, of Eq. (9–13)] which, according to our argument, is the ratio between the magnitudes of our theoretical Forces of Diversification and of Unification, is a mathematical parameter that can be—and in later examples will be—disclosed empirically. Yet our alleged Forces of Diversification and of Unification are by no means mathematical parameters, but are merely theoretical factors; the same is true of our theoretical Force of Innovation. Not until we have operational units of measurement of these theoretical Forces, such as we have for sheer physical force (e.g., a unit of horsepower), will the Forces in question be anything but theoretical.

The preceding thirteen equations, which are all related, are basic to the argument of our lemma. Yet before we take leave of our lemma, there remain a few odds and ends that merit summary discussion.

We assumed initially in our lemma that everyone will receive a $1/C$ share of each of the m different kinds of goods for which he will give a $1/C$ share of the total work of production. In short, we have assumed an equality of production and of consumption which we find in actual practice is by no means the case—for reasons that we shall discuss in Chapter Eleven. But though this complete equality—or equalitarianism or "egalitarianism"—is neither realized nor realizable in practice, it does stand as a *collective goal* for reasons that we shall now attempt to set forth in brief.

In the first place, if we remember that the m different kinds of goods of the system have developed over the years, under the Force of Innovation, as economical means of living, then we can understand how everyone who knows of these m goods will want his share of them. (This factor is obviously important in the spread of culture.) We can also understand how no person can expect to receive these goods gratis without any compensatory work on his part, since such a gift would represent the fruit of the labors of others from which they would receive no compensatory return.

On the other hand, from the viewpoint of the individual person, it is the acme of economy, as every mother's son knows, to receive one's own individual needs completely gratis, without any compensatory labor whatsoever in return. Indeed, figuratively speaking, if it were not for man's congenital dislike of seeing his neighbor receive more than himself, or work less than himself, there would be no tendency towards an equality of labor and of reward. As it is, this *social envy*—that is, the proverbial desire "to keep up with the Joneses" not only by imitating them, but also by trying

* Though our concept of m diversity of goods reminds us of the Principle of Economical Versatility and Permutation and Specialization of tools (Chapter 3) we have no interest at present in pointing out the applicability of the Tool Analogy to social systems, since this applicability is obvious.

both to frustrate their rewards and to increase their difficulties—has, as an end result, *the equality of production and of consumption* as a *collective* goal of equalitarianism, in its aspect of enviously frustrating the rewards of others while adding to their difficulties. Needless to say this *social envy* of equalitarianism can inhibit individual initiative and enterprise which are necessary if m is to be increased, yet which will not operate under the Principle of Least Effort unless additional rewards are available as incentives for above-average work or ingenuity. An unrestrained equalitarianism can effectively kill a social system in the sense that it can actually cause m to decrease.

On the other hand, the collective goal of an equality of production and of consumption does set a lower limit of toleration upon the qualities of goods and of services, below which goods and services cannot fall if they are to be accepted by others in exchange for work or the fruits of work. In other words, though a person may try to get his reward with less work, nevertheless society sets a lower limit of toleration to its standards; if work is skimped to such a point that the product does not meet the lower limit of acceptability, then the work is lost.

We mention this matter of lower thresholds for two reasons; first, it suggests a general economic basis for social standards of goods and services. Second, it ties in with our previous argument about the artisan in our Tool Analogy in Chapter Three where we made the point, in effect, that though the artisan was obliged to devise means for saving work in producing goods, he was not allowed, in so doing, to reduce the quality of his products below that of their acceptable standards. So much, then, for the assumption of equal production and consumption.

Before leaving our lemma, however, there is a further matter that merits mention. In initially defining the $(M + L)_h$ cost of goods, we did not include the cost of the raw materials used. Since the cost of these raw materials may also be expressed in terms of M and L—say $M_a + L_a$—we need only to redefine $cost_h$ as $(M_a + L_a) + (M + L)_h$, or some such thing. This new definition of cost will in no way alter the validity of any of our preceding equations, although the new definition has the undeniable advantage of emphasizing the inertia of the Force of Diversification, which will tend to locate production ever nearer to the raw materials as $M_a + L_a$ increases—as was inferentially the case when we initially defined cost simply in terms of $(M + L)_h$.

With either definition of cost, it is evident from our equations that the communities of larger P sizes will produce goods of lower cost per $1/C$ share. More specifically, the cost of a $1/C$ share of any of the m_h kinds of goods that are produced in a community of a total P size seems to be inversely proportional to the fourth power of P (i.e., P^4). For we know, from Eq. (9–3), that the F_h number of $1/C$ shares that are made in an h production center is inversely proportional to the square of their $(M + L)_h$ cost. Since from Eq. (9–5), P_h is inversely proportional to $(M + L)_h$, it follows that F is directly proportional to P_h^2. Since $P = P_h^2$, it follows that the total F shares of all m kinds of goods produced in P is equal to P^4; and since the total amount of work that is used in making and delivering these F shares is directly proportional to P (i.e., there is a P number of $1/C$ units of work), it follows that the cost per $1/C$ share of each of the F different shares in question is inversely proportional to P^4.

In short, cheap goods and services seem theoretically to be connected with large P communities. Yet here a note of caution is in order! We have been speaking all along of $1/C$ shares—that is, of a $1/C$ share of the production of a given kind of goods over an interval of time, say, a year. A $1/C$ share may be 300 packages of cigarettes, or a right to a 1/20th of a gold watch, or to a 1/50th of a grand piano, or to a 1/10,000th of the services of a rare specialist in obscure brain diseases. Hence, when we say that the cost of a $1/C$ share is inversely proportional to the P^4 of the community that produces it, we must make some provision for the f frequency of usage of the goods or services in question. If grand pianos were consumed as often as loaves of bread, there would be piano factories around the corner, like bakeries.

If we say that goods flow D work-distances that are inversely proportional to their $(M + L)_h$ cost, and if we remember that every person is both a point of origin and a point of destination for a $1/C$ share of the total traffic of the system, then we can understand why those communities of larger P sizes and larger domains will tend to export goods whose per capita annual cost is very much cheaper.

In short, as m increases, its increase *tends* to be through the addition of ever cheaper h kinds of goods, as is apparent from our equations.

Let us not make the mistake of assuming that m must invariably be increased in every society. After all, the factor m is by no means a maximum. We have merely tried to show the alterations in population distribution that will attend an increasing m (and inferentially a decreasing m).

As long as we are in a materialistic civilization then *perhaps* m will continue to increase apace. Yet overnight, for all we can know to the contrary, people may become weary of a materialistic civilization, and prefer rather to seek their happiness in their own hearts and in those of their friends. In that case m would presumably decrease—and such a decrease might well betoken what is meant by the loose term, *Dark Ages*. Yet be the "ages" ever so "dark," as diagnosed subsequently by the learned professoriat, our equations should still be able to describe their social organization.

For in our lemma we have not restricted our argument to any value of C, or of m, or of q, or of p. We have begun our lemma with a group of soldiers whose degree of social organization was so low that p was virtually zero. Yet in the course of our lemma, in which the diversity of activity increased, we arrived at conditions which were fairly representative of those of the United States at the present time.

In propounding a lemma for the purpose of disclosing general principles that govern the distribution of populations and their various kinds of activities over the terrain—under the general heading of the economy of geography—we cannot restrict our argument to any particular stage of materialistic development. Though we have mostly treated of fairly large values of m, let us not forget that m can be so small that it can be produced by a single family or a tiny clan at the very source of raw materials without any trade at all. Such a small m kind of life is still a social organization to which our theory will apply.

Now for a final critique of our lemma before we leave it. In our discussion of production we have not distinguished between producers' goods and consumers' goods; nor have we dwelt at length upon differences between raw materials, semifinished goods, and finished goods. Instead we have spoken merely of the consumer. Yet in this connection let us also remember that we have never said that our goods of production inevitably had to pass into individual usage, as is commonly understood by the term consumption. Instead they can pass, say, into the consuming hoppers of factories for further processing, and so on, as their $(M + L)_h$ cost is thereby increased. This further processing does not invalidate any of our equations, since at every stage of the processing there is a value of $(M + L)_h$ of the goods in question, and since there is a relationship between the amount of goods put into the hoppers, and the number of persons in the factory, and the number of ultimate consumers of the goods that are further processed.

In order to envisage the situation let us simply view goods as a flow from their natural state, through production, to consumer. The greater the $(M + L)_h$ cost is, the proportionally shorter will be the D work-distance of its flow. Since $(M + L)_h$ refers to the cost of a $1/C$ share of goods, we can understand also that as goods keep on flowing farther and farther through additional processing, they will be broken up into a larger number of $1/C$ shares of an increasing diversity of goods (whether producers' goods or consumers' goods). Although we cannot dwell longer upon this topic at present, let us at least suggest the possible inference that there may be a rectilinearity in the frequencies, kinds, and costs of all different sorts of all kinds of goods. In this connection, we might reflect that all these goods of production are *tools* which are used directly or indirectly to make life easier. In Chapter Three we saw that there might be a law that governs the frequencies of usages, and the costs of usages of n different kinds of tools.

The Tool Analogy was cast in terms of a single artisan in one dimension, and yet not a great deal needs to be altered to make the Analogy applicable to C different artisans in essentially two dimensions who pursue common ends by means of common rules.[4] We mention this matter not in order to suggest that we have made it explicit, but merely to point out that we have not ignored its existence in a lemma that refers to a field of activity whose scope is truly enormous.

Instead of reviewing now in summary the various steps of the lemma we have just presented, let us prefer to use the material as a background for our following Section II, where we shall develop a formal analogue under quite specific postulates with an eye to an empiric verification to be undertaken in Section III.

In this formal analogue (II) we shall meet once more some of our thirteen equations which, except in the case of the ones that are more basic to our argument, we shall not take the space to establish again. From these thirteen equations we shall derive further ones of considerable practical utility that happen to be particularly easy to test empirically. Because of the extensive argument of our present Section I, the argument of our following Section II will be presented with considerable brevity.

II. THE HYPOTHESIS OF THE "MINIMUM EQUATION"[5]

In the present section we shall formulate much of our previous argument in terms of definite assumptions about the distribution of raw materials over the terrain. In so doing, we shall meet a selected few of our previous equations and shall also derive several new theoretical equations that will be of considerable value when we undertake our empiric test in Section III.

As to our new assumptions about the distribution of raw materials, let us take the view that in the course of centuries man has so spread out that in the humanly inhabited parts of the earth the amount of labor per spot is about the same. We shall assume explicitly that the different kinds of raw materials necessary for the social system in question are so distributed that the amount of individual human labor necessary to extract them, per unit of area, is the same.*

Apart from the preceding postulate, which refers to the homogeneous distribution of raw materials in terms of labor costs, we make no new postulates, although the two postulates of our lemma still apply. Thus, *first,* we shall continue to assume a total constant C population, each member of which contributes a $1/C$ share of the total work, in return for which he receives a $1/C$ share of each of the m different kinds of goods (including services) that are produced; and, *second,* we shall continue to assume that the movement of all materials into the system, through production, to consumption, and out of the system, will be such as to minimize the sum of the products of all masses (including persons), when multiplied by the distances moved.

This immediately preceding postulate is familiarly that of our "minimum equation," after which, for convenience, the hypothesis of the present section is named. Although the minimum is expressed in terms of *work,* it obviously refers to *probable work,* or *effort,* since, as we know from experience, the plans made by persons and groups are virtually always cast in terms of the probable future.

With the above postulates in mind, let us turn to the question of the number or *m diversity,* of different kinds of raw materials used. From our

* This postulate refers to highly idealized conditions, since some terrain, like mountain tops, may be uninhabitable, while there may be vast differences in the concentration of needed raw materials in inhabitable terrain (e.g., the labor density necessary to work a square mile of coal fields versus that for a square mile of corn fields). Some of these differences may be unappreciable statistically in large terrains; thus, the miles upon miles of corn fields may preponderate over those of ore-bearing land. Yet where the terrain is grossly nonhomogeneous in respect of the labor of procuring raw materials, our theoretical equations, which are intended to serve as norms for the efficient distribution of a population and its activities, will obviously not apply. The case is analogous to that of physics: although all trajectories are theoretically parabolic, nevertheless, in the history of this planet there probably has not been one single case of a trajectory that represented a pure parabola.

argument in Part One we know that as an ever larger m diversity of raw materials is used, the probability decreases rapidly of finding them all together in one spot.* Therefore, an increase in the total area of the terrain, as well as in the rate of trade within the terrain, will tend to be directly related to an increase in the m diversity of raw materials used. As a possible example of this direct relationship between m diversity, area, and rate of trade, we might cite the tendencies towards fewer and larger countries, and towards imperialism and a vastly expanded international trade, that attended the increased diversity of raw materials that were needed by the new kinds of goods and services that were introduced by the Industrial Revolution.

The size of the m diversity of needed raw materials will also influence the n number and P population sizes of the communities in which our theoretical C population lives, as we have already noted in our lemma.

Thus as long as a small m diversity of raw materials is used, with an increased likelihood of finding them in a restricted area, there is the economy of our familiar Force of Diversification in living at the very source of the raw materials, in order to minimize the work of transporting the raw materials to production. As a result, the C population will be broken up into a large n number of communities of equally small P population sizes which will be equally spaced in the terrain and virtually autarchical, since they will have no need for trade or communication with one another. Each of these n different autarchical communities can be viewed as an independent social system in the light of our definition of a social system, since each represents a group of individuals who pursue like objectives by means of like rules. (Later we shall see that the structure of a single community is dynamically similar to that of a system of communities.)

On the other hand, as the m diversity of needed raw materials increases, with the decreasing probability of finding them all in a single spot and with an increasing need for trade, the economy emerges of bringing the entire C population together into one single community—according to our familiar Force of Unification—where all production will be performed; for, by so doing, the system saves work in transporting the goods to the consumers.

Since the C members of the population cannot live simultaneously both at the sources of raw materials and in one big city where all production and consumption occurs, it follows that the actual locations of members of the population will depend upon the comparative magnitudes of the two Forces in question.

Since the Force of Diversification makes for a larger n number of communities of smaller P population size, and since the Force of Unification makes for a smaller n number of communities of larger P population size, then—if we interpret the relationship as a best straight line on doubly

* Indeed, the probability of finding all m different raw materials together in one given spot is equal to the product of the m probabilities of finding each individual kind of raw material in a given spot.

logarithmic co-ordinates—the result will be that the n number of different communities, when ranked, r, in the order of their decreasing P size, will follow the equation:

$$r \cdot P^q = K \qquad (9\text{–}1a)$$

where r is integral and positive, and where the exponent, q, represents the ratio of the magnitude of the theoretical Force of Diversification when divided by the magnitude of the theoretical Force of Unification. Eq. (9–1a) is the same as Eq. (9–12) in our lemma where, incidentally, the point was made explicitly that the variables of our equation are concrete mathematical parameters that can be disclosed empirically, whereas our two alleged Forces are merely theoretical factors.

Eq. (9–1a), as we already know from our previous argument, can be expressed in terms of the following equation of the generalized harmonic series:

$$P \cdot Sn = \frac{P}{1^p} + \frac{P}{2^p} + \frac{P}{3^p} + \ . \ . \ . + \frac{P}{n^p} \qquad (9\text{–}2a)$$

where $P \cdot Sn$ equals the total C population of the terrain, and where P is the population of the largest community [or, $P = K$ of Eq. (9–1a)], and where the exponent, p, equals $1/q$ of Eq. (9–1).

We know from our preceding discussion that as the m diversity of the system increases, the exponent, p, will increase and n will decrease, under the increasing relative magnitude of the Force of Unification.

Let us digress momentarily in order to visualize the dynamic operation of an increasing Force of Unification, as p increases. Since the system must minimize work, the system will continually seek new materials and methods that will produce the same goods and services with less labor; this is one aspect of the Force of Innovation which, as we pointed out in our lemma, also acts in the direction of producing new kinds of goods. The search for new methods and materials under the Force of Innovation will concentrate itself comparatively more upon those portions of the system whose comparative efficiency is less, since that is where the comparatively greater savings are to be effected. Hence, by and large, the system will tend to become equally efficient everywhere—in production, transportation, and distribution—with the result that the number of persons who become unemployed at any point, because of the general action of the Force of Innovation, will be proportional to the population at that point.

Obviously those persons who become unemployed as a result of the Force of Innovation will temporarily cease to be producers, in the sense that they will temporarily cease to contribute their respective $1/C$ shares of production. Nevertheless, they will still continue to be consumers with a right to a $1/C$ share of each of the m different kinds of goods of production, and as consumers they are more economically located in the communities of larger size—and proportionately so, since these larger communities are proportionally more the sources of consumable goods than of raw materials.

But since the larger a community is, the ever more suitable it is to absorb the surplus population from the outside,* and the ever less it is impelled to eject its own unemployed, it follows that the ever larger communities will grow ever more at the expense of the number and sizes of the smaller communities. In this fashion the larger communities will grow to a size depending upon their rank in Eq. (9–2a); or, *rate of growth* $= P/r^p$, which corresponds to Eq. (9–10) of our lemma. Consequently the available free labor market for new enterprises in a community will also be a function of its rank. Hence as the m diversity of the entire system increases by the adoption of new materials, methods—and goods—this increased m diversity is likely to be allotted to communities as a function of their P sizes.

Since this relationship between P and m diversity is basic to our argument, let us inspect it more closely. For convenience, we shall say that a community's m diversity of activity consists of successive h unit increments of kinds of activity that are added to the original stock. That is, as m increases from m_1 to m_2, by the addition of 1 h increment, the original m_1 kinds of activity are not abandoned; instead a new h kind is added. For example, if m_1 includes a barber shop, this barber shop is still kept while the new h kind of enterprise—say, a beauty parlor—is added. Yet let us note well that *this added h will serve the needs of an increasing number of persons* (or an increasing *domain* of persons, if we borrow a term from our preceding lemma) *who live outside the community* and who will come to the growing community to have their features beautified, even though they may still get their haircuts at home. In short, the population *domain* of customers for an h kind of goods-services will tend to increase with the rank of h.

Laborers must be imported to make the new h goods, thereby increasing the size of P. And since these new laborers must be supplied, further laborers must be imported to increase the n number of establishments of antecedent h. Indeed the n number of establishments of all kinds will increase with P (e.g., any increase in P will proportionately increase the number of stores, doctors, etc.), or:

$$n \text{ establishments} = P/_c \qquad (9\text{–}3a)$$

Because the new h laborers are *both* producers *and* consumers, they will have a double effect upon the size of P. Whatever economy makes P attractive as a center of increased production (by adding the new h producers) makes it equally attractive as a center of increased consumption, as further persons move into P, both to consume the new h goods, and to supply the new h producers. Hence we can see that P will grow at a rate that is faster than that of m. Indeed, as we know from Eqs. (9–9), (9–10), and (9–11) of our previous lemma, whose demonstration we shall not repeat here, the

* If, instead of a fixed C population, we have an excess of births over deaths with further additions to the population from foreign immigration—thus increasing C by a *surplus* of population—this surplus would tend to migrate to communities in proportion to their P sizes, for obvious theoretical reasons.

rate of P growth is twice the rate of m growth. Since P grows according to $P^p = P/r^p$), then, with a c constant understood:

$$m \propto P^{p/2} \tag{9–4a}$$

Moreover, since the argument we used about the n number and m diversity of establishments of Eqs. (9–3a) and (9–4a) applies also to the occupations of the persons in the communities, we may conclude that the n number of different persons of like occupation, and the m diversity of their occupations will be subject to the same equations as apply to the establishments themselves. From this argument we deduce that if the communities of the social system follow Eq. (9–1a) [and therefore (9–2a)], then both the m different occupations and the m different establishments will follow the same equations, when ranked, r, in the order of the decreasing N number of their members, or:

$$r \cdot N^q = C_p \tag{9–5a}$$

in which C_p is directly proportionate to the population of the total terrain, if all occupations and establishments throughout the terrain are included; and where C_p is also proportionate to the population of any community, if only the occupations and establishments of that community are studied.

We have spoken above about the *domain* of consumers of a community's successive h's of different goods, with the radius of the domain increasing with h. Let us turn now from a consideration of domains to the question of the *density* of persons within the domains in which, we remember, the cost in work increases in direct proportion to D work-distance to the center.

Since the term *density,* or *population density,* means the number of persons per unit of area, we can understand, under our assumed homogeneity of terrain, how the actual population density around the center of a community will be inversely related to the square of the distance to the center or, in terms of an absolute $density_D$ at a D distance from any P^p community (in which $P^p = P/r^p$), we have the equation:

$$density_D = P^p/D^2. \tag{9–6a}$$

In this connection, visualize n different magnets whose respective P strengths, when ranked in the order of decreasing strength, follow Eq. (9–2a) with an almost infinitesimal value of the exponent, p. Then imagine that these magnets are placed simultaneously at various points in a field of equally dense steel filings, and that the magnets will interfere with one another in their actions upon the filings. As p increases in the series, the radii of the effective domains of the magnets, whose respective circumferences are determined by a common arbitrary lower limit of disturbance of the filings, will increase in proportion to P/r^p, with the absolute $density_D$ of filings around each magnet being in proportion to Eq. (9–6a).

Eq. (9–6a) refers only to the manner in which the filings within the domain are heaped. As to the actual total number of filings in a domain, that will be in proportion to P/r^p. Therefore, if for each community we take a given outer degree of density—such as might be determined for a city by the economical density limits of a unified municipal system of water supply, sewage disposal, police and fire protection—then we shall find that the therein contained filings will be proportional to P/r^p. We mention this consideration in order to suggest that there are natural boundaries to cities which over the long run tend to be approximated by functional political boundaries of some sort (e.g., our Metropolitan Districts), and to protect ourselves against the criticism that it is impossible to use political boundaries for our statistical studies. In this connection let us reflect that as politicians extend the city's boundaries ever farther, they assume responsibilities at a rapidly decreasing rate of return; and conversely. Hence there is an equilibrium point for a municipal boundary of fixed services. A similar argument will be presented for nations in Chapter Ten.

Magnet analogues are not new to social language, in which the terms "pull" and "push" are quite frequent. Our above analogue, however, is incomplete because it makes no provision for moving the magnets themselves by comparative distances that are inversely proportional to their respective values of P/r^p. This shortcoming could be rectified by having the magnet's mass increase with its strength; or better still, to have its mass consist of its collective steel filings with the magnetic constant changed to a gravitational constant in two dimensions.

Under the above conditions what would be the interspacing of our communities? According to our general argument up to this point, the N number of communities of approximately equal size will be approximately equally spaced under the Force of Diversification in our homogeneous terrain. What, then, is the N number of different communities of approximate like P population size? This relationship is a corollary of Eq. (9–1a), which we have already set forth in Chapters Two and Three for the case of words and which we now present in the following equation:

$$N \cdot (P^{q+1} + b) = K \qquad (9\text{–}7a)$$

in which b represents a small constant (about ¼) that is appreciable only for very small values of P. Incidentally, Eq. (9–7a) also describes the N number of different domains of like radius, as well as the N number of linear D work-distances of like size between communities of like size (multiplied by a constant).

This last consideration of linear D work-distances leads to a further one, if we recall that all communities are sending h goods-services throughout their respective h domains. Since each P community contributes a P/C share of the total C work expended, and since it receives in return the same share of the total C goods of production, then there must be a transportation of exchanged goods-services between communities.

Let us assume that this intercommunity transportation is effected by porters who carry a constant unit of *exchange value* of goods-services per mile-hour; they will carry their positive flow of goods-services in a single trip from their respective immediate origins to their respective immediate destinations for further processing, and they will then return home the same way with the negative flow of goods which they have received in exchange.

Let us now inquire into the N number of single trips (or of round trips, if one will) of like D_T trip distance that the porters will carry throughout the entire domain during an interval of measurement; for we remember that every person is a point of origin for a positive flow of a $1/C$ share of the work of production, and a point of destination for a negative flow of a $1/C$ share of the goods of production.

Each community will contribute a share of the total work of the system in proportion to the fraction P/C, in which P is its relative population size. In exchange it will receive from the system a P/C share of other kinds of goods in return. (For convenience we shall ignore interchanges within the community since, as we shall later note, the same principle applies.) Porters, therefore, will be carrying the same amount, *by value,* out of the community as they carry into it. For this interchange each community will have a number of porters that is proportionate to its P size. All these porters of each community will carry goods of all sorts in value units per porter to all other communities in proportion to the products of their respective P sizes and inversely proportional to their intervening least D work-distances. The reason for this is that the probability that any *kind* of goods is at hand in P is directly proportional to P; whereas the probability of finding it there is inversely proportional to D by precise geometric probability (in the sense that the angle subtended at a point by a given disc is essentially inversely proportional to D distance to that point; nor is the situation altered by substituting D work-distance). Hence the y interchange of $1/C$ value units of goods between any two communities, P_1 and P_2, will be:

$$y/C = \frac{P_1 \cdot P_2}{D} \qquad (9\text{–}8a)$$

This equation sheds light on Eq. (9–4a): whatever makes any P attractive as a locus for the production of new h kinds of goods, thereby increasing P by the amount of the new producers, will make P equally attractive as a probable supply of goods, thereby increasing the density of traffic to and within P by *once again* the same amount.* Moreover, Eq. (9–8a) gives us the necessary information about the N number of different trips of like D_T distance, if we remember that both the N number of communities of like

---

* In the case of raw materials of a comparatively high degree of concentration, like previously mentioned coal mines, the resulting high density of population will attract production centers towards them in order both to consume the coal, and to supply the miners and other workers. In this connection let us note that the $R(n)$ number of relations among n number of different individuals is:

$$R(n) = n(n-1)$$

which, when increased by unity, becomes:

$$R(n+1) = (n+1) \cdot n$$

and where the difference in turn becomes:

$$R(n+1) - R(n) = \Delta R(n) = (n+1) \cdot n - n(n-1) = 2n.$$

This relationship may be defined as the *square effect* of increasing n.

P size, and their intervening D distances are inversely proportionate to P^{q+1} (approximate) of Eq. (9–7a), or:

$$(N + \alpha)(D_T{}^{q+1} - b) = C \qquad (9\text{–}9a)$$

in which α is a constant that must be added since, in a closed field, a decreasing number of persons have the opportunity to go longer distances (e.g., conceive of a circle cut into city blocks; only those living at the circumference have the opportunity to walk the longest diameter, D_T, in a straight line, and so similarly as distances become shorter; $N + \alpha$ corrects for this). Eq. (9–9a), therefore, will describe all movement of persons by bus, train, automobile, and foot; it will also describe the distances of telephone calls, telegrams, mail, express packages, etc., *provided* that the cost per mile is constant per unit-value of shipment, and provided also that all persons are equally able to pay the costs.

As to the circulation of all different m kinds of goods throughout the entire domain, we remember that, as the h of m increases, the radius of its domain increases proportionately. To make a long story short, the total f_h frequency of usage of the goods-services of the successive h increments of the m different classes of goods throughout the entire domain will be inversely related to the size of h. Indeed, if the $cost_h$ of a person's daily share of usage of h goods increases with h, then we may say:

$$f_h{}^q \cdot (cost_h) = m = P^{p/2} \qquad (9\text{–}10a)$$

in which P represents the population of the community of rank 1. In other words, and in general, the most frequently used goods-services tend to be the cheapest and the nearest, and the reverse. Thus the air that we use continually is at our nose; the water that we drink is generally at hand—and if not, that fact may exert an important influence upon the location and activities of the population in question.

Eq. (9–10a), which ties in with the argument of the closing paragraphs of our lemma in Section I, goes far, like our Tool Analogy in Chapter Three, towards describing a theoretical condition of maximum efficiency which may be useful for measuring the comparative efficiencies of actual systems, and for suggesting where f frequencies (i.e., sales) can be profitably increased or decreased, as well as costs to consumer. In this respect, Eq. (9–10a) may go beyond the well-known Law of Supply and Demand by suggesting that, say, an increased relative cost (or, conversely, with supply) may effect not only a decreased supply, but also an altered m diversity of goods. In other words, with a constant total supply of labor—and hence with a constant total purchasing power—increased costs of particular goods may not merely reduce the frequency of consumption of the goods in question, it may also decrease the m diversity of total goods consumed, and conversely. Of course, by increasing the efficiency of the total system, in the sense that more is produced per unit of available labor, m diversity can be increased even with constant rates of consumption of the old kinds of goods.

Eq. (9–10a) refers ultimately to a *per capita* consumption of the m different kinds of goods in terms of units of exchange value, in some form of money, whether gold, cigarettes, or beaver skins. The *per capita* consumption of some kinds of goods is low [that is, in terms of our lemma in Section I, its $(M + L)_h$ cost is low]. Of others, it is high. Theoretically, as the *per capita* consumption of a given kind of goods becomes lower, its production is located in fewer communities of larger P size—and conversely—as we have tried to make clear in the present chapter.

Therefore, the rarely used and so-called highly specialized goods and services tend to be found in the larger P communities—and theoretically proportionately so. From the viewpoint of the purveyors of these rarely used goods and services, the larger community is an economical location because of the increased probability of finding someone in the community who will need the goods or services in question. From the viewpoint of the total population, however, the large city stands out as a place where unusual goods and services are likely to be found; indeed, as we have argued shortly before, the probability that any particular kind of goods or services will be in a given community increases in proportion to the P of the community. Hence, those who have culturally unusual demands to satisfy migrate to the larger communities; and so too those with culturally unusual goods and services, including skills, for sale.[6] As a result, the inhabitants and activities of a large city may seem queer to the rest of the population, and the reverse.

Yet when we speak of the tendency of the diversity of goods and services to increase with the P size of a community according to Eq. (9–4a) or according to Eq. (9–9) in our lemma, we mean *all* kinds of goods and services, regardless of whether the goods are raw, semifinished, or finished and, if finished, whether they are producer's goods or consumer's goods; and regardless of whether the services are those of a common laborer or of a surgeon, lawyer, teacher, engineer, or cultural artisan in esoteric fields. For that reason we may suspect that theoretically the respective frequencies of the m different kinds of goods may be doubly logarithmically rectilinear, like the m different kinds of occupations, as described theoretically by our Eq. (9–5a). In that case, our goods, like our services (and our language), are culturally standardized according to stereotypes.*

And yet "odd" or nonstandard sizes are also sometimes needed, and one goes or writes "to the city" for them. For that reason, for a typical example, a large department store in a large city, like Marshall Field in Chicago, or Jordan Marsh in Boston, will have a larger *assortment* of styles and sizes and prices than a smaller store in a smaller community does or could have. There is an economic advantage in sheer large assortment, or diversity, because of the increased probability of being able to satisfy one's needs there.

---

* For example, a man buys 6, or 8, or 10, or 12 penny nails (instead of 7, 9, or 11 penny ones) because those are the standard sizes and hence cheaper because of the economies of mass production; yet, on the other hand, the standard sizes are produced in mass because of the large demand for these standard sizes. For most purposes the nails of odd penny weight would do equally well. In the question of *kinds* or *standards,* demand determines supply, as well as supply determines demand.

Since, however, many persons who may want a wider diversity of goods cannot travel to the big city, the whole large field of mail-order merchandising has sprung up, with elaborately illustrated catalogues, such as those by Sears-Roebuck and Montgomery Ward, that both tell the outlying public what goods are available and teach them what demands are current, while offering to fulfill their demands at a fair price. It is regrettable that a rank-frequency study of the items and prices of mail-order sales is not available.

Some kinds of goods, like soap, bread, and cigarettes, are staple, in the sense that they have a large constant demand, the satisfaction of which is merely a matter of the customer's *convenience.* Hence, one can buy soap, cigarettes, and perhaps bread, in the corner store, whether that store be a drugstore or a grocery store. *Convenient* goods are mostly cheap goods of large *per capita* demand.

With goods of higher cost, however, like automobiles, washing machines, etc., the customer must ever more ponder the question of purchase. These are the *deliberative* goods,* whose centers of merchandising will be sought out. For that reason we often find that rare goods of high price and low demand will be sold in very out of the way places.

As to the *new kinds* of goods that are being continually placed on the market, in respect of which the public must be both taught of their use and reminded of their existence, these are most advantageously exhibited in the most populous parts of the most populous stores. Thus, for example, the chemicals and biologicals of a drug store, which will be *deliberately* sought out, are often scarcely in evidence in the store, whereas the soda fountain, being a matter of *convenience,* is in plain sight and easily reached by a route that is lined with *new kinds* of brands and gadgets. The dynamics of a store, with its aisles and showcases, may not be unlike that of a city with its streets and show windows, in which, incidentally, the latest hairdo, gadget, style, or importation is far more likely to be exhibited than the staples of bread, soap, or cigarettes. Indeed when *convenient* goods are conspicuously exhibited, their exhibition may betray inventory troubles.

We mention these considerations, however, not in order to contribute anything to the theory or practice of merchandising, which is elaborate; rather do we suggest that the dynamics of merchandising may be subject to the exigencies of Eq. (9–10a). And yet this equation refers not merely to one store, but to all stores. A department store, after all, can reach such a size and diversity that its difficulties of internal traffic and information [7] may drive many potential customers to seek their goods in specialty shops and in the corner store, thereby increasing the number of specialty shops on the one hand, and the diversity of goods in the corner store on the other. The number, kinds, and sizes of stores (in terms of payroll or profit) in a community of P size is, therefore, not a matter of caprice.

Some insight into the question of the number, kinds, and sizes of stores can be gained if we once again view the growth of a community in the light of the magnet analogue presented a few pages back, in which the p exponent

* The terms *convenient* and *deliberative* in the above sense are borrowed from current business usage.

of the magnets increases according to Eq. (9–2a) (i.e., the equation of the generalized harmonic series). We have argued that the "magnets" will "pull" persons into the larger P communities at rates that are proportional to P/r^p, but that is not the whole story, for they will also "pull" the smaller outlying communities into the larger communities. The smaller and nearer the outlying communities, the more likely they are to be absorbed (i.e., inversely proportionate to their respective values of P/D). The larger a community is, the greater will be the number of communities that it attracts.

In view of our Eqs. (9–7a) and (9–9a), we can understand how a larger attracting community will consist of harmonically seriated [Eq. (9–2a)] absorbed communities which, for convenience, we shall call *trading centers.* Hence, theoretically, the frequency distribution of these trading centers within a city, when ranked in the order of decreasing number, sizes (in terms of employees, payroll, or net), and the diversity of their stores—as well as the amounts and diversity of their goods-services in terms of their assortment of styles, sizes, and prices—will all follow Eq. (9–2a) (with the exponent, p, being that of the country, and the constant being proportionate to the city's size). In short, our equations apply theoretically not only to the entire social system, but also to the subsidiary systems within the inclusive system.

Therefore our hypothesis of the "minimum equation" can be tested at various parts of a social system, as we shall now attempt to show, as we turn to the problem of empiric test in Section III. Before turning to Section III, let us remember that we have made certain explicit assumptions about the terrain which permit us to state equations in a definite form. Where actual conditions deviate widely from those of our assumptions, we may not expect to find the distributions of our equations.

III. EMPIRIC TESTS

In the present section we shall test empirically the theoretical formulations of our preceding section. Since many of our corollary equations depend upon the relative population sizes of the communities of the total system, we shall begin our test with the rank-population distributions of Eqs. (9–1a) and (9–2a).

A. The Generalized Harmonic Distribution

In Section II we argued that when the communities are ranked, r, in the order of decreasing P population size, they will follow Eq. (9–1a) (viz., $r \cdot P^q = K$), with values of r being integral and positive, and, of course, the value of q being positive. This relationship we also stated in terms of the generalized harmonic series of our Eq. (9–2a) which we shall not repeat here.* Since our argument referred to the natural boundaries of

* The first person to my knowledge to note the rectilinear distribution of communities in a country was Felix Auerbach in 1913 who, however, generalized incorrectly upon the value, $p = q = 1$, and was quoted therein by A. J. Lotka. In 1931 R. Gibrat reported the rectilinearity of the larger communities of Europe with a value of p (Eq. 9–2a) less than 1.

communities, as opposed to their political boundaries, we shall use the data for the P populations of Metropolitan Districts in the U. S. A. in 1940, although in Chapter Ten we shall find that politically bounded communities follow the same equation.

In Fig. 9–2 is presented the rank-frequency distribution of the 100 largest Metropolitan Districts in the U. S. A. in 1940 as reported by the Sixteenth Census. The line drawn was calculated by least squares and has a slope of $-.9835 \pm .0677$, or, in equation form, $\log y = -.98 \log x + 7.05$. Since the

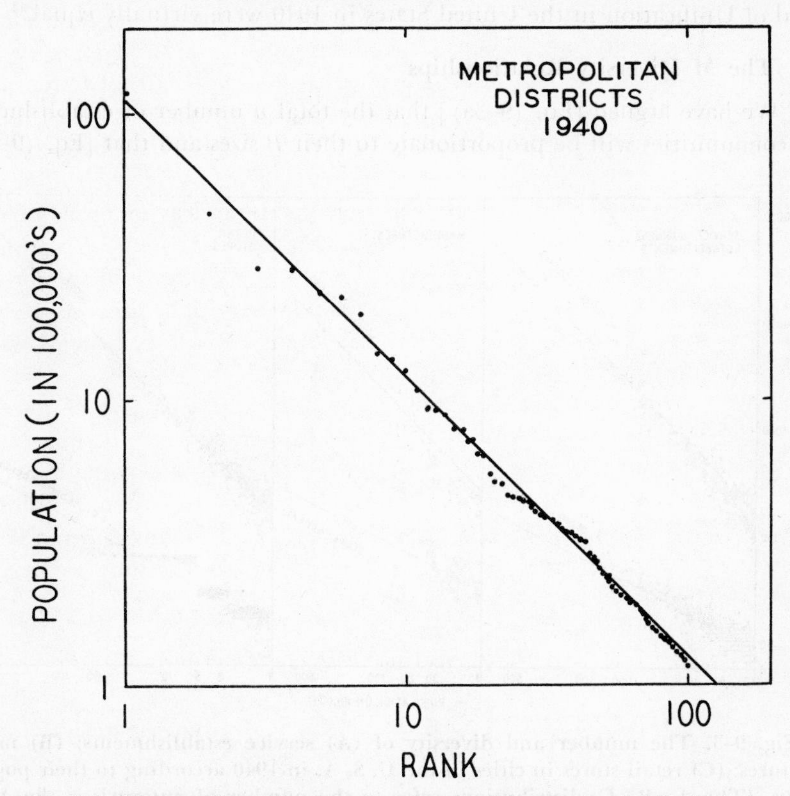

Fig. 9–2. Metropolitan districts. One hundred largest in the U. S. A. in 1940, ranked in the order of decreasing population size.

negative slope of this line is equal to the positive value of p of Eq. (9–2a), we may say that the value of p for Fig. 9–2 is approximately 1.00 (a legitimate value for our observed $-.9835$ slope with a probable error of .04). The antilogarithm of 7.05 is about 10 million, which is theoretically the population of the largest Metropolitan District (New York), which is the value of P in Eq. (9–2a).[9]

The value, $p = 1.00$, is also found if we calculate the rank-frequency distribution of all 140 Metropolitan Districts, which represent all the cities of 50,000 or more persons with immediately surrounding populations as defined by the Sixteenth Census. Specifically the slope for these 140 Districts

Further extensive treatment appeared by the author in 1941. All these studies were made on the basis of politically bounded communities.[8]

is $-1.0365 \pm .0362$ (or, $\log y = -1.0365 \log x + 7.1179$), which again is not far removed from -1.00 which we are adopting for the value of p and q.

The total population of the first 100 Districts is 59,459,800; of the second, 62,865,550. Hence, Fig. 9–2 represents nearly ½ of the country's total population.*

The above $p = q = 1$ value can be expected to be found in all our equations that refer to U. S. A. populations at approximately 1940. Theoretically, this value means that the magnitudes of our Forces of Diversification and of Unification in the United States in 1940 were virtually equal.[11]

B. The M Diversity Relationships

We have argued [Eq. (9–3a)] that the total n number of establishments of communities will be proportionate to their P sizes and that [Eq. (9–4a)]

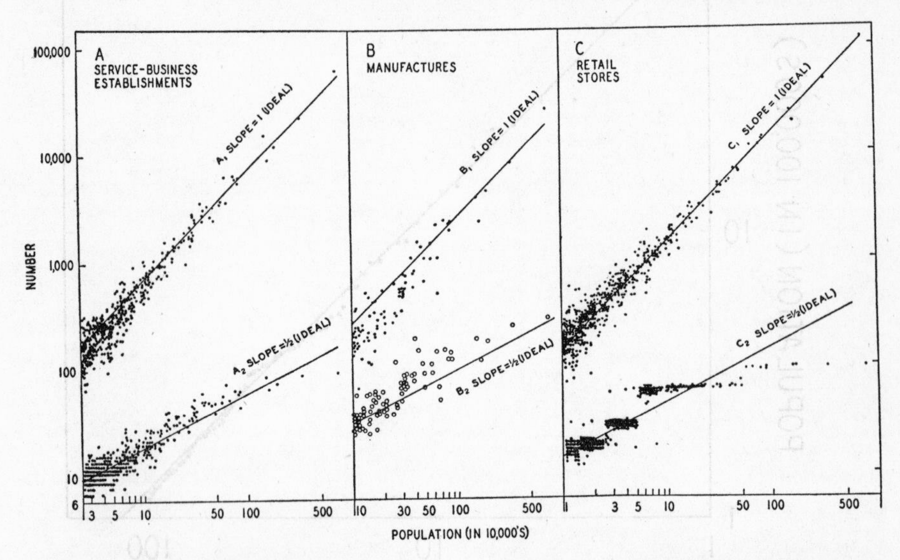

Fig. 9–3. The number and diversity of (A) service establishments; (B) manufactures; (C) retail stores in cities in the U. S. A. in 1940 according to their populations. (The A_1, B_1, C_1 distributions refer to the number of enterprises; the A_2, B_2 and C_2 distributions refer to their diversity.)

the m diversity of these establishments will be proportioned to $P^{\frac{1}{2}}$. Let us now test these equations with U. S. A. data for approximately the time of those of Fig. 9–2.

In Fig. 9–3 are presented the data for (*A*) personal and business service establishments including transportation services; for (*B*) manufactures; and for (*C*) retail stores including chain stores—all for the year 1939 in the United States as enumerated by the Sixteenth Census. Population in all cases is measured logarithmically on the abscissa, with the *A* data referring to all cities of over 25,000, *B* over 100,000, and *C* over 10,000 inhabitants

* The y-density of the 140 Districts of x population is, by least squares, $\log y = .3192 \log x + 1.2688$, P.E. $\pm$ .1520. For the first 100 Districts it is $y = .3815 \log x + .9116$, P.E. $\pm$ .1412.[10]

in the states from Alabama through New York, alphabetically arranged (about half the cases).

Each of the three sets of data of Fig. 9–3 consists of two distributions: an *upper* and a *lower*.

The *upper* sets of points (i.e., A_1, B_1, and C_1) refer to the total n number of the respective enterprises of all kinds in the cities in question which, according to Eq. (9–3a), should be directly proportional to P population. In each case the points are not inconsistent with an approximation of a straight line of + 1.00 slope, as suggested by the ideal line of that slope, added for the reader's convenience. Therefore, the total number of service establishments, manufactures, and retail stores of a city of P population seems in each case to be directly proportional to P, times a constant. Hence Eq. (9–3a) is confirmed empirically. The perhaps slightly greater slope of B_1 we shall discuss in a few pages.

The *lower* sets of points (i.e., A_2, B_2, and C_2) refer to the m number of different kinds, or classes—that is, to the m diversity—of the respective enterprises of the various cities under discussion. This m diversity, we remember from Eq. (9–4a), should be proportional to the square root of the population; as graphed in Fig. 9–3, the distribution should have a positive slope of ½. The points of A_2 and B_2 seem in each case to group themselves about the line of that slope which was added for the reader's convenience, thereby confirming Eq. (9–4a) to the effect that m is proportional to $P^{\frac{1}{2}}$ (or to the square root of the n number of establishments of Eq. (9–3a), with a constant). The points of C_2 do not fit the line so closely; the reason for this may be the less discriminating scheme of classification adopted by the Bureau of the Census for stores, as becomes clear from an actual inspection of the classes employed; nevertheless, the results are not inconsistent with the line drawn. In both lines of A and C, the points are, in fact, much denser at the bottom than they appear, since many of the points fall together, as is to be expected from the increasing number of cities of approximately like size, as P decreases.[12]

But though the *lower* set of data of Fig. 9–3 tells us that the m diversity of social-economic activity of a city is proportionate to the square root of its population, the data tell us nothing about the extent to which the different cities agree in their kinds of enterprises. Thus, for example, P_1 might have one "vocabulary" of different kinds of enterprises, while P_2 has a totally different one. An inspection of the underlying data reveals that the larger cities increase the diversity of their enterprises simply by adding further kinds to those of the smaller cities (cf. Eq. (9–11) of lemma: *rate of m growth* $\propto P^{p/2}$), so that we may say that m grows by adding further classes according to P.

If we remember in this connection, however, that the cities in question in 1939 closely approximated the proportions of a harmonic series, as previously reported, when ranked, r, in the order of decreasing P population size, with $p = q = 1$, then we can see that the rank-frequency distributions of (A) personal and business service establishments, of (B) manufactures, and of (C) retail stores will follow Eq. (9–5a) (viz. $r \cdot N^q = C_P$) in which

$q = 1$. In short, the distribution will be that of the harmonic series, just as in Fig. 9–2 for the Metropolitan Districts, if communities grow in m diversity at a rate that is proportional to P. That such is the case will be evident from Figs. 9–4, 9–5, and 9–6.*

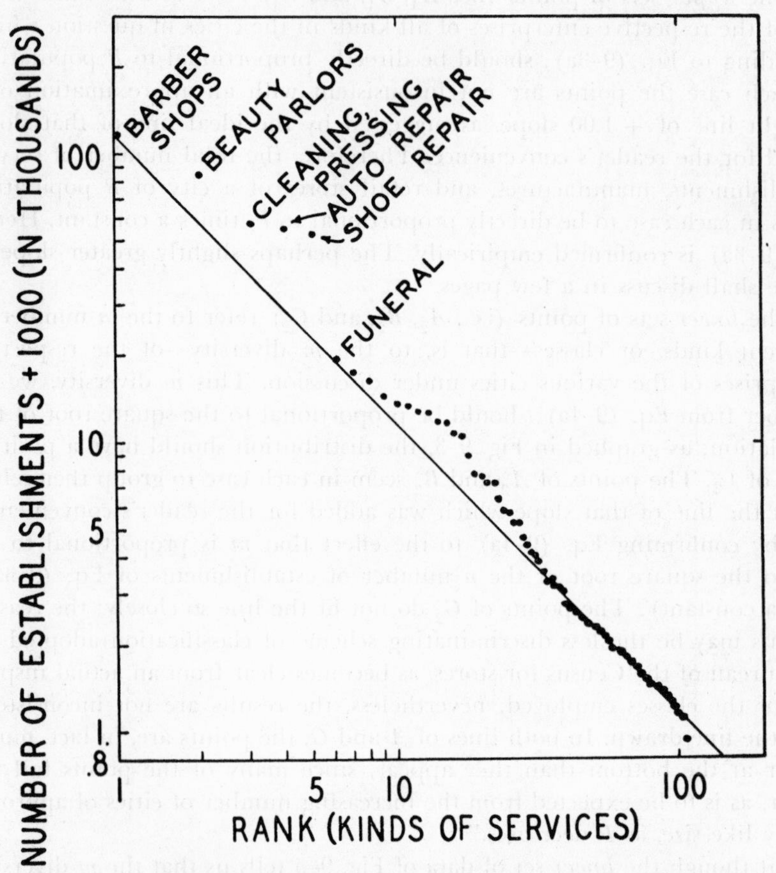

Fig. 9–4. Service establishments; (personal, business, and those relating to transportation) U. S. A. 1939 when ranked in the order of decreasing number of establishments of like kind. (Line drawn has ideal slope of -1.00.)

In Fig. 9–4 [13] are presented the data for the personal and business service establishments for the entire U. S. A. in 1939, with r rank plotted logarithmically on the abscissa, and with the N number of like establishments plotted logarithmically on the ordinate after shifting the origin by + 1000, [or,

* The preceding argument can be stated differently with the harmonic distribution of cities in the U.S.A. in 1939, and with m diversity proportional to $P^{\frac{1}{2}}$; then, if m grows at the rate of $P^{\frac{1}{2}}$, there will be a small N number of different kinds of enterprises of very high f frequency of occurrence, and an increasing N number of enterprises whose frequency of occurrence will decrease according to f^2, if larger cities merely add to the diversity of smaller ones. In short, $N \cdot f^2 = a\ constant$ (approximate). We know from our discussion in Chapter Two that when this relationship is stated in terms of ranked frequencies, it becomes $r \cdot f = C$.

$r \times (N + 1000) = C_p$]. The need for this shift of the origin may result from the fact that the Bureau of the Census excluded service establishments that were "conducted from the residence of the proprietor without a sign or other means of identification," thereby eliminating doubtless numerous cases of small establishments (e.g., upholsterers, painters) that are locally known without the need of signs. The deviation of some of the points above the line suggests the difficulty of classification of which the Bureau of the Census is well aware. Further reasons for deviations may be the fact that many service establishments also retail finished goods, while many of them are ancillary to further services and retailing. On the whole, however, Fig. 9–4 confirms our hypothesis.

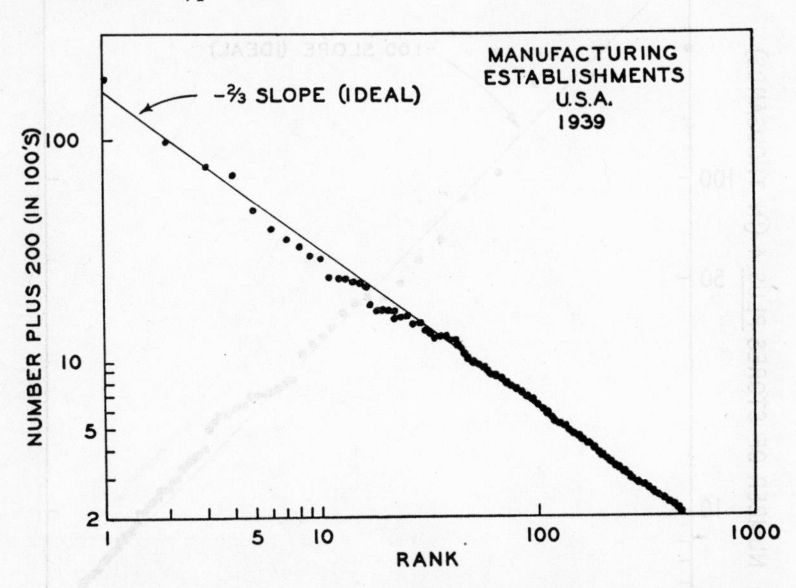

Fig. 9–5. Manufactures in the U. S. A. in 1939 when ranked in the order of the decreasing number of manufactures of like kind.

In Fig. 9–5, with co-ordinates the same as before, is presented the rank-frequency distribution of manufactures in the U. S. A. in 1940,[14] which seems to approximate the line of – ⅔ slope (ideal) that is drawn. This deviation in slope is significant, and may represent a theoretically "excessive" amalgamation of plants of different kinds under a single management (in spite of the efforts of the Bureau of the Census, from 1937 on, to enumerate the different plants regardless of a common income tax return). Thus, for example, a fruit packing concern might include a box factory to make its crates; an automobile manufacture might in fact include a glass factory or a foundry, with nothing in common between them except a unifying direction which by no means eliminates the need to enumerate the subsidiaries independently. Incidentally, the reader may choose to see a +1.50 slope for the B_1 data of Fig. 9–3, and a +⅔ slope for the B_2 data of the same figure to correspond to the –⅔ slope of Fig. 9–5. For whatever the slope is for a given distribution throughout the entire country will be the slope for the distribution within the individual cities, with the constant C_p being proportionate to the population in question.[15]

In Fig. 9–6, with co-ordinates and origin shift as before, is presented the rank-frequency distribution of all stores of like kind [16] with the line drawn having the theoretically expected − 1.00 slope (ideal). The y-origin is shifted, but only by + 4. Since every retail establishment in the United States was included, "if readily recognizable as a place of business," we may perhaps infer from the comparative smallness of the shift of the origin that

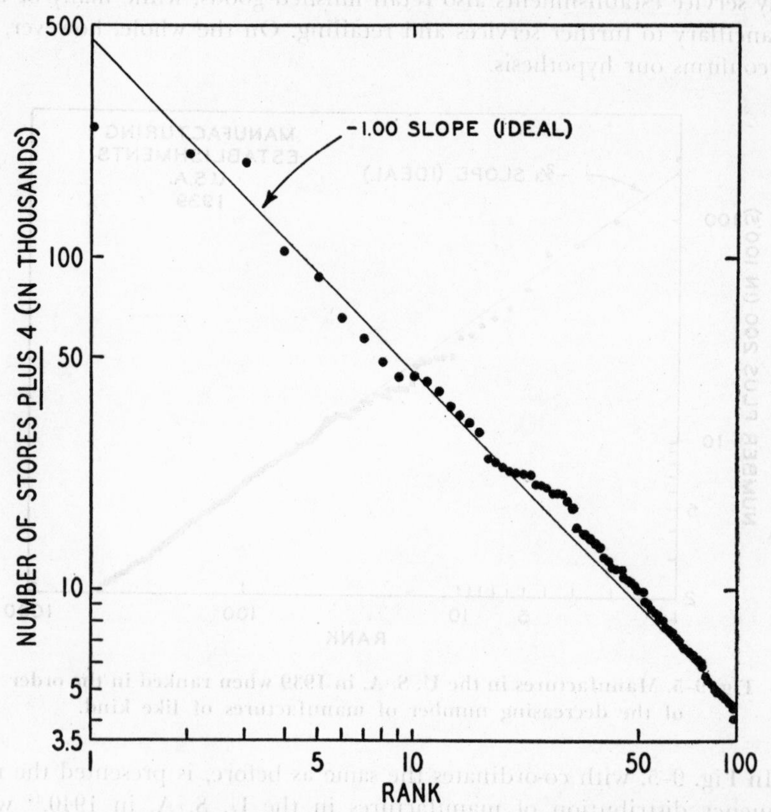

Fig. 9–6. Retail stores (including chain stores) in the U. S. A. in 1939, ranked in the order of decreasing number of stores of like kind.

stores advertise themselves better than service establishments and manufacturers.

Theoretically, closely related to the preceding data on the frequency of enterprises is the frequency of occupations which, as we remember from Section II, may also be expected to follow Eq. (9–5a), and therefore, too, the corollary *number-frequency relationship* (in which the x number of different occupations of like y number of members will, in the present case, be inversely proportional to y^2). We mention this corollary equation because the occupational data of Fig. 9–7 are graphed according to it.

In Figure 9–7 are two different sets of occupational data,[17] each of which is the number-frequency distribution of the x number of different kinds of occupations ("generic" and "specific") of the same y number of members. The slopes of each of these sets of data should be – ½ (with a slight downward concavity at the bottom to compensate for b), if the whole is harmonically seriated according to Eqs. (9–1a) and (9–2a). This *number-frequency* method of graphing was adopted instead of the *rank-frequency* method for a greater convenience in discussing the data in connection with

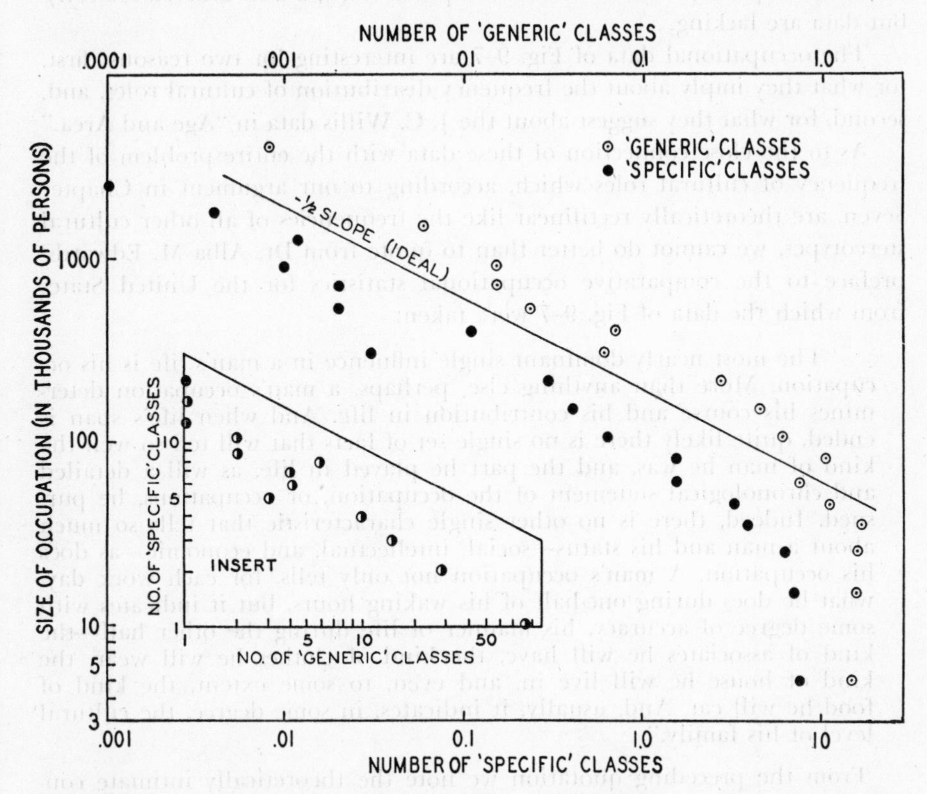

Fig. 9–7. Occupations in the U. S. A. in 1939. The number of different kinds, or classes, of "generic" and "specific" occupations of like number of members.

those of J. C. Willis on biological genera and species which we presented in Chapter Six and which were graphed as in Fig. 9–7.

We note that in Fig. 9–7 there are two methods of classification of occupations—the "generic" and the "specific"—which are each graphed doubly logarithmically as indicated in reference to the selected class middles. The generic occupations were the nonindented occupations in the original tabulation for 1940; the specific occupations were the indented occupations, except that when a nonindented generic occupation had no indented specific one, it was considered to be both generic and specific. The insert at the lower left-hand corner represents the number of generic occupations that have a like number of specific occupations; this insert was added to facilitate our brief discussion of the corresponding relationship of the J. C. Willis data.[18]

The line drawn in Fig. 9–7 has an ideal slope of $-\frac{1}{2}$ which, theoretically, should be approximated by both sets of data, and which is approximated by all but the lower 2 or 3 points in each case. Hence, Eq. (9–5a) is again confirmed.* It is regrettable that data on professions are lacking since these too should follow the same equation.[19] From the data of Figs. 9–3 to 9–7 we can anticipate that the x number of different labor unions of like y membership should follow the same equations (*in a well ordered society!*) but data are lacking.

The occupational data of Fig. 9–7 are interesting for two reasons: first, for what they imply about the frequency distribution of cultural roles, and, second, for what they suggest about the J. C. Willis data in "Age and Area."

As to the close connection of these data with the entire problem of the frequency of cultural roles which, according to our argument in Chapter Seven, are theoretically rectilinear like the frequencies of all other cultural stereotypes, we cannot do better than to quote from Dr. Alba M. Edwards' preface to the comparative occupational statistics for the United States from which the data of Fig. 9–7 were taken:

> "The most nearly dominant single influence in a man's life is his occupation. More than anything else, perhaps, a man's occupation determines his course and his contribution in life. And when life's span is ended, quite likely there is no single set of facts that will tell so well the kind of man he was, and the part he played in life, as will a detailed and chronological statement of the occupation, or occupations, he pursued. Indeed, there is no other single characteristic that tells so much about a man and his status—social, intellectual, and economic—as does his occupation. A man's occupation not only tells, for each work day, what he does during one-half of his waking hours, but it indicates with some degree of accuracy, his manner of life during the other half—the kind of associates he will have, the kind of clothes he will wear, the kind of house he will live in, and even, to some extent, the kind of food he will eat. And, usually, it indicates, in some degree, the cultural level of his family."

From the preceding quotation we note the theoretically intimate connection between a man's occupation in life and the total cultural role he plays, as briefly discussed in Chapter Seven, where we arrived theoretically at the rectilinearity of the frequency distributions of cultural roles. Indeed this rectilinearity of occupations goes far towards supporting our contention that all cultural stereotypes are rectilinear.

The occupational data of Fig. 9–7, when viewed against the broad background of our entire preceding argument, are closely related to the distribution of biological genera and their species, as observed by J. C. Willis and discussed in Chapter Six. By this we do not mean merely a similarity of mathematical description from which, incidentally, one may not at all infer a similarity of dynamics. Rather do we mean that the distribution of occu-

* The problem of classifying occupations is a difficult one upon which Dr. Alba M. Edwards has been working since he joined the Bureau of the Census in 1909. Yet what is a correct classification? If our hypothesis of the Minimum Equation be correct, and if the distributions of Fig. 9–7 approximate the line drawn, then Dr. Edwards is to be congratulated upon the improved schemes of classification which he has devised and introduced.

pational types over the terrain is such that few have a wide area of dispersion, while an increasing number have a decreasing area of dispersion (according to the inverse square, as indicated by our data). Moreover, theoretically, the occupations of ever smaller areas of dispersion are the comparatively more specialized ones—indeed, virtually by definition (as we argued, *mutatis mutandis,* with the Willis data). Whether those "generic" occupations with the greater number of "specific" ones are also the older ones is a neat question that can only be answered by historical examination; surely the insert at the lower left of Fig. 9–7 might be so interpreted, thereby intimating that the evolution of cultural roles has the same dynamics as that of biological species. In that case, the evolution of cultural varieties would be but a special instance of the general evolution of biological varieties. Indeed, our argument in Chapter Six about the evolution of types or "species" was so cast as to rationalize both the Willis data and the present occupational data and, therefore, does not merit a statement here.*

We can see that the data of Figs. 9–3 to 9–7 all belong together theoretically, and provide a helpful insight into the dynamics of the conditions that are frequently described by the phrases "too many" or "too few" persons in any kind of occupation, or "too many" or "too few" of any particular kind of store, service, or manufacture in particular communities, or in the terrain as a whole. Though the question of the "too many" and the "too few" is usually scrutinized against the background of the Law of Supply and Demand, we can see that the question goes much deeper than the Law of Supply and Demand, which merely states that there are dynamic equilibria between supply and demand, without specifying what the particular equilibria are in terms of the m diversity and the N membership of the total occupations, goods, and establishments of the social system at a particular time.

Before leaving the present topic let us remember that we have argued theoretically that the larger P communities would also tend to have the larger establishments. Thus, as we go to a larger city we may expect theoretically to find not only more services, stores, and manufactures, and a greater diversity of the same; we may also expect to find larger services, larger stores, and larger factories, in terms of number of employees, net sales, payrolls, inventory sizes and inventory diversity. Is such the case? Although the Census gives a great deal of information along these lines for groups of enterprises, I cannot find detailed studies about the actual number and sizes of individual enterprises in different cities. Nevertheless, some deductions are possible from the more general data.

Thus, for example, there is a classification of manufacturing establishments according to their average annual number of wage earners in 1939, even though the extensive data are broken down into only nine classes of number of wage earners, viz., 1+, 6+, 21+, 51+, 101+, 251+, 1001+, and 2,500+. Yet, if we rank on the abscissa the manufacturing establishments

* In times of economic depression, do not the comparatively rarer and more specialized goods-services suffer more, as we have argued to be the case with the more specialized species?

in the decreasing order of their number of wage earners on the ordinate, using the above frequency classes for the cumulated terminal ranks (i.e., the 176 manufactures of more than 2,500 wage earners are represented by 176 on the abscissa and 2,500 on the ordinate, and so on), we have in Fig. 9–8 a distribution that is approximately rectilinear, with an approximate slope of $-\frac{2}{3}$, if we shift the *y*-origin, as indicated.

In view of the fact that the wage earners belong to, and help constitute, the populations of the cities in which the manufactures are located, it is evident that the manufactures with the greatest number of wage earners *can* only be located in the larger cities, whereas the smaller ones *may* also be in the larger cities. The probabilities of the case are like those of a sieve

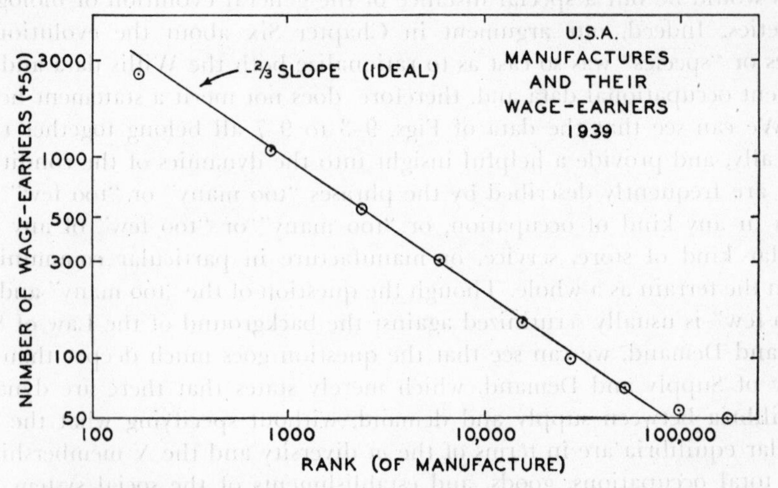

Fig. 9–8. Manufactures and their wage earners in the U. S. A. in 1939, with the manufactures ranked in the order of their decreasing number of wage earners.

with holes of various sizes for stones of varying size, except that with cities, each city will apparently have a total number of manufactures in proportion to its *P* size.[20]

Incidentally, we have argued in our lemma of Section I [cf., Eqs. (9–7), (9–8), and (9–9)] that the P_h population of persons that work at the production and distribution of a given *h* kind of goods in a given *P* city will be proportional to *P* . If a manufacture's P_h may be construed as its wage earners, then the data of Fig. 9–8, in conjunction with those of Fig. 9–5, are quite consistent with the argument of our lemma. Nevertheless, a more discriminating statistical classification on the part of the Census would be welcome.

Further data on the sizes of enterprises—this time in the case of service establishments—seem to shed some light indirectly upon the question of city size and the comparative size of its enterprises. Thus in Fig. 9–9 are plotted doubly logarithmically, with the respective origins of each set of data shifted in each case two cycles to the right: (1) the gross receipts, (2) the number of full-time employees, and (3) the total average payroll of all of the different ranked personal and business service establishments as graphed in Fig. 9–4. In other words, consider the respective values of Fig. 9–9 plotted for each different service graphed in Fig. 9–4, and in that order. The points in each case, in representing the totals of each service in question, also represent the averages. These averages are important.

For, as we pass from left to right in each distribution, the points, in spite of a very wide variation, seem on the whole to descend at a somewhat steeper angle (slope = – 2?) than we observed for the rank-frequency distribution of the same establishments in Fig. 9–4. That may mean, of course, that the more numerous kinds of services do individually a proportionately greater business in terms of gross receipts, number of employees, and payroll—a

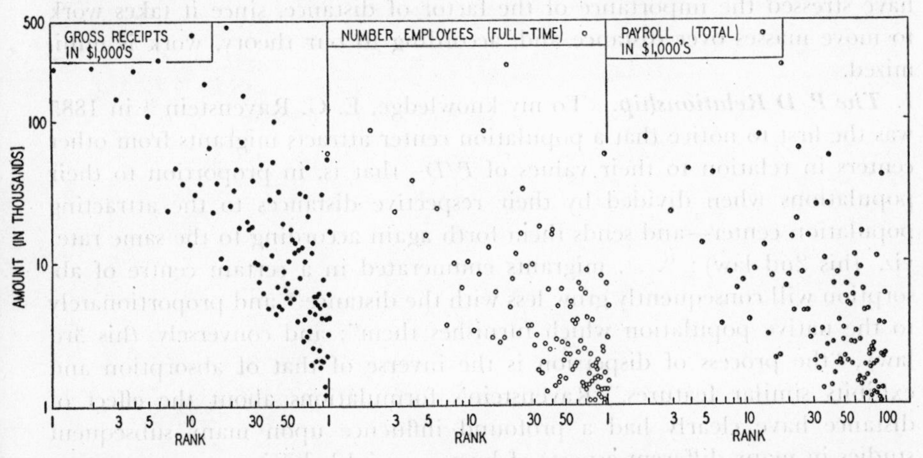

Fig. 9–9. Gross receipts, number of full-time employees, and total payroll of service establishments in the U. S. A. in 1939 when the service establishments are ranked in the order of their decreasing number of members as in Fig. 9–4 *supra.*

condition that would be difficult to visualize, since many of these establishments, like barber shops, beauty parlors, and shoe repair shops, are in very small communities. On the other hand, all these establishments are also in very large cities in which, as we know from experience, the service establishments often have a very considerable size and thereby bring up the national average. Because of the sizable variation in Fig. 9–9, which precludes curve-fitting in view of the large probable error of any fitted curve, we can draw no conclusions. The data do, however, suggest the value of more detailed data for the sizes of enterprises in individual communities. For it is not unthinkable, in the light of our theory, that the sizes of all stores, or of manufactures, or of service establishments, in a given community, when ranked in the order of decreasing number of employees, will be rectilinear according to Eq. (9–1a), with the value of the K constant in each case being in proportion to the P population of the city in question. That would mean that large cities have both small and large enterprises, as they cater both to intracity and extracity trade, with the disparity in size between the largest and the smallest increasing in a city with its P population. Later, in treating of the topic of intracity traffic, we shall come upon this question again.

In any event, as we reflect upon the data presented in Figs. 9–3 to 9–9, we note a very high degree of orderliness in the number and diversity of enterprises and occupations in individual cities and throughout the entire country—an orderliness that indicates that one's occupational and business life is by no means a matter of randomness or caprice, nor entirely within one's control. Instead it is subject to what we are calling the *m* diversity relationships.

C. The Factor of Distance

In both our lemma of Section I and in our analogue of Section II we have stressed the importance of the factor of distance, since it takes work to move masses over distance and, according to our theory, work is minimized.

1. The P/D Relationship. To my knowledge, E. G. Ravenstein [21] in 1885 was the first to notice that a population center attracts migrants from other centers in relation to their values of P/D—that is, in proportion to their populations when divided by their respective distances to the attracting population center—and sends them forth again according to the same rate: viz. (his 2nd law): ". . . migrants enumerated in a certain centre of absorption will consequently grow less with the distance * and proportionately to the native population which furnishes them"; and conversely (his 3rd law), "the process of dispersion is the inverse of that of absorption and exhibits similar features." Ravenstein's formulations about the effect of distance have clearly had a profound influence upon many subsequent studies in many different aspects of human social behavior.

Thus, Professor John Quincy Stewart [23] of Princeton University observed that the older "national" universities (i.e., Princeton, Massachusetts Institute of Technology, Harvard) attracted their students from different states according to the white P populations of the states when divided by the D distance of the state from the university in question—or according to P/D. He observed, however, that the correlation applied only within the United States and not to Mexico and Canada. This limitation to the correlation is quite understandable, for reasons that we shall present shortly. Although we cannot tarry longer with Dr. Stewart's observation, let us briefly submit by way of rationalization that, in general, universities seek students and students seek universities, just as all tools seek jobs and all jobs seek tools. Moreover, Dr. Stewart's observed relationship, like Ravenstein's and others [24] that relate to distance, in my opinion consists of at least two factors that involve work. *First,* there is the work of finding out about the university at all, which is not different from the general *work of gaining information* about any other kinds of goods and services at a distance. *Second,* there is the actual work of going to and from the university, which obviously in-

* Strictly considered, Ravenstein did not specify the precise function of distance by which migrants grow less. The function in question was precisely specified in similar problems by William J. Reilly [22] and by J. Q. Stewart, *vide infra.*

creases with D distance. But since this second factor of distance is by now quite obvious, let us concentrate our attention upon the first factor—*the general economy of gaining information about events at a distance.*

We previously pointed out that the probability of finding anything from a D distance is inversely proportional to D by a precise geometric probability (in the sense that the angle subtended at a point by a given disc is essentially inversely proportional to D distance to that point; nor is the situation altered by substituting D work-distance). This applies not only to students' finding universities, and to universities' finding students, it also applies to finding grandpapa's mislaid spectacles and to finding anything else. In short, it is basic to the acquisition of information about things at a distance. And since, on the whole, information about conditions and events at a distance is prerequisite to a deliberate movement thither (or farther thence), the probability of gaining information about conditions and events at a D distance is obviously a vital factor in a great many problems that involve movement.

The economy of gaining information at a distance is perhaps nowhere more readily understandable than in the phenomenon of a newspaper which both (1) gleans information about events at varying D distances, which it prints (cf. Chapter Five), and (2) sends its printed information forth to persons at varying D distances. Here clearly both in the (1) gleaning of information, and in the (2) purveying of it in printed form, we are dealing with the above-mentioned factor of a probability that is inversely related to D distance. Yet how will this factor manifest itself objectively in a newspaper?

Restricting our argument for convenience to the gleaning of information about human events that occur within the social system—and thereby excluding information about purely physical phenomena, like earthquakes and solar eclipses, and also about international events and discoveries (like a new scientific cure or principle) that are anational—we can see that the probability of occurrence of a human event of "newspaper value" in a community of P population size is directly proportional to P, if we assume that all persons in the system are equally likely to produce a human event of "newspaper value." Yet, as we know, the probability of finding out about it at a D distance is inversely proportional to D. Hence, theoretically, the y number of news items that are printed in any newspaper over a long interval of measurement about events that happened in a P community at a D distance will tend to be directly proportional to P, and inversely proportional to D, or, in equation form, $y = P/D$. (This equation is obviously corollary to our Eq. (9–8a) in Section II.) This equation can be tested empirically by counting the y number of different news items in a newspaper that reported events which occurred in an arbitrary set of communities whose populations are P_a, P_b, P_c . . . which are located at distances D_a, D_b, D_c. . . . For, theoretically, the y number of items from each community should be directly proportional to P_a/D_a, P_b/D_b, P_c/D_c. . . .

In Fig. 9–10 are presented the results of an examination of the y number of different news items that referred to events with datelines in 48 arbitrary cities in the U. S. A. as reported on pages 2, 3, 4, and 5 of *The Chicago Tribune* for the period from January, 1937 through April, 1940, with the exception of November, 1939, which was missing from the files of the Harvard College Library which were consulted for this purpose. The tabulation of the items according to datelines was generously undertaken by some of my students.[25]

In Fig. 9–10 the *y* number of news items is measured logarithmically on the ordinate against the value of P/D of each community, multiplied by

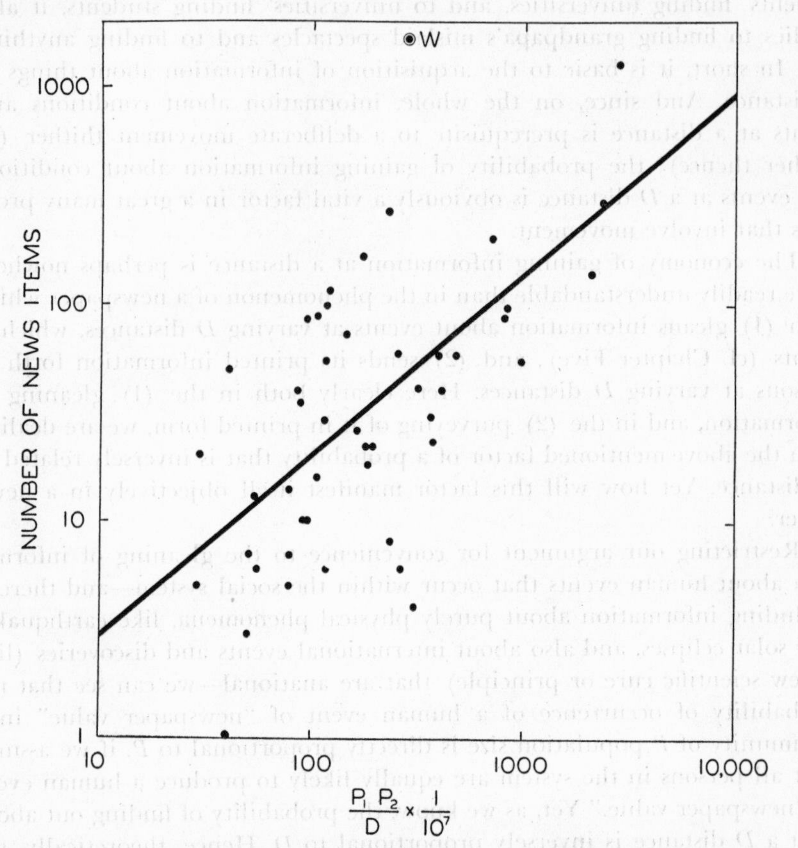

Fig. 9–10. Number of different news items in *The Chicago Tribune* (*W* is the dateline of Washington, D. C.).

the constant population of Chicago (or $P_1 \cdot P_2/D$), which is measured logarithmically on the abscissa. (The value, $P_1 \cdot P_2/D$, which was selected to facilitate comparison with other sets of data, does not alter our argument because we have merely multiplied by a constant.)

The general rectilinearity of the data of Fig. 9–10 is obvious, except for the point marked *W*, which refers to the number of news items that had Washington, D. C. as a dateline. The reason for this particular deviation may be that in many cases Washington merely served as a clearing house during those troublous times for events that happened elsewhere—with the result that the Washington dateline was often misleading.

In any event, the slope of the best straight line, by least squares, of the data *with* Washington is $0.83 \pm .51$ and this is the line drawn (i.e., $\log y = 0.83 \log x - .37$). *Without* Washington the slope drops to $0.80 \pm .45$. In view of the sizes of the respective errors, either slope is a fair approximation of the theoretically anticipated $+1.00$ slope. Hence, the data of Fig. 9–10 confirm our hypothesis.

In Fig. 9–11 is presented another set of data which refers to a particular class of news items, *obituaries,* that were printed on the page opposite to the editorial page on weekdays, and on the two pages of obituaries of the Sunday edition of the *New York Times* during the odd months of 1938,

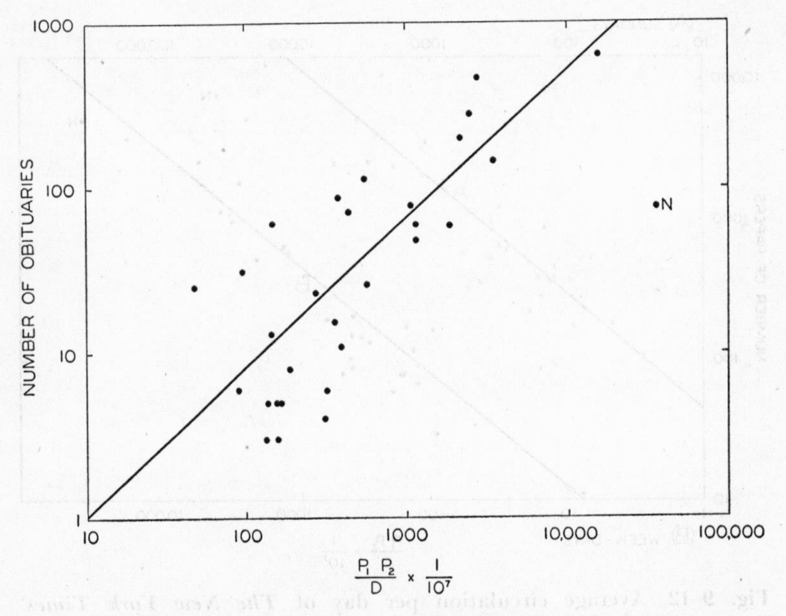

Fig. 9–11. Number of obituaries in *The New York Times* (*N* represents Newark, New Jersey).

with the exception of July, and the odd months of 1939 and 1940, and January, 1941, as disclosed by the same students who tabulated the preceding set of data. Only obituaries with datelines for 30 arbitrary cities were taken, with the place of the death being assumed to be that of the dateline. The *y* number of obituaries are plotted against $P_1 \cdot P_2/D$ for New York, doubly logarithmically, as indicated.[26]

The general rectilinearity of the points, with the exception of the point for Newark, N. J., marked *N,* is obvious. (Newark may have been an unhappy choice since some of its population may have died in New York hospitals nearby, and been locally reported without dateline.) The best straight line fitted to the data by least squares *with* Newark has a positive slope of $0.71 \pm .46$, which is a legitimate though not a comfortably close fit to our theoretical value of $+1.00$ slope. On the other hand, the best straight line *without* Newark has a $+0.90$ slope $\pm .43$, which may be viewed as an acceptable approximation to the expected slope. This slope is that of the line drawn (i.e., $\log y = 0.90 \log x - .87$).* Fig. 9–11, therefore, also confirms our hypothesis.

The hypothesis can be tested further on news items in other newspapers, and on other particular classes of news items.

Having now shown in the above two figures that the frequency distribution of news items in newspapers follows our P/D hypothesis, let us turn to the case of the circulation of the newspapers themselves which, theoretically, should also follow the same equation. For, as we know, one way of finding out about what is happening in a community is to subscribe to a newspaper that is published there. The probability of anyone's doing

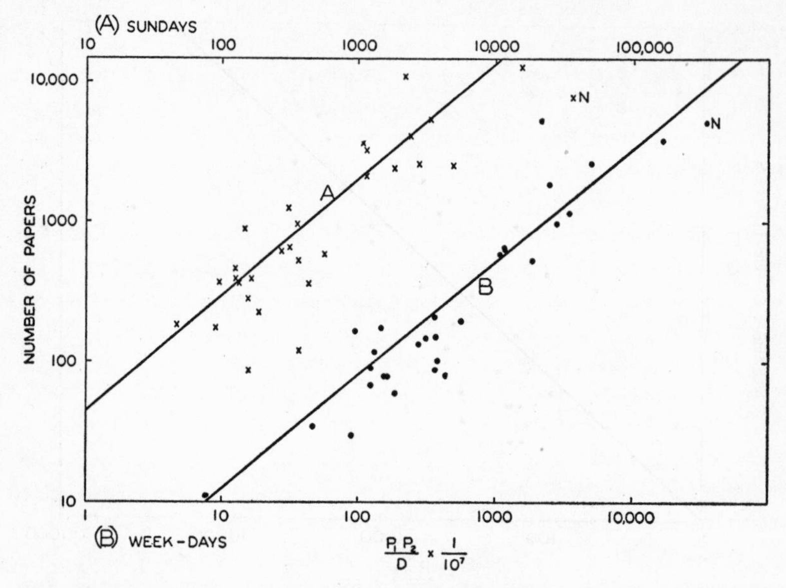

Fig. 9–12. Average circulation per day of *The New York Times* (*A*, Sunday circulation; *B*, weekday circulation).

so at a community of P population at a D distance is theoretically proportional to P/D.

In Fig. 9–12 we present data from the Audit Bureau of Circulation for the circulation of the *New York Times* in the same set of cities as in the preceding Fig. 9–11, for the (*A*) average Sunday circulation, and for the (*B*) average weekday circulation during the 12-month period ending September 30, 1941.[27]

Both the *A* and *B* sets of data are rectilinear. For *A* the slope is $0.73 \pm .32$ with Newark (marked *N*), and $0.83 \pm .30$ *without* Newark. For *B* the slope is $0.80 \pm .44$ with Newark (a fair approximation to 1.00), and $0.84 \pm .45$ *without* Newark. A reason for this deviation of Newark may be that persons

* In the original publication, the y total *lengths* of obituaries of the 30 cities was also presented. These are not reproduced here because the average *length* of obituaries is *not* correlated with differences in P, or D, or P/D. For Dr. Henry Dyer's calculation of r for correlation between *number of items* and their *total* lengths ($r = 0.97$, or 94% of the variance in common) see original publication.

living in Newark but working in New York, which is only a dozen odd miles distant, may buy their *Times* in New York.

There are further corroborative data,[28] already published, for the circulation of *The Chicago Tribune,* in which the circulation is broken down into zones of increasing distance from Chicago for the purpose of studying the effect of delayed delivery upon sales at a distance; the data do not merit being presented again here.* Later under a separate heading, *D,* the *k constant,* we shall present many further confirmatory observations of the circulations of newspapers.

But though the sheer probability of learning of events of "newspaper value" in a *P* population at a *D* distance is an important factor in understanding the dynamics of the circulation of information, let us not forget that there is the further factor of the comparative value of known events at varying *D* distances. Thus, as a given opportunity is situated ever farther away, it becomes ever less valuable because of the increasing work of getting to it; and the same applies to an event of negative news value that is threatening. If we listen to proverbs, "a boil on your own neck will worry you more than a famine in China"; yet as your location is ever nearer to China, the comparative magnitude of your worry about the famine will increase proportionately—even to the point that the boil is forgotten. The same applies to the comparative proximity of known human events: a murderer at large seems to be increasingly less dangerous as his presumable distance increases. Yet, in general, the probability of occurrence of a particular kind of event increases with *P* population; and so, too, the probability that anyone will find the particular event of positive or negative value.

The basic incentive for gaining information about events anywhere is, theoretically, the need to minimize the effort of one's living, either by procuring an easier situation or by avoiding a more difficult one. In either case the increasing work of an increasing intervening *D* work-distance is obvious. Indeed, were we to visualize the circulation of information as a vast telephone or telegraph network over which news is continually "flowing" —not unlike what is actually the case with the various press associations— we could visualize the value of news as decreasing, or "wearing out" with distance as it flows along the wires. Indeed, if a wire ran to each person who both gives news and receives news—just like an actual telephone sys-

* Moreover J. Q. Stewart reported in 1942 [29] the observation that the circulation of a St. Louis newspaper in counties in Missouri and Illinois followed the *P/D* relationship, though (1) he noted a limitation to the circulation at 120–160 miles which he ascribed to competition from Chicago and Kansas City newspapers, and though (2) he noted that "close at hand the newspaper, in order to conform to the inverse distance rule, as calibrated by distant sales, would have to sell considerably more than one copy per family. Here we have a 'saturation' or 'clean-out' effect the necessity of which is obvious." As to his first (1) limitation we believe that he was striking the outer limit of the particular newspaper's circulation domain; as to his second (2) limitation, our own observations reported below under the heading *D, the k constant,* do not confirm it. Theoretically, the newspapers from Chicago and Kansas City were competing with the unnamed St. Louis newspaper right in St. Louis itself. In 1929 William J. Reilly noticed this general relationship in the circulation of newspapers in Texas from a study of the data of the Audit Bureau of Circulation *(op. cit.)*.

tem—the message should theoretically flow in number according to the P/D relationship, or better still, according to the $P_1 \cdot P_2/D$ relationship which, as we shall see in our following section, is very much the case.

Before turning to our following section let us first present a set of P/D data that refer only circuitously to the circulation of information. In Fig. 9–13 are presented the percentages of total Jordan Marsh charge accounts (on the ordinate) in 96 different cities and towns in Massachusetts, New Hampshire, and Maine whose values of P/D (absolute D) are plotted on the abscissa.[30] Jordan Marsh in Boston is the largest department store in

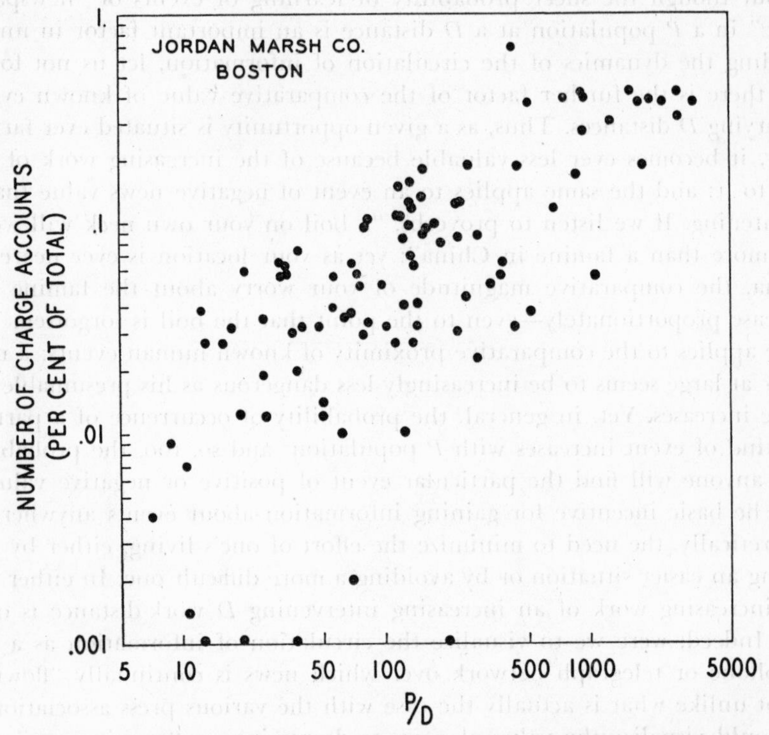

Fig. 9–13. Charge accounts of Jordan Marsh Co., Boston, in 96 cities and towns in Massachusetts, New Hampshire, and Maine, with their percentages of total charge accounts plotted against the communities' values of *P/D*.

New England, to whose generous kindness I owe the data. These points fairly approximate a + 1.00 slope, with the variation accountable to some extent by the fact that some of the communities had accounts of summer visitors whose populations were not enumerated in the Census.*

Naturally, the Jordan Marsh accounts imply the sales of goods whose kinds and costs must somehow be made known through the circulation of

* William J. Reilly in 1929 studied empirically the competition of two cities, P_1 and P_2, for the retail trade of the territory between them, and observed a "general formula for the law of retail gravitation" (i.e., directly proportional to $P \cdot P$ and inversely proportional to D^2 as estimated by the mode of his observations). In this connection see our discussion of *domains* below.

information—in this case, advertising, which, although a special field, does not necessarily have a special set of dynamics divorced from those under discussion.

As with the Jordan Marsh data, so too presumably with the data for other stores, services, and manufactures. For that matter, the P/D relationship should be discernible in the places of origin of the guests of a hotel register, or the frequenters of a bar.

2. The $P_1 \cdot P_2/D$ Relationship. The preceding P/D relationship is obviously only a corollary of the $P_1 \cdot P_2/D$ relationship of Eq. (9–8a) of Sec-

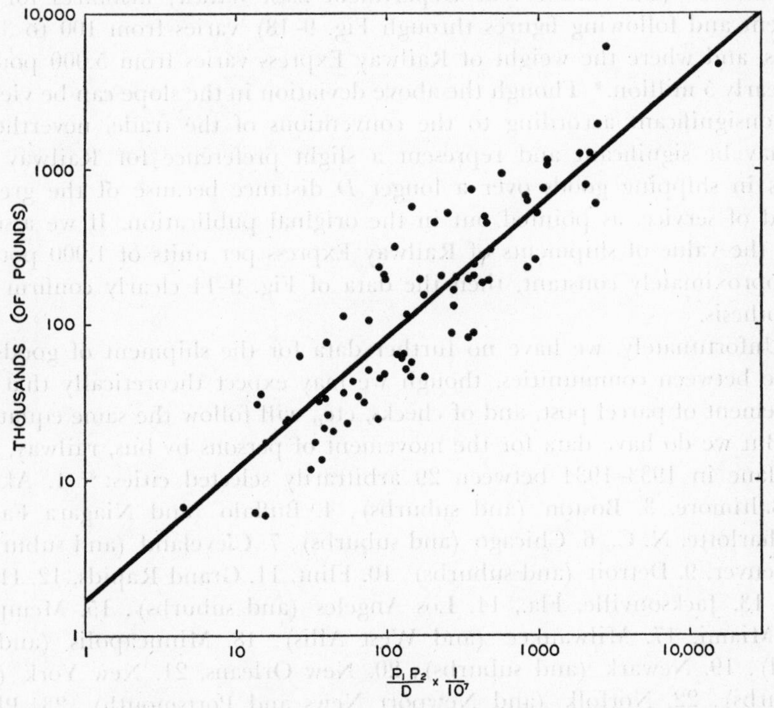

Fig. 9–14. Railway express. The movement by weight (less carload lots) between 13 arbitrary cities in the U. S. A., May 1939.

tion II. This relationship goes a little further than Ravenstein's original formulations in that it specifies a C constant for the population of the entire social system, as we noted in our argument in Section II. Though this argument need not be repeated here, we remember that it referred to the *values* of goods that are interchanged between any two communities, P_1 and P_2, separated by an intervening shortest D work-distance; it also referred to the y number of porters who carried the goods hither and thither in the interchange.

In Fig. 9–14 are presented the data for the movement of goods by Railway Express [31] in units of one thousand pounds (in less than carload lots) in May, 1939 between thirteen arbitrarily selected cities in the United States—or 78 pairs of cities (i.e., 1. Boston, 2. Buffalo, 3. Chicago, 4. Cleveland, 5. Detroit, 6. Los Angeles, 7. Milwaukee, 8. New York, 9. Philadelphia,

10. Pittsburgh, 11. St. Louis, 12. San Francisco, 13. Washington, D. C.) as generously made available to me by President L. O. Head of the Railway Express Agency. The y number of pounds is plotted logarithmically on the ordinate against the logarithm of $P_1 \cdot P_2/D$ on the abscissa.

The rectilinearity of the data is unmistakable. The line drawn was calculated by least squares and has a + 0.85 + 0.31 slope (i.e., $\log y = 0.8472 \log x + .2157$). With *P.E.* of .2, the value, 0.85, may be viewed as a nonsignificant variation from our theoretically expected + 1.00 slope in a set of data of four variables in which P varies from 500,000 to 7.5 million, and in which D (the official War Department *least railway distances* for the present and following figures through Fig. 9–18) varies from 100 to 3,000 miles, and where the weight of Railway Express varies from 5,000 pounds to nearly 5 million.* Though the above deviation in the slope can be viewed as nonsignificant according to the conventions of the trade, nevertheless it may be significant and represent a slight preference for Railway Express in shipping goods over a longer D distance because of the greater speed of service, as pointed out in the original publication. If we assume that the value of shipments of Railway Express per units of 1,000 pounds is approximately constant, then the data of Fig. 9–14 clearly confirm our hypothesis.

Unfortunately, we have no further data for the shipment of goods by value between communities, though we may expect theoretically that the movement of parcel post, and of checks, etc., will follow the same equation.

But we do have data for the movement of persons by bus, railway, and airplane in 1933–1934 between 29 arbitrarily selected cities: [32] 1. Akron, 2. Baltimore, 3. Boston (and suburbs), 4. Buffalo (and Niagara Falls), 5. Charlotte, N. C., 6. Chicago (and suburbs), 7. Cleveland (and suburbs), 8. Denver, 9. Detroit (and suburbs), 10. Flint, 11. Grand Rapids, 12. Houston, 13. Jacksonville, Fla., 14. Los Angeles (and suburbs), 15. Memphis, 16. Miami, 17. Milwaukee (and West Allis), 18. Minneapolis (and St. Paul), 19. Newark (and suburbs), 20. New Orleans, 21. New York (and suburbs), 22. Norfolk (and Newport News and Portsmouth), 23. Philadelphia (and suburbs), 24. Pittsburgh (and McKeesport), 25. St. Louis (and East St. Louis), 26. San Diego, 27. San Francisco (and suburbs), 28. South Bend, 29. Washington, D. C.

These 29 arbitrarily selected cities—or about 400 pairs of cities—to which our data on travel by bus, railway, and airplane refer, vary sufficiently in size (roughly from 100,000 to 7½ millions) and are sufficiently scattered over the United States to constitute a fair sample. Smaller communities would not have shown any passengers in some cases during the comparatively short interval of measurement (and when in the below data that happened to be the case, no value is given in the figure).

On the other hand, the above entities included in some cases suburban populations whose sizes were impossible to disclose. Hence, in our following figures the values of P refer to the populations of cities *exclusive* of

* On the other hand, the recurrence of this particular deviation from 1.00 in samples of several different types of material suggests that the deviation may very well be significant.

those within parentheses above. This will introduce a certain amount of variation in our data which will be neither favorable nor unfavorable to our hypothesis; yet because of the ambiguity of our P values, no lines were calculated. All data were taken from *Appendix I* of the *Passenger Traffic Report* prepared by the Section of Transportation Service under the office of the Federal Co-ordinator of Transportation. All data refer to

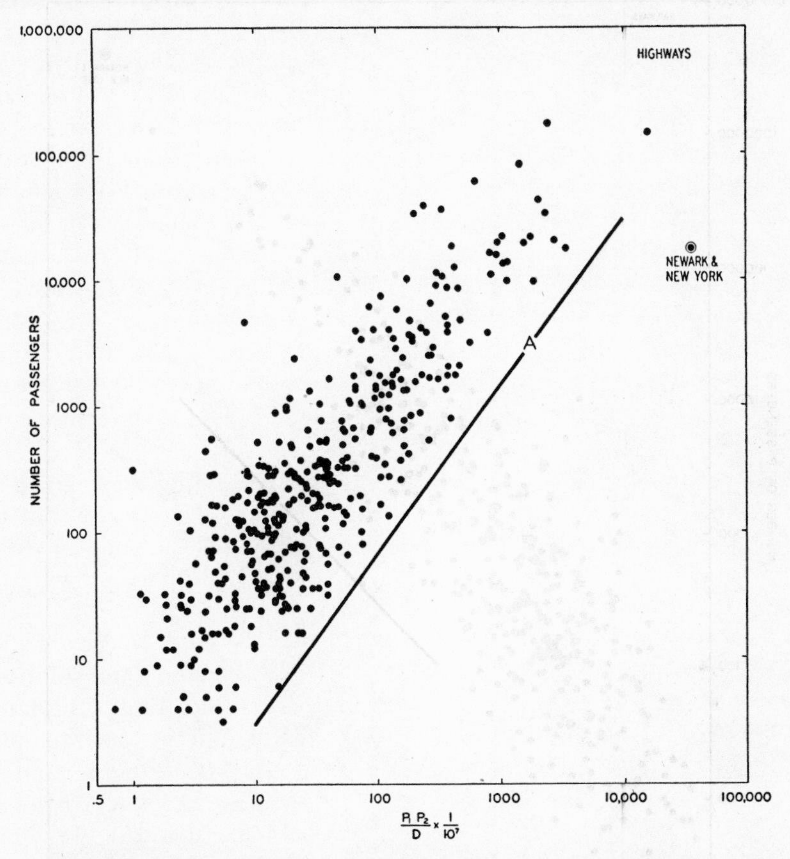

Fig. 9–15. Bus passengers. Movement of persons by highway bus travel between 29 arbitrary cities during intervals of measurement in 1933 and 1934. Line A has an ideal 1.25 slope.

tickets (single and round trip) sold during the periods of measurement, and not to tickets actually collected, which we should prefer.

In Fig. 9–15 are presented doubly logarithmically, as indicated, the y number of bus passengers that travelled over the highways between the above 29 communities during December, 1933 and July, 1934. The line, *A,* with an ideal slope of 1.25, which has been added to aid the reader's eye, represents about the *upper* limit of the slope of the distribution which, in view of the considerable amount of variation, is quite consistent with our theoretically expected 1.00 slope (the reader may cover up *A* and draw a line of his own). In any event the rectilinearity of the data—*extending over 5 logarithm cycles*—is unmistakable. The position of the point for

Newark–New York is understandable if we remember the excellent competitive rail service between these two cities. The factor of seasonal variation is discussed somewhat in the previous publication.

In Fig. 9–16 are presented the data for railway passengers of all classes between the above cities during one month in each quarter of 1934 and

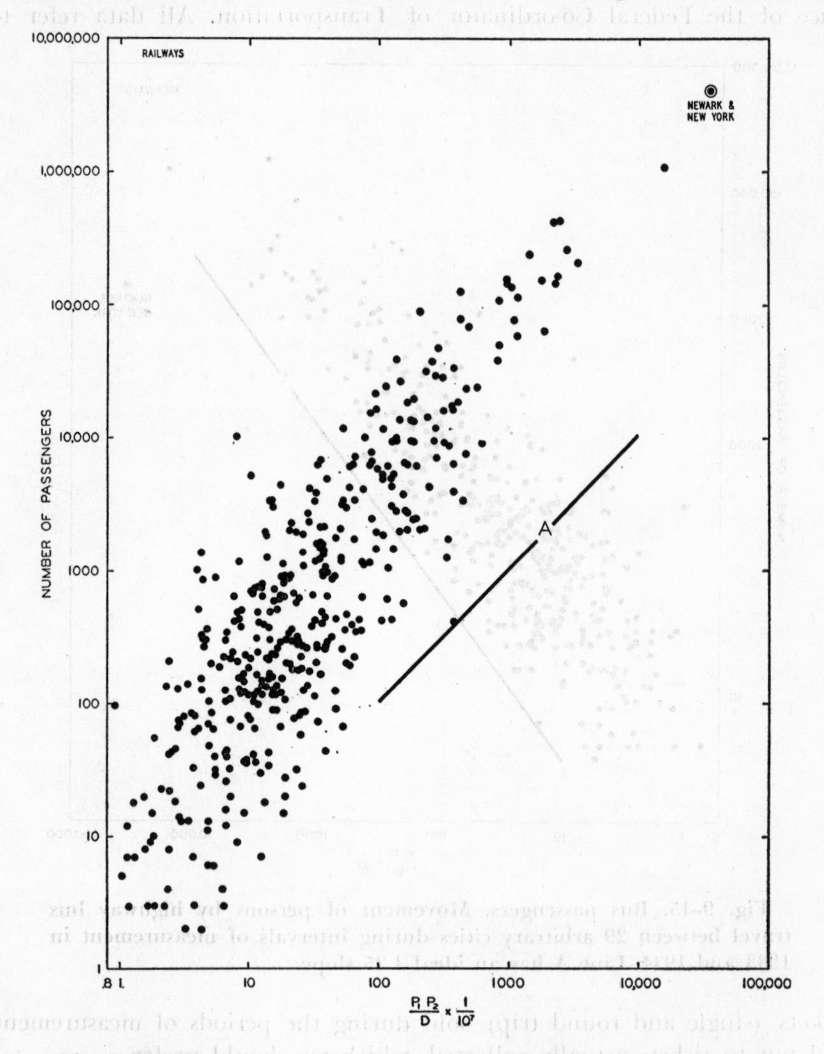

Fig. 9–16. The number of passengers travelling by railways between 29 arbitrary cities during one month in each quarter of 1933 (line A has an ideal 1.00 slope).

plotted as indicated, with the line, *A,* added with the theoretically anticipated ideal slope of + 1.00 in order to aid the reader's eye.

The existence of a correlation between our factors in Fig. 9–16 is unmistakable. Equally unmistakable is its divergence from the expected slope (since the slope of the data is much nearer 1.50). This divergence is significant for us (as well as for the Federal Co-ordinator of Transportation, who apparently undertook this study in order to ascertain what was wrong with the railroads in the 1930's). After all, there was no such marked divergence from the slope of 1.00 with the highway bus data of Fig. 9–15.

This divergence of Fig. 9–16 means that as $P_1 \cdot P_2/D$ increases, the number of passengers increases by approximately the 1.5 power thereof. In short, there is a systematic premium upon shorter D distances, since the same 29 cities are used throughout with D's of varying sizes.

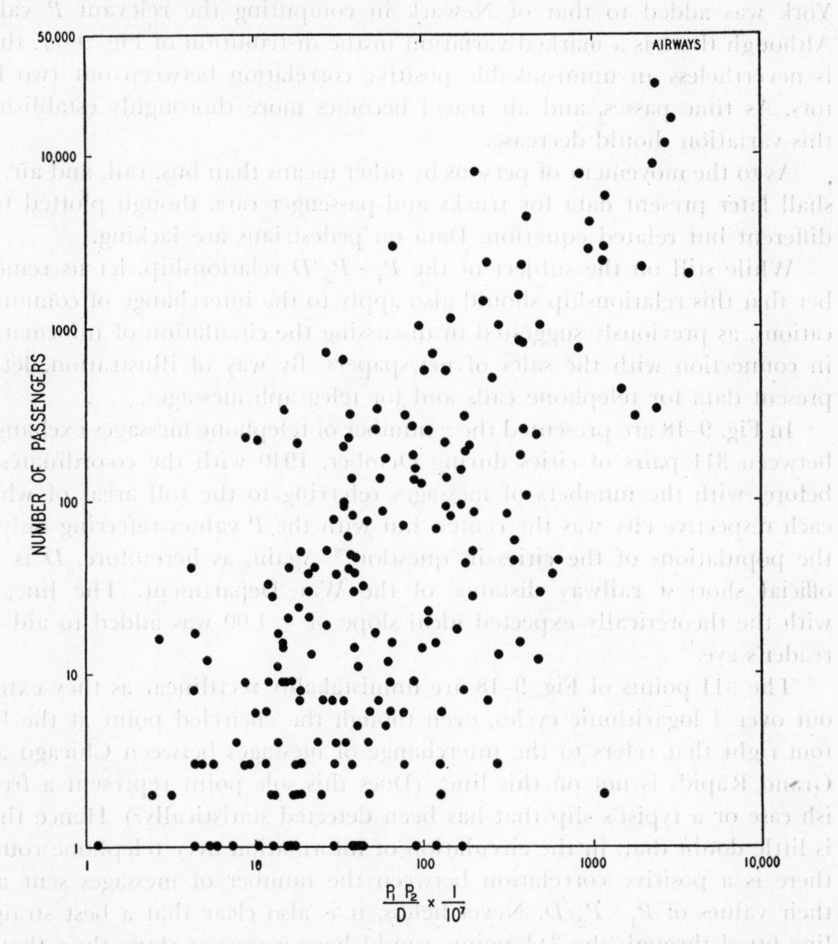

Fig. 9–17. The number of passengers travelling by airway between arbitrary cities in 1933.

This systematic premium upon small D distances may mean, in view of the Pareto income curve to be discussed in Chapter Eleven, which presumably applies to the distribution of incomes within cities, that railway fares, in comparison with bus fares, were so high that a logarithmically decreasing number of persons out of those that travelled *could* afford to take trips of increasing D distance. In other words, as D increased, the resulting absolute increase in cost prohibited an ever increasing percentage of persons from travelling by rail. This reason, which is sufficient, may explain why the cheaper bus travel approximated our theoretical value more closely. For further possible reasons, the reader is referred to the original publication.

In Fig. 9–17 are presented rather for completeness than for decisive information the data for railways during all of 1933 (when commercial air travel was scarcely in its infancy) for such pairs of our 29 cities as had air passengers. Since New York's airport is in Newark, the population of New York was added to that of Newark in computing the relevant P value. Although there is a marked variation in the distribution of Fig. 9–17, there is nevertheless an unmistakable positive correlation between our two factors. As time passes, and air travel becomes more thoroughly established, this variation should decrease.

As to the movement of persons by other means than bus, rail, and air, we shall later present data for trucks and passenger cars, though plotted to a different but related equation. Data on pedestrians are lacking.

While still on the subject of the $P_1 \cdot P_2/D$ relationship, let us remember that this relationship should also apply to the interchange of communications, as previously suggested in discussing the circulation of information in connection with the sales of newspapers. By way of illustration, let us present data for telephone calls and for telegraph messages.

In Fig. 9–18 are presented the y number of telephone messages exchanged between 311 pairs of cities during October, 1940 with the co-ordinates as before, with the numbers of messages referring to the toll areas of which each respective city was the center, but with the P values referring only to the populations of the cities in question.* Again, as heretofore, D is the official shortest railway distance of the War Department. The line, A, with the theoretically expected ideal slope of $+ 1.00$ was added to aid the reader's eye.[33]

The 311 points of Fig. 9–18 are unmistakably rectilinear as they extend out over 4 logarithmic cycles, even though the encircled point at the bottom right that refers to the interchange of messages between Chicago and Grand Rapids is not on this line. (Does this sole point represent a freakish case or a typist's slip that has been detected statistically?) Hence there is little doubt that, in the circulation of information over telephone routes, there is a positive correlation between the number of messages sent and their values of $P_1 \cdot P_2/D$. Nevertheless, it is also clear that a best straight line fitted through the 311 points would have a steeper slope than that of 1.00 represented by A.

The reason for this deviation in slope may conceivably be connected with the fact that the number of messages refer to the population of toll areas which are larger than the values of P taken; on this point only more precise data can give clarification. Yet the deviation may also result from

---

*** Akron, Baltimore, Boston, Buffalo, Chicago, Cleveland, Denver, Detroit, Flint, Grand Rapids, Houston, Jacksonville, Los Angeles, Memphis, Miami, Milwaukee. Minneapolis, Newark, New Orleans, New York City, Norfolk, Philadelphia, Pittsburgh, San Diego, San Francisco, South Bend, St. Louis, and Washington, D. C. For some pairs of cities information was unavailable.**

the distribution of incomes according to the Pareto curve, as mentioned above in connection with the railway passenger data of Fig. 9–16. For, after all, if the cost of telephone calls increases with D distance, then a logarithmically decreasing number of persons can afford to pay for the longer calls, as would not be true if we were dealing with the case of first class mail for which, alas, quantitative information is not available.

This very deviation in the telephone data may be instructive for several reasons. In the first place, if our Pareto explanation be valid,* the

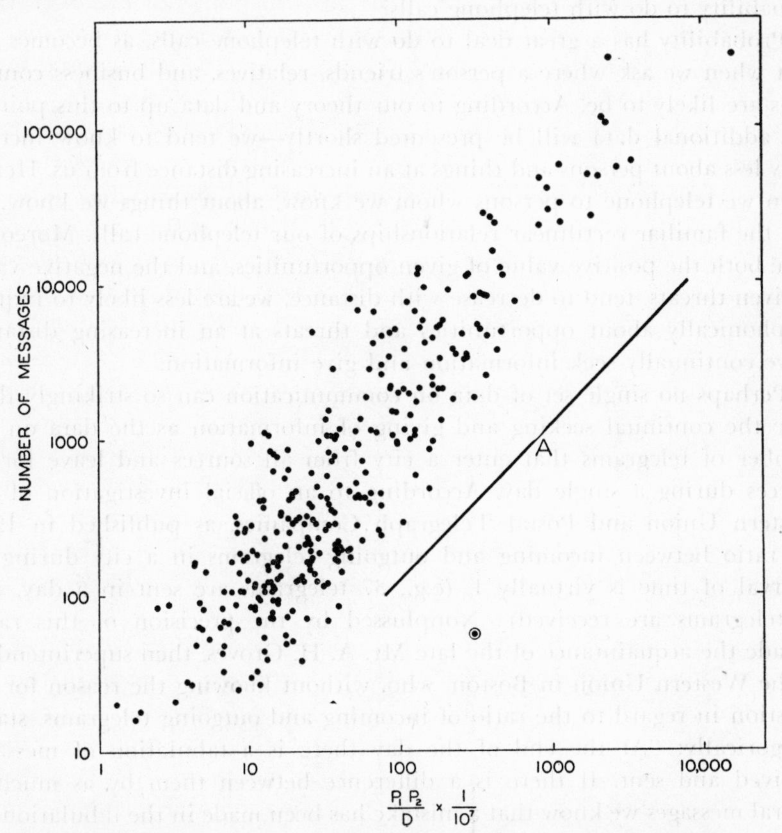

Fig. 9–18. Number of telephone messages interchanged between 311 arbitrary pairs of cities in 1940 (line A has an ideal 1.00 slope).

deviation illustrates how an additional factor can modify the distribution in a quite orderly manner; moreover, it is of about the size to be expected; in that event our $P_1 \cdot P_2/D$ relationship provides a subtle measuring rod. In the second place, this deviation, like the previous ones, forcibly reminds us of the fact that further economic factors may destroy both the slope and the rectilinearity of the distribution.†

* See Chapter Eleven for discussion of income distributions with supporting data.

† The case is analogous to the law of three-dimensional gravitation in physics, whose rectilinearity and slope can be disturbed by other forces (e.g., leaves rise in the wind). Not until one has worked out theoretically in advance what is to be expected can one appropriately apply a *chi*-square test for the goodness of a fit.

The data on telephone messages in Fig. 9–18 are likely to be perplexing if we view them apart from the other data in this chapter and merely concentrate upon that aspect of our theory which refers to the probability of finding things at a distance. For, after all, in actual practice we *deliberately* make telephone calls to *definite* persons whose names, telephone numbers, and even addresses, we either know or ascertain in advance. More specifically, we deliberately call our friends, our relatives, our business connections—we do not pick telephone numbers at random.[34] What, then, has probability to do with telephone calls?

Probability has a great deal to do with telephone calls, as becomes evident when we ask where a person's friends, relatives, and business connections are likely to be. According to our theory and data up to this point—and additional data will be presented shortly—we tend to know increasingly less about persons and things at an increasing distance from us. Hence, when we telephone to persons whom we know, about things we know, we find the familiar rectilinear relationships of our telephone calls. Moreover, since both the positive value of given opportunities, and the negative value of given threats, tend to decrease with distance, we are less likely to inquire telephonically about opportunities and threats at an increasing distance, as we continually seek information and give information.

Perhaps no single set of data on communication can so strikingly illustrate the continual seeking and giving of information as the data on the number of telegrams that enter a city from all sources and leave for all sources during a single day. According to an official investigation of the Western Union and Postal Telegraph Companies, as published in 1909, the ratio between incoming and outgoing telegrams in a city during an interval of time is virtually 1 (e.g., 37 telegrams are sent in a day, and 37 telegrams are received). Nonplussed by the precision of this ratio, I made the acquaintance of the late Mr. A. H. Groves, then superintendent of the Western Union in Boston, who, without knowing the reason for my question in regard to the ratio of incoming and outgoing telegrams, stated categorically: "At the end of the day there is a tabulation of messages received and sent. If there is a difference between them by as much as several messages we know that a mistake has been made in the tabulation."[35]

These telegram data, which should have a counterpart in incoming and outgoing letters even in units of mail bags, suggest that P populations are both the sources of news in proportion to their P sizes, and also the recipients of news in the same proportion. Or, in terms of the artisan of our Tool Analogy in Chapter Three, a community consists of a P population of artisans whose existence and activities are of interest to others, whether as competitors or as allies, and who in turn are interested in the existence and doings of others in the same capacities. Moreover, according to our statistics and according to the postulates of our lemma, people tend to be more or less equally interesting and equally curious—at least on the average in large groups.

Yet our telegraph data, like our telephone and newspaper data, are understandable only when viewed against the entire background of our hypothesis that governs not only the circulation of information, but also the circulation of goods, services, and persons—all these being dynamically interrelated.

Naturally, the $P_1 \cdot P_2/D$ relationship, like the P/D relationship, refers only to a condition of static equilibrium and makes no provision for determining the P sizes of cities, their intervening D distances, and their growth. These static relationships, therefore, are secondary to the primary and more far-reaching relationships of Eqs. (9–1a) and (9–2a) which define the area of the terrain to whose organization the secondary equations apply.*

3. Trips, Spacings, and Density of Communities. In elaborating our hypothesis of the Minimum Equation, we argued that the number, sizes,

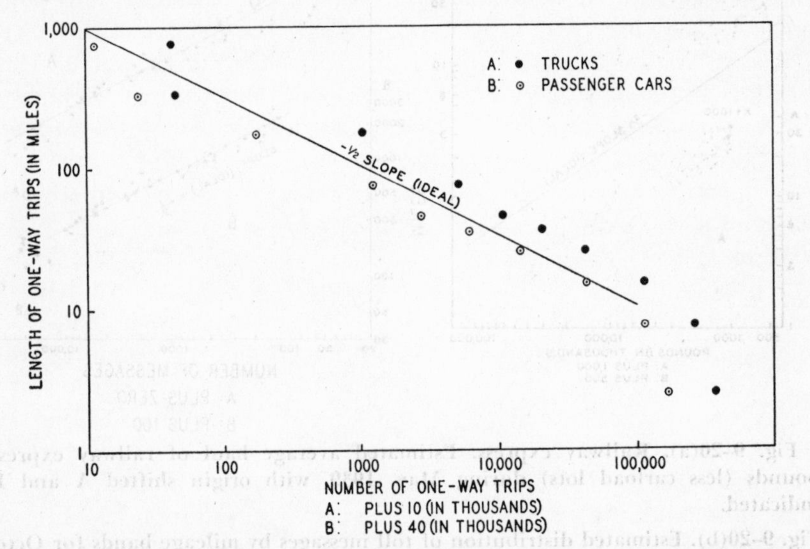

Fig. 9–19. Trucks and passenger cars: the number of one-way trips of like length.

interspacings, and densities of the n communities of the theoretical system should be such that the N number of "trips" of our imaginary porters —or any other class of movement in respect of whose costs and availability all persons would be equal—would be according to Eq. (9–9a).† In the case of the United States, the N number of trips of like D distance should be approximately proportional to the inverse square of D, after an appropriate shift of the origin (i.e., $N + \alpha$).

In Fig. 9–19 are presented the $(N + \alpha)$ number of one-way trips of A trucks and B passenger cars originating in 11 widely scattered states in

* For that reason the interchange of goods and persons between communities separated by a national boundary will not be at the same rate as between communities within the same nation. This explains the limiting effect of national boundaries upon the place of origin of students in American Universities as first observed by Dr. J. Q. Stewart; McGill will draw Canadian students more than Princeton, which in turn will exceed McGill in drawing American students.

† Closely related theoretically to this equation is Dr. N. J. Fine's analysis of what he calls "The Jeep Problem" (cf. *The American Mathematical Monthly,* Vol. 54, Jan. 1947, 24–34). I am grateful to Prof. J. L. Walsh for calling my attention to this article.

1936, as measured by the U. S. Bureau of Public Roads.[36] The A data are based upon an analysis of 22,268,882 one-way trips; the B data on that of 42,407,204 one-way trips. The need for positive shifts of the origin for the N number of trips was explained when discussing Eq. (9–9a). The data are plotted doubly logarithmically with N number as abscissa, and with D distance as ordinate. The downward concavity at the bottom is the result of two factors: *first,* the b constant of Eq. (9–9a), and *second,* the *slight* positive shift of the y origin that should have been made because the origin of the trips was reckoned at the city limits and not at the city center.

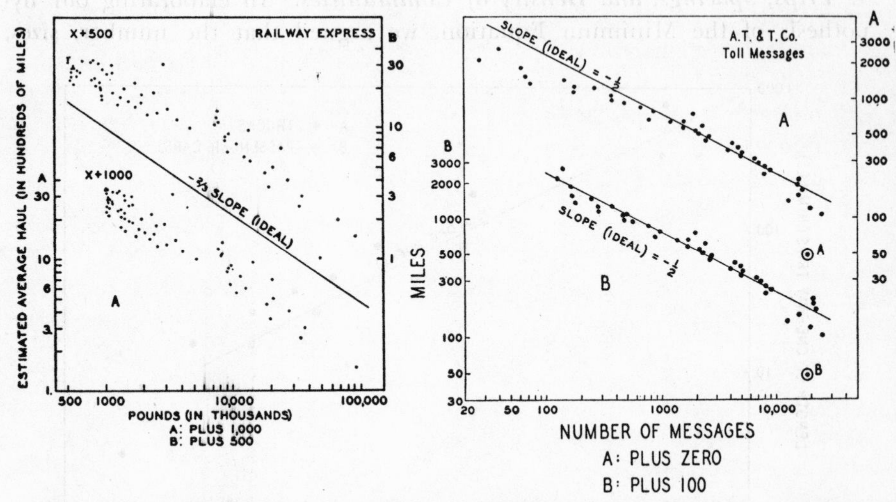

Fig. 9–20(a). Railway express. Estimated average haul of railway express in pounds (less carload lots) during May, 1939, with origin shifted A and B as indicated.

Fig. 9–20(b). Estimated distribution of toll messages by mileage bands for October, 1948 (traffic over A. T. & T. lines only).

The reader can assess for himself how closely all but the respective two lowest points are approximating the theoretically anticipated line of $-\frac{1}{2}$ slope (ideal) that was added for the convenience of comparison.

And let us remember that these data of Fig. 9–19 will be rectilinear, theoretically, only if the n number of communities are interspaced in respect of their P population sizes according to Eq. (9–7a) which is therefore indirectly confirmed by the data of Fig. 9–19.

In Fig. 9–20 are presented the data for Railway Express in pounds (less carload lots) for 1939 in units of 100 miles with the X origin shifted + 1000 for the lower A distribution and + 500 for the upper B distribution. The arbitrary line drawn with an ideal $-\frac{2}{3}$ slope (which to the eye seems to be approximated by these sets of points) indicates that Railway Express is preferred for more distant shipments, as previously suggested when rationalizing the $P_1 \cdot P_2/D$ distribution of the Railway Express data for the thirteen cities discussed in Fig. 9–14. Since the data of Fig. 9–14 are included in those of Fig. 9–20, we can see graphically the close connection between Eqs. (9–8a) and (9–9a).

Intimately connected with the above data on Railway Express are those on the estimated distribution of telephone toll messages by mileage bands for the month of October, 1940, for traffic only over the lines of the American Telephone and Telegraph Company as presented in Fig. 9–20(b).* The *A* data represent the number of messages measured logarithmically on the *X*-axis against the number of miles (class middles) measured logarithmically on the *Y*-axis (scale at right); these data, thus plotted, are not poor approximations of the line drawn through them with an ideal $-\frac{1}{2}$ slope. Yet when these same data are plotted with the origin shifted $+100$ on the *X*-axis, as is the case with the *B* data (scale at left), the points approximate with astonishing closeness the line with the ideal $-\frac{1}{2}$ slope there drawn. The need for the origin shift has been explained previously. The point at the bottom for each set of data (encircled and marked *A* and *B*) for messages from 0 to 96 miles, is obviously untrustworthy, since it does not include local nontoll messages that dynamically belong there.

Perhaps no single set of data so immediately tests our entire hypothesis as these for toll messages, with their close approximation to the "inverse square." For these are calls from one person to another; they tell us where one's friends, the sources of one's supply of goods, and the location of one's customers and clients are likely to be. Our theory extends, of course, to intracity calls, for which data are badly needed. Indeed it exetnds to all communication, even to the interchange of talk at a cocktail party. Incidentally, the above distribution of toll calls seems to presuppose that the communities of like size, etc., are spaced in the manner that we have already discussed theoretically.

Turning now to the question of the spacings of communities of like size, which should follow Eq. (9–7a) and to whose validity our preceding Figs. 9–19 and 9–20 indirectly contributed empirically, the only extensive empiric data of which I am aware are the graphical measurements of the interspacings of communities in South Germany, as made with meticulous care by Dr. Walter Christaller in support of his theory of the central city, and which, when judged by eye, support our present contention.[37] Dr. Christaller's measurements in conjunction with others will be found brilliantly discussed in Dr. Edward Ullman's excellent article.[38]

Turning now to the question of the density of populations, according to our Eq. (9–6a), we refer to the exhaustive original empiric research of Dr. J. Q. Stewart, whose measurements and maps have answered the question of density beyond the peradventure of a doubt, and which certainly confirm our own particular theoretical expectations.[39] In this connection we call attention to Dr. Stewart's ingenious analogue of a "sand-pile citizen," on the basis of which he has constructed an interesting theory of static equilibrium.[40]

---

* These confidential toll data were put at my disposal many years ago by the then Chief Statistician, Mr. S. L. Andrew, under the promise that their source should not be revealed publicly. In August, 1948, Mr. O. C. Richter, the present chief statistician, with the consent of Mr. Andrew, now retired, kindly released me from this promise. I am deeply grateful to these gentlemen, and to Mr. Walter Gifford, for their kindness in helping me with my research.

Before leaving the topic of trips and the spacings and the density of communities, let us reflect that the general theory behind all this intercity movement and the location of populations does not stop at municipal boundaries. Instead our theory applies to intracity conditions as well as to intercity ones, as we shall now see, even though a municipal boundary with the introduction of new sets of municipal rules (ordinances) may slightly influence density, etc., at the actual boundary.

4. On Intracity Conditions. The location and movement of persons within a community are theoretically governed by the same principles that we have been discussing. Since this topic is vast, we shall present only a few measurements which nevertheless will have very extensive theoretical implications.

a. City Traffic. City planners have long known that the density of traffic towards the center of a city is inversely related to the square of the distance to the center, except at the actual center, where the traffic tapers off decidedly[41] (as indeed it would have to, since there would not be sufficient two-dimensional space for the automobiles which, unlike man, can only with difficulty employ the third dimension of a skyscraper).* This traffic-density relationship is confirmed by our own origin-destination studies of the recent official traffic surveys of Denver, Fort Wayne, Kansas City, Milwaukee, New Orleans, Providence, and Tulsa, in which maps are presented for the zones of approximately equal area. For each zone there is given the number of persons who during an interval of measurement set out from it (i.e., origin) in all directions, plus the number of persons who arrived there (i.e., destination) from all directions: hence the term, *origin-destination*. Additional maps were also given for the origins-destinations of passenger automobiles, trucks, and rapid transit passengers. In the light of these data, traffic is unquestionably denser by the inverse square of distance to the center, as originally disclosed with qualifications by the city planners.

But that is not the entire story. For in our theoretical discussion in Section II relative to the magnet analogue, we argued that communities as such would be "attracted" into the city limits where they would become *trading centers*. Without reviewing our then argument, let us recall that these trading centers when measured by the relative density of their traffic (i.e., origin-destination), as well as by other factors mentioned at the time, would be rectilinear according to Eqs. (9–1a) and (9–2a). In other words, hypothetically, if the trading centers of a city were ranked in the order of the decreasing size of their origin-destination traffic, they would follow approximately the proportions of the generalized harmonic series, on the assumption that the relative density of traffic of a trading center is directly indicative of the relative size of the trading center in terms of the number, diversity, and sizes of its stores and business services.

---

* Apparently the number of persons who get on and off an elevator at a given floor of a high building is inversely related to the distance of the floor to the bottom (thereby making the problem of city movement that of a "solid hyperbola"?)[42]

With this theoretical expectation in mind, let us turn again to the above-mentioned traffic surveys whose origin-destination data refer to zones that are for the most part of roughly equal areas, and which therefore can be ranked according to decreasing density with a fair degree of approximation.

In Fig. 9–21 are presented as labelled on doubly arithmetic co-ordinates the various zones ranked in the order of decreasing density of traffic for trucks, passenger cars, and rapid transit passengers respectively for the city of Milwaukee, which is representative of all the traffic surveys studied and

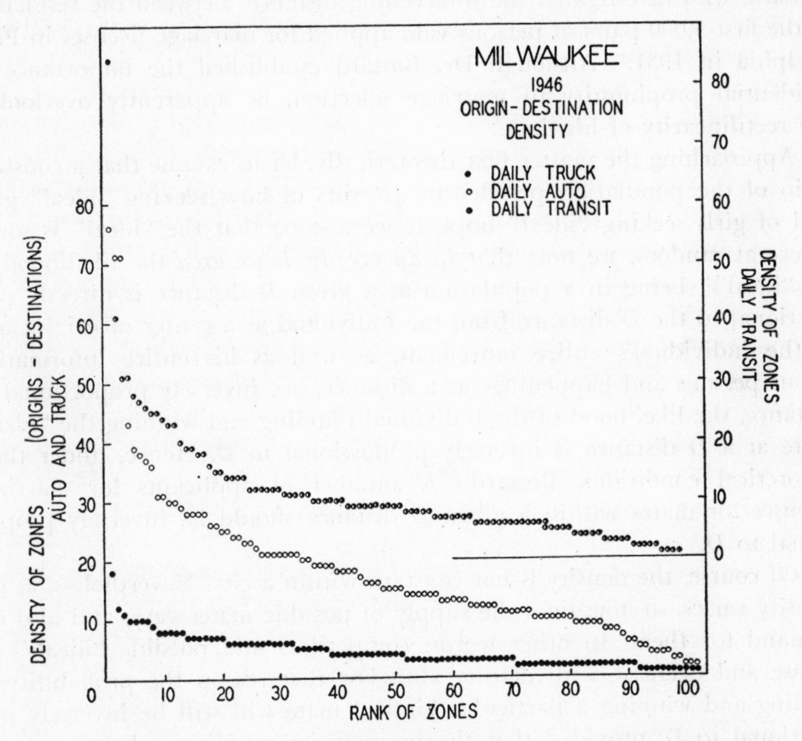

Fig. 9–21. Density of zones in Milwaukee in terms of origin-destination of traffic, with zones ranked in the decreasing order of their density.

which was selected for graphical presentation merely because it was alphabetically the middle one.[43] The "hollow curves" of Fig. 9–21 on doubly arithmetic co-ordinates are not inconsistent with our hypothesis; on doubly logarithmic co-ordinates, however, they are not completely rectilinear, even after shifting the origins, although they are largely so. The differences in constants in the three "hollow curves" are instructive.

The present topic of city traffic can be further explored by studying the number of telephone calls between suburban areas, the number of intracity charge accounts of widely scattered stores, etc., etc. Moreover, its further exploration is recommended for genuinely practical reasons of municipal finance since, for the most part, municipalities derive their income from real estate taxes, which in turn are assessed on the basis of appraisals of real estate including the assessment of land.[44] If land values for commercial purposes decrease logarithmically with distance from the point of 100% traffic in a trading center,* then that fact should be taken into consideration in the assessment of land values if real estate appraisal is to be equitable and objective.

b. Dr. Bossard's Marriage Data. Persons move hither and yon for reasons other than commercial ones, and yet the same principles of economical movement should apply regardless of the motives. To illustrate this point, let us briefly inspect the important measurements of Dr. J. H. S. Bossard, who investigated the intervening distances between the residences of the first 5,000 pairs of persons who applied for marriage licenses in Philadelphia in 1931.[45] Although Dr. Bossard established the importance of residential propinquity in marriage selection, he apparently overlooked the rectilinearity of his data.

Approaching the matter first theoretically, let us assume that a constant ratio of the population per density consists of boys seeking "ideal" girls and of girls seeking "ideal" boys. If we assume that the "ideal" is somewhere at random, we note that *in an evenly dense area* the likelihood of an "ideal's" being in a population at a given D distance is directly proportional to the D distance from the individual as a center of origin; and if the individual's entire movement, as well as his entire information about persons and happenings at a distance, are inversely proportional to distance, the likelihood of the individual's finding and winning the "ideal" mate at a D distance is inversely proportional to D. Hence, under these theoretical conditions, Bossard's N number of applicants for marriage licenses for mates within a given D distance should be inversely proportional to D.

Of course, the density is not constant within a city. Nevertheless, as the density varies, so, too, does the supply of possible mates vary, and also the demand for them. In other words, competitors and possible "ideals" increase and decrease with density also. For that reason the probability of finding and winning a particular kind of mate will still be inversely proportional to D, provided that the prerequisite supplies and demands for "ideals" are distributed at random throughout the population according to densities. The problem is nevertheless moot.

In Fig. 9–22 are plotted doubly logarithmically Dr. Bossard's data for all y applications for marriage licenses between partners separated by a like x distance (in units of city blocks with the middles of Dr. Bossard's classes) for all distances within 20 blocks down to, but not including, distances of 1 block or less. The distribution is clearly linear. The least-square slope and error of the data are $-.8166 \pm .0652$; if we add the 859 cases of one block or less, including cases at the same address, the slope increases to

* Real estate brokers, in describing the location of a store, speak of a "percentage location" (e.g., "60% location") which refers to the pedestrian traffic there in comparison to the point of maximum (i.e., 100%) pedestrian traffic of the trading center in question. I am deeply indebted to Mr. Joseph C. Leighton of Cambridge, Massachusetts, the official appraiser for many New England cities, banks, and insurance companies, for his kindness in making available to me the principles of objective real estate appraisal, on which he is a recognized authority.

$-.8425 \pm .0568$ error. Both these deviations from -1.00 are significant. Hence, perhaps "distance lends enchantment." With the maximum distance being merely 20 blocks, no shift of the origin would be appreciable.

The possible enchantment of distance was even greater in New Haven in 1931, if we judge by the careful data of Maurice R. Davie and Ruby Jo Reeves, which limitations of space preclude our presenting.[46] Though unmistakably rectilinear, the slope is appreciably less.

On the other hand, the 5000 cases in Philadelphia for each of 1885–86, 1905, and 1915, as reported by Dr. Roy H. Abrams, are definitely not recti-

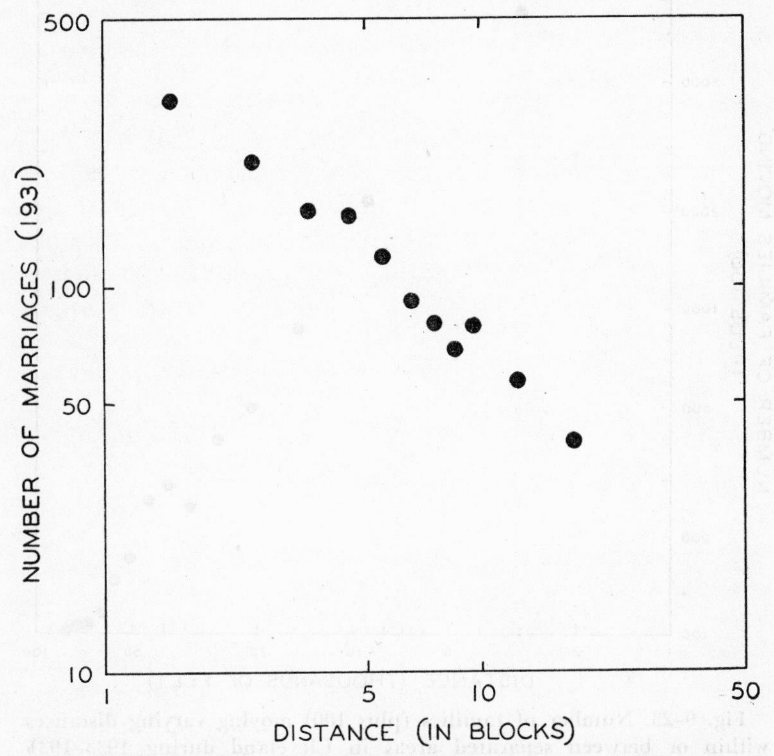

Fig. 9–22. Number of marriage licenses issued to 5,000 pairs of applicants living within Philadelphia in 1931 and separated by varying distances (the data of J. H. S. Bossard).

linear, though *D* is obviously a factor.[47] The theoretical meaning of his data is that a slight disadvantage attaches to matings within 4 or 5 blocks, since that portion of the curve is concave downwards.

Before leaving these data on an intimately personal aspect of human life, let us remark that tendencies to marry persons of like race, religion, or national origin will influence the rectilinearity of the distribution. On the other hand, as we know from Chapter Seven,[48] persons of like race, religion, culture, etc., will theoretically tend to congregate.*

* The war interrupted a study of the cities of origin of persons outside Boston who applied for marriage licenses in Boston (the fragmentary data suggest the P/D relationship). Similarly interrupted was a study of the distance from Cambridge of the 1940 resi-

c. Dr. Stouffer's data on the change of family residence. Our entire preceding argument applies also to residential changes, as landlords seek tenants and as tenants seek landlords (or sellers seek buyers, and *vice versa*), and with competition increasing with density. But here further factors enter into the picture that act unfavorably upon distance. Thus, even though prospective migrants are likely to know of vacancies in proportion to their D distance, and even if we assume that the probabilities of migration and of vacancies are constant per density, nevertheless, as every real estate broker

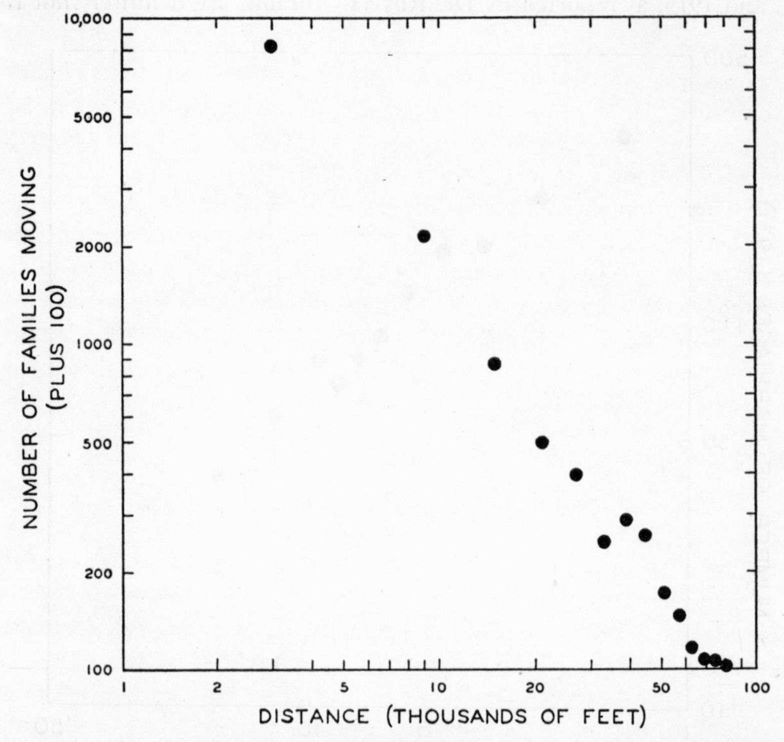

Fig. 9–23. Number of families (plus 100) moving varying distances within or between separated areas in Cleveland during 1933–1935 (adapted from the data of S. A. Stouffer).

knows, man dislikes moving far away from his friends. Hence, distance may be said to lend horror, since the farther off a person moves, the harder it is for him to return to visit his friends. Because of this premium upon shorter residential movements, the negative slope of the $y + \alpha$ families that move a given distance should be greater than unity.

In 1940 Dr. Samuel A. Stouffer published in his Table One the results of his brilliant study of residential movement in units of distance of 1,000 feet for 12,292 families within 12 White Census tracts in Cleveland during 1933–35.[49] Seven of these tracts were on the west side of Cleveland, and five

dences of Harvard alumni; according to preliminary data, the P/D relationship was evident, with a slight positive correlation between birthplace and place of post-college settlement. Both topics merit further investigation.

on the east side. Between these two tracts was an area whose distance was presumably included but which provided neither origins nor destinations. Hence, the y origins for the number of movements must be shifted to $y + \alpha$.

In Fig. 9–23 are presented Dr. Stouffer's extensive and careful observations after we have taken the liberty to shift his y origin an arbitrary $+ 100$. The rectilinearity of the distribution is striking, and the negative slope, by eye measure, is greater than unity, as expected. In this figure, as in the preceding one, we note the astonishing extent to which the intimate details of one's social life are subject to the exigencies of the hypothesis of the minimum equation. Dr. Stouffer's studies have stimulated further important research by Dr. D. S. Thomas on interstate migration, and by Dr. E. Isbell on internal migration in Sweden, which limitations of space regrettably prevent our discussing.

The same limitations of space prevent our discussing in detail the interesting "theory of intervening opportunities" that Dr. Stouffer presented with his data, and which in a way harkens back to the laws of migration of E. G. Ravenstein. Suffice it to say that if "opportunities" are defined as opportunities to minimize work, and if distance is defined as work-distance, our preceding pages contain much about the probable frequency distributions of opportunities at distances under both static and dynamic conditions.*

D. Domains and the *k* Constant

The entire argument of our hypothesis of the Minimum Equation was based on the explicit postulate that every person received a $1/C$ share of each kind of the total goods of production. Although all the preceding data of this chapter confirm the validity of this postulate, we nevertheless shall produce a set of data that refer directly to what we shall for convenience call the k constant of a particular h kind of goods-services $(k = 1/C)$.

As soon as we explore the topic of the individual consumption of a particular h kind of goods, we come upon the problem of the h domain in which the h kind of goods circulates. Although we have briefly discussed the problem of domains in our previous theoretical sections, we have largely ignored their existence in presenting our quantitative data. Therefore, we shall approach the problem of the k constant by first noting the influence of the domain. This will be easy in the present instance since, for our empiric study of the k constant, we have selected the sales of newspapers, in which the domain influence happens to be quite transparent.

We have already seen that the circulation of news follows the $P_1 \cdot P_2/D$ relationship because the probability of occurrence of any class of human events in a P community is proportional to P, and because the probable interest in that class of events by a person at a D distance is inversely proportional to D.

* Lest we seem pedantic, the difference between distance and work-distance can radically alter a frequency distribution. Thus, for example, the movements of persons in a city on the side of a hill will not be the same as in one on a level plane, if sheer distance is alone considered.

This argument is still valid if we cast it in terms of the occurrence of human events of news interest to persons at an increasing *D* distance. Thus, the probability of occurrence of such events—as of any other class of human events—in a *P* community is directly proportional to *P*. By and large, therefore, the likelihood of occurrence of human events of far-reaching interest is quite small in a small community, and all but negligible in a single family.

The probable interest at a distance in a community's happenings (which is intimately connected with the problem of the domain) can perhaps best be visualized if we first consider the case of community radio stations that broadcast news.[50] If every community has a radio station, the economical power of each station will be proportional to the *P* of its community; and this power will delimit the radio domain, since the comparative interest in the newscasts of its local happenings will probably not extend beyond the limits of its domain. Indeed, as we have argued before in general, the radius of the domain for a given *h* kind of goods-services around the community of its origin tends to be directly proportional to the community's *P*, with *h* demand decreasing in direct proportion to least work *D*.

Bearing the above conditions in mind, let us derive more precisely the limits of the domain. If the radius of the parent city is 1 *D*, then the proportion of persons in the city and in each successive ring around the city —if we recall Eq. (9–6a) on density—will follow the series $1/D$, $\frac{1}{2}D$, $\frac{1}{3}D$, ... Furthermore, if all these persons are buying from the city in amounts that are also inversely proportional to their *D* distance (i.e., the P/D relationship), then the demand for the *h* kind of goods-services will decrease according to the series:

$$1/1D,\ 1/2^2D,\ 1/3^2D\ .\ .\ .$$

At this point let us note that the first member, 1, of this last series represents about 60.79% of the sum of the entire series, as A. J. Lotka has shown.[51] Theoretically, therefore, approximately 60% of a particular *h* kind of goods-services will be sold in the city of origin, and the remaining 40% will be sold outside the city in the rest of the domain, thereby determining the limits of the domain.*

This theoretical 60%/40% ratio for intracity and extracity sales is useful in the matter of an empiric test in a problem that involves a domain. Thus, in the case of our fictitious radio stations, about 60% of the listeners will be inside the city itself.

Moreover, the same ratio should apply to the circulation of newspapers, of which 60% should be in the home city (provided, of course, that the newspaper contains news and is not slanted for rural or extracity demand). In this connection we report that for the seventeen newspapers named in Table 9–1, the mean circulation within the respective home city zones was 59.23% ± 12.25%. This percentage is sufficiently close to our theoretical

* The above percentages are only approximate, since the series $1/n^2D$ is a convergent series with an infinite domain, whereas the harmonic series (with $p \leq 1$), and all its corollary equations are divergent, thereby yielding a domain of finite radius.

60% to justify our belief that the circulation of a newspaper is a domain phenomenon.

The question now arises as to whether all persons throughout the entire United States buy a *k* constant number of newspapers according to our hypothesis (newspapers are a happy *h* kind of goods-services to study, since virtually everyone can afford a newspaper). If our entire hypothesis, including the *k* constant, be correct, then, newspapers of such numbers and circulation sizes will be established in such cities throughout the United States that a constant *k* number of papers will be sold *per capita* throughout the entire population of the country.

Inspecting Ayer's Directory for 1941,[52] we note that the total weekly circulation of newspapers originating in a given city of *P* population is approximately 50% of its population (actually somewhat less). If approximately 60% of the circulation is intracity, then we may say that within a city a newspaper is sold to 60% of 50% of its population—or approximately to every 3+ persons (for convenience let us say that $k = 3$ persons, though more precisely it is ⅓ of a newspaper per person).

The question now arises as to whether this *k* constant applies also to extracity sales. The reports of the Audit Bureau of Circulation for the year including April 1940 were analyzed for the seventeen newspapers named in Table 9–1. For each newspaper a sample of the first 100 alphabetized communities that bought 25 or more copies and whose populations were enumerated in the Sixteenth Census were selected (except for the *Chicago Tribune,* the *New York Times,* and the *Kansas City Star and Times* for which 3, 3, and 2 samples of 100 communities were taken respectively, as indicated by letters in Table 9–1). In some cases the samples were arbitrarily scattered among surrounding states. We assume that a sale of 25 papers in a community is sufficient to indicate that it lies within the newspaper's domain.

Then for each community in each sample the value of P/D was computed (for ease, *D* was the shortest distance) for a grand total of 22,000 communities. The absolute circulations in the communities of each sample were then divided by their respective values of P/D; the resulting quotient represented the *k* value of the newspapers in question in each city. Then the 100 calculated values of *k* of each sample were taken, and the mean *k* was computed for the entire sample.[53]

This mean *k* for each sample is given in Column III, with its standard deviation in Column IV. According to the null hypothesis, the mean *k* could be almost any value into the hundreds of thousands. Hence in spite of the obvious variations in *k for the first 15 papers,* the correspondence is truly astonishing.

The median value of mean *k* for the first 15 papers (19 samplings in all) is 3.68, which is not too far off from the theoretically expected.

The mean *k* for (16) the *Kansas City Star and Times* and for (17) the *Oregonian* is way off. That is because the sales to the 100 communities in question included "motor route" circulations which represented numbers of newspapers that were sent to the respective communities for further expe-

TABLE 9–1

The Calculated Mean *k* Constant Number of Persons Purchasing Newspapers in *P* Sized Populations Living at *D* Distances as Derived from 22 Samples of 100 Communities Each for 17 Different Newspapers.

I Sample Number	II Newspaper	III Mean *k*	IV Stand. Dev.
1	Augusta Chronicle	6.20	3.68
2	Boston Herald	2.01	1.72
3	Boston Post	5.13	3.79
4	Chicago Daily News	4.50	2.20
5-*a*	Chicago Tribune	8.19	6.25
5-*b*	Chicago Tribune	7.24	4.36
5-*c*	Chicago Tribune	6.99	4.48
6	Cincinnati Times Star	5.28	3.82
7	Cleveland Plain Dealer	3.83	5.26
8	Cleveland Press	1.70	1.30
9	Detroit Free Press	6.77	5.68
10	Detroit Times	4.02	3.48
11	Los Angeles Examiner	6.11	8.35
12	Los Angeles Times	5.82	3.87
13-*a*	New York Times	4.93	7.93
13-*b*	New York Times	2.72	3.40
13-*c*	New York Times	.70	.65
14	Pittsburgh Post Gazette	3.41	2.38
15	Pittsburgh Press	1.36	.81
16-*a*	Kansas City Star & Times	41.8	18.6
16-*b*	Kansas City Star & Times	28.4	12.9
17	The Oregonian	18.2	2.6

dition by motor to populations that lay beyond their city limits. Therefore, the *k* constant is naturally considerably larger.

The data of Table 9–1 go far towards substantiating our hypothesis to the effect that newspapers of such numbers and circulation sizes will be established in such cities throughout the United States that a constant number of persons will buy newspapers with least work throughout the entire population. In short, newspapers theoretically spring up in numbers and circulation sizes at locations throughout the entire country so that everyone will have his $1/C$ share with a minimum of work.

This situation is perhaps more readily apparent from Fig. 9–24, in which are plotted doubly logarithmically both (*A*) the *x* number of communities of like *y* population size in the United States in 1940 that issued daily newspapers, and (*B*) the *x* number of newspapers in the United States in 1940 of like *y* circulation size, with the class middles as indicated, and with an ideal line of $-\frac{1}{2}$ slope added for the reader's convenience, and with the upper limit, for convenience, at one million, which excludes only five cities and one newspaper (the lower bends at the bottom which have been discussed in a previous publication are ignored now as being inconsequential to the present argument). Strictly speaking, we have shown no connection between the A and B sets of data, in the sense that large cities tend also to have newspapers of a correspondingly large circulation size,* even though we note from an inspection of the tabulated data that such is the case with a very high value of r if it were calculated. Hence, we shall here merely assume the direct relationship between the corresponding magnitudes of the A and B data.

Although Fig. 9–24 tells us nothing that we could not infer from our preceding argument, it has a certain didactic value in showing graphically

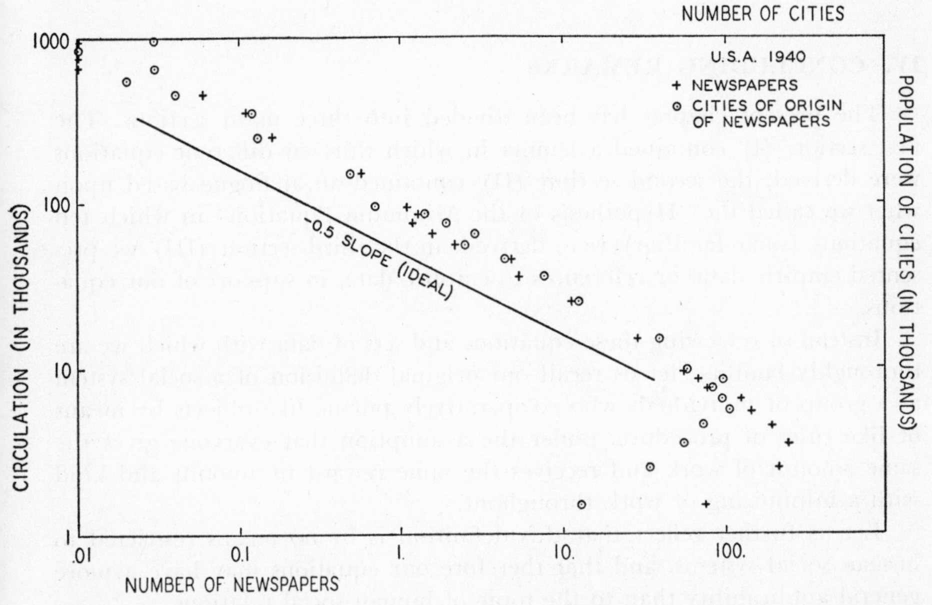

Fig. 9–24. Number of newspapers of like circulation size and the number and population sizes of the cities of origin of the newspapers in the U. S. A. in 1940.

how, with a constant demand for newspapers throughout the population, individual newspapers, in order to satisfy this demand, will spring up with the same orderliness that governs the emergence of communities. Large communities will tend to have newspapers of large circulation both because of a greater likelihood of having more news to report and of having more persons who are interested in the news reported (naturally, as a paper grows in size it can afford a more extensive and therefore more expensive news coverage).

Most important of all, let us reflect that this argument is not restricted to the sale of newspapers, whose particular h domains and k constant we happened to select for study. The same argument applies theoretically to any other h kind of goods and k constant—to kinds of stores, to kinds of

* There is a slight tendency for the number of different newspapers that issue from a city of P size to increase with P. For report of preliminary studies of proportions of local, national, and international news items, see original publications.[54]

manufactures, to kinds of goods and services—which will theoretically also spring up in response to the same demand, with some growing greatly in size, while others fail or merely hold their own. In other words, Fig. 9–24 is of general illustrative value for any and all h kinds of goods and services, if one merely relabels the co-ordinates for the particular h in question, and alters the constant appropriately.

With this brief but quite conclusive single piece of evidence on domains and the k constant in the important case of newspaper sales, we have now provided empiric tests of virtually all the salient points of our hypothesis of the Minimum Equation, which was based upon the assumption of a minimizing of work.

IV. CONCLUDING REMARKS

The present chapter has been divided into three main sections. The first section (I) contained a lemma in which thirteen different equations were derived; the second section (II) contained an analogue based upon what we called the "Hypothesis of the Minimum Equation" in which ten equations (some familiar) were derived; in the third section (III) we presented empiric data, or references to empiric data, in support of our equations.

Instead of reviewing these equations and sets of data with which we are thoroughly familiar, let us recall our original definition of a social system as a group of individuals who co-operatively pursue like objects by means of like rules of procedure, under the assumption that everyone gives the same amount of work and receives the same reward in amount and kind with a minimizing of work throughout.

Let us further reflect that this definition is by no means restricted to human social systems, and that therefore our equations may have a more general applicability than to the topic of human social relations.

By way of illustration of this point, let us in our mind's eye take one of the maps of the city traffic surveys that we have mentioned previously, in which the increasing density of street traffic towards the central part of the city is represented by correspondingly increasing thicknesses of lines. These converging fewer lines of increasing thickness remind one of the root systems and branch systems of many trees. Can it, therefore, be that a tree is a social system of cells to which our equations apply when cast in terms of three dimensions, with every cell contributing on the whole a like amount of work for which it receives on the whole a like amount and kinds of return?

The same question applies to our blood and nervous systems, as has been pointed out often enough in the past. Do our equations similarly hold as goals of maximum efficiency for their behavior? We have been told that the brain is like a telephone switchboard. Would it perhaps be more felicitous to suggest that it, with the rest of the nervous system, is like an entire telephone-telegraph system which, as we know, is so thoroughly integrated with the entire manufacturing and transportation systems in question that one cannot separate them? If so, our human social system may provide a valuable analogue for the study of physiological systems. In that case the study of human social systems may give valuable aid in formulating questions in physiology.[55] In other words, as suggested in Chapter Six, a study of routes of traffic and communication in human social systems, with all their alternatives for detours and provisions for substitute activity in the case of breakdowns, dynamic changes, and cultural lags, may provide a useful theoretical perspective for studying analogous physiological phenomena.

One striking feature of our equations is the repeated occurrence of integral exponents. May we perhaps generalize upon this? Thus is the volume of a cell's nucleus an integral root of the volume of the cell? Only meticulous empiric studies can answer this question. Nevertheless, it is at least a question.

Just as we have argued that Part One of this book provides a useful approach to the problems of Part Two, so also does Part Two shed light on the problems of Part One.

Yet there is a difference between the two parts. For in Part One we developed Effort (i.e., probable least average rate of work) as the minimum, whereas so far in Part Two, sheer work has been the minimum. Actually this difference is more apparent than real, since human beings, after all, are the elements of the social group and, in providing the action of the group with least effort, they will make the group action one of least effort. Thus, for example, when railroads or highways are laid out, thought is generally given to probable future needs.

The present Chapter Nine contains in many respects the main body of Part Two, as the reader can easily see. Nevertheless, it is not complete even for the needs of an introductory study of biosocial dynamics. We have repeatedly pointed out that rectilinear distributions are not at all times inevitable, and that inflexibly fixed boundaries are by no means always the case. The topic of the deviations from rectilinearity we shall treat briefly in our Chapter Ten.

After postulating an equal $1/C$ share of work with an equal $1/C$ share of reward for all persons in the group, we pointed out the inapplicability of this assumption. The more particular dynamics of reward will therefore be considered briefly in Chapter Eleven.

Finally, there is the question of "like rules of procedure for all" which broaches again the problem of culture, which we shall treat briefly in Chapter Twelve.

Hence, our following three chapters will essentially add further elaborations and qualifications to our preceding argument.

Up to this point we have presented data which, in the light of the null hypothesis, virtually establish the existence of natural social laws. Whether our theory, however, is logically firmly knit and applicable—and all theories that apply to empiric data can stand further conceptual sharpening—only the reader can decide for himself.

CHAPTER TEN

INTRANATIONAL AND INTERNATIONAL COOPERATION AND CONFLICT

In our preceding chapter we developed a hypothesis on the economy of geography which we tested empirically with data that referred exclusively to conditions in the United States at about 1940. In the present chapter we shall first (I) extend the range of observations, and then (II) consider cases of unstable intranational equilibrium, which will in turn lead us (III) to questions of stable and unstable international equilibrium. Our argument will refer in all cases to the theoretical analysis presented in the preceding chapter.

I. CANADIAN DATA

Our most urgent need is to show that the rectilinearity of our data for the rank-frequency distribution of communities in the United States in 1940 is not unique. Since the data we present in this chapter will refer to populations of communities within their official city limits, unless otherwise specifically stated, let us recall that in our theoretical discussion of the Hypothesis of the Minimum Equation in Section II of our preceding chapter, we made the point that political boundaries of communities will tend in the long run to approximate their natural dynamic boundaries, if only because these latter are the economical limits to the extension of municipal services. Without reviewing the argument in detail we shall proceed in the belief that the rank-frequency distributions of the populations of politically bounded communities will tend to approximate our equations when other conditions of our Hypothesis are met.

That such may be the case is illustrated by the data of Fig. 10–1 for Canadian communities of 1,000 or more inhabitants at the moments of measurement of the six Canadian decennial censuses from 1881 through 1931, with rank plotted logarithmically on the abscissa, and with population size plotted logarithmically on the ordinate.[1] For comparative purposes, the rank-frequency distribution of the populations of politically bounded communities in the U. S. A. in 1930, with sizes under 1 million and over 2,500, are also presented (the same data for the U. S. A. will be found again in fuller form in Fig. 10–2).

Despite the irregularities in the curves of Fig. 10–1, there is little doubt that they may be fairly viewed as approximating the rectilinearity and slope of the value, $p = 1$, of Eq. (9–2a). Hence, however remote the probability may have been that the rectilinearity of the data for the Metropolitan Districts of the U. S. A. in 1940, as presented in Fig. 9–2, represented merely a fluke of chance, the probability is now even vastly more remote because of the confirmation of the Canadian data, particularly for 1931.

For the earlier years, and notably for 1881, there are undeniably serious bends in the Canadian data which with passing years have largely disap-

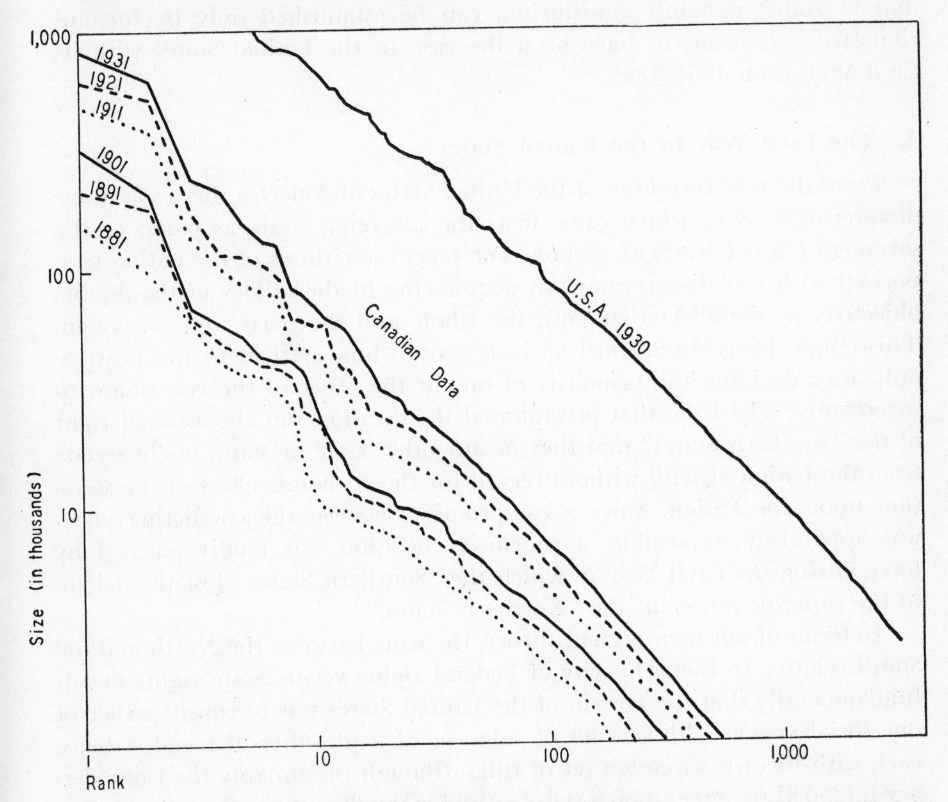

Fig. 10–1. Canada 1881–1931. Communities of 1,000 or more persons, ranked in the decreasing order of population size.

peared. These bends, we believe, may indicate conditions of an unstable intranational equilibrium, as we shall now attempt to show from similar bends in earlier U. S. A. distributions.

II. UNSTABLE AND STABLE INTRANATIONAL CONDITIONS

In our theoretical analyses of Sections I and II of Chapter Nine, we defined a social system as a group of individuals who, among other things had like objectives which they pursued co-operatively by means of like rules of conduct. In effect, we have been arguing that nations represent such social systems.

But although we may assume theoretically that the inhabitants of a nation agree as to their national objectives and rules of conduct, this agreement is historically by no means always the case. Instead there is almost always a continual alteration of objectives and of rules of procedure which is generally accomplished directly or indirectly by common consent, as we argued in Chapter Seven.

Nevertheless, changes in objectives and in rules of procedure may not always be effected by common consent. For it may happen that regional, financial, or cultural interests are so divergent in a nation, that a condition of stable dynamic equilibrium can be established only by forceful civil strife, as seems to have been the case in the United States with its Civil War from 1861–1865.

A. The Civil War in the United States

From the very inception of the United States of America there was grave disagreement as to which came first: the sovereign states as parts; or the sovereign United States as a whole. For years the citizens of the nation temporized with this disagreement by acquiescing in the fallacy of the double objective, to the effect that both the whole and the parts were sovereign. This temporizing lasted until an issue arose whose settlement was possible only after deciding the primarity of one or the other of the two claims to sovereignty. The issue that precipitated the decision was the asserted right of the "Southern States" that they or any other state or states might secede from the Union at will, without regard for the economic effect of the secession upon the Union. Since a compromise between the conflicting views was apparently impossible, a conclusive decision was finally reached by force during the Civil War in which the "Southern States" lost the debate to the superior power of the "Northern States."

In terms of our own present theory, the issue between the North and the South relative to the primarity of Federal rights versus State rights meant fundamentally that the terrain of the United States was to consist either of one social system with one set of rules, or of a plurality of social systems, each with its own sovereign set of rules (though presumably the Confederacy intended to agree upon a set of rules for the "Southern States").

As long as only one set of rules was valid throughout the terrain, then the population of the terrain, in seeking to organize itself with maximum efficiency, would be distributed in such a way as to approximate the conditions of our equations.

On the other hand, if the terrain were to consist of a plurality of systems—each one of which would theoretically seek to organize itself with maximum efficiency, and hence theoretically to approximate our equations on its own behalf without any regard for the action of other systems—then the entire population of the whole terrain would not be distributed according to our equations. On the contrary, the entire population of the terrain might represent the sum of a number of different independent harmonic distributions; and this sum would by no means yield a harmonically seriated whole.* Instead the summated distribution would be nonlinear with conspicuous bends.

* The harmonic series cannot be divided into two or more *complete* harmonic series, since each fraction occurs only once.

In general, when two or more harmonic series are added, the graphical effect on doubly logarithmic co-ordinates is that of a connecting horizontal line (or lines) that results from the fact that there are two (or more) successive ranks for communities of the same size.

Thus, for example, if there are two independent social systems of equal population size whose respective communities are each harmonically seriated, and whose largest communities in each case are one million, then, when the two systems are combined, there will be two cities—rank 1 and 2—of one million inhabitants each; and that condition will be reflected graphically by a horizontal line that connects rank 1 with rank 2 at the point, one million, on the ordinate. The rest of the curve, however, will be rectilinear with the slope of negative unity, since all other ranks will have been multiplied by the constant, 2.

Horizontal bends can also appear elsewhere. Thus, if we assume explicitly for the remainder of the chapter that the smallest *n*th community of a harmonic series contains an arbitrary constant small number of persons—say 2 or 3—then, if a shorter harmonic seriation is added to a longer one, there will obviously be a horizontal line connecting the first member of the shorter harmonic seriation with the member of corresponding size of the larger harmonic seriation.

Nor are horizontal bends the only possible ones. Thus, if one or more extraneous fractions are inserted into a harmonic series, the curve will become convex upward at the point(s) of insertion; on the other hand, if one or more member fractions are deleted from the harmonic series proper, the series will become convex at the point(s) of deletion.* Bends of these types may be of historical importance. Thus, in the annexation of populated land, extraneous fractions may be added with the result of an upward convexity in the resulting distribution (a condition of *surfeit*). On the other hand, when populated lands are ceded, fractions of the harmonic seriation may be lost, with the result of a downward convexity (a condition of *deficiency*).[2]

This discussion of bends in the graph refers, in the present instance, to the graphical effects of the alteration of populations in terrain, such as might result from a schism in objectives and rules of procedure, or from the addition or secession of parts, such as threatened to be the case with the Southern States of the United States during our Civil War, to the consideration of which we now return.

Recalling the essential conflict between the Northern and Southern States, and bearing in mind our previous discussion of the possible meaning of bends, we present in Fig. 10–2, as labelled, the rank-frequency distributions of the communities of the U. S. A. at the decennial censuses from 1790 through 1930, insofar as data are available.[3]

Inspecting these data, we note the emergence of a horizontal-like bend at about 1820, which became quite pronounced by 1840 when the North–

* E.g.: the harmonic seriation, 1, ½, ⅖, ⅓, . . . has the extraneous fraction, ⅖. The seriation, 1, ½, ¼, ⅕, . . . has lost the member fraction, ⅓.

South secession controversy began to flare, and which more or less disappeared by 1870 after the Civil War had ended.

The appearance of this horizontal-like bend from 1820 onwards—much as if the whole were splitting into two or more sovereign parts—is not inconsistent with the view that the Civil War was a conflict between two

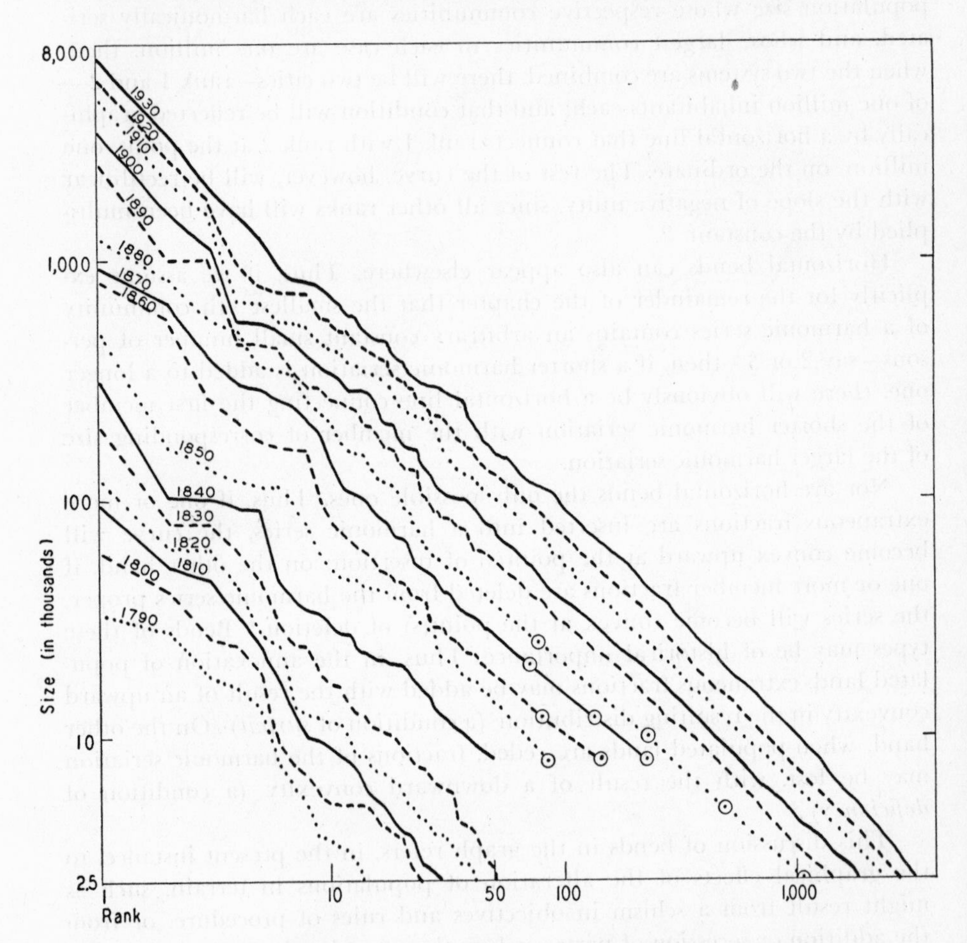

Fig. 10–2. U. S. A. 1790–1930. Communities of 2500 or more inhabitants ranked in the decreasing order of population size.

competitive social systems, each one of which had a set of objectives and rules of procedure of its own.

This view is further confirmed by the data of Fig. 10–3, in which are presented separately the rank-frequency distributions of the communities of the Northern States and of the Confederacy in 1860, as ascertained by my former student, Mr. Richard Lehman. Each distribution, we note, is independently a fair approximation to harmonic series. Regardless of the merits of the issue of the Civil War, the Northern States had the superior population, and did in fact defeat the Southern States and absorb them into the Federal rules of procedure.

In our terms, we repeat, the quarrel between the North and South was primarily about a rule of procedure: viz., were all persons to be equal before the law, or were colored people to be chattels. Although Abraham Lincoln may not have been historically correct in stating that no nation can

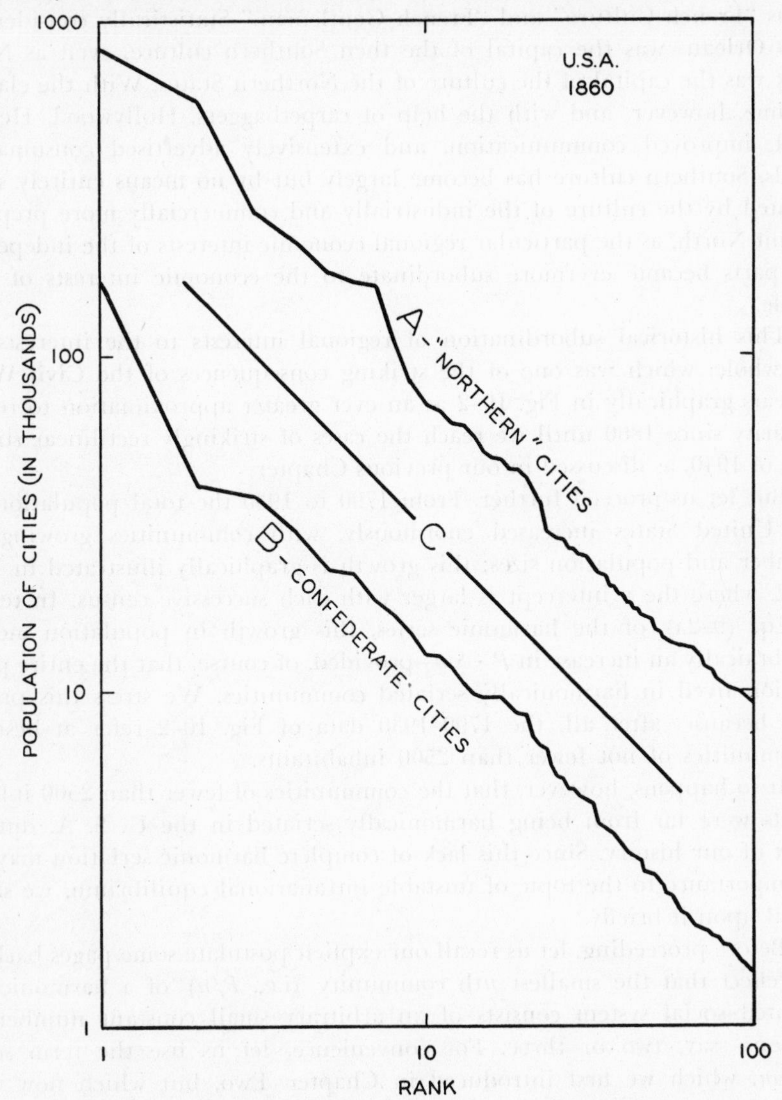

Fig. 10–3. U. S. A. 1860. (A) "Northern" cities, and (B) CONFEDERATE cities, ranked in the decreasing order of population size.

long exist half slave and half free, since nations have existed for centuries with the institution of slavery; nevertheless, he was quite right in implying that no nation can long exist according to two basic rules of procedure that are contradictory—even if the rules of procedure do not refer to slavery.

Naturally, any such differences as those of Fig. 10–3 will have many further cultural connotations if we remember the general discussion of culture in Chapter Seven. Different social systems, after all, may have different cultural vocabularies, as seems historically to have been the case with the North and South. The terms "Southern Living" and "Southern Gentleman" were not vain, sentimental epithets but had as much meaning as the terms "French Culture" and "French Gentleman." Statistically considered, New Orleans was the capital of the then Southern culture, even as New York was the capital of the culture of the Northern States. With the elapse of time, however, and with the help of carpetbaggers, Hollywood, Henry Ford, improved communication, and extensively advertised consumable goods, Southern culture has become largely but by no means entirely supplanted by the culture of the industrially and commercially more preponderant North, as the particular regional economic interests of the independent parts became evermore subordinate to the economic interests of the whole.

This historical subordination of regional interests to the interests of the whole, which was one of the striking consequences of the Civil War, appears graphically in Fig. 10–2 as an ever greater approximation to rectilinearity since 1860 until we reach the cases of strikingly rectilinear structure of 1940, as discussed in our previous Chapter.

But let us proceed further. From 1790 to 1930 the total population of the United States increased enormously, with communities growing in number and population sizes; this growth is graphically illustrated in Fig. 10–2, where the y intercept is larger with each successive census. In terms of Eq. (9–2a) of the harmonic series, this growth in population means algebraically an increase in $P \cdot Sn$—provided, of course, that the entire population lived in harmonically seriated communities. We stress this provision because, after all, the 1790–1930 data of Fig. 10–2 refer at best to communities of not fewer than 2500 inhabitants.

It so happens, however, that the communities of fewer than 2500 inhabitants were far from being harmonically seriated in the U. S. A. during most of our history. Since this lack of complete harmonic seriation may be of importance to the topic of unstable intranational equilibrium, we shall dwell upon it briefly.[4]

Before proceeding, let us recall our explicit postulate some pages back to the effect that the smallest nth community (i.e., P/n) of a harmonically seriated social system consists of an arbitrary small constant number of persons—say, two or three. For convenience, let us use the term *saturation,* which we first introduced in Chapter Two, but which now will describe a condition where the entire population of a terrain is distributed in communities whose respective sizes follow the proportions of the generalized harmonic series of Eq. (9–2a), with the smallest nth community having an arbitrary small constant number of inhabitants, say 2 or 3.

If we reinspect the curves of Fig. 10–2, it is evident that the slopes of the distributions are approximately negative unity, with the result that the value of the exponent, p, in our Eq. (9–2a) is approximately one. Under these conditions, if the entire population of the United States during a given year was *saturated* in the sense just defined, then the summation of all the n harmonically seriated communities for that year would be $P \cdot Sn$, which in turn will represent the total population of the United States for that year.

Assuming now that the total population of a saturated terrain is $P \cdot Sn$, then if we divide the total population, $P \cdot Sn$, by P, which is the population of the largest community whose rank is 1 (i.e., New York, in the case of the United States), then we obtain the value, Sn, which represents the sum of the n fractions of the harmonic series (after dividing the populations of all communities by P). And from this value of Sn we can calculate the total n number of different communities in the population, by using Euler's formula; $Sn - log_e n = .577$ (approximate).

If the entire population is saturated, then the nth smallest community should have a population (P/n) that is $1/n$th of the population, P, of the largest community.

By way of illustration of the foregoing method of calculation, as well as for the sake of showing the lack of saturation in the United States for that year, let us take the census data for 1930 for which Sn has the value of about 17.5, as obtained by dividing the total population of the United States (i.e., 122,775,046) in 1930 by the population of New York (i.e., 6,930,446) for that year.

This value, $Sn = 17.5$, fixes n at approximately 22,400,000. Hence in 1930 if the United States had been saturated, there should have been 22,400,-000 communities. The smallest community, therefore, would have had the rank, 22,400,000 and its population should have been 1/22,400,000 of the population of New York. Since New York had only 6,930,446 persons in 1930, then, if the entire United States had been saturated, this smallest community would have had to consist of approximately ⅓ of a person—an obvious absurdity. Hence in 1930 the United States was not saturated for communities of fewer than 2500 persons. Of these latter there must have been a *deficiency*.

Since the size of Sn was ever larger at earlier censuses (e.g., in 1920, Sn was 18.8, in 1910, 19.2; in 1900, 22.1; in 1880, 26.2; in 1860, 26.9), it follows from our argument that there should have been an ever larger n number of communities as we go back in American history, if during our entire history the United States had always been in a condition of saturation. Clearly, if the above conditions of 1930 with a theoretical ⅓ of a person in the nth community was absurd, then the far smaller theoretical fractions of earlier decades would be even more absurd.

From the preceding argument and graphs we may infer that if we had complete census data for all communities of all sizes, including the families of isolated farmers, so that the rank-frequency distribution for each Census would include the entire population, then in each case there would be a point somewhere below $y = 2500$ on the graph where the curve would bend downward as an indication of a deficiency of smaller communities. This point, incidentally, might well be viewed as the demarcation between the traditional classes, *urban* and *rural*.

This hypothetical *urban-rural* point obviously does not need to be quantitatively the same for each census year, for we know both from our analysis and from an inspection of the actual census data that the United States throughout its history became urbanized at a faster rate than that of its total population growth.

We have just referred to the urban-rural classes, about which many valuable historical-descriptive treatises have been written. Since our own interests, however, are in dynamics, we are confronted by the question as to what this urban-rural dichotomy may mean when viewed dynamically against the background of the theoretical argument of our preceding chapter. Although the dichotomy may result from many factors, may we not suggest that one factor for the deficiency of population in the rural classes might have been the well-known fact that rural communities through 1930 did not share equally in the m different goods and services of the United States, even though the rural inhabitants most certainly contributed their share of the work? Surely recent rural political history supports this view.

For since 1930, and even earlier, rural organizations, or "farm blocs," began to exert a very serious pressure upon the Federal Government in order to make more readily available to the rural population the goods and services that all along had been quite easily available to urban dwellers. The extensive rural electrification programs, educational programs, health programs, merchandising co-operatives, and the like, might be viewed as some of the results of the powerful collective efforts of many small rural groups which, if operating alone, would have been statistically insignificant. In short, the events of recent history corroborate our theoretical view that the presumable bends in our straight line for the rank-frequency distribution of communities of fewer than 2500 inhabitants arose from the want of an equal share in the nation's goods and services—a want that is being fulfilled by means of political pressure.

We have previously remarked that the rate at which the United States has become urbanized has been consistently greater than the rate of its total population growth. If this faster rate of urbanization continues, then sooner or later the country may well become saturated, as has been argued in some historical detail in an earlier publication where, incidentally, the point was also made that in the late 1930's a condition of saturation might already have been obtained in view of the rate at which Sn has been decreasing over the decades. As far as we can see, there is no dynamic reason for a permanent deep dynamic cleavage between the urban and rural.

On the other hand, nothing is gained by being dogmatic about the urban-rural cleavage in respect of which other views are clearly much to be desired. In this connection, we emphatically call attention to Dr. J. Q. Stewart's important and unequivocal observation that, from 1790 down to the present, the n number of urban communities of the census enumerations—that is, in effect, the communities of at least 2500 inhabitants that are ranked in Fig. 10–2—has at every census been a close approximation to the square root of the total population at that time.[5]

Dr. Stewart gives no reason for his observation, nor do we find one implicit in our preceding argument, although our type of argument in Chapter Eleven about the pariah class may be applicable here.* Any attempted rationalization would presumably have to explain dynamically, *first,* the emergence of the rural-urban classes at all and, *second,* the number 2,500 as a critical point in the classification. Here we might remark that in France in 1936 there was a pretty close approximation to rectilinearity for villages down to about 700–800 inhabitants, and hence well below 2,500 persons; German communities from 1875 have been on the whole rectilinear down to the size of 2,000 inhabitants, below which information is not available. Finally, there is the distribution of Metropolitan Districts in 1940 as presented in Fig. 9–2, to which Dr. Stewart's square root rule will presumably not apply. The important dynamical problem of the urban-rural dichotomy, therefore, remains as moot as it is real, though undeniably Dr. Stewart's observation, for which, incidentally, he has additional data and a more refined equation that will cope with values of p that are less than 1, is an extremely promising approach to its solution.

In a field of such vast scope as that of intranational equilibrium there are clearly many, many more problems than those we have discussed. Thus, for example, the Metropolitan Districts of 1940 were rectilinear with $p = 1$, and similarly rectilinear were the politically bounded communities of that time, some of which were constituent members of the larger Metropolitan Districts; moreover, the same rectilinearity apparently attaches also to the different "trading centers" within the politically bounded communities—an orderly dynamic concatenation that presents a problem upon which we have merely touched in our discussion of density in the preceding chapter.

But, be all that as it may, our discussion of the underlying condition of unstable equilibrium that eventually led to our Civil War has at least served to dispose of the naive belief that we shall always find only cases of true rectilinearity, as Auerbach and Gibrat apparently believed. Our discussion has also served to suggest that absences of rectilinearity may represent the presence of serious conflicts that result from actual conditions that are far removed from the ideal conditions of our lemma and analogue, where every person of the population magnanimously agrees upon a vocabulary of rules of conduct according to which each person contributes a $1/C$ unit of work for which he receives a $1/C$ share of each of the different kinds of goods and services produced.

The case of unstable equilibrium of the United States which we have just discussed in part may be typical of any other social system where small groups at one or more points expand over terrain by sheer force of aggressive conquests while routing or enslaving the previous occupants if not actually massacring them (e.g., "a good Indian is a dead Indian"). Such was the history of Rome and of many, many other social systems as well

* We refer specifically to our discussion of the "square effect" in Chapter Eleven (q.v.) and merely suggest that Dr. Stewart in his above disclosure may have found a case of the "square effect."

as of our own. Theoretically, however, if the successful aggressors are not plagued later by "upstart" aggressors, a more stable equilibrium will eventually appear, in which the rules of conduct will have become largely a matter of agreement (at least among members of the elite class, as defined more particularly in our following chapter).

Civil Wars, therefore, may be likened to the psychotic episodes of individuals, or to the growing pains of adolescents: a mechanism whereby a greater unity of the whole may become established, albeit at the risk of a total destruction in the event that harmony fails to ensue.

B. The Case of Germany[6]

At the end of the Franco–Prussian War in 1870, Germany headed into a direction of unification that was quite comparable to that of the United States after the Civil War. Germany was also similar to the United States in the extent to which she placed enormous emphasis upon technological progress, with the result that the m diversity of its goods and services increased markedly. It is the effect of this increased m diversity upon the growth of German cities that will concern us primarily now.

In this connection we remember from our lemma and analogue in Chapter Nine that one possible effect of an increased m diversity is a concomitant increase in the size of the exponent, p, of the generalized harmonic series of Eq. (9–2a). In other words, as m increases, the slope of the line (absolute slope $= p$) of the rank-frequency distribution of communities also increases according to our equations of Chapter Nine.

As to the actual rate of increase of m in Germany, the present writer is uninformed. Nevertheless, we do have the official census data on the population sizes of German communities from 1875 through May 1939 (which includes the populations of the Sudetenland and Austria). The rank-frequency distributions of these data are presented doubly logarithmically in Fig. 10–4.

An inspection of Fig. 10–4 reveals strikingly the increase in the slope (and p) with passing years, as expected theoretically from an increasing m diversity. Of interest also are the horizontal bends towards the tops of the earlier distributions, which become less pronounced in passing years, much as if there had been a problem of the sovereign whole versus the sovereign parts which was slowly solved with time.

Incidentally, this orderly increase in the slopes of the curves of Fig. 10–4, which so strikingly confirms our hypothesis, also raises the question as to why the analogous curves for the U. S. A. from 1790–1930 in Fig. 10–2 did not show similar increases in slope, since during this interval the American m diversity presumably also was increasing.

The answer to this question may be that the German technological development took place in a terrain that was already populated with a fairly homogeneous culture, and hence in a terrain that more nearly approximated the conditions of our lemma in Chapter Nine, than did that of the United States, which expanded over effectively uninhabited territory during the increase in the m diversity of its goods and services. While Germany had to adapt its increasing *m* diversity to previously existent cultural givens, the United States could and did alter its cultural vocabulary to suit its innovations, and even extended the bounds of its territory quite considerably with

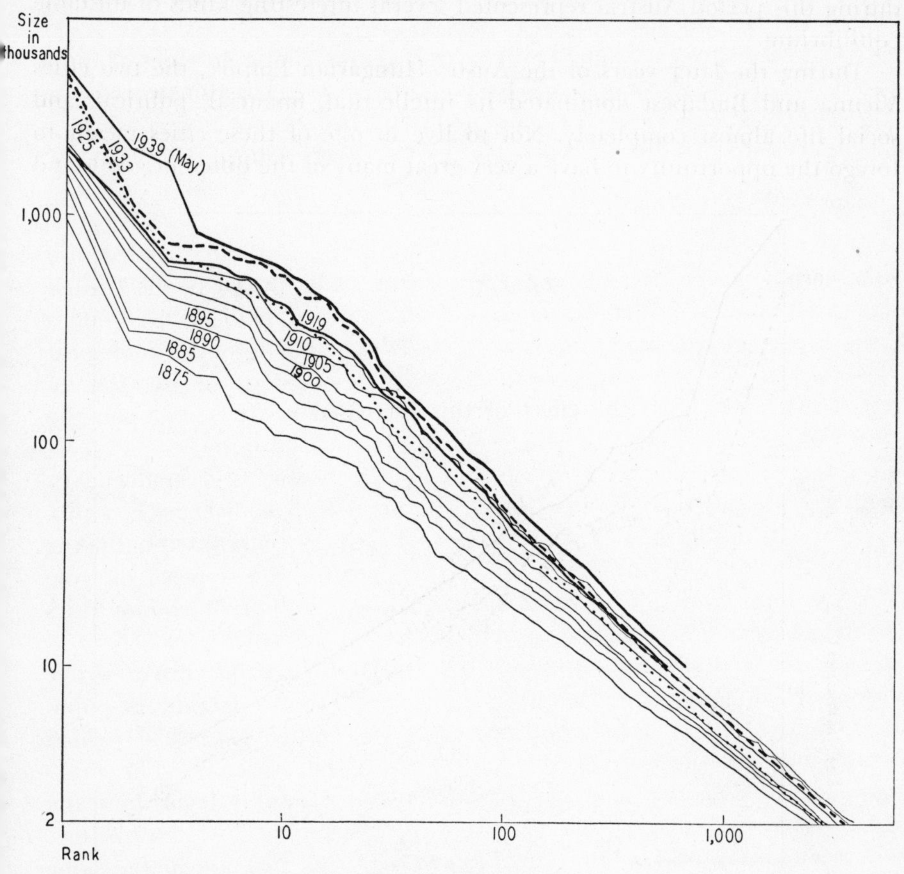

Fig. 10–4. Germany, 1875–1939 (May). Communities ranged in the decreasing order of population size.

the object of providing sources of raw materials for its finished goods and services.

C. The Case of Austria

In the lemma and analogue of our previous chapter we assumed an equality of objectives, of labor, and of rewards on the part of the population of a terrain. Such was not completely the case in the United States, where we found a disagreement in objectives. In Germany it was more nearly the case, though we—perhaps erroneously—placed under the heading of unstable equilibrium the marked increase in the German *m* diversity of goods and services that occurred historically.*

---

* This increase in *m* without a concomitant increase in terrain (i.e., the area-diversity relationship) was theoretically possible only with a vastly expanded foreign trade, which itself can disturb international equilibrium, as discussed in Section III following.

Now let us consider the case of Austria from the time of (1) the Austro-Hungarian Empire in 1910 through (2) the period of Austria's separate independence, to the time of (3) its absorption into Germany in 1939, for during this period Austria represented several interesting kinds of unstable equilibrium.[7]

During the later years of the Austro-Hungarian Empire, the two cities Vienna and Budapest dominated its intellectual, financial, political, and social life almost completely. Not to live in one of these cities meant to forego the opportunity to have a very great many of the different goods and

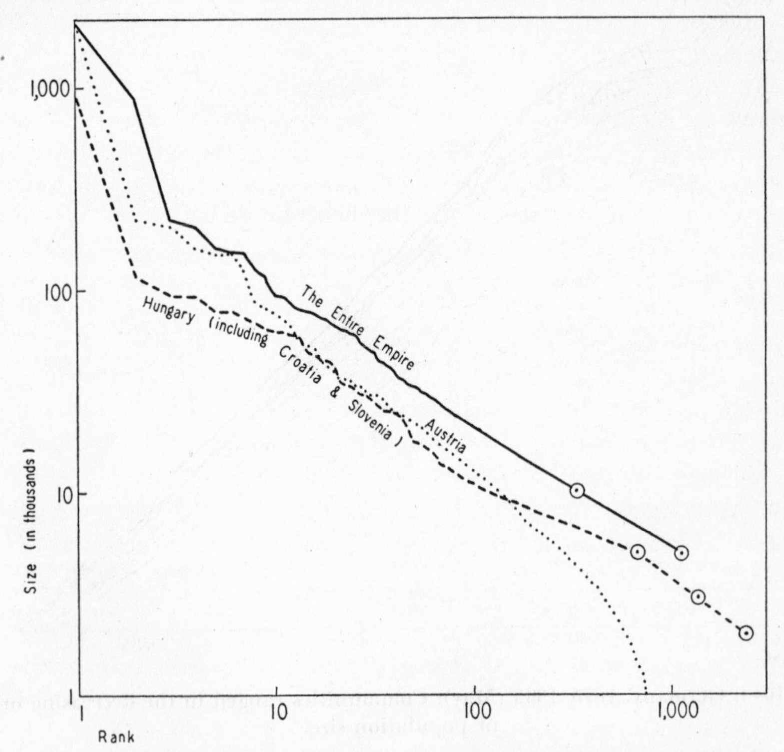

Fig. 10–5. Austro-Hungarian empire 1910. Communities ranged in the decreasing order of population size in (a) the entire empire, (b) Austria, and (c) Hungary.

services of the country. Hence, there existed a cleavage between these two ancient capitals on the one hand, and the rest of the Empire on the other.

Further complicating the situation was another factor. There was a hereditary nobility of great wealth and large retinue who tended to spend in the large cities most of their sizable incomes, which were derived to a considerable extent from the land. As a result, we can understand how the population of these two capitals would grow at a disproportionately greater rate than the rest of the country, since by and large the rest of the country was expending work without a commensurate reward. In other words, though the outlying populations contributed their individual $1/C$ shares of work, they did not receive in return their individual $1/C$ shares of the goods and services of production. At least that is the traditional view.

This traditional view seems to be supported by the rank-frequency distribution of Austro-Hungarian communities in 1910 as presented in the unbroken line of Fig. 10–5, where the top two ranks represent Vienna and Budapest respectively. Should this traditional view be correct, then we have in the present case a graphical illustration of an instance of unstable intranational equilibrium that arose from a radical maldistribution of production, and with an excessive urbanizing of consumption and production. Of course, we may not overlook the alternative explanation that Vienna and Budapest were the cultural and economic capitals of Balkan and Central European terrain that lay beyond Austro-Hungarian boundaries at a time when tariffs and other restrictions to trade were comparatively low in Europe.

Nevertheless, in support of the traditional view of the general "top heaviness" of the old Austro-Hungarian Empire, we also may not overlook the fact that many of the repressed persons in outlying rural districts revolted in 1918–1919 and seceded from the Empire entirely, in order to found independent countries with the neurotic resuscitation of cultures that had lost effective economic meaning centuries ago—and all this at a time in the twentieth century when, theoretically, according to the area-diversity relationship, nations should rather have been increasing in size and decreasing in number than the reverse.

That the old Austro-Hungarian Empire was "top heavy" is a view with which the present author does not care to quarrel; yet, that a more stable economic equilibrium could be established by simply splitting it into its medieval speech-minorities would seem to border on genuine schizophrenia. In Fig. 10–5 are presented gratuitously in broken lines the rank-frequency distributions of the Austrian part and the Hungarian part (including Croatia and Slovenia) in 1910. Even though the old Empire was astonishingly rectilinear except for its two largest capital cities, the independent Austrian and Hungarian parts were far from being rectilinear.

After World War I, Austria was stripped of her possessions by the treaty-makers at Versailles who, confessedly in the interest of world peace, deliberately carved up the old Austro-Hungarian Empire in such a way that there would inevitably exist an enduring conflict between what was left of Austria and Hungary and the newly formed nations. This was the period of "Brave Little Austria."

In Fig. 10–6 is presented, in the curve at the bottom, as labelled, the rank-frequency distribution of communities of "Brave Little Austria" in 1934. This distribution, which is convex downward throughout, is a clear-cut example of a condition of (urban) *surfeit,* as previously defined, which resulted from the removal of much of Austria's supporting population.

At the top of Fig. 10–6 are two curves. The unbroken line is for Austria in May 1939 after she had been joined to Germany and the Sudetenland. The dotted line is for the U. S. A. in 1930 and has been added for the reader's convenience in assessing the high degree of rectilinearity and the close approximation to a slope of negative unity of the Austro-German data.

Well, that is that! What a vast amount of blood has been spilled and treasure destroyed since those data were first published by the present writer in 1941.[8] In that publication were objective discussions of the dynamics of boundary fixing, and of the dire consequences that will result from the imposition of such inanities as the famous "Morgenthau Plan" (for anyone who was resident at Harvard University during the early months of the war—when President James B. Conant was at the heighth of his political war-agitation—and who looked behind the scenes at what was going on could easily have foretold the ultimate appearance of some sort of a "Morgenthau Plan" that was all so carefully rationalized and so highly endorsed by the "intelligentsia").[9] There were further predictions

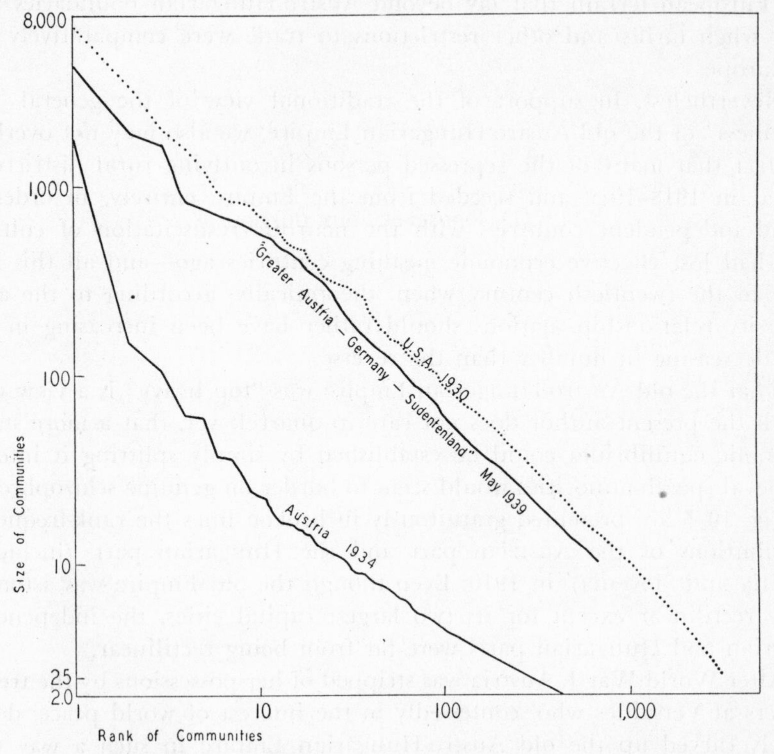

Fig. 10–6. "Greater Austria-Germany-Sudetenland" May, 1939. Communities ranged in the decreasing order of population size, with comparative data from Austria, 1934, and U. S. A., 1930.

there too—about the impending decline of the British Empire, the freedom of India, and the ultimate destruction of certain types of pressure groups —including "religious" and "educational" pressure groups.

These predictions were not nice. In fact, the present writer was viciously attacked for having made them.[10] Our motives were impugned, and so on. Nevertheless, the predictions had one supreme virtue in the light of ensuing history, as, I think, will be evident to those who read them now. We mention these considerations in order to intimate that objective social science as represented by such principles as, say, "The Harmonic Law," may be a far safer conceptual guide for the future well-being of the American people and of mankind than the "intuition" of such persons as Mr. Henry

Morgenthau, Jr., and the then dominant academic and nonacademic "intelligentsia."[11] The oft-heard excuse, "At least they were sincere," loses its lustre somewhat when we reflect that the poor person who believes that he is Napoleon is also doubtless quite sincere in his belief.

We mention these considerations also lest, in turning abruptly to a further demonstration of the Principle of Least Effort, we seem to leave out of consideration the earlier events that necessitated the "bravery" of "Brave Little Austria," as well as the events that are necessitating the bravery of still other brave little states in Europe to whose present "Protector," Russia, Mr. Morgenthau so generously presented the engraved plates of the United States invasion currency.

Our present interest, after all, is solely the demonstration of the Principle of Least Effort. If we have indulged in an *obiter dictum* in which we criticize the academic and nonacademic persons who provided the effective political leadership in American foreign relations during the last several administrations of Mr. F. D. Roosevelt, our purpose is undisguised. We do not indict them on the grounds of their emotional—and perhaps at times even their hysterical—thinking, since no one is completely free from the same; neither on the grounds of the specious logic, spurious correlations, verbalistic argument, and apparently deeply rooted personal biases or even venomous vindictiveness in their judgment, since no one is completely free from these. We indict them because in critical moments they rarely seemed capable of rising effectively above these things and of taking an objective deliberate view of affairs against the background of the best long-term short-term intranational and international interests of the United States—a statement that is by no means true of all other persons. If the above "intelligentsia" claim that the adoption of any one of the numerous possible other policies that were suggested would have led to even direr national consequences, let them produce as a controlled experiment some duplicate planet-earths in which all else remains the same except for the adoption of the respective alternative policies. Until they can do so, their alleged claims of the dire consequences that would have resulted from other procedures remain conjectures, whereas the actual dire consequences of their own effective policies are matters of observable fact. Or would they perchance choose to argue on the basis of the observations of objective social science? In any event, they cannot claim that their type of national defense and world salvation, as well as their type of mentation, have been overlooked in the present book.

D. The Case of India

There is a further possible manner of development that seems to be represented by India, say from 1911 through 1931.[12] The manner of development to which we refer is the utilization of laborsaving devices to increase the number of establishments (under an increasing population) without any appreciable increase in the m diversity of goods and services.

Thus, if the birthrate is very high, as in India, then the population size will be stopped at a point where the country's facilities can support no more persons. At that point the deathrate will balance the birthrate.

If, now, laborsaving devices are introduced in the then extant means of production, so that the same amount of goods and services can be produced with less labor, then the surplus free labor that is made available may be used in one (or both) of two ways. First, it can be used to increase the m diversity of goods and services, as discussed in our previous chapter; and second, it can be used to increase the *total amount* of the extant m kinds of goods and services so that they will be available to an increasing number of persons (i.e., $P \cdot Sn$ increases while m remains stable).

If m diversity is primarily increased, then the slope of the rank-frequency distribution will theoretically increase, as we argued was the case with Germany, as indicated by Fig. 10–4. If, however, all extant establishments

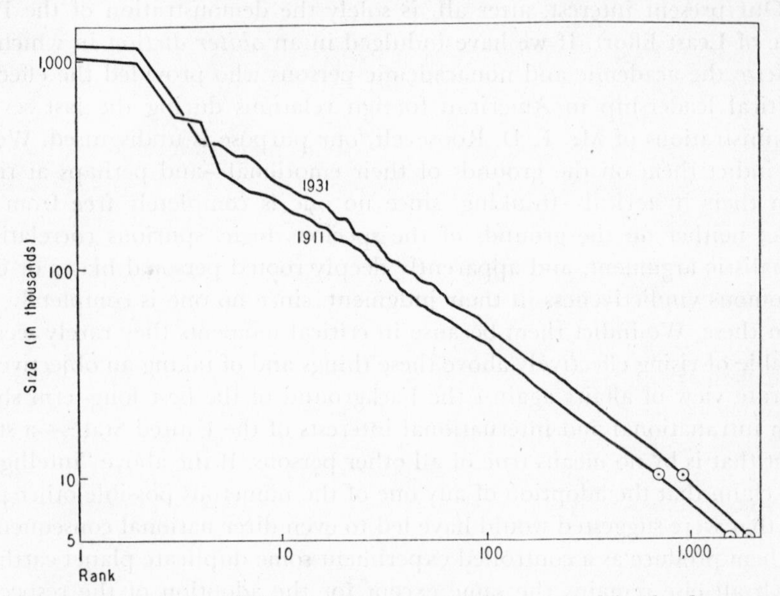

Fig. 10–7. India in 1911 and 1931. Communities ranked in the decreasing order of population size.

are merely increased in number, while the populations of all communities simply grow in proportion to their sizes, then the slope of the distribution will remain the same, though the y intercept will increase.*

It is too much to argue that any population during recent years has followed exclusively this second course of development. Nevertheless, the data for India in 1911 and 1931 respectively, as presented in Fig. 10–7, where we note that the line essentially moves upwards and parallel to itself, do at least illustrate the question at hand.

The horizontal line at the top between ranks 1 and 2 suggests the presence of two separate social systems in India (thereby *perhaps* indicating that India's present-day cultural schism may have an economic counterpart). In a previous publication we argued, perhaps erroneously, that the

* The case of India will be discussed again from a different angle in Chapter Eleven under the heading of *the Imperial two-third slope* in connection with the general problem of equilibrium in a dominance system.

downward concavity at the top might indicate the omission of London, which in those years was both the political and economic capital of India.

On the other hand, the rectilinearity and slope of the data of Fig. 10–7 indicate that India was organized economically, though with a standard of living, in terms of a theoretical *m* diversity, that was appreciably lower than that for Germany and the United States in 1939.

E. Concluding Remarks

The problem of unstable intranational equilibrium is vast. We have merely pointed out what we think are four different kinds of unstable equilibrium, as represented by the history of the United States during the Civil War, the history of Germany, the history of Austria, and the case of India.[13]

Although these distributions may be interpreted differently by others, they are at least not without a certain didactic value as presented. In the first place, they show that rectilinearity is by no means always the rule. In the second place, they show that social systems tend to develop rectilinearity with the elapse of time even if wars and revolutions are sometimes resorted to in the process.

III. Stable and Unstable International Equilibria

Up to now we have mostly treated cases of single national social systems, with primary emphasis upon internal structure and with little regard for relations between two or more national systems (i.e., international relations). We know, however, that few if any national social systems, as the term is commonly used, actually exist in complete isolation; on the contrary, the structure of one system quite generally both influences, and is influenced by, the structures of other systems, with the result that international relations are virtually always an important factor in national organization, and the reverse.

In using the term *international relations,* we are tacitly suggesting that the earth's surface must inevitably be organized into more than one *nation.* The mere fact that the earth always has been organized into a plurality of nations, however, does not mean that it must inevitably continue forever to be so organized. Indeed, before we can inquire into the question of stable and unstable international equilibrium we must first inquire into the possibility of a single all-inclusive "One World Nation." [14] And that in turn will necessitate a definition of a *nation.*

In Chapter Nine we described a theoretical social system that seemed to have a striking counterpart in the historical nation, the United States. In this theoretical system we postulated (1) that each person would give a $1/C$ share of the total work of the system for which he would receive a $1/C$ share of each of the *m* different kinds of goods and services produced; and (2) that all persons would react towards this common production-consumption according to the same rules of procedure (or cultural vocabulary).

The chief shortcoming of this definition of a *nation* is that it may include very much smaller groups than those that are generally known historically as nations.

Nevertheless, this shortcoming is not relevant to our question as to whether a single "One World Nation" is possible, since at present we are interested rather in how large a group can be included in our definition of a nation, and not how small a one. Our present interest in this topic, incidentally, is purely scientific, without any reference to present-day schemes of political action, or to the general desirability or undesirability of a one-world government today, since the implications of our data for such projects, as they seem to me, have already been presented in an earlier publication.[15]

Let us assume, as usual, that the necessary raw materials for our human problems are distributed at random as far as human needs are concerned. Let us then increase the m diversity of needed raw materials until, according to the area-diversity relationship, the entire humanly inhabitable area of the earth's surface is needed for the procurement of needed raw materials. Finally, let us ask where the least work center will be in this "One World" field of activity, so that we may locate there our primate city (i.e., $r = 1$), for theoretically this primate city will arise under the Force of Unification if there is to be a "One World Nation." This hypothetical single primate city at the least work center will be the theoretical "One World Capital."

Yet in view of the curvature of the earth's surface, and with our assumed even distribution of population and random distribution of needed raw materials, can any such single primate city in a hypothetically unique least work center preserve its primacy indefinitely? In this connection, let us remember that the population that lives in the hemisphere that is opposite to this "One World Capital" can conceivably save a great deal of work of transportation by founding a second capital city in their own hemisphere, which will produce the goods and services of the erstwhile "One World Capital," by exploiting as far as possible the raw materials of their own hemisphere, and by trading for the freakishly few raw materials that they do not possess.*

In actual practice it may happen temporarily that some one spot or small section of the world may have a quasi-monopoly of an essential raw material, or of essential skills, or of an essential site in world transportation, as seems to have been the case with England in the nineteenth century. In that event, which we shall find illustrated in our data below, the spot in question may very well become the site of a world primate city, but only for such a period as the monopoly in question can be maintained. During that period there will doubtless be a single world system.

In general, however, world domination by a single system seems to be virtually impossible to establish (except for a fluke of chance), and also virtually impossible to maintain for any very great length of time. The cry

* As soon as we have two different nations we have the problem of international relations. (Today we may be emerging into a state of hemispheric nations, although it may be only one of continental nations.)

that is so dear to the political propagandist—"He is trying to dominate the world!"—may be accurate as to the intent of the person in question; yet it is vain and empty as far as any great likelihood of actual achievement is concerned. For we remember that increasing space means increasing work, and that a rapidly increasing number of persons may be adversely affected by the expanding nation. Sooner rather than later, the expansionist's plans *may fall before the exigencies of space;* sooner rather than later *it may cost more to coerce the subject populations than the subject populations can be made to produce*—the sorry lesson that every would-be world conqueror and every would-be world "savior" apparently has to learn the hard way. This argument will be repeated in Chapter Eleven.

We have defined a nation as a group of persons who contribute equal shares and receive equal shares of the *m* different kinds of goods and services of production (all according to a common set of rules of procedure). And we have suggested that—barring freakish incidents—the whole earth cannot be *permanently* organized into a single nation.

It may be rightly objected, however, that this definition of a nation is too narrow, since not all persons may need or desire a like share of all the different *m* kinds of goods and services of production. Thus, for example, a person in the tropics will not need the same goods and services as a person in the arctic.

To obviate this potent shortcoming of our definition of a nation, we shall modify it to the end that everyone must work a like amount, for which he will receive a like reward in value, with the right to buy whatever he wants. This modification makes the definition more applicable (and incidentally gives an economic justification for money as permits for free choice as well as for *tokens* of exchange).*

Even with this modification of our definition, will a single "One World Nation" still be permanently possible? Or will the modified definition merely lead to specialized local cultures with specialized demands and with specialized production centers to fill the specialized demands? With the development of these specialized local cultures, the language of the world will cleave into dialects and "species," for reasons presented in connection with the J. C. Willis data in Part One. This cleavage into different dialects will be matched by cleavages in economic interests, for, as we saw in Chapter Nine, "a boil on your own neck will worry you more than a famine in China."†

---

* In our discussion of *fashions* and *prestige symbols* in Chapter Twelve, we shall note reasons why persons will tend to *desire* the same *m* kinds of goods.

† Because of these differences in dialects and in economic interests, effective communication about social-economic problems will be possible only in terms of an objective language of human ecology and of biosocial dynamics (cf. Chapter Twelve, Section VI) and not in terms of any cultural speech, including Basic English, which is bound to have, or to develop, differing emotional connotations for differing persons, social strata, and cultures. To my mind, not the least of the difficulties that led to World War II was that of verbal misunderstandings. Strictly considered, the terms, *"isolationism"* and *"internationalism"* have little meaning as exclusive positions in present-day realities, where there will presumably be at least some international trade (i.e., the Force of Unification)

Local cultural differences that result from differences in climate, accessibility, and value of terrain promise, therefore, to remain forever present, with varying degrees of gravity and with the emergence of various national organizations to reflect their varying cultural interests. The most that we can say today about a stable international equilibrium at a given moment of measurement is that everyone should be working at about the same rate, and should be rewarded at about the same rate throughout the world at that moment of measurement. Depending upon the actual conditions at the time, this may or may not admit of a "One World Government," that is, a single *dominance system* (defined in Chapter Eleven).

Even so, a stable equilibrium of today may become unstable tomorrow, as the result of a new discovery or of a sudden shortage somewhere that will alter the comparative rates of work and of reward.

In international organization, as in all biosocial organization, the ultimate definition of *stable equilibrium* may have to take cognizance of Mendel's famous Law of Balance, and therefore include in it the concept of an oscillation about a norm. As to the present-day meaning of the term *international equilibrium,* nothing can yet be formulated with assurance in objective dynamic terms. Although people talk about "unhealthy" and "abnormal" international conditions, they never tell us what a healthy, normal condition is.

We for our part shall say, as a working definition, that those human systems are most nearly ones of stable equilibrium whose members both most nearly give and most nearly receive at equal rates. We shall view wars and revolutions as potential equilibrating devices for effecting a more stable equilibrium, even though the more stable equilibrium may be in terms of a very meagre existence. Yet this is merely a working definition from which we can at best hope only to understand our question more clearly.

The empiric data of our following cases will represent what are commonly believed to be cases of unstable equilibrium. We shall discuss them in terms of our above working definition and in terms of the theoretical and empiric analysis in our preceding chapter, for whatever light they may shed upon our question.

A. The Case of the British Empire

In the remaining pages of the present chapter we shall discuss a few recent historical cases in the light of our theoretical Principle of Least Effort. We shall begin with the case of the British Empire, which in a previous publication [16] was discussed in detail before 1941 in terms of probabilities that in the meantime, alas, have materialized. Our present discussion, therefore, will be brief.

---

and some local trade (i.e., the Force of Diversification). Aside from all ethical and aesthetic considerations, and viewed purely as a matter of gaining information and of seizing opportunities and of avoiding threats, a given Joe Doakes will tend to know more and to care more about events of his environment in an inverse proportion to their *D* distance from him; and he may appropriately view with suspicion the motives and loyalty of those who claim that the well-being of a person at the opposite side of the earth is as important to him as that of his neighbor next door.

Let us remember that Great Britain did in fact make important discoveries that helped to initiate the Industrial Revolution, and that for years she possessed, for all intents and purposes, a virtual monopoly of highly important skills. Hence, she was in a position to produce many valuable new kinds of goods and services for export to other parts of the world which could profitably buy them in exchange for their own local raw materials. Furthermore, Great Britain was in a geographical position at the time to dominate by force the sea lanes of the world, and thereby to frustrate the aspirations of others in the same direction. Finally, she understood how to manipulate to her own advantage the native leadership of other countries (e.g., India, the African Colonies, the United States) during critical periods of her history.

The above is familiar, nor is the story complete.

As a result of this British Hegemony there was a long period, culminating in World War I, during which the world could in fact be viewed as approximately constituting a single economic system, since, to a very considerable extent, the rest of the world did export raw materials and local goods to Great Britain in exchange for British finished goods. Moreover, Britain largely established and arbitrated the prevailing rules of international conduct in international relations, even if the conquest and subjugation of independent states were necessary to that end. Indeed, so great was Britain's cultural domination at the time that today many persons in the United States whose formative periods came to an end before Queen Victoria's demise, still tend to look upon these past British ways and British views as something that is eternally and absolutely correct in every moral, economic, cultural, and political sense (e.g., "Queen Victoria put this world in order once and for all, and anyone who tries to upset it is a nasty thing"). Although this neurotic view is doubtless both amusing and politically dangerous, let us not forget that, comparatively speaking, the underlying principles of British Imperial action could not have been completely unsound dynamically, since they otherwise would not have worked successfully during many long decades.

In Fig. 10–8 we present doubly logarithmically the rank-frequency distribution of those cities of the world which, at about 1920, had not fewer than 100,000 inhabitants. The community rank 1 is London, for which there are two points: the lower point was London's official population size, whereas the upper point represents the then size of "Greater London."

This rank-frequency distribution for 1920, which represents about the end of British world hegemony, is not far off from rectilinearity, even though it does show a *deficiency* of communities of about 500,000 and fewer persons in the world in 1920. As to the more nearly straight upper portion of the curve, "Greater London" is undeniably the primate city with about the correct size.

That "Greater London" at that time was dynamically a world Capital and not merely the Capital of the British Empire is evident from Fig. 10–9, where we present the rank-frequency distribution of communities of 50,000 and more persons in the British Empire at about 1921.

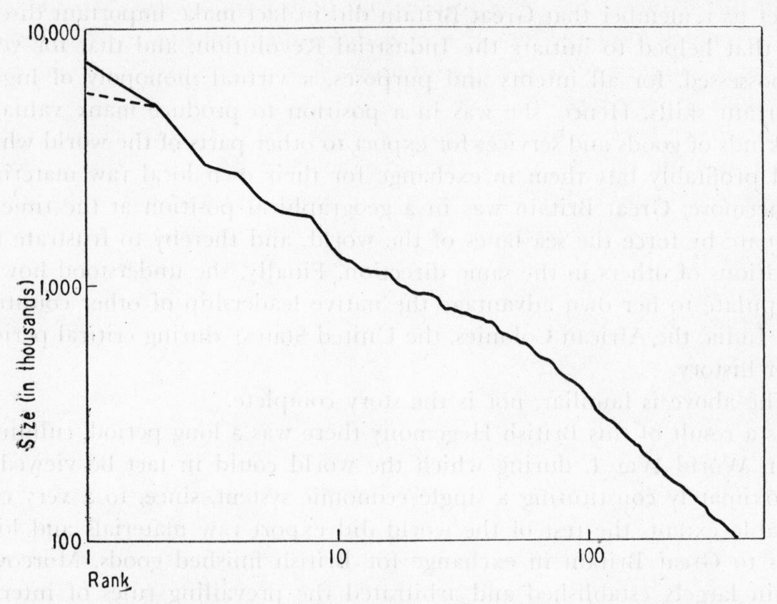

Fig. 10–8. Cities of the world (about 1920) with at least 100,000 inhabitants, ranked in the decreasing order of population size.

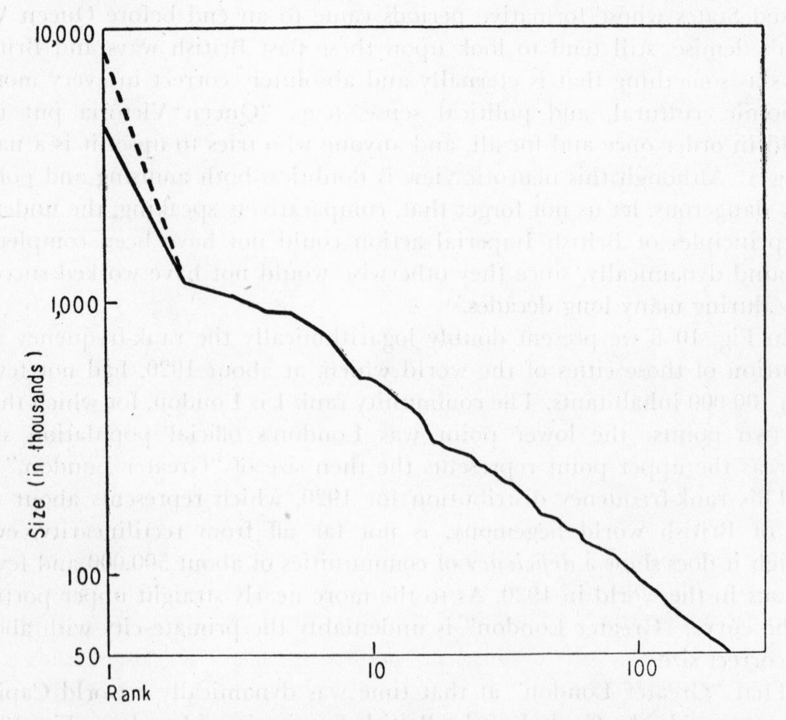

Fig. 10–9. British empire (about 1921). Communities with at least 50,000 persons, ranked in the decreasing order of population size.

An inspection of Fig. 10–9 reveals that both London and "Greater London" are much too large for the rest of the British Empire, thereby indicating that London was the first community of a system that included much more than its own Empire.

The lower part of the distribution of Fig. 10–9, beginning with about rank 8, is quite rectilinear. If we study the separate rank-frequency distributions of the major parts of the British Empire, as presented in Fig. 10–10,

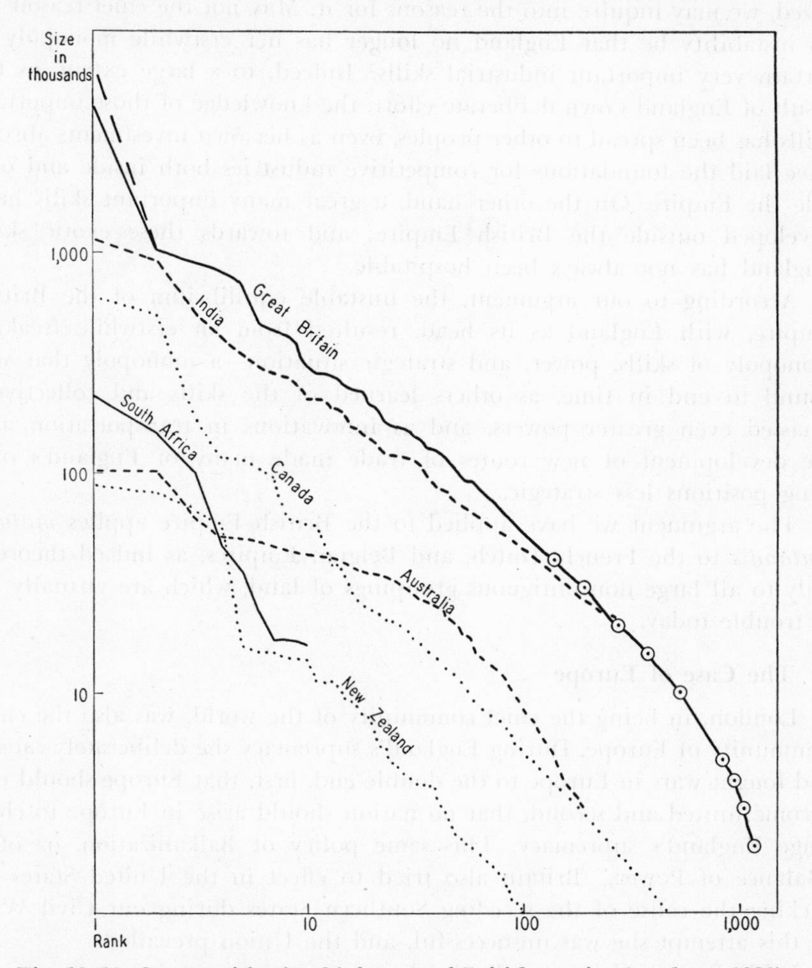

Fig. 10–10. Communities in chief parts of British empire (at about 1921).

we find that those for India and Canada, as already presented (Figs. 10–1, 10–7) are alone of striking rectilinearity. Indeed, it is the tremendous population of India that statistically almost engulfs the communities of the rest of the Empire, and that is largely responsible for the rectilinearity of the distribution of Fig. 10–9.

Today India is breaking away politically from Britain, and Canada is virtually independent. Without the inclusion of the Indian and Canadian populations in the Empire, both London and "Greater London" will be even more out of line with what remains of her empire. Theoretically, this disproportionately large size of London—and for that matter of Great Britain—will dynamically result in one or both of two things: the decrease in British population by death or migration, and/or the findings of new supporting terrain. Both these eventualities have been recognized for years by persons of competence in Great Britain.

Now that the highly unstable position of Great Britain is well recognized, we may inquire into the reasons for it. May not the chief reason for its instability be that England no longer has her erstwhile monopoly of certain very important industrial skills? Indeed, to a large extent, as the result of England's own deliberate effort, the knowledge of those important skills has been spread to other peoples, even as her own investments abroad have laid the foundations for competitive industries both inside and outside the Empire. On the other hand, a great many important skills have developed outside the British Empire; and towards these exotic skills England has not always been hospitable.

According to our argument, the unstable equilibrium of the British Empire, with England as its head, resulted from an erstwhile freakish monopoly of skills, power, and strategic situation—a monopoly that was bound to end in time, as others learned of the skills and collectively amassed even greater powers, and as innovations in transportation and the development of new routes of trade made many of England's outlying positions less strategic.

The argument we have applied to the British Empire applies *mutatis mutandis* to the French, Dutch, and Belgian Empires, as indeed theoretically to all large noncontiguous groupings of land, which are virtually all in trouble today.

B. The Case of Europe

London, in being the chief community of the world, was also the chief community of Europe. During England's supremacy she deliberately caused and fought wars in Europe to the double end, first, that Europe should not become united and second, that no nation should arise in Europe to challenge England's supremacy. This same policy of Balkanization, or of a "Balance of Power," Britain also tried to effect in the United States by backing the cause of the seceding Southern States during our Civil War. In this attempt she was unsuccessful, and the Union prevailed.

With Europe, however, England was more successful in temporarily obstructing a larger and more economical union of the continent, even though her obstruction may not have been quite so profound as our history books lead us to believe.[17]

Since the middle of the nineteenth century, continental Europe has become highly industrialized, with the development of valuable new skills and a very valuable intracontinental trade, in which, incidentally, England took part. In other words, Europe, in spite of England's obstructionism, and in spite of serious cultural differences, has already taken long steps towards an effective economic unity.

The question now arises as to whether there is any reflection of this developing European unity in the rank-frequency distribution of collective European communities.

In Fig. 10–11 we present for about 1880 and for about 1920 respectively, the rank-frequency distributions of the cities of Europe of not fewer than 100,000 inhabitants.

According to these data, there was in 1880 a marked horizontal line between ranks 2 and 3 that is quite similar to what we observed in the data for the conflict-ridden United States before the Civil War. During the period

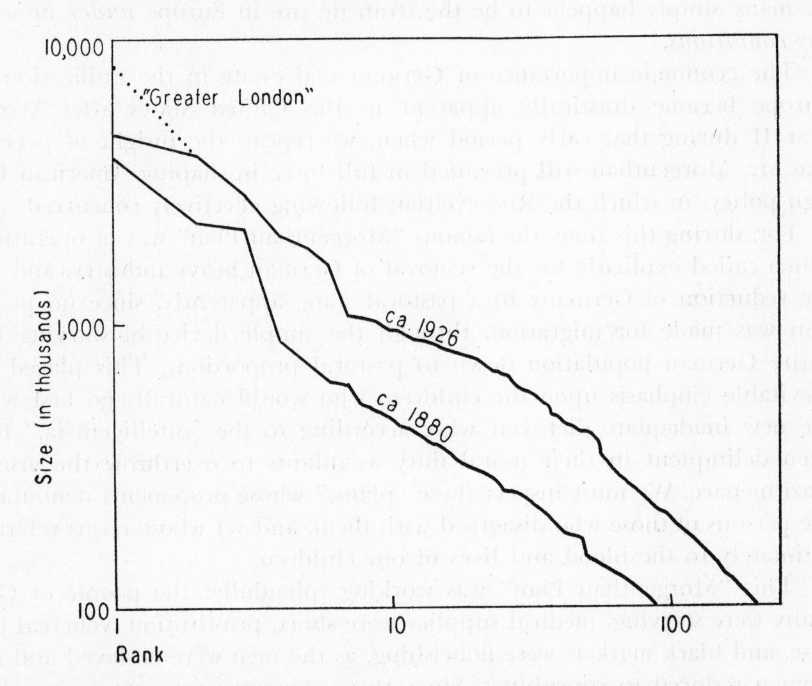

Fig. 10–11. Cities in Europe of not less than 100,000 inhabitants in 1880 and 1920 (approximately).

from 1880 and 1926, however, this horizontal line in Europe had managed to disappear, much as if a greater effective unity had emerged during that time. Indeed, the curve for 1926, with "Greater London" as the chief community, is not far off from rectilinearity. In other words, judged by Europe's larger communities, Europe was indeed becoming a unified social system, with London as its primate city.

Yet let us ask whether there were any enduring economic conditions that made London's (and England's) primacy in Europe permanently necessary. Surely other harbors in Europe are just as convenient for international trade as England's. England by 1920 had very few goods and services for export that were uniquely her own, and quite obviously neither London nor England are centrally located in Europe.

Indeed, as a matter of sheer geometry, the least-work center of Europe lies somewhere within the terrain that is now Germany. If Europe is to be unified, then the real estate of Germany seems destined to be its center, even though the then inhabitants of the real estate in question will no longer be Germans if persons of the political and economic insight of the ex-Secretary of the U. S. Treasury, Mr. Henry Morgenthau, have their way (witness, the famous "Morgenthau plan" which was endorsed by a certain college president).

Therefore, it may not have been entirely accidental, nor merely the consequence of an innate germplasmic bad taste that Germany has been the chief opponent to British domination of the world and of Europe. Germany simply happens to be the strategic site in Europe *under present-day conditions.*

The economic importance of German real estate in the unification of Europe became drastically apparent to the United States after World War II during that early period when, we repeat, the insight of persons like Mr. Morgenthau still prevailed in full force in shaping American foreign policy, in which the Rooseveltian following effectively concurred.

For, during this time, the famous "Morgenthau Plan" was in operation, which called explicitly for the removal of German heavy industry, and for the reduction of Germany to a pastoral state, apparently, since no provision was made for migration, through the simple device of starving the entire German population down to pastoral proportions. This placed an inevitable emphasis upon the children, who would naturally go first with the new inadequate diet, but who, according to the "intelligentsia," had been delinquent in their moral duty as infants to overthrow the armed Nazi menace. We must inspect these "plans," whose proponents denounced the persons of those who disagreed with them, and yet whose terms referred ultimately to the blood and lives of our children.

This "Morgenthau Plan" was working splendidly: the people of Germany were starving, medical supplies were short, prostitution, venereal disease, and black markets were flourishing, as the men were enslaved and the women reduced to concubines. Since these consequences were foreseeable, they were presumably deliberately desired. Above all, the population was being "re-educated" into paths of American Democracy and into the beauties of the United Nations with the esoteric propaganda of the school of brave Mr. Archibald MacLeish, whose writings, if we may so interpret his statement, quoted in Chapter Seven, were constantly being molested by Nazi attempts to sabotage his meanings.

Why then was this eminently successful and highly moral foreign policy suddenly reversed? For, if memory serves, almost overnight the anti-fraternization and "hate Germans" propaganda was withdrawn and, as soon as possible, replaced; food and medical supplies were shipped, and every effort was undertaken to unify Germany politically and to raise her level of production.

Why?

This reversal of foreign policy was admittedly undertaken for two reasons. First of all, we found at long last by actual experience that Europe was economically very largely unified as a whole and in terms of a German industry; in short, we found what the empiric data presented in this book have shown all along. Second, we suddenly realized that Russia, even before Mr. Hitler came to power and made her a mere "bogeyman," had all along been cognizant of the value of German real estate, and also, we might add, of the value of the technical skills of German scientists, which at least one important group in the United States wished vindictively to keep excluded from our shores after the war in spite of our imperative national need for their information.

Today, with the co-operation of British leaders, American foreign policy is in the direction of a unified Western European economic reconstruction by means of Western European co-operation and Western European self-help. Though European cultural hatreds may seem to run so high today as to inhibit any effective co-operation, let us remember that they ran even higher during the Thirty Years War, after which the opposing parties did get together for the simple reason that they had to.

Knowledge gained by random trial-and-error experimentation in the political and social field can apparently be costly for mankind. So, too, the adoption of policies that are speculatively conceived without reference to actualities and to scientific principles, and whose only buttressing is their proponents' intuitive and often intellectually smug insight into a claimed eternal *veritas*.

C. Summary

The term *stable equilibrium* means in general that things do not change with time. In the course of the present and preceding chapters, we have assumed certain conditions which we have suggested may represent conditions of stable equilibrium. We have by no means shown that our assumed conditions do in fact represent stable equilibrium, even though we have discussed cases of intranational and international organization and conflict in terms of them.

The question of international equilibrium is, after all, a large question; and not the least of disturbances to the establishment of a more stable world equilibrium may be a dogmatic attitude towards it.

In view of the havoc that a dogmatic attitude can cause, and has caused, let us not be too eager with a definition of international equilibrium, in any other sense than that of a working hypothesis. Instead, let us content ourselves with the hope that we may have helped somewhat to clarify the question.

Perhaps the question of intranational and international equilibrium can best be studied against the general background of intraspecies and interspecies equilibrium as discussed in Chapter Six. Viewed simply as a species, people should theoretically behave in a like manner in like situations. The only difficulty therein is that people differ so widely in their knowledge. Moreover, man has evolved a social system in recent centuries whose very existence depends upon an assembly of raw materials from the four corners of the earth, and whose functioning depends upon a knowledge and an information service of simply tremendous proportions. Any monopoly or control of knowledge or of information or of the flow of raw materials and of goods and services can obviously cause some persons to work harder than others, and to assume greater risks than others, and to be rewarded at a far smaller rate than others—all to their own personal disadvantage.

And yet what is biosocial equilibrium? What is the perfect human society? Is the perfection of society a question of more material goods for all, or is it a question of establishing a "City of God" in every person's heart? Is biosocial equilibrium a static condition, or is it something that is constantly changing as it oscillates about a changing norm?

The answer to these questions may depend upon first ascertaining what the particular factor is that is minimized in biosocial dynamics. We are still engaged in demonstrating that the dynamic minimum is *effort*. The argument of the present chapter, with its supporting data, is but an extension of that in our previous chapter, where we explained the meaning of the Principle of Least Effort in terms of human social behavior.

CHAPTER ELEVEN

THE DISTRIBUTION OF ECONOMIC POWER AND SOCIAL STATUS

In this chapter we shall investigate a far-reaching economy that up to now we have barely mentioned. We refer to the obvious economy of having another individual do one's work if the other individual can be induced to do so. This new economy, which is present everywhere, will modify somewhat the argument of our preceding chapters, in which we assumed that everyone performs precisely a $1/C$ share of work for which he receives precisely a $1/C$ share of all the m different kinds of goods and services of production.

But, although this new economy will modify our previous argument, it will by no means invalidate it. On the contrary, our previous argument will serve to show us the limits to which one or more individuals can manipulate others, even to the economic disadvantage of those others. Indeed it is rather the limits to the economical manipulation of the "other fellow" than the economy of the manipulation itself that will concern us.

The economy of manipulating the "other fellow" to one's own advantage is only one particular aspect of the general economy of trying to manipulate one's entire environment to one's own advantage, as studied in considerable detail in Part One. The chief difficulty of manipulating the "other fellow" arises from the fact that it is also economical for the "other fellow" to do a little manipulation on his own account, while resisting manipulation by others.

Thus arises the age-old problem of economically exploiting others—or of economically dominating others—a problem which, according to the thesis of this book, will be with mankind forever, since (1) it will always be economical for a person to get others to do his work for him, and since (2) man will always tend to behave with maximum economy. Even though the terms *dominance* and *exploitation* may have an ugly connotation for those who lay great weight upon "the finer things in life," we shall not argue with the fact.* Indeed, curiously enough, we shall have occasion to note that what we call the "advance of human civilization," including the "advance of the arts and the sciences" and other "finer things in life," is almost entirely the result of the economy of exploitation.

---

* *Exploitation* in our usage means merely *"to get the good out of something"* (not in the bad sense of, say, *extortion*). Whatever A does to B, B can do to A (i.e., the rules are impartial). An organization can be beneficial both to the exploiting organizers and to the exploited organized.

I. THEORETICAL CONSIDERATIONS

The economy of exploitation can perhaps best be approached theoretically if we begin by assuming that each member of the fixed C population produces a $1/C$ share of the total production of the group, and that each person can successfully survive from a $(1/C - a)$ share of the total production. The a increment that is left over is important, since it is theoretically the largest amount that can be taken from a person without killing him. The product, $C \times a$, or Ca, is important because it represents the total amount that *exploiters* can take from the entire C population. For convenience we shall assume initially that all exploiters come from outside the C population (this initial assumption will save us the bother of operating with the term, $C - n$, with n representing the number of exploiters). We shall also assume initially that a is fixed.

A. Competition Among the Exploiters: The *Ca* Hypothesis

In the preceding paragraph we stated that Ca represented the total amount of exploitable earnings of our fixed C population of exploiters, of whom each provides a single fixed exploitable a increment. With these definitions in mind let us explore the dynamics of distributing this total Ca income to the elite of exploiters.

Our exploration will be in terms of two successive analogues. The *first* (1) analogue will be similar to that of distributing the fixed space of a newspaper to n different news items of varying S size, as discussed in Chapter Five. The *second* (2) analogue will be similar to that of the $\bar{N}$ number of communities of like P size, as discussed in Chapter Nine. Both analogues will lead to the same familiar equations; and one analogue will lead to the other.

1. The First Analogue. Any *exploiter* who wishes to increase his income can do so by increasing the N number of subjects, or *exploitees,* that are tributary to him. Hence, to increase one's N is one device for increasing one's Na income. Nor has this device been frowned upon historically. For, as history shows, the conquest of territory for the sake of acquiring additional populations of tribute-paying workers has long been one of the motives of aggressive warfare.

History also shows that there is an opposing economy, or Force, which tends to curb the ambition of any one exploiter. For, in simple terms, as one exploiter increases the Na amount of his income in a fixed C population, he thereby decreases the opportunity of other exploiters to increase their incomes. For that matter, as any exploiter increases his Na income, he does concomitantly two other things: (1) he correspondingly increases his threat to other would-be exploiters, if we assume that his strength is in proportion to the size of his Na; and (2) he becomes an increasingly more profitable person for others to despoil.

Yet the lesson of history does not stop there. For it also tells us of the economical device for an exploiter to utilize, both for the sake of increasing his Na income, and for the sake of defending it. This economical device is none other than sheer physical force, or its threat, by means of which one kills or incapacitates the competitive exploiter, loots his estate, kills and enslaves his servants, and so on.

Since this physical force must be exerted and directed by persons, we can understand how an exploiter may profitably hire a retinue of individuals who will fight, both in order to defend their master's exploitation, and in order to extend it. This retinue must be paid by the exploiter from the exploiter's *Na* income. We shall shortly see that this payment of the retinue will itself involve the problem of economical exploitation. For the time being let us inspect the problem of the economical n number of exploiters of a system and of the comparative sizes of their *Na* incomes—a type of problem that is quite familiar to us by now.

From the *viewpoint of any single exploiter,* there is *always* an *individual* economy in alone possessing the entire *Ca* exploitable surplus, with the result that the n number of exploiters will be 1. This the single exploiter will attempt to accomplish both by decreasing the $n - 1$ number of his competitive exploiters and by decreasing their respective *Na* incomes. If the lesson of history means anything, the procedure is to gain strength by despoiling the weak, and then to join with the weak in order to despoil the strong. From the viewpoint of the individual exploiter there is hypothetically always the urge to gain *everything* by despoiling others. Of course, as the single exploiter becomes increasingly more successful, in the sense of acquiring an increasing *Na* income, he thereby becomes increasingly more a person who is to be feared and who is worth despoiling. In other words, he will tend increasingly more to unite the other exploiters in an alliance that is designed to oppose and to despoil him, and which, by its very nature, entails collective action. This alliance of the remaining exploiters to oppose and to despoil the successful exploiter represents an economy that acts in the direction of increasing the n number of exploiters at the expense of the large *Na* incomes of the rich whose estates will be partitioned.

But if we now take the *viewpoint of the system as a whole,* which is the viewpoint that we shall henceforth adopt exclusively, we can see that every actual or aspiring exploiter can adopt one of two alternative courses of action. *First,* he can join with the stronger to despoil and to decrease the weaker (this is our erstwhile Force of Unification); or *second,* he can join with the weaker to despoil and partition the stronger (this is our erstwhile Force of Diversification). Clearly the *first* alternative is to his advantage when there are many small exploiters and no markedly rich ones, since he can gobble up these weak exploiters one after another. On the other hand, the *second* alternative is to his advantage when there is a decreasing number of increasingly rich exploiters; for although these rich exploiters will be more difficult to overcome, they will offer correspondingly more lucrative spoils when once vanquished. Equilibrium may be said to exist *from the viewpoint of the system* when the above two alternatives are equally advantageous (or equally disadvantageous) for the actual or aspiring individual exploiter.*

* The above Forces of Unification and Diversification are defined in terms of the organization of the system as a whole. The enduring desire which we impute to every *individual* exploiter to gain everything either by joining the few and rich in order to

Indeed, *from the viewpoint of the system* the case is analogous to that of the division of the space of a newspaper into an n number of different news items of varying S size as explained in Chapter Five, where we argued that equilibrium was established in a rank-frequency distribution according to the equation of the equilateral hyperbola, $r \cdot S = C$. For in this equation, the magnitude of the Force of Unification, which acts in the direction of reducing n to 1, is equalled by the magnitude of the Force of Diversification, which acts in the direction of increasing n to such a point that, in the case of our exploiters, each exploiter will receive, say, a small $(1/C - a + b)$ income that is just enough to keep him alive.

Although this concept of the balance of Forces will be discussed again in our *second analogue,* nevertheless, our foregoing argument suffices to suggest that equilibrium, because of the nature of the factors that are involved, will be represented by a distribution of the n exploiters that is hyperbolic, in the sense that the n number of different main exploiters (including their retinues) when ranked, r, in the order of the decreasing sizes of their Na incomes (with, say, c, the smallest income) will be:

$$r \cdot (Na) = nc \tag{11–1}$$

For convenience of later argument, we shall also postulate that the smallest exploiter $(r = n)$ will receive an income $(1/C - a + b)$ that is only slightly larger than $(1/C - a)$. We shall also assume for the time being that Ca is fixed.

Thus distributed, the n number of exploiters will hold each other in check, in the sense that the risks of despoiling one another are as great as the rewards. We shall return to this argument later when we shall state it in a second analogue.

Eq. (11–1), for reasons already presented in Chapter Two, can also be stated in the form of the equation of the pure harmonic series (in which A represents the Na income of the richest exploiter): [1]

$$A \cdot Sn = \frac{A}{1} + \frac{A}{2} + \frac{A}{3} + \ . \ . \ . + \frac{A}{n} \tag{11–2}$$

Here let us remember that our two preceding equations represent concrete mathematical parameters that are subject to empiric test; yet our Forces of Unification represent only theoretical factors which we cannot measure objectively since we do not know of any measureable unit.

Let us also note, lest we overlook it, that our Eq. (11–1) refers to the proportions of the simple harmonic series which would have the value $p = 1$, if stated in terms of the generalized harmonic series. As we pass down the series, we pass from the few exploiters who are powerful because of their greater *individual wealth,* to those exploiters who, though individually less wealthy, are powerful because of their *collectively greater numbers.* It is this aspect of the simple harmonic series, or of the equilateral hyperbola, already quite familiar to us, that we are stressing now.

---

despoil the many and poor, or to join with the latter to despoil the former may be viewed as a quasi third Force.

Reflecting upon the implications of the two above equations, we note that if the two equations with their slopes of negative unity on doubly logarithmic co-ordinates represent a condition of dynamic equilibrium, then any upward convexity above this line (a condition of *surfeit*) will mean that too few are getting too much at that point, thereby indicating a probable future increase in the Force of Diversification at that point. Conversely, any downward convexity below this line (a condition of *deficiency*) will mean that too many are receiving too little, thereby indicating a probable future increase in the Force of Unification at that point. Bends from our theoretical line of equilibrium will therefore have meaning.

At the beginning of our argument we pointed out that exploiters must have *retinues* to help them; and that the exploiters must reward the members of their respective retinues from their *Na* incomes, which are the only sources of the exploiters' wealth. Hence, the *Na* incomes of our preceding two equations are *group incomes* (i.e., incomes that are paid to the exploiters, from which they pay their retinues) and not net incomes to the exploiters after they have paid their retinues.

Once we inquire into the *net incomes* that accrue to the individual exploiters as well as to the individual members of his retinue—hereinafter the distribution of *individual incomes*—we ask a different question. For convenience we shall henceforth assume that the exploiter and his retinue constitute the group we are calling a *retinue* (i.e., the exploiter is the chief member of the retinue). Moreover, a group may be so small that it consists only of a single person who is both exploiter and retinue.

In order to keep the two kinds of incomes apart, let us view *group incomes* as the incomes of competing independent principalities, as in Europe in the Middle Ages, or in erstwhile India, or as in the independent cities of Renaissance Italy, or in American corporations.* The *individual incomes,* on the other hand, are the net incomes that are paid to the individual executives (or to the members of the *elite,* as we shall later say) of those principalities, cities, corporations, and so on.

Since the economy of exploiting the "other fellow" is theoretically common to all beings, we can understand how competition may arise among the members of a retinue for larger individual shares of the *group income.* This competition between the members of a retinue may be considered either from the viewpoint of the chief exploiter of the group—say, the king —who tries to keep the remainder of the retinue from despoiling him or abandoning him; or from the viewpoint of the individual members of the entire retinue, who severally organize themselves into subsidiary cliques for the sake of collectively increasing their individual shares of the *group income.*

As far the the king, or chief exploiter, is concerned, if he is too niggardly in rewarding his retinue associates, either (*a*) because he wants to keep too much for himself, or (*b*) because he wants to have a very large n_2 number of persons in his retinue, then (*a*) his followers may unite and

* The rank-frequency distribution of the populations of said competing principalities, etc., should be approximately that of our generalized harmonic series (another way of viewing the data of Chapter Nine).

despoil him, or (*b*) they may abandon him for another chieftain who pays better—thereby reducing the size of n_2 by the amount of their defection. On the other hand, if the king rewards too generously, thereby decreasing the n_2 number of his followers, then he risks having too small a retinue for the royal defense and the royal aggression against other groups. Hence a king, or any other retinue leader of any sort who wants to maintain himself as the controlling head of his retinue, must bestow his largesse in the "right amounts" to the "right" n_2 number of members of the retinue. For that reason there will be a "right amount" of income to be paid to the "right" n_2 number of individual members of the total retinue.

This problem of the "right amount" of income to be paid to the "right" n_2 number of retinue members can perhaps best be fathomed if we view the n_2 members of a retinue as actively competing for larger individual shares of the distributable Na group income. For then we note that the problem of the respective sizes of the individual incomes that are paid to the n_2 members of the retinue in their competition for larger incomes will be precisely parallel to the problem of the competition among the n different exploiters (i.e., *social groups*) for the entire Ca income as previously discussed.

For, once again, the Force of Unification will make for 1 single large G individual income which takes the entire Na income of the whole group, whereas the Force of Diversification will make for a larger n_2 number of incomes with proportionately smaller G *average individual incomes.* Moreover, these two Forces will be of equal magnitude and opposite direction, for precisely the same reasons as in the case of competition among the n different exploiters for larger Na group incomes out of the total Ca exploitable surplus. In each retinue, n_2 will be a point of equilibrium between the two hypothetical Forces.

Let us inquire theoretically into the determinants of the size of n_2 in any retinue. In this connection we have just used the term, G to describe the *average income* that is paid to the individual n_2 members of a group whose total group income is Na; or, in equation form:

$$n_2 \times G = Na \tag{11–3}$$

Here let us note that the Force of Unification will act in the direction of increasing G at the expense of n_2 whereas the Force of Diversification will act in the opposite direction of increasing n_2 at the expense of G. If, as we assume, the two Forces are of equal magnitude and of opposite direction, then, for any social group, we may make the following statements which are analogous to those derived in Chapter Two and which we shall presently verify with numerical examples:

$$n_2 = G \tag{11–4}$$

$$n_2^2 = Na \tag{11–5}$$

$$n_2 = (Na)^{\frac{1}{2}} \tag{11–6}$$

Moreover, if we remember that the rank-frequency distribution of the n different *social groups* (i.e., exploiters) according to the size of their *group incomes* is harmonically seriated according to Eq. (11–2), then the following Eq. (11–7) will describe the distribution of the sizes of the retinues of these social groups when ranked in the order of decreasing size:

$$Elite = A^{\frac{1}{2}}Sn = \frac{A^{\frac{1}{2}}}{1^{\frac{1}{2}}} + \frac{A^{\frac{1}{2}}}{2^{\frac{1}{2}}} + \frac{A^{\frac{1}{2}}}{3^{\frac{1}{2}}} + \ldots + \frac{A^{\frac{1}{2}}}{n^{\frac{1}{2}}} \qquad (11\text{–}7)$$

In this equation $A^{\frac{1}{2}}$ represents the n_2 number of members of the retinue of the largest social group [whose Na income is A in Eq. (11–2)]. Indeed the n different social groups of Eq. (11–7) will have the same rank as in Eq. (11–2).

The term $A^{\frac{1}{2}} \cdot Sn$, which represents the summation of all the members of the retinues of all the n different social groups of Eq. (11–2), we shall define as the *elite* of the C social system. Since, according to Eq. (11–4) $n_2 = G$, we see that Eq. (11–7) also describes the rank-frequency distribution of the G average incomes of the n different groups, provided that the term $A_{\frac{1}{2}}$ is redefined to represent the G of the largest group.

Eq. (11–7) which gives us information about the average individual incomes within the n different retinues, would seem offhand to tell us nothing about the rank-frequency distribution of individual incomes among the n_2 members of each individual retinue.

If we remember (1) that the same argument about the Forces of Unification and of Diversification in reference to the allocation of the system's total exploitable Ca income to the n different exploitation groups will also apply, *mutatis mutandis,* to the allocation of a group's Na income to the n_2 members of its retinue, then it follows (2) that Eq. (11–7) will also describe the allocation of individual incomes to the n_2 members of each group's retinue, provided (*a*) that n_2 is substituted for n; and provided (*b*) that for the term $A^{\frac{1}{2}}$, we now substitute the term A_2, which represents the largest income paid to any member of any n_2 retinue; and provided (*c*) that each individual member of the retinue is viewed as a group (and indeed the richer ones may well have a private retinue of their own).

After the above substitutions (*a, b,* and *c*) have been made, the following equation will theoretically describe the n_2 individual incomes in any *retinue,* or:

Individual incomes:
(to members of retinue)

$$A_2Sn = \frac{A_2}{1^{\frac{1}{2}}} + \frac{A_2}{2^{\frac{1}{2}}} + \frac{A_2}{3^{\frac{1}{2}}} + \ldots + \frac{A_2}{{n_2}^{\frac{1}{2}}} \qquad (11\text{–}8)$$

If we now ask for everyday examples of what Eq. (11–8) may describe, we might submit that it describes the rank-frequency distribution of the salaries paid to the n_2 number of persons on the executive staff of General Motors Corporation, or of Ford, or of Du Pont, or of General Electric, or of the Standard Oil Company of New Jersey, or of any other well-managed corporation. Eq. (11–2), on the other hand, describes the total incomes that accrue to the individual corporations themselves (e.g., to Ford, to General Motors, to Du Pont, etc.).

The question now arises as to the distribution of individual incomes to all members of the elite in the entire social system regardless of their retinue memberships. In short, what is the rank-frequency distribution of the *individual incomes* of all the n_3 members of the entire $A^{\frac{1}{2}} \cdot Sn$ elite?

In the light of Eqs. (11–2), (11–7), and (11–8), the answer to this question as to the distribution of the n_3 individual incomes of the entire elite is:

$$\text{Individual incomes:} \quad A_3 \cdot Sn = \frac{A_3}{1^{\frac{1}{2}}} + \frac{A_3}{2^{\frac{1}{2}}} + \frac{A_3}{3^{\frac{1}{2}}} + \ldots + \frac{A_3}{n_3^{\frac{1}{2}}} \qquad (11\text{–}9)$$

where A_3 describes the largest individual income that is paid to a member of the largest retinue, and, in everyday terms, the individual incomes in the United States, or any other country, will theoretically be distributed according to Eq. (11–9). This last equation, incidentally, is the same as that of the Pareto income distribution *except* that the Pareto school [2] argues that the exponent, *p*, in terms of our own equation, will be ⅔ instead of ½ as we are arguing.*

It is evident that our preceding nine equations depend in the last analysis upon the total *Ca* income that can be exploited from the *C* workers of the social system (these *C* workers we shall henceforth call the *pariah class*). Clearly, as *Ca* increases, and if the smallest individual income, $1/C - a + b$, that is paid to any member of the elite remains the same, then an increasing n_3 number of persons can be supported in the elite. Yet regardless of how large or how small the *Ca* exploitable surplus is, our equations will still hold.†

Our preceding argument is cast in terms of the comparative sizes of incomes that are paid to members of the elite from a *Ca* exploitable surplus. These incomes of varying sizes refer to shares of varying sizes of the goods and services of the production of the social system in question. Hence, our equations, technically speaking, represent the distribution of economic power in terms of the capacity to buy goods and services from others.

Yet because of that very fact, our equations may also represent what might be called the *distribution of relative power in a dominance system,* since the larger incomes can also buy better professional advice of all sorts (i.e., legal, medical, religious), and can also alter their environments more

---

* Much more belongs theoretically to the distribution of incomes than that described by Pareto's famous law (*vide infra*). There is also the question of the group incomes (of Eq. (11–2)) as well as the question of the wages paid to the "exploited" *C* workers (or the *pariah class*) which we shall consider later.

† It seems that the n_3 number of members of the elite will be a function of the square root of *Ca*. Thus, (1) $A \cdot Sn = Ca$; $A = Ca/Sn$; (2) $Elite = A^{\frac{1}{2}} \cdot Sn = (Ca/Sn)^{\frac{1}{2}} \times Sn$; (3) $Elite = (Ca)^{\frac{1}{2}} \times Sn^{\frac{1}{2}}$. The variable, $Sn^{\frac{1}{2}}$, is very small (e.g., 4 or 5 at the most in the U. S. A. in recent years). This "square root function" may ultimately be of some value in computing national incomes. Rousseau, curiously enough, argued that the size of the elite (i.e., government) varied with the square root of the population, if I understand correctly.[3] There may well be a connection between the elite and the population. The elite of a given group tends, therefore, to be a relatively small fraction of the total *C* population of the system.

to their own liking, including an alteration of the objectives and rules of procedure of the entire social system itself. For that reason our concept of a dominance system (or of a power system) in equilibrium according to our above equations may also include the distribution of political power, including police power, in the selection of social objectives and of the methods of procedure whereby the objectives are pursued, as will become even more apparent, I think, in our *second analogue.*

2. *The Second Analogue.* One drawback to the theoretical argument of our foregoing first analogue may be the difficulty of envisaging it in concrete terms. To obviate this difficulty let us restate our argument in terms of a *second analogue* that is modeled on the analogue of the n number of communities of varying P sizes as presented in Chapter Nine. In the present case, the P size of the community becomes the A size of the income of the social group; while the size of the p exponent in the equation of the generalized harmonic series is stabilized at 1.

If we take a large terrain that is populated with a C number of serfs who produce a Ca exploitable surplus as previously defined, we can see how a large N_1 number of *local squires* might emerge with retinues to skim off the Ca surplus. Since the squire's life is one of comparative ease, there will be a tremendous desire for persons to enter the *squire class,* thereby increasing the N_1 number of squires to such a point that each squire will receive a $1/C - a + b$ share of income that is barely more than the almost starvation $1/C - a$ share of a serf. This extreme increase in the N_1 number of different squires represents an extreme operation of the Force of Diversification.

On the other hand, the king will also want for himself the entire Ca income; and to that end he will coercively exact tribute from those beneath him under the threat of extermination. The king, if he succeeds in getting the entire Ca income, will represent an extreme case of the Force of Unification.

Now clearly, with Ca fixed, the king can increase his own personal income only by *exacting tribute* from the N_1 number of squires who are expropriating serfs at the bottom; and yet, as the king exacts an increasing amount of tribute, the N_1 number of squires will decrease correspondingly, since the amount paid to the king in tribute will not be available for the support of so many squires. Since the squires extort the Ca surplus from the serfs, it follows that the Na number of serfs that each of the N_1 squires extorts will be inversely proportional to N_1 [or, in equation form, $N_1 \cdot (Na) = C$]. If we designate the Na number of a squire's serfs as his *tributary domain,* we can see that the *Na size of his tributary domain* will increase as the N_1 number of squires decreases.

The term *tributary domain* recalls the *domains* of the analogue for the N_p number of communities of like P size (and of like domain size) in Chapter Nine. There we noted that when the magnitudes of the Forces of Unification and of Diversification are equal, then the n different communities of the system, when ranked in the order of decreasing P size, will follow the proportions of a harmonic series (or, $p = 1$ of the generalized harmonic series). In that case the N_p number of communities of like P size will be inversely proportional to the square of P (i.e., $N_p \cdot P^2 = C$); and the same will apply to the N number of domains of like size.

The question now arises as to whether the community analogue of Chapter Nine can be made to apply to a *dominance system* in which there is an intervening hierarchy of *classes of lords* between the N_1 squires at the bottom and the king at the top. Here we shall assume that each member of each y class of lords has a *y domain* that consists of an $N_{(y-1)}$ number of lords from the $y - 1$ class immediately below. We shall further assume that each of the $N_{(y-1)}$ lords of each y domain will pay tribute to their y lord of the domain, who in turn will pay tribute on his own behalf to his own $y + 1$ lord. This hierarchy of classes of lords from the squires (i.e., $y = 1$) at the bottom to the king at the top will constitute our *dominance* system.

Yet the dynamics of our dominance system will be indeterminate unless we make a provision for the rates at which tribute is both collected from the $(y - 1)$ class below and paid to the $(y + 1)$ class above. Since these rates are critical for the structure of our system, let us make a few clarifying definitions and preliminary assumptions.

To begin (1) we shall define any y lord's A_y income as the balance that is left over after he has collected tribute from his $N_{(y-1)}$ domain of $(y - 1)$ underlords, and after he has paid tribute to his own $(y + 1)$ overlord above. Then (2) we shall assume that throughout the entire dominance system, it will cost a constant amount in terms of the number of lords to exact a given amount of tribute from an underlord. As a result, the total N_y number of lords in any y class will be directly proportional to the total amount of tribute that is to be collected from all the $N_{(y-1)}$ lords of the entire $(y - 1)$ class.

Now if each lord keeps for himself merely the actual cost, including personal expenses, of exacting the tribute from the underlords of his domain, and loyally and conscientiously turns over the entire balance to his overlord, then every lord, regardless of his y status, will have exactly the same A income until we reach the king at the top who will appropriate the entire balance of the tribute for himself without paying any tribute to others. Hence, the king under these conditions will have the most enviable status.

Naturally, if each lord is removing a fixed A income from the "flow" of *Ca* goods and services from the squires at the bottom up to the king at the top, then as the "flow" passes through each successive y class of lords it becomes proportionally more "diluted" by the removal of the A incomes of the y lords; and since the "flow" is becoming proportionally more "diluted" as y increases, it follows that a proportionally smaller N_y number of lords will be necessary to exact the tribute as their y status increases from the squires $(y = 1)$ at the bottom to the king. In other words, if all A incomes are the same, then the N_y number of lords in any y class will be inversely proportional to y, or, in equation form, $N_y \cdot Y = constant$.

Obviously, if the N_y number of lords of each y status is inversely proportional to y, then the size of the y domain of each y lord will be directly proportional to y, or, in equation form: $domain_y = y$. In other words, the Na_y number of serfs in any y lord's domain will be directly proportional to the lord's y status; and we remember that these Na_y serfs represent the ultimate wealth and source of power of the y lord.

Yet there is a fatal weakness in our dominance system as described up to this point. For although we have provided an adequate N_y number of lords to exact tribute from the $N_{(y-1)}$ lords below, in which each lord throughout the entire hierarchy gets exactly the same A income while loyally and conscientiously passing the balance on up to the king, we have made no provision for the individual cupidity of each lord who, with an understandable economy, will want to increase his own A income. Since any A income can be increased only at the expense of the royal tribute that is delivered to the king, it follows that the entire hierarchy will envy the king and covet his royal tribute. If the king, therefore, does not somehow alter the structure of this dominance system, he will be dethroned and despoiled by his underlings who will confiscate his wealth.

Before considering how the king can protect his wealth by altering the structure of the dominance system, let us first recall that the y domain of each y lord increases directly with his y status. Since the Na number of each y lord's tributary serfs, who are the source of all power, is also proportional to y, it follows that the R_y *rebellion potential* of any y lord (or of all y lords) is proportional to y, if the y lords can only persuade the tributary lords of the inferior $y - 1$ classes to join the y lords in revolt. Yet the $y - 1$ classes of lords will have no incentive for joining the y lords in revolt unless the y lords agree to divide the royal plunder with them by increasing the A amounts of the respective incomes of the members of all the inferior $y - 1$ classes of lords.

Yet by how much should the y lords increase the A incomes of their underlings? As the y lords increase their underlings' A incomes they add to the underlings' incentives for joining them in the revolt; on the other hand, y lords will thereby decrease their own incentives for leading the revolt, since an ever smaller net amount will be left over for themselves. If the y lords give their underlings too small a share of the royal plunder, then the $y - 1$ lords can in turn lead a revolt against the y lords—and so on successively down the hierarchy until the $(y = 1)$ squires at the bottom revolt against the $(y = 2)$ class of lords above them and keep the entire tribute for themselves under an extreme Force of Diversification.

Hence, *there is a real problem in giving to each y class of lords just the "right amount" of A_y income in order to elicit their support of the class above while protecting them against revolt from their underlings below.* If perchance the king can solve this problem of the "right amount" of A_y income to be paid throughout the entire hierarchy, he too will have no need to fear a revolt from his underlings.

Let us suppose that the king shrewdly allows each lord to keep an A_y income that is directly proportional to the lord's y status (and to his erstwhile R_y potential), while the king keeps for himself a royal A income that is only proportional to his top y status. By this simple act the king will have so altered the N_y number of lords of any like y status that the *increasing* strength of their *individual* A_y *wealth* (the Force of Unification) will be counterbalanced by the *decreasing* strength of their *collective y class wealth,* $N_y \times A_y$ (the Force of Diversification). At the same time, as we shall later see in detail, the envy by the y lords of the $(y + 1)$ lords, and the y lords' fear of the envy by the $(y - 1)$ lords will tend to keep the entire hierarchy in balance, because of the relationship between N_y number of lords of like y status and the size of their like A_y incomes.

To elucidate the above point, let us note that as soon as the king gives each y lord an A_y income that is proportional to his y status, then the king *doubles* exponentially the rate at which the upward "flow" of the *Ca* stream of goods and services is "diluted." In other words the N_y number of lords of like y status, and hence of like A_y income, will not be inversely proportional to y, as was previously the case, but to y^2; or in equation form, with A_y substituted for y:

$$N_y \cdot A_y^2 = c \qquad (11\text{–}10)$$

Since we see from this equation that $N_y = c/A_y^2$, and since the *total amount* paid to the entire y class is equal to $N_y \cdot A_y$, we find by substitution that the *total amount* paid to the y class equals c/A_y. In general, therefore, as y status increases, the individual reward, A_y, *increases* in direct proportion to y, whereas the total y class reward *decreases* in direct proportion to y.

Hence, the more that the king needs to fear the y class of lords *individually,* the less he will need to fear them *collectively.* And conversely. In general, as y status increases, the lords will tend to side ever more with the king in order to seek protection against the more numerous covetous lords of lower status; on the other hand, as y status decreases, the lords will side ever more with the king in order to seek larger incomes. In this fashion the king can play off large numbers against large incomes, and *vice versa,* among his underlings; and so likewise can every other lord behave with his underlings in his domain.

Eq. (11–10), as we know from our argument in Chapter Two, is corollary to Eq. (11–1) of the *first analogue* of this chapter. In other words, since y status is positive and integral, it follows that if all the n different lords of the hierarchy, as described by Eq. (11–10) are ranked, r, in the order of the decreasing size of their A incomes, then they will be distributed according to Eq. (11–1) which, in the language of the present analogue, will be $r \cdot A = n$. This in turn is the same as Eq. (11–2) of the simple harmonic series (or the value, $p = 1$, of the generalized harmonic series).

Moreover, if we equate the A incomes of the n different lords with the P population sizes of the n different communities of our analogue in Chapter Nine, then our present analogue will parallel that for the distribution of communities in Chapter Nine (in the special case where $p = 1$). Later we shall find that the two analogues are so closely related that they can be combined into one "grand" analogue.

Now that we have observed the general structure of this dynamic system, let us inspect more closely some of its details and implications. To that end we shall inquire, *first,* into the incentives of a greedy and venturesome outsider who wants to supplant some y lord of the system, and then, second, into the incentives of a y lord to display some $(y + n)$ lord above him.

As to the incentives, *first,* of the greedy and venturesome outsider who wants to supplant some y lord of the system, we can see that as the y status of a lord increases, his A_y income increases proportionally, and therewith his attractiveness to the bold outsider. In short, the y lord's attractiveness is proportional to A_y. On the other hand, as the A_y income increases, the N_y number of y lords who have that income decreases according to c/A_y^2, with the result that the N_y opportunities of supplanting a y lord decrease more rapidly than the A_y income increases.

If A_y represents the incentive, and c/A_y^2 the opportunity, then cA_y/A_y^2, or c/A_y, represents the total net attractiveness of any y status to any outsider with no income of his own who wants to procure an A income for himself by supplanting someone in the system. (Here we may conceive of a physical analogue in the form of a table with n different holes of varying A areas distributed at random over the table according to the proportions of Eq. (11–2); if pellets of the diameter of the smallest hole are dropped at random, the preceding function, c/A_y, describes the likelihood of hitting any hole of A_y area.) Hence, as A_y increases, its attractiveness decreases; the king with the largest A_y income has the least attractive position for any outsider who desires an A income.

If the outsider happens to have a following of f adventurers to help him and with whom he must divide his arrogated A income, then the total net attractiveness must be divided by f; or, $1/(A_y \cdot f)$. Hence, we may expect that, historically, raiding bands of adventurers will tend to pick on the lords of lower y status for their plunder if the raiders have no income of their own.

As soon as we assume, however, that the outsider has an income of his own, then we come in effect to the *second* case in which a y lord who is already in the system and has an A_y income of his own, covets the $A_{(y+n)}$ income of a superior $(y + n)$ lord.* If we assume that every lord (except the king at the top) desires thus to increase his y status and his A_y income, then the attractiveness of the $A_{(y+n)}$ income is directly proportional to $A_{(y+n)}/A_y$, whereas the $N_{(y+n)}$ number of opportunities to supplant an $A_{(y+n)}$ lord is proportional to $c/A^2_{(y+n)}$. Consequently, if we multiply the incentive to supplant any $A_{(y+n)}$ lord by the $N_{(y+n)}$ number of opportunities to do so, or

$$[A_{(y+n)}/A_y] \times [c/A^2_{(y+n)}] \cdot \cdot \cdot$$

we find that the total net attractiveness is proportional to $c/[A_y \cdot A_{(y+n)}]$.

Moreover, since A_y income varies directly with y status, we may say that the E_y envy of any $(y + n)$ status is proportional to $1/[y \times (y + n)]$; or

$$E_y \textit{ envy of } (y + n) = 1/y(y + n) \qquad (11\text{–}11)$$

---

* We ignore the case in which all N_y lords of the y class desire the total income of all the $N_{(y+n)}$ lords, since we have already seen that y class income is inversely proportional to y.

Eq. (11–11) tells us three things. First, as the n disparity between any two statuses, y and $(y+n)$, increases, the E_y envy of $(y+n)$ and reciprocally the $(y+n)$ fear of the y underling decreases. Consequently, *second,* the $(y+1)$ status will always be the status that is most envied by the y lord; in other words, the greatest E_y envy will be of the $(y+1)$ lord next above. And *third,* Eq. (11–11) tells us that as y status becomes lower, the E_y envy of the $(y+1)$ lord becomes greater [since, in effect, E_y envy of $y+1$ is inversely proportional to $y\ (y+1)$, or to (y^2+y)].

Hence, one's envy of the immediately superior status increases very rapidly as one's status decreases; by the same token, one's relative suspicion and fear of one's underlings, or one's feeling of *status insecurity,* will increase as one's status decreases. Conversely, as one's status increases, one's covetousness of one's superior as well as one's relative suspicion and fear of one's underlings diminishes, with the result that one's *status complacency* (i.e., the reciprocal of *status insecurity*) will increase.

These concepts of *status insecurity* and of *status complacency* are psychologically interesting. One effect of the envy and covetousness of the immediate $(y+1)$ lord, is to cause a natural affinity to arise between all lords of odd y status (i.e., $y = 1, 3, 5, \ldots$) on the one hand, and between all lords of even y status (i.e., $y = 2, 4, 6 \ldots$) on the other. That in turn serves to explain the frequently observed phenomenon that a person feels that his own $(y+1)$ boss is a "bootlicking incompetent" whereas his boss's own $(y+2)$ boss is really a fine person who regrettably lets $(y+1)$ pull the wool over his clear $(y+2)$ eyes. Nevertheless, it is dangerous for y to complain to $(y+2)$ about $(y+1)$, lest $(y+1)$ in turn complain to $(y+3)$ about y and even about $(y+2)$, with the result that one or both may be dismissed from the hierarchy on the grounds of being "troublemakers" with "unfortunate personalities" who do not "co-operate." [4] Potential mutiny lies in a connivance between members whose status is that of y and $(y+2)$.

In general, no matter how great y's E_y envy of $(y+1)$ may be, the $E_{(y-1)}$ envy by $(y-1)$ of y will be still greater. Therefore, an easy defense by $(y+1)$ against y is to incite $(y-1)$ against y. And that applies to all status through the entire hierarchy.

So we have an envy on the part of each y lord in each "y box" against his superior $(y+1)$ lord in each "$(y+1)$ box" all the way up the line, and a reciprocal distrust by the superior "box" of the inferior "box" all the way down the line. As we approach the "boxes" of higher status, the feeling of *status complacency* increases; as we approach the "boxes" of lower status, the feeling of *status insecurity* increases. In a later section we shall note that these lords of lower status and of greater status insecurity will be the chief defenders of the conventions of the *status quo* of the system. They are the ones who are under the greatest pressure by the would-be social climber and, indeed, seem to represent the most vulnerable points of attack by an enterprising revolutionary.

Turning now to the question of the relative S_y size of the retinue that each y lord must retain in order to collect the tribute from his N_y number of $y - 1$ lords below, let us remember that the *Ca* "flow" of goods and services from the squires at the bottom to the king at the top is being "diluted" at a rate that is proportional to the square, or 2nd power, of y status. That is because the y lords do not receive an A_y income in proportion to the tribute they extract from the $(y - 1)$ lords but in proportion to their y status. Therefore, the relative amount of S_y retinue power in terms of unit fighting men that the y lord will need in order to exact tribute from his domain of $(y - 1)$ lords will vary according to the square root of y status, which is the same as the square root of A_y income: or,

$$S_y \; retinue = A_y^{\frac{1}{2}} \qquad (11\text{–}12)$$

This function is theoretically quite interesting, if we assume that S_y represents the rate of y work, whereas A_y represents the rate of y reward. For, in that case, it may be that, as a general proposition, the A_y rate of reward varies with the square of the S_y amount of work. Such a function, which might be called the "square effect" would be of considerable value in social studies (e.g., "reward in proportion to the square of the risk"?).

Yet the y lord is by no means safe after he has hired his S_y retinue, since the members of his S_y retinue will both covet the y lords' A_y income and have the force to overthrow him. The y lord must, therefore, buy off his retinue by introducing therein a status ranking that will have an analogous relationship to that of the status ranking of the lords themselves that we have just considered. Without discussing the details of the status ranking of the individual retinues, let us merely remark that if the y lord pays his retinue "too little," he will learn the appropriateness of the ancient adage: "always beware your second in command" (which is not far removed from the injunction to beware the lord of next lower status).

By continuing the above argument, which by now has become the same as that of our *first analogue,* we could derive all nine equations, (11–1) through (11–9), of the *first analogue*. These equations, we remember, represent a condition of stable equilibrium in which everyone envies everyone else, and desires both to withhold tribute from those above and to increase tribute from those below, and yet in which no one can safely do either. As a result our lordlings will philosophically resign themselves to brotherly love and Christian charity while hunting grouse on each other's estates, as their wives, in imitation of those above, make merry at the social pretentiousness of those below. As long as S_y is not increased beyond $y^{\frac{1}{2}}$, those above need not worry; as long as it does not fall below $y^{\frac{1}{2}}$, those below can swallow their chagrin. If, perchance, our equations are too complicated for the royal understanding, then there will occur one revolt after another until some blood-stained rebel who "understands" the equations will mount the throne, and establish and maintain peace.

This *second* analogue, which has led us to the same equations as the *first analogue,* is, as we pointed out at the time, quite parallel to the *community analogue* that we developed in Chapter Nine for the n communities of P population size in a social system. To make more vivid the relationship between our erstwhile *community analogue* and our present *lord analogue,* let us ask a favor of our fine lords.

Thus let us say: "Sweet lords, build yourselves castles and spend your handsome A_y incomes that your C serfs are producing for you; yet remember that work must be minimized."*

Instantly each y *lord* will build his castle in the least-work center of his y domain, where he will "spend his A_y income" on his castle and on goods and services (including his retinue) at rates that are a function of his y status. And equally instantly the analogues, the equations, and the entire argument of Chapter Nine will be absorbed into this new "grand" analogue, which will also contain the analogues, equations, and arguments of the present chapter. As a result this new "grand" analogue will refer not only to the movement of persons and of raw materials and of goods and of services, but also to the distribution of "power" that makes them move.

Although the details of our new and more inclusive "grand" analogue are obvious, let us nevertheless note certain rather interesting aspects of it. In the *first* place each y lord's production in terms of the P number of working "serfs" (or *pariahs*) will be in proportion to each y lord's A_y; therefore the P populations around the castles will be harmonically distributed. *Second,* these "serfs" must be exploited by "bosses" whom the y lord hires, with the result that there will arise castle dominance systems whose dynamics will be similar to that of the S_y retinue; consequently the m_y number of different kinds of production that a y lord can have will vary directly with the square root of his A_y income. Moreover, *third,* trade between the $(y - 1)$ lords and the y lords and the $(y + 1)$ lords of the respective domains will follow our equations for the exchange of goods in Chapter Nine, if we view the lords as using their respective A incomes to buy goods from one another. In that case, however, the "flow" of tribute will give place to a "flow" of profit, in which the lord of higher y status will receive profit at a greater rate in any trade that he may make.

We mention the preceding considerations not because they are not obvious but because they will suggest further questions for the reader to ask of the analogue (e.g., the harmonic distribution of incomes within a P community in terms of a k constant that varies with P), thereby both broadening and integrating our field.

At this point, let us note that although the analogue is cast in terms of A incomes, it will nevertheless also apply *mutatis mutandis* to the distribution of assets, as becomes apparent as soon as we inquire into the respective "asset values" of the various y lords' castles and of their productive facilities (whether in terms of the assets' replacement costs, or in terms of their number of employees, or in terms of a constant rate of capitalization). Upon inspection, we note that the y lord's "assets" will vary directly with his A_y income, with the result that our equations will describe the distributions of *group assets* and of *individual assets;* and that is dynamically understandable, too, since a y lord's wealth will tempt others to rob and to despoil

* Our Eqs. (11–11) and (11–12) introduce the concept of probabilities and, therefore, of probable work (or effort).

him quite as much in proportion to his A_y assets as in proportion to his A_y income.

There is, incidentally, a further possible value of our present "grand" analogue that merits inspection: the fact that the value of the exponent, p, of the equation of the generalized harmonic series is fixed at 1 for the *group incomes* (and at ½ for *individual incomes*) in any dominance system anywhere that is in a condition of stable equilibrium. That in turn *may* explain why the value $p = 1$ may represent a condition of equilibrium in the rank-frequency distribution of the P sizes of the n communities of a social system. We remember that in Chapter Nine we gave no reason why the value $p = 1$ should represent equilibrium. On the other hand, lest we become prematurely dogmatic, let us also remember that we found cases where the rank-frequency distribution of the P sizes of communities of a system had a value of p that was less than 1 (e.g., in India and in 19th century Germany). These smaller values of p for the communities need to be explained before our "grand" analogue is satisfactory.

One possible explanation of these values of p for communities that are smaller than 1 may be that they do not meet the criteria of our social system. To illustrate this point let us briefly *sketch in barest outline* a different social system in which the value of p will be less than 1.

Let us assume that each lord belongs to two hierarchies, a *Regal hierarchy* and an *Imperial hierarchy,* with the latter consisting of large number of Regal hierarchies. Each vassal will therefore pay tribute to two kinds of overlords while keeping some income for himself, with the result that there will be three Forces in operation. Since either hierarchy can join with the lower vassals of the other hierarchy in order to overthrow the other hierarchy, the three Forces will be in a condition of equilibrium if there is no rebellion. Yet it would seem that the effect of these three different Forces in terms of the distribution of the n different communities of varying P population sizes will be such as to yield the value $p = ⅔$ of the generalized harmonic series for the entire Empire, since the Imperial Force of Unification would in effect be opposed by the combined Regal and Vassal Forces, which will act together in withholding tribute from the Emperor and, therefore, in the direction of a double Force of Diversification. In any event this value, $p = ⅔$, seems to describe the distribution of communities both in recent India and in early Imperial Germany, as is evident from an inspection of the data in Chapter Ten. Both of these may be viewed as Imperial-Regal systems.*

Nevertheless, this theoretical value of $p = ⅔$, which for convenience we shall call the *Imperial ⅔ slope,* will represent a condition of equilibrium that is highly unstable since, as we have already observed, there is always the opportunity of playing off one hierarchy against the other, by siding either with the Emperor or with the Kings, to the obliteration of the opposing hierarchy and to the greater unification of the whole. The past history of Germany and the present history of India may both represent a

* The same may be true of Europe, which has been plagued and is being threatened by wars with the avowed intention of a European unification.

condition in which the local kings and princes lose to the "Emperor" (i.e., a single whole). The value $p = 1$ will therefore represent an ultimate stability. This same value of p will also emerge if the Emperor loses to the Kings, except that there will then be a large number of different dominance systems instead of a single one.*

According to our argument, the value $p = 1$ will in the long run represent a condition of stable equilibrium. Yet it is interesting to reflect that other systems may exist in which different *integral* values of our theoretical Forces of Unification and of Diversification will represent conditions of a temporarily stable equilibrium.

Since it takes physical force to move matter over distance, physical force will be continually expended in the manufacture and distribution of goods and services in our analogue. Yet our analogue refers also to the distribution of *potential power* in coercing persons to do things—a *potential power* that becomes *actual coercive force* as soon as equilibrium is disturbed, and which ceases to be expended only when equilibrium has been restored (*vis medicatrix naturae*). In short, force restores equilibrium. Yet behind the *potential power* and *actual coercive force* of our analogue lies the concept of economy—the economy of getting someone else to do one's work. Primary to our analogue, therefore, is what may be called the *distribution of economic power* which we have attempted to explain in terms of relative *social status.*

How far our present analogue may be used in rationalizing the distribution of incomes in present-day America, where corporations, for example, do not employ soldiers, is an interesting question. And yet if we view the "spirit of co-operation" as the Force of Unification that acts in the direction of making fewer larger corporations; and if we view the "spirit of competition" as the Force of Diversification that acts in the direction of making a greater number of smaller corporations; then we see the applicability of our previous analogues in terms of the number and sizes of A corporation incomes as well as of the salaries of the individual executives. Consequently, all the equations of the analogues will apply to corporate incomes (including incomes of partnerships) and to individual incomes; and we must visualize a person, or a group of persons, in a social system as having the choice of either joining some business that is already established, or of founding a competitive business.

Since the foregoing relationships are quite obvious in the light of our analogues, we shall not expand upon them further beyond remarking that the respective incomes that accrue to corporations and to the members of their executive staffs, and even to the shareholders who own the corporation,

* The *Imperial 2/3 slope,* in addition to representing a lower limit to the value of p in the distribution of community sizes, may be of considerable value in semantic dynamics (or better, *semantic potentials* in the present instance) if, instead of speaking of the y "boxes" of lords with their S_y retinues, we speak of y "boxes" of words with their S_y meanings. In that case the distribution of holophrases, as in present-day Nootka, Plains Cree, etc., as discussed in Chapter Four, may conceivably be viewed as representative of the *Imperial 2/3 slope,* with "Diversification" having twice the Force of "Unification."

theoretically, constitute a subtle problem of balance, with bankruptcy facing those who fail to solve the problem correctly, and with increasing competition awaiting those whose solution is too successful.

Hence, our equations may indicate what a "reasonable" profit is, and a "reasonable" salary and wage, thereby indicating when the struggles of strikes and lockouts are in order in a dominance system that is based upon financial force and not upon force of soldiers (except indirectly).

Indeed, a dominance system may function that is based neither upon financial nor upon military force but rather upon the rank-order of the prevalence of one's will, or upon the rank-order in which one is allowed to die off in times of scarcity. Thus, in a religious order in which no member owns property and where all have the same habit, fare, and shelter, the dominance system may be based upon the relative right to have a voice in framing policies or to represent the group. Moreover, in the event the brethren, say, take a sleigh ride and are pursued by wolves, our equations may suggest the rank-order, from bottom to top, in which the brethren are thrown overboard. In the event the brethren have insignia of office, the frequency distribution of the insignia should, theoretically, be those of our equations—a consideration that seems to be related to the rank-frequency distribution of occupations discussed in Chapter Nine.

Indeed, the possession of any prestige symbol that will induce deference, or the possession of any privilege to perform a respected cultural rite, will represent the possession of capital and power in the dominance system in question.[5]

At the bottom of a dominance system, and serving as a foundation, there will in all cases be theoretically a *c* number of "serfs" or pariahs, upon whom the elite is built, and with whom the elite is closely related.*

B. The Elite-Pariah Relationships

Our foregoing discussion referred primarily to the dynamics of elite organization, with only secondary reference to the *pariah class,* whose members provide the labor that is exploited by the elite. Now we shall turn our attention to the pariah class, with particular reference to the relationship between the pariah class and the elite.

For the sake of a greater verisimilitude, let us assume that members of the elite can originate anywhere; that is, they can come from outside the system, or they can come from within the system, either from the progeny of the elite or from the pariah class. This assumption is obviously quite reasonable in the light of historical fact.

Let us further assume that all persons have the urge to increase their relative incomes—i.e., the relative rate of return for their work. This urge does not mean that individual income *per se* is to be maximized in the *Ca* field, but rather that an increase in the relative size of an individual's income makes him relatively more powerful in altering his environment to

* Consider a military organization with a number of officers of various ranks constituting an elite that is built upon a class of soldiers who virtually have neither responsibility nor authority.

his own personal advantage. In other words: by increasing one's individual income one saves effort.

With the above in mind, we shall inquire into the various individual and collective methods for increasing one's individual income as derived from the equations of our foregoing section. Henceforth *Ca* is no longer fixed. The main steps of our impending inquiry are fourfold. In the first place (1) we shall discuss the economy of increasing the size of the *C* membership, as already suggested in our previous section. Then (2) we shall inspect the economy of decreasing the amount that is paid to the lowest members of the elite; this economy has also been touched upon previously. Then (3) in the light of the above two economies we shall derive and discuss what seems to be a far-reaching exponential law of incentives—a topic of timely interest since we are witnessing attempts today to construct national social systems in which, oddly enough, there are to be no incentives at all. The next step (4) is an exploration of the economy of increasing the size of the *a* increment in the total exploitable *Ca* surplus; this economy is the one that underlies the creation of capital. Then finally (5) we shall briefly describe the elite economy of devising *ad hoc* moral codes in order to hallow elite positions and to hoodwink the pariah class (i.e., *Pied Piper Morality*).

1. The Economy of Increasing C. One manner of increasing one's individual *A* income is to increase the size of the total tributary *C* population, as we have previously pointed out; for by increasing *C*, we increase *Ca*. This increase in *Ca* will accomplish two things. *First,* it will increase the absolute shares of all persons in the elite (if we assume that the lowest elite income, $1/C - a + b$, remains constant). *Second,* it will increase the n_3 number of persons who can be admitted into the elite, thereby increasing the probabilities of every member of the pariah class that he will become a member of the elite. Because of these two factors, an increase in *C* is one device for increasing the probable income of every member of the social system.

For that reason expansionist programs which promise increased territory tend to be popular with the entire population. Naturally, the upper members of the elite stand to gain relatively far more than others from a successful venture and, therefore, may be expected theoretically to be the chief warmongers. Nevertheless, the pariah class stands to gain also from the increased likelihood of becoming members of the elite. Nor should we forget that in the case of a successful expansion, new recruits both for expanding old retinues and for founding new ones are frequently enough selected from those members of the pariah class who have distinguished themselves for *bravery* and *cunning* on the battlefield—the two eternally necessary characteristics of successful elite membership.

The rank and file of the pariah class, when considered as a statistical aggregate, have probably little to gain from expansionist programs. But by the same token they also have comparatively little to lose in case the expansionist program is a fiasco, since, for example, the peasant will still jog along behind his oxen and merely pay tribute to a different master.

The upper members of the elite, on the other hand, may perish in the event of an unsuccessful venture, as they are killed off as "war criminals," or as "enemies of the people" or of "democracy" or as "aggressors"—or whatever the "moral-legal" fiction may be as devised by the elite of the winning side (cf., the discussion of *Pied Piper Morality* in Section 5).

2. The Economy of Decreasing b; Status Insecurity. We have arbitrarily defined $(1/C - a)$ as the amount that is left for each of the C members of the exploited pariah class. We have defined $(1/C - a + b)$ as the sum that is paid to the lowest paid person of the n_3 number of different members of the elite. Moreover, in presenting the analogues of a preceding section we have noted the enormous pressure from all nonmembers of the elite to tend to crowd into the elite. One effect of this pressure will be to displace the inefficient members of the elite. Another effect is to decrease the size of b, as we have already pointed out, so that the difference between $(1/C - a)$ and $(1/C - a + b)$ will be negligible, with the result that the n_3 members of the elite will be as large as possible. Indeed it is the continual pressure of outsiders to become members of the elite by increasing n_3 that decreases b.*

Because b is very small, the actual difference between a very poor "elite man" and a member of the pariah class may be largely one of insignia and of class feeling. Except for this difference, the actual material life of the poor "elite man" may even be shabbier than that of the pariah, thereby indicating the comparatively high *status insecurity,* or *status worry,* of the poor "elite man," as explained in our previous section. With this increasing *status worry* comes an increasingly uncompromising conventional bigotry and an increasingly ruthless intolerance of any attempt by a pariah to enter the elite, since any successful attempt to enter the elite is likely to be at the expense of some poor "elite man."

Conversely, a high social status with its concomitant *complacency* will tend to lead to a greater tolerance—up to a certain point.

These differences in *status worry* and *status complacency* are important in understanding the matter of incentives.

3. The Exponential Nature of Incentives and the Frequency-Distribution of Pariah Wages. In our foregoing discussion, we have suggested that an elite man's feeling of social and economic security tends to decrease as his elite income decreases and thereby brings him ever nearer to the pariah class. This consideration of the alteration of one's feelings towards society with an alteration of one's comparative economic standing—or social status —serves to introduce the interesting problem of the exponential nature of incentives, with which a wide range of social phenomena are correlated.

a. Incentives (the Exponential Law). Let us begin our study of the nature of incentives by first inspecting the effect of a constant percentage cut—say a cut of 90%—in all elite incomes. Here we note two considerations: *first,* all incomes will shrink by a constant percentage amount, and *second,* the progressively lower individual elite incomes will both approach,

* Because b is very small there will be no hiatus in the total income curve between elite incomes and pariah wages.

and even pass through, the bottom $(1/C - a)$ starvation level at a faster absolute rate.

To illustrate these two considerations, let us assume that the lower threshold of existence, or $1/C - a$, is about $500—or any other arbitrary sum. Now let us assume that all elite incomes are cut by 90%.

In that case the one million dollar income is reduced to 100 thousand dollars; the 100 thousand dollar income is reduced to 10 thousand dollars; the 10 thousand dollar income is reduced to one thousand dollars. All of these persons can obviously still survive, and many of them can still survive quite comfortably. Moreover, each one can console himself with the thought that all other elite members are faring equally badly—as indeed they all are on a percentage basis.

Yet this consolation will be in vain for the person whose income had formerly been less than 5,000 dollars a year, since, with a 90% cut he will be reduced below the starvation point of $500 and will die.

Although a constant percentage cut in incomes will, by its very nature, decrease all incomes proportionately, nevertheless it will decrease the "safety cushion" above starvation for the n_3 members of the elite at rates that increase in direct relation to the comparative smallness of their respective incomes; and that applies not only to the starvation level but to any other arbitrary level.

On the other hand, if one wishes to reduce the entire elite at the same rate to the $(1/C - a)$ pariah level so that all members of the elite will hit this income level at the same instant, then the incomes may be decreased logarithmically (or, differently expressed, *exponentially*) in the sense that the exponent, p, of the generalized harmonic series will be decreased progressively from ½ to 0. In that case all members of the elite will approach the lower threshold at the same rate in time.

The converse is also true. Any percentage increase—or any absolute increase—in the individual incomes of the elite will be "appreciated" at rates that are inversely related to the recipient's income. Thus, for example, a ten dollar a week raise will be appreciated increasingly less by a person of increasingly larger income, and exponentially so. Therefore, if an income increase is to be equally "appreciated" by all members of the elite, the income increase should follow a fixed power of the income of the recipients (i.e., it should be an exponential increase), and conversely, if members of the elite are to be equally restrained (see below for discussion of taxation).

In general, *the sheer amount of income increase that is necessary to evoke a given amount of response from a member of the elite will vary directly with a power of the member's individual income (and conversely)*. Or, if one will, *y incentive is an exponential of x income*. For convenience we shall call this the (theoretical) *Exponential Law of Incentives,* which, if true, may well be of considerable didactic value for many different kinds of phenomena.[6]

For although we are primarily arguing that in order to get a man to expend a given amount of additional work in the performance of a given job, he must be rewarded by an amount that is in proportion to a power of his income, nevertheless, the same argument applies to any attempt to evoke a given amount of his gratitude and favor (or "appreciation"), or to restore a given amount of his "confidence," or to appease his wrath, or to quiet his anxious nervous system, or to induce him to expend (or to restrain him from expending) a given amount of work in any cultural or acultural direction.

Since we have argued, theoretically, that all nonmonetary, or partially monetary, dominance systems follow the same doubly logarithmic principles of dynamics, the same theoretical Law may be expected to apply to the y amount of flattery, deference, and the like, which will be necessary to provide incentives. In short, the Exponential Law will theoretically describe all social stimuli and responses in all social interaction.*

Indeed, by extension of the argument, the theoretical Exponential Law of Incentives may be connected with the *growth of P populations* of communities under Eq. (9–2a). It may also be connected with changes in the frequency, and, therefore, of the "popularity" of words and phrases—and of other cultural signals—as discussed in Chapter Three in connection with the generalized harmonic series. That leads in turn to a consideration of the waxing and waning of vogues and fashions, to which we shall more particularly turn our attention in our following chapter, after we have finished our present treatment of incomes and wages. In short, the theoretical Exponential Law of Incentives has a considerable scope.

b. Pariah Wages. If we assume explicitly that members of the pariah class are unequal in skills and strength, as seems to be the case, then their individual incomes will not all be $1/C - a$, because the members of the elite will compete with one another for the services of the most useful pariahs. This competition will be in terms of offering additional incentives in the form of higher wages to the more skillful pariahs.

And yet, because of the structure of the elite, not all members of the elite can afford to give the same wages for a given service; therefore, the competition for the pariahs will not be equal. For according to the Exponential Law of Incentives, the cost of a sacrifice by members of the elite must be exponentially the same if it is to be felt as the same. Thus, for example, the payment of one hundred dollars per month for the wages of a cook will seem to be increasingly small to the person whose income is increasingly large.

Yet if the competition for the services of pariahs is not equal, but in accordance with the income distributions of our equations, it will follow that by and large the actual wages that are paid to members of the pariah class will tend to be ordered exponentially. For though the elite will strive

* By extension this theoretical Law will explain the often observed tendency of persons to interact with members of the same socio-economic status. For if Joe Doakes can only afford five dollars for an evening's entertainment of a girl, he must seek a girl in a socio-economic class in which the five dollars will provide an adequate incentive. With fixed cultural givens and a random distribution of supplies and demands, all social interaction will tend to be within like socio-economic classes, or status. To facilitate this interaction, persons of like status tend to reside near to one another, as is on the whole observably the case, cf. argument of Chapters Seven and Nine.[7]

to get the services of the pariahs as cheaply as possible, and though the pariahs, being disorganized, will simply go to the highest bidder, nevertheless the elite, in paying the "same," will tend to pay exponentially. As a result, the rank-frequency distribution of pariah wages will be arithmetic-logarithmic, with r rank plotted arithmetically against the logarithm of y wages, or:

$$r + (c \log y) = constant \tag{11–13}$$

This equation does *not* mean that pariah capacities, or human capacities, are distributed arith-logarithmically in this world; on the contrary, insofar as anything is known about "intelligence," the I.Q.'s of a population are distributed according to the normal curve (even though one may suspect at times that the units of the abscissa are not arithmetic, since the difference between an I.Q. of 100 and that of 60 does not seem to be merely that of 40 times the difference between an I.Q. of 61 and 60, even after allowing for roughness of measurement). Neither does Eq. (11–13) mean that like goods in like units (e.g., coal or gasoline) cost more per unit for the elite. It does mean, however, that slaves or oil paintings at the auction block, where the units of trade are not equivalent, will tend to be exponentially priced.

For though no member of the elite will want to pay more than another for a given good or a given service, nevertheless, in those cases where there is a difference in quality which admits of no objectively discernible unit of utilitarian value, as is often the case in "luxury" or "prestige" goods, the purchaser's judgment of value may be biased exponentially by the size of his income.*

c. Personal Damages. The theoretical exponential law of incentives will also apply to the settlement of personal liability claims. By a personal liability claim we shall mean a plaintiff's claim for compensation against a defendant who has damaged him through negligence as defined by the social code in question.

To objectify this problem, let us restrict our argument to the special case of automobile liability damages, under the assumption that every automobile owner carries compulsory liability insurance of "adequate" coverage. (By this assumption we delete from the problem the question of the probable ownership of automobiles, and of the probable financial responsibility of their owners.) These automobiles will cause personal damages for which the insurance companies will be liable.

Here let us note that the problem of damages is not one of the "intrinsic" value of a lost eye or of a broken leg, since presumably every person values

* Differently expressed, the elite buys two kinds of goods: (1) daily needs which he shares with the pariahs, the total costs of which may vary with A income, as Engel has observed, and (2) "luxury" goods, or "prestige" goods, whose costs may vary exponentially with the income. But the problem is moot. The m diversity of goods and services purchased has been referred to above in the *second analogue*.[8] Implicit in our argument is the quasi-paradox that a more menial position in a richer establishment is to be preferred by the gifted person since the ultimate reward for his services, if brought to the attention of the master, is likely to be an exponential of his master's income.

his own bodily parts and functions equally highly. Instead the problem involves (1) the comparative wealth of the defendant, which measures his comparative power in hiring gifted counsel and in taking his case to expensive higher courts, and (2) the comparative amount of damages that must be paid to *satisfy* the plaintiff's aggrieved feelings about his personal damage (and here enters the exponential law of incentives).

If we assume that the likelihood of sustaining a given damage is distributed at random throughout the population, then the probability that persons of varying sizes of income will sustain the damage will be distributed according to Eq. (11–9) where the value of $p = \frac{1}{2}$; and this equation will also measure the comparative *power* of the persons to urge their claims. Nevertheless, it will not measure the comparative sizes of the settlements which the respective plaintiffs will consider to be satisfactory, since the sizes of these settlements must vary exponentially with the income, if all plaintiffs are to feel equally satisfied.

If our *second analogue* is correct, to the effect that reward varies with the square of "S_y power," then the settlements of liability suits will vary directly with the square of the defendant's income. Consequently, the *rank-frequency distribution of the sizes of settlements of liability claims will follow Eq. (11–2) where the value of* $p = 1$.

Thus for example, because of the exponential law of incentives, a Rockefeller will receive far more for the loss of his feet than will a taxi driver. In this connection, let us not forget that the defendant's lawyer who eyes his client before suggesting what he thinks is a "reasonable" settlement will also be subject to the exponential law of incentives as he calculates the cost of suit against the probabilities of winning. (We leave to the reader the problem of the position of the courts in a dominance system even in regard to the frequency distribution of fines and of lengths of sentences in jail for the bad behavior of the rich and of the poor.)

Our above argument, which applies to the settlement of claims for compensation under automobile liability insurance will by no means necessarily apply to claims in the matter of fire insurance and of life insurance. In the case of fire insurance, if we assume that all persons insure, say, their dwellings and outbuildings at a constant fraction of their replacement cost, and if we assume that the likelihood of a total fire loss, or of a given percentage fire loss, is distributed at random, then the rank-frequency distribution of the sizes of the settlements of fire claims will follow Eq. (11–9) (i.e., $p = \frac{1}{2}$) if every *individual,* according to our *second analogue,* does in fact have a "house" (or "castle") whose value is in proportion to his income.[9]

Life insurance claims will follow the same Eq. (11–9) since life insurance is a need that will presumably vary directly with income.

The empiric tests of the foregoing theoretical expectations, as presented later in Section II, will constitute interesting support of our entire theory of the exponential law of incentives and the distribution of economic power in terms of income and assets.

d. The Exponential Attraction of a "Popular" Following. Closely related to our foregoing arguments as well as to the problems of vogues to be discussed in the following chapter is the drawing power of a popular leader of whom it may be said that "nothing succeeds like success." For as the size of the leader's following grows, and therewith his power, it will become correspondingly more advantageous for others to join his group. This is presumably the dynamics of the proverbial "bandwagon psychology" with its exponential mushroom growth.

Nevertheless, the same exponential function will apply theoretically in reverse to the dissipation of the popular following when it is seen either that the entire enterprise is futile, or that the prospective reward nowhere nearly justifies the size of the following. In that case the members of the following will climb off the "bandwagon" with an exponential *crescendo.*

Naturally if the venture promises to be more and more highly successful, with large rewards, then its leader, almost without exception, is impelled to resort to "liquidations" and "purges" (to borrow from the recent Stalin-Roosevelt vocabulary) that are directed primarily against his erstwhile closely associated henchmen and conspirators, so that the leader can convert his somewhat opportunistic popular following into a more enduring dominance system in which the popular leader will alone occupy the top status in an erstwhile revolutionary movement that now congeals into an elite. If the leader is successful with his "liquidations" and "purges," his newly created elite will receive rewards according to our earlier equations.

e. Taxation and the Bureaucratic Elite. It is obvious that if a tax is to be felt as "reasonable" by the members of the elite it must, theoretically, be exponential in nature, since a flat percentage tax upon incomes or assets will fall increasingly more heavily upon the lower elite incomes, and therefore will unequally decrease the elite's incentives for production. Indeed, as we noted in an earlier section, any percentage decrease in income, whether from taxation or from other causes, will increasingly depress the lower elite classes (or the *petite bourgeoisie*). This increasing burden upon the more populous lower elite classes can be doubly dangerous, since any corrective reforms that the lower elite may instigate can inadvertently open the door to a far-reaching revolution.[10]

A system of double taxation, in the sense that a corporation's income is taxed as well as the incomes of the individual owners of the corporation, may contain in it a concealed constant percentage individual tax of the type above mentioned. Thus, the effects of a corporation tax fall equally upon its owners, share and share alike. If these shares, like all other capital assets, are distributed to individuals according to Eq. (11–9), then the burden of the corporation tax will fall like a fixed percentage tax.* Corporation taxes should therefore be avoided if the effects of a fixed percentage tax are not wanted.

Just as taxation can curb incentives, so too can tax exemption offer incentives. Thus, for example, if a social system wishes to encourage the

* By taxing to the individual shareholder all corporation profits whether paid out in dividends or kept in the treasury (as is the case with beneficiaries of a Massachusetts Trust) the tax will become equitable—and quite obviously the profits will tend to be distributed as dividends.

procreation of offspring by the device of allowing a certain amount of tax exemption for each child produced, then it must carefully weigh the rate at which it offers exemption. A flat rate for all will merely encourage the lower members of the elite to propagate; an exponential exemption will make the incentives equal throughout; an exponential exemption that increases exponentially with each successive child will throw the joys of procreation upon the upper income groups.*

The ultimate effect of a tax does not necessarily mean a curbing of the productive capacity of the system. Indeed, if the proceeds of a tax are used to provide services such as schools or police and fire protection that meet the common needs of all, then the tax will by no means be a curb upon the incentives to produce. Instead it falls under the heading of production.

On the other hand, the sheer fact that the proceeds of taxation provide a distributable sum that is both collected and expended by governmental agents may lead to the formation of a *governmental bureaucratic elite* that increases its power by selling its favor until it becomes an independent dominance system of its own. The goal of the bureaucratic elite will *always* be that of an increased taxation, and its chief device for achieving this goal will be the purchase of a following from the pariah class by means of variously disguised gifts from the public treasury which is supported by a taxation of the productive elite whom the bureaucratic elite threatens and calumniates.

If the bureaucratic elite grows, its hierarchy may in time represent what in an earlier section of this chapter we called an Imperial hierarchy (we remember the *Imperial 2/3 slope*). In other words, the Force of the rewards of the bureaucratic elite will equal the Force of managerial rewards. The long term instability of this three-cornered arrangement of a social system we have already pointed out. Ultimately, either the productive elite will overthrow the bureaucratic elite and take the government again into its own hands, or the bureaucratic elite will supplant the productive elite and assume its managerial functions. In either case a single dominance hierarchy will ensue, which our equations will describe.

Historically, it may be difficult to tell whether a bureaucratic elite or a productive elite is actually in control without inspecting the distribution of incomes in the system. Thus, the royal court and royal army may control business, or they may be tied to the pursestrings of business, for all that one can tell at the time from outward appearances. Yet in the long run, and one way or another, the productive elite will prevail and will control the royal army, while the royal court may be kept, as in England, only to preserve a useful conventional middle-class morality that is deferred to by the pariahs and the intellectually and socially insecure (cf., discussion of *Pied Piper morality* below).

* The commonplace observation that the birthrate tends to fall with a rising standard of living, as investigated in particular by Dr. Karl Sax, may conceivably be connected with the fact that the asset value of a child as a helper is fixed, and that therefore there is a decreasing incentive for the wealthy to have children as far as asset value is concerned.[11]

Up to now we have said nothing about the taxation of the pariah class. Theoretically, any taxation of the pariah class will fall upon the elite since, in the last analysis, it will decrease the *a* increment that the elite exploits. For although a processing tax or a sales tax may be absorbed by consumers who are for the most part pariahs, the result will mean, theoretically, that the wages of the pariahs will have to be increased commensurately (i.e., an increase in the "take-home pay"). If the pariahs are fooled by these indirect taxes, the elite seem to be even more fooled; and it is upon the lower members of the elite, in whom we believe the greatest threat of revolution lies, that the greatest burden of the indirect tax will fall.*

The assessment of real estate for purposes of taxation, which we mention only in passing, offers a further interesting problem for our theoretical exponential law of incentives. That the concept of an exponential factor may not be lacking in assessments is suggested indirectly by the words of the distinguished real estate appraiser, Mr. Joseph C. Leighton of Cambridge, Massachusetts: "If a person's assessment is raised by so much as a dime he should complain; otherwise the assessment will be raised until he does complain." Yet what is the amount that an assessment can be raised before a home owner will go to the trouble to file a request for an abatement and plead before an appeal board?

Closely related to the question of the assessed valuation of real estate is the question of the rate of its depreciation. Depreciation, we remember, consists both of the asset's physical deterioration and of its obsolescence as a result of factors that operate outside the premises. According to Mr. Leighton, the rate of depreciation of dwelling houses in terms of resale value tends to increase with their cost because, as Mr. Leighton says, "there are progressively fewer persons who can afford to buy the more expensive houses." Here again there seems to be evidence of an exponential factor in the rate at which dwelling units depreciate in value, though the problem is clearly complex.†

f. The Distribution of Assets. In our *second analogue* we suggested that the distribution of individual and of group assets will, theoretically, be the same as that of individual and of group incomes. If we again mention the problem of assets, it is because it also comes under the heading of the exponential law of incentives.

That the relationship between the distribution of incomes and of assets is close becomes apparent when we remember that the ownership of assets is fundamentally the possession of the control of instruments and of agents that are useful in altering the environment to the advantage of those who

* A system's labor unions are members of the social system's elite, just as much as is a corporation. Fights for control of a labor union are fights in a dominance system. A labor leader is not only under pressure from above but also under pressure from below. A revolution in the social system is no more to his advantage than to that of a corporation or its executive staff.

† The question of whether the allowable rate of depreciation of dwelling units for tax purposes is to be a "straight line" depreciation (i.e., a certain percent per year) or according to some exponential system may have important consequences in expediting Veteran housing projects.

possess the control; one feature of an asset is its capacity to produce income for its "owner," and to induce deference to its "owner." It is doubtful whether the term *ownership* has any other significance in a social system than that of possession of a greater or lesser degree of control of the entity in question, regardless of whether the entity in question be real or personal property, or the members of one's family, or even of one's own self. (Surely contemporary history will not controvert this statement.)

From the above considerations we can theoretically derive others. Thus, for example, whatever operates throughout the system as an asset—whether it be one's employees or one's house—may be rectilinearly distributed according to relative value.* Moreover, all those things which, like longevity, good health, good education, or freedom from jails, are enhanced by the degree of one's control of one's environment will be positively correlated with one's wealth.

And yet there is a further factor in the matter of assets, if we assume that all groups and persons are building up reserves for expansion in addition to reserves for contingencies and depreciation. Since these reserves for expansion will be only potentially productive capital until the expansion has actually taken place, then the presence of these expansion reserves may slightly modify the rank-frequency distribution of assets by increasing the values of p for groups and for individuals slightly above their respective values of 1 and $\frac{1}{2}$, if we assume on the basis of our theoretical law of incentives that the urge to expand is an exponential. We mention this matter since the data for assets in Section II reveal a slightly greater slope than that which is anticipated theoretically.

g. Cultural "Orthogenesis." While still on the general topic of the exponential law of incentives, let us briefly note the effect of intellectual rigidity, as discussed in Part One, upon a person's behavior after his status has been changed upwards or downwards because of the vicissitudes of fortune. We remember that because of the increasing intellectual rigidity of increasing age, a person's earlier habits are likely to perseverate.

With this perseveration of earlier habits there will also, theoretically, tend to be a perseveration of the exponential incentive rate of an earlier status. Thus, the newly rich may either continue to pinch pennies in a fashion quite exemplary for an earlier more humble status or, by way of overcompensation, they may expend at a rate that exceeds what their new status justifies. By the same token a person who has fallen from a higher status may find it difficult to reduce his scale of spending; furthermore, he may foolishly underrate the value of new opportunities because he erroneously assesses them in the light of his former higher status that is no longer definitive.

---

* This type of argument applies to all constant or random behavior in reference to our distributions. Thus if noses are blown at random or at a constant rate, then more noses will be blown by poor men than by rich ones; so too the probability that a person will blow his nose at a D distance from his house will decrease as D decreases, since that is the probability that he will be a D distance from home at any moment selected at random.[12]

Since this perseveration of earlier status evaluations is commonplace, let us describe it with the term, *cultural orthogenesis*. The extent to which parents impart to their offspring their own excessive thrift and extravagance may be an interesting problem in orthogenesis; so too the tendency of the successful revolutionary to continue to suspect everyone who wears a "white collar," and to "purge" beyond need.

h. Summary: The Exponential Law of Incentives. In the foregoing pages we have outlined, if at times only briefly, various aspects of what we believe is an exponential law of incentives which, if correct, is of considerable importance in human ecology since it suggests the comparative Force with which we approach towards, or are restrained from, the objectives of life. These objectives of life, which we discussed in Part One, are presumably continual and all-pervasive in our activity; so too, then, theoretically, the principle that governs the degree of incentive with which they are pursued or frustrated. Our own suggested principle, or theoretical law, relates to the rate at which the incentive is increased in relation to the rate of increase of the intensity of the activity.

4. The Economy of Increasing the Exploitable a Increment; The Elite as the Creator of Capital. We assumed initially that the *a* increment exploited from each individual pariah is a constant but, as we shall now see, such a constancy of *a* in terms of actual goods and services is by no means the case.

For just as there is a continual incentive for the elite to indulge in expansionist programs that will increase *C* and thereby the total exploitable *Ca* surplus, so, too, there is the same continual incentive for the elite to increase the *a* increment so that, in this way too, *Ca* will be increased. This incentive to increase the *a* increment may be called the *creativeness of the elite* since, in the last analysis, the *a* increment can only be increased by the invention of more efficient tools and skills, as the economists have long since pointed out and as Dr. Carl Snyder has argued in detail.[13] It is the role of the *elite as the creator of capital* that will now concern us.

One way to understand the role of the elite as a creator of capital is to begin by assuming that every individual produces all that he consumes, and consumes all that he produces; the condition is one in which the Force of Diversification is extreme. Then, next, let us assume that a *strong man* arrives and expropriates something—an *a* increment—from each of the *C* persons in the neighborhood; at this point the Force of Unification will begin to operate.

The strong man can use his thus exploited *Ca* income in one or both of two ways. He can *consume* it, or he can invest it in capital outlays. To expedite our argument we shall assume that he *invests* at least a sizable amount of it. For example, he builds, say, a grist mill.

The grist mill will save labor for the entire *C* neighborhood, since it can grind grain more economically than could the *C* laborers; and since the *C* laborers are all still working the same amount of time, it is evident that they will produce more during that time. As a result, the exploitable *a* increment and *Ca* surplus will increase.

The strong man skims the surplus again; and again he invests the exploited sum either in better production or in better transportation—or in a better defense, since these *C* slaves of his are becoming valuable assets that merit careful defense and tending. The *C* slaves are still working the same amount; the only difference is that they are using more efficient tools and skills which have been forced upon them by a man (or group) of superior strength and vision.

The foregoing kind of story is familiar in economic history. If we elaborated the story further we should presently find ourselves in one of our analogues on the economy of geography that we presented in Chapter Nine —as the strong man tries to increase *Ca* both by increasing *C* and by increasing *a* through a greater specialization of tools and labor.* But instead of elaborating the story further, let us inspect, *first,* the incentives which the strong man may have in investing his exploitations, and *second,* the weaknesses that may be inherent in his position.

One important incentive that impels the strong man to save and invest some of his income so that he will become still richer and more powerful in his fear of the second strong man on the other side of the hill against whom he must defend himself. Indeed, it is the vying of strong men for increased power for their successful defense and expansion that puts a premium upon the discovery of new tools and skills that will increase *a*. So great is this premium upon the new in defensive and offensive weapons that spies are sent across borders to procure the latest lethal inventions of other systems, although smart leaders will also spy out all new inventions that will increase the general standard of living. For it is to the strong man's advantage that the soil is well tilled, that the roads are in repair, that there is a high standard of public health, that persons of capacity are well trained both to fill positions of responsibility and to devise more effcient tools and skills for the strong man's defense and aggression and for his sensuous entertainment and for the philosophical easing of his mind. Hence, as odd as it seems, it is the fearful and aggressive vying of strong men that creates and advances material and intellectual and artistic civilization by the simple device of expropriating the pariah class whom the strong men force to work more and more efficiently. As long as some men are born more cunning and stronger than others, they will force those others to work for them, and the *a* increment will increase.

There is a weakness, however, in the strong man's position as his wealth and power increases with an increase in his *C* number of slaves and in the size of the *a* increment. For as the strong man's dominance system increases in size and diversity, he must rely increasingly upon the administrative and managerial help of other strong men against whom he must also defend himself. For the same education that makes a pariah a more efficient servant will also make him a more dangerous competitor.[14] So the strong man,

* We may suspect that in the long run the Force to increase *C* will equal that to increase *a;* or that the urge to expand equals the urge to innovate. It may be that nations that have expanded at a rate greater than that of their innovations are less to be feared than those nations of which the reverse is the case. Does *Ca* vary with C^2?

in order to acquire both the services and the good will of those of his underlings who are strong, gifted, and well-trained, will have to grant his agents quite sizable rewards—with the result that we promptly find ourselves once again in the problem of the ordering of a dominance system to the discussion of which the two analogues of the present chapter were devoted. Those two analogues, we remember, apply not only to the distribution of a fixed amount of *Ca* exploitable surplus, but also to the dynamics of an increasing (or decreasing) *Ca;* and they reveal both the strength and weakness of the strong man.

An inevitable theoretical consequence of an increasing *Ca* is a rise in the standard of living of the pariah class, whose members will naturally benefit from the increased efficiency of a common defense, from a common transportation, and from a common code of law that will tend to minimize intrasystematic friction. Moreover, as is evident from an earlier argument, the pariahs will also benefit from the fact that the members of the elite who compete for their services are becoming richer and richer. This competition among the elite for the services of the pariahs will take the form of including more goods and services in the real wages of the more gifted pariahs, even though they, like all pariahs, will continue to contribute their respective $1/C$ shares of the total work of production.

Curiously enough, although the real wages of the pariah will increase as a result of the competition among the elite for his services, nevertheless, the *relative* social status of the pariah will remain unchanged in spite of any advance in civilization. Thus the actual real wages of a pariah today in the American national dominance system are far higher than the real incomes of some princes of the blood a few centuries ago, or even of some princes today in out-of-the-way parts of the world. But since the pariah, like everyone else, tends to think primarily in terms of his own contemporary system, in which his real risks and opportunities lie, he will naturally also tend to think primarily of his own actual low social status; and hence he will continue to envy the status of those above him whose wealth and good things he will covet. It is this envy and covetousness on the part of the underling, with his attempt to imitate and to supplant those above, that theoretically makes the system grow in wealth and in efficiency, and in the homogeneity of its cultural code. Nor is the envy of the pariah confined to the elite, since those pariahs who receive lower wages will envy the pariahs who receive higher wages.

In spite of the "rise of civilization," the individual pariahs will still continue to contribute a $1/C$ share of the labor of production, in return for which they will simply receive an increasing amount of goods and services, except for the least desirable pariahs at the bottom, who will theoretically receive merely a $1/C - a$ amount from which they will survive at a level that is just above starvation.

Obviously, most of the goods and services of production will go to the pariahs because of their relatively large numbers. Moreover, since the pariahs will all be imitating the elite, and since they will all be receiving *approximately* the same amount and kinds of goods and services, and since they make up most of the population, we were perhaps not overbold in Chapter Nine when we postulated that every member of our theoretical system will contribute a $1/C$ share of the total work of production, in return for which he will receive a $1/C$ share (approximately) of the m different kinds of goods and services that are produced.

The elite is relatively small. It is paid its handsome rewards for directing the pariahs and for forcing them to work. For by expropriating the extra slice of black bread from the pariahs many centuries ago, the elite ultimately made possible the automobiles for the pariahs of today.

For the sake of the argument, let us now suppose that the pariahs so envy the elite that they refuse to work for them, and instead prefer to slow down their production so that Ca will decrease. In that case the Force of Diversification will increase, and the once great system will begin to disintegrate into many smaller independent systems, while our previous argument that led to the one great system now applies in reverse. Yet what will be the ultimate consequences of this disintegration, and who will suffer most? If the "slow-down" is carried to an extreme, the pariah will once again enjoy unmolested that extra slice of black bread that was expropriated from him. How much the extra slice of bread will cost the pariah is a real question, as he continues to expend the same $1/C$ share of work.

But, alas, mankind being what it is, ere long the strong man will appear again in order to "fill" the proverbial "political vacuum."

In the foregoing discussion of the elite as the creator of capital we have repeatedly used the phrase, *more efficient tools and skills.* Let us now inquire, first, into what is to be included in the more efficient tools and skills and, second, into who is to be called the owner of the same. Let us note that the toolage of a system consists not only of the actual physical tools but also of the knowledge or skill to produce, maintain, and use the tools. For, as we saw in Part One, a tool is meaningless without a knowledge of its use, and valueless without the skill to use it. Indeed, knowledge and skills are tools. Moreover, since knowledge and skills exist only in the persons who possess them, the persons who possess them are also tools of the system. Since, theoretically, everyone in the system is productive, everyone in the system is a tool, whether actual or potential. In other words, the structure of a social system of the type under discussion is similar to the structure of the Tool Analogy that we developed in Part One. If we view the entire toolage as a cultural system, then we see how the persons who are born into the system become creatures of the system who are "moulded" educationally into the system of cultural "tools" or occupational roles of the system.*

If we define tools and skills in the above fashion, we note that the question of the "ownership" of these tools is quite difficult. Theoretically, as previously pointed out, no one owns the tools. Instead the members of the system possess varying degrees of control over various tools, including themselves, with the entire system "owning" itself. The case is not unlike that of a corporation whose entire shares are allotted beneficially to its officers

* It is not by chance that the equations of our Tool Analogy of Part One are found again in Chapters Nine and Eleven.

and workers in proportion to the amount of their wages during the period of their employment; if the shareholders select the directors who run the business and employ the workers to whom the shares are allotted, then the problem of ownership becomes a highly academic matter. Yet the problem of the individual and collective possession of the controls is by no means an academic matter.

Our view of a person as a serviceable tool of society has the advantage of broaching the question of what society should do with those persons who, because of misfortune or of advanced age, are no longer useful as actual or as potential tools. Upon first thought it would seem to be economical for the system to dispose of its useless members in order to save the cost of their continued support; and some systems have been known to do so. If we remember, however, that all members of the system exist also as individuals who, theoretically, wish to live their entire individual lives with least effort, and to whom the problem of personal misfortune and old age is of grave individual concern, then we can understand how it can be economical for society to assume the responsibility for these individual misfortunes in order to ease the individual's worry and thereby to increase his efficiency. In other words, by crassly viewing an individual as a social tool, we arrive at a splendid economic motive for a humane course of social action that is sometimes scorned on the grounds that it is wasteful and sentimental. Those who say "There but for the grace of God go I," and who also reflect that no one can ever tell when or where "lightning is going to strike," will understand the economy of providing collectively an insurance against misfortunes that may befall any individual person.

In other words, our view of the elite as a creator of capital in a dominance system in which all persons are simultaneously competing and cooperating contains in it the economy of a collective defense, or insurance, not only against an attack from the outside, but also against the onset of individual misfortunes and incapacitations within. Yet the precise structure of the collective defense or insurance is not a matter of caprice but a very definite economic problem, lest it otherwise either put a premium upon malingering or else fail to insure.

5. The Elite as the Creator of Status-Hallowing Morality (i.e. "Pied Piper Morality"). The creativeness of the elite is by no means limited to the task of increasing capital. In addition, it extends to the fabrication of marvelous metaphysical and ethical systems that are intended to hallow the *status quo* and thereby to protect the incumbents of elite positions by making it wicked for the underling to compete or to disobey. This *status-hallowing morality* we shall poetically dub a *Pied Piper Morality,* since it seems to be designed to elicit a following of persons who are either weak and gullible or else easily induced to destroy furtively what may stand in the way. The Pied Piper morality in question is useful not only in preserving status but also in gaining a following for the purpose of overthrowing the hierarchy, since rebels are "righteous" too.

The concept of this type of morality is not new. Indeed, Pareto treated the topic at length under the terms, *residues* and *derivatives.*[15] It is intimately connected with our discussion of culture and of the superego in Chapter Seven, particularly in reference to those correlations that are empirically unverifiable. Our present interest in the topic is largely in the economy that leads to the structure of such ethical and metaphysical systems and in the danger that lurks therein.

In order to understand the economy and danger of Pied Piper morality, let us begin by noting that because of the doubly logarithmic distribution of the elite, it is easier for a member of the elite to fall to a lower position than to rise to a higher one. Since all members of the elite will have a common incentive in not falling, they will have a common incentive in preserving themselves as a class against falling. Therefore, they will find it economical to seek devices to achieve that end—that is, devices that will discourage attempts to displace them. Suitable devices are not readily available in the *real* world of human ecology, since the very existence of the elite is the result of envy and competition. Therefore, suitable devices are sought in an *imaginary* world—a *supernatural* world—and once they are found, the elite takes on the character of a leisure class.

The chief value to the elite of a Pied Piper morality is that of a deterrent. Thus, an aspirant to elite membership has not only the physical problem of supplanting someone in the elite by sheer force and cunning, but also the initial problem of overcoming his own conscience before attempt-to do so. The elite, on the other hand, has no conscientious scruples about annihilating the aspirant; on the contrary, the elite's self-defense becomes a highly moral act of which the entire hierarchy has been taught to approve. This same moral righteousness gives added momentum to any expansionist program of the elite for its own selfish aggrandisement, since the elite, with its moral righteousness, can easily blind the gullible in Pied Piper fashion, while silencing with the threat of ostracism or of death anyone who might choose to inquire objectively into the probable value and cost of the enterprise. Those citizens who follow the Pied Piper, whether from gullibility or from cowardice, have the temporarily comforting feeling of moral superiority while they commit what are only too often outright abominations and sadistic atrocities whose only purpose is to give vent to an aggressiveness and cruelty of temperament.

Another economy of a Pied Piper morality, as far as the leaders are concerned, is that it can quite cheaply bestow rewards upon the loyal followers in the inexpensive form of a moral approbation or of an eternal life of glory after death—with a medal thrown in as a token thereof. The reader can doubtless think of further economies of these splendid codes of Pied Piper morality whose solemn details fill the pages of contemporary comment.

The dangers of a Pied Piper morality are also obvious and well known. First of all, it tends to preserve incompetence in power and, if carried sufficiently far, it will cause the social system to develop into a caste system with "religious" status and occupational status closely combined; as a result of this incompetence, the productivity of the system will decline. Second, it will lead to crazy intranational and international ventures; though these ventures may benefit the elite for a short term, they may nevertheless be highly deleterious to the entire system, including the elite, over the long term. Third, a Pied Piper morality may lead to a feeling of moral frustration on the part of a sizable number of the population who, having been duped again and again, finally reach a condition of dejection (and defection) in which they no longer know what or whom to believe, and hence fall the easier prey to aspirants to power who try to stir up feelings of vengeance against the self-hallowed elite while promising to bestow lush rewards upon those who help to overthrow it (cf., our previous discussion of the exponential nature of a popular following). These aspirants to power, if memory serves, also make use of Pied Piper morality in their talk of "social justice" and the "common good" and the "common man" and "equality for all." Rebels, if successful, are always "righteous," or become so.

This feeling of moral frustration in a social system can be socially dangerous. Some observers believe that the present so-called "younger generation" in the United States, with its doubts and lack of clear objectives, reveals the effects of the monstrous deceit, duplicity, subterfuge, and fake righteousness on the part of America's effective intelligentsia up to and during World War II. Indeed, this fake righteousness of the war party of World War II together with the complete postwar fiasco for the United States and the world, as far as the problem of peace and human well-being is concerned, serves nicely to illustrate the dangers of a Pied Piper morality.

World War II also serves to illustrate one of the problems of personnel in promulgating, or of propagating, a Pied Piper cause since, to date, God himself does not seem willing to do so. The sole prerequisite of being a Pied Piper moralist in defense of the elite is apparently that the populace must be willing to defer to the superior intuitive insight of the Pied Piper in question. In the olden days the clergy were popularly supposed to have this superior intuitive insight into the ways of God and man. Today, in the United States at least, we defer rather to the intuitive insight of moving picture actresses, college presidents along the Atlantic seacoast, columnists, radio commentators, and the like—a motley array of self-righteous Pied Piper moralists whose mentation finds a fitting monument in the present postwar confusion. "The moral dignity of man!" "Social justice!"—these were only a few of the tunes of the moral crusaders who devised the chaos of Central Europe (i.e., the Morgenthau Plan), and let loose the atom bomb, thereby controverting their own loudly expressed "moral" principles.

While there is every reason both for examining the structure of a Pied Piper morality for its value as clinical material, and for studying the personalities of the Pied Piper moralists, who are often interesting cases of paranoia,* professional frustration, sadism, repressed homosexualism, and other types of sexual maladjustments (from which, incidentally, the aca-

* At a certain university the present writer, covertly by an actual test that used a certain familiar psychiatric device, found in a sample of the faculty that about 3 out of 7 had "significant indications" of paranoia. This fact was also apparent from their public utterances (the same applies to members of the administration).

demic profession and the editorializing classes are by no means immune), nothing is apparently gained either by arguing with Pied Piper morality itself or with its moralists. For to rout one Pied Piper is merely to make room for another; furthermore, since the Pied Piper moralist is almost always a skillful verbalist, the inquirer will merely pursue the Pied Piper moralist through the "opalesque labyrinth" of his schizophrenia and at best only disclose the type of personal conflict at the base of his particular brand of morality. Moreover, if the Pied Piper moralist happens to have marked paranoid tendencies, as is certainly not unknown, and if he also happens to occupy a strategic position, then it may be personally hazardous for the objective inquirer to controvert him (cf. Chapter Seven). For that reason the elite does well to prefer persons in strategic positions for their Pied Piper agents.

The best and perhaps the only way to get rid of all Pied Piper morality is to construct empirically an objective science of society that may be used as a frame of reference for an *empiric* system of ethics, as has been advocated again and again by persons of intellectual status like George A. Lundberg, H. W. Odum, E. B. Wilson, Wesley Mitchell, Reed Bain, W. F. Ogburn, Stuart Dodd, Robert Angel, F. S. Chapin, E. W. Burgess, R. R. Cottrell, Alfred Korzybski, Louis Gutman, Frank Lorimer, Donald Young, Irving J. Lee, and a *few others,* in addition to those whose contributions we have discussed more particularly in this book.[16]

If we use the term a *few others,* it is to suggest that the total number of students of the natural science of society is by no means large today. The reason for this fewness of numbers may be found in the published observation [17] of E. B. Wilson to the effect that those who bestow academic positions tend to reward more highly a poor picture of the ideal world than a good study of the real one.* Of course, Professor Wilson's observation, like many other similar observations, may be subject in part to the restrictions of the *P/D* hypothesis as discussed in Chapter Nine. Professor Wilson, we find, resides in Brookline, Mass. Hence, things may not be so sad for the social empiricist as *D* distance increases thence; according to all indications, social empiricism is flourishing in the Middle and Far West and South.

Perhaps the most trenchant attack against what we are calling a Pied Piper morality, as well as a brilliant defense of social empiricism, can be found in Dr. George A. Lundberg's little classic, "Can Science Save Us?" (Lundberg, we remember, is the author of the pioneer study, "Foundations of Sociology").[18] Dr. F. Stuart Chapin in a recent article [19] has applied his wide knowledge and shrewd insight to the problem of the social obstacles that stand in the way of an acceptance of the actual scientific knowledge about the structure of social behavior that is available today; in other

* Theoretically, this will be the case only if the picture of the ideal world in question elaborates with zeal the private psychoses of those who bestow the positions; for in general we should expect to find that a genuine adulation of the king's moral wisdom, like the applause of the king's wit, will be a profitable pastime all the way down the hierarchy, according to our equations; while preferment up the scale will go to those who are "moral" and have a "good sense of humor."

words, he has treated the resistance to natural social science as a problem in social psychology and societal pathology; among other points in his study, Dr. Chapin neatly analyzes the effect of intangible and trite verbalistic behavior. This has also been brilliantly analyzed by Count Alfred Korzybski in his writings and in his Institute of General Semantics.[20] The enormous intellectual confusion to which such verbalistic behavior has led in present-day American life has been objectively and succinctly set forth by our excellent colleague, Dr. Wendell Johnson.[21]

After all, why is it not in the public interest that the Pied Piper and his tunes should be selected as fit subjects for an objective social study, as the Pied Piper now appears over the radio for a friendly "fireside chat," and now appears in a cap and gown with a golden tassel and whistles a baccalaureate sermon that is a clarion call to those who will follow.

As far as the present book is concerned, we are but attempting to disclose objectively some of the impersonal principles that govern the individual and his social relations. Although it is true that persons may differ in their genetic gifts and in their cultural "clothing," yet, except for these differences, persons seem to be essentially the same. For although cultural "clothing" is relative to time and place—and different climates have different flowers—nevertheless, all cultural systems seem to be the same in their dynamics. Viewed dynamically, "thou" and "thy neighbor" are the same; and that fact may be of considerable importance.

There are many who sincerely believe that the key to all human relations is found in the ancient commandment: "Thou shalt love thy neighbor as thyself." This commandment is difficult to obey until we know objectively in dynamic terms both what *thy neighbor* is, and what is meant by the term love. Social empiricism, in disclosing the nature of these things, can only help to provide an empiric ethics; in short, we should view social empiricism as a constructive ethical "force" that will help effectively in the rout of nihilism, and by no means contribute to it, as is often feared by the naive.

It is perhaps true that the "fall of the dice" may favor some over others, with the result that those who lose must be patient. Doubtless the day will never come when we can no longer say: "man's inhumanity to man makes countless thousands mourn"; therefore, let each person forgive as he hopes to be forgiven, and to measure others as he is willing to be measured. On the other hand, the advance of social empiricism will at least help to put an end to the Pied Piper type of organized morality which with its alleged *"humanity to man"* has succeeded historically in needlessly destroying mankind by the countless millions.

C. The Elite As a System of Roles in Revolution: Summary

Up to this point the argument of the present chapter has fallen into two main sections. First (*A*) we have developed two theoretical analogues on the distribution of economic power and social status; these analogues yielded a family of equations that we are about to test empirically. Second (*B*) we discussed in considerable detail certain corollary relationships that were inherent in the two analogues. Chief among these were the distribution of assets, the distribution of pariah wages, and the exponential law of incentives.

Now (*C*) by way of summary, let us briefly allude to certain aspects of our foregoing theory that seem to merit emphasis because they are closely related to our discussion of culture and of cultural roles in Chapter Seven.

A social system may be viewed as something that tends to endure as a structure although its members are transient. Indeed, it may be viewed as a *system of roles of relative control* which are acted by the members of the social system who enter and leave the system one way or another as time passes.

Our equations describe the distribution of the relative amounts of control in a system that is in a condition of stable equilibrium. Dynamically viewed, there may, of course, be a continual rising and falling of persons within the scheme of status even though the system itself is in a condition of equilibrium, since our term, equilibrium, refers solely to the distribution of the controls. On the other hand, as we have already pointed out, deviations from our equations represent unstable conditions which are theoretically corrected by "revolutions." (Consider the "intensity of a revolution" as something that varies *directly* with the size of the deviation that is to be corrected, and *inversely* with the length of time during which the revolutionary correction occurs; thus conceived, a social system may be continually *in revolution,* with our equations representing only norms about which the phenomena oscillate.)

Even though dominance systems will, theoretically, agree in the distribution of their points and relative amounts of control, they may nevertheless differ vastly in the cultural details of the actual roles and in the insignia of status of the roles. As we noted in earlier chapters, different cultures are dynamically similar despite their differences in form.

If we choose, we may view a social system as a dominance system of cultural roles that is described, theoretically, by our accumulated equations, provided that the system is in a condition of stable equilibrium as we have defined the term. Our insistence upon the need of precisely defining the concept of equilibrium in all human social activity springs from the conviction that no system of dynamics is possible without a precise definition of equilibrium. In our own system of dynamics, *effort* is theoretically the minimum.

But now that we have elaborated our theory and derived a dozen odd equations for the distribution of economic power and of social status, the question remains as to whether our equations, and therewith our theory, will sustain an actual empiric test. Obviously this question as to the empiric verifiability of our argument can be answered in only one way.

II. EMPIRIC DATA

In the theoretical construct of our foregoing section we arrived at a family of equations which we shall now test empirically. For convenience we shall test them in the following three main groups. First (*A*) we shall test all those equations that refer directly or indirectly to the income and wages of individuals; then (*B*) we shall test our theory of the distribution of the incomes of corporations, which will be followed (*C*) by a test of the equation for the distribution of corporation assets.

A. Individual Incomes and Wages

According to our theory, we should expect that the rank-frequency distribution of (1) individual incomes, and of (2) the salaries of the executive staffs of corporations should follow the equation of the generalized harmonic series with a value of p that is equal to $\frac{1}{2}$. This value of p is expected, theoretically, (3) to rise to 1 in the case of the settlement of liability claims against automobile insurance companies, though it will again drop to $p = \frac{1}{2}$ in the settlement of claims against fire insurance and life insurance companies. In addition to the above we have also argued in detail as to the meaning (4) of the term *bureaucratic elite,* in illustration of which we shall present a set of data. Thence, we shall turn (5) to a consideration of the rank-frequency distribution of pariah wages which, according to our theory, will be rectilinear on arithmetic-logarithmic co-ordinates.

1. Income Tax Data. The traditional place to look for information about the distribution of individual incomes is in the income tax data as published by the taxing bodies of the various countries. We shall defer to tradition by first consulting this kind of information, even though we can suspect that there may be difficulties of definition, since what is to be officially considered as *net income for taxable purposes* may or may not be the equivalent of an individual income. Furthermore, there is the question of fraudulent tax returns which, as we shall later note, may introduce the question of an exponential law of incentives for honestly reporting one's income.

But though we may be critical of income tax data, we can scarcely argue that the data are of no value whatsoever. Instead, as we shall see from the following samples of seven different countries, the observed approximation of the data to the theoretically expected value, $p = \frac{1}{2}$, is often quite close. The data will in all cases be presented graphically, with the addition of an ideal line, *A,* of $-\frac{1}{2}$ slope that represents the theoretically expected slope, and which will be convenient for purposes of comparison. No slopes have been calculated because (1) the pariah wages have often been included in the data (as is evident from the downward bend of the slope at the bottom) thereby necessitating an arbitrary decision as to where the upper elite part of the curve may be said to stop; and because (2) a fitted curve of such data would tell us little more than the eye. The method of graphical presentation is familiar: *rank* (or the cumulative frequency of all persons who receive not less than a given y amount of income) is plotted logarithmically on the abscissa against the logarithm of y income on the ordinate. The data represent in all cases the official data of the countries in question.[22]

In Fig. 11–1 are presented the individual income data for the United Kingdom surtax for six different years as indicated. In Fig. 11–2 are those for France for seven years. In Fig. 11–3 are those for Denmark for four years.

In Fig. 11–4 are those for the Netherlands for six years. In Fig. 11–5 are those for Finland for four years. In Fig. 11–6 are those for Germany for five years. In Fig. 11–7 are those for the family consumer units for the

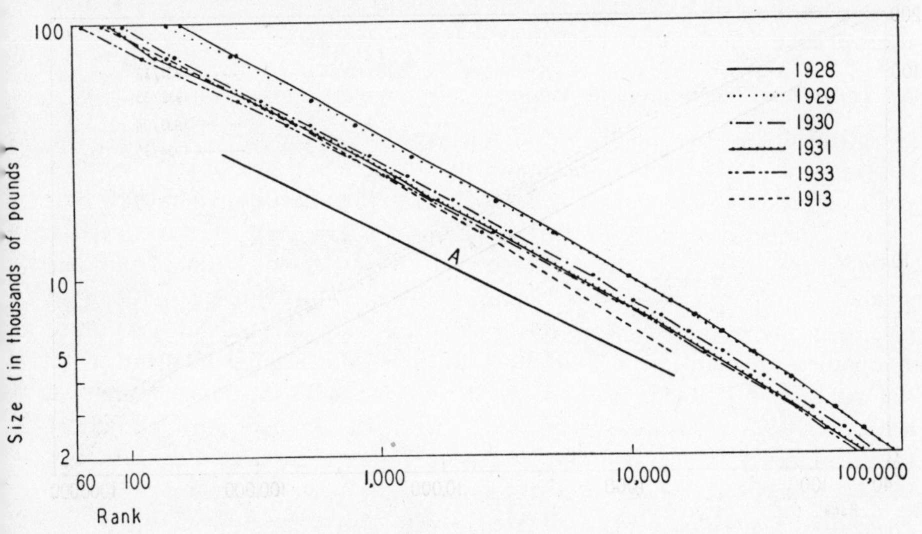

Fig. 11–1. United Kingdom: incomes for six years (for surtax). (Line A has an ideal − ½ slope.)

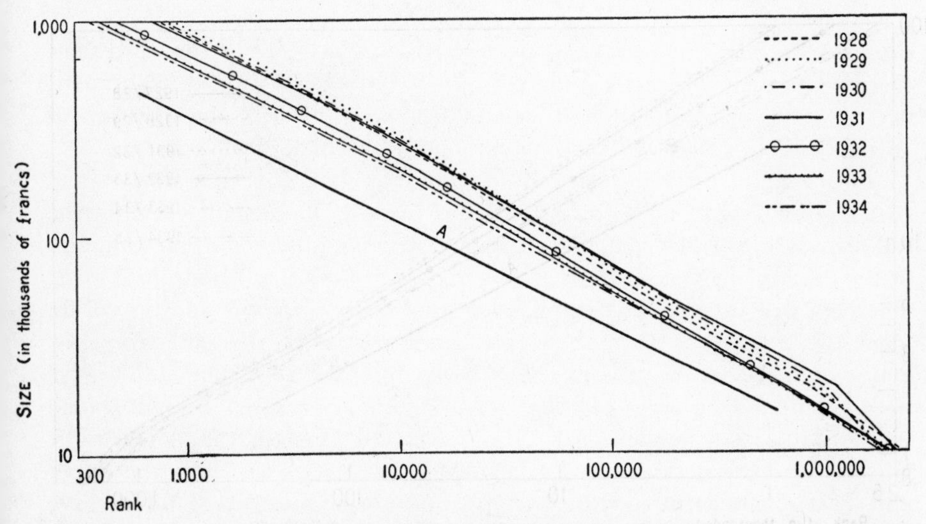

Fig. 11–2. France: incomes for fiscal years, 1927–28 – 1933–34. (Line A has an ideal − ½ slope.)

U. S. A. for the fiscal year 1935–1936. The seven different figures represent a total of 33 different annual samples.

At the bottom of the curves of many of these figures, where the very low income brackets are included, we find a concave downward bend which is to be anticipated theoretically, since these very low income brackets presumably include pariah wages which, theoretically, will not be doubly logarithmically rectilinear. The bend at the bottom of Fig. 11–7 for the U. S. A. will be analyzed later (cf. Fig. 11–10) as an empiric test of our

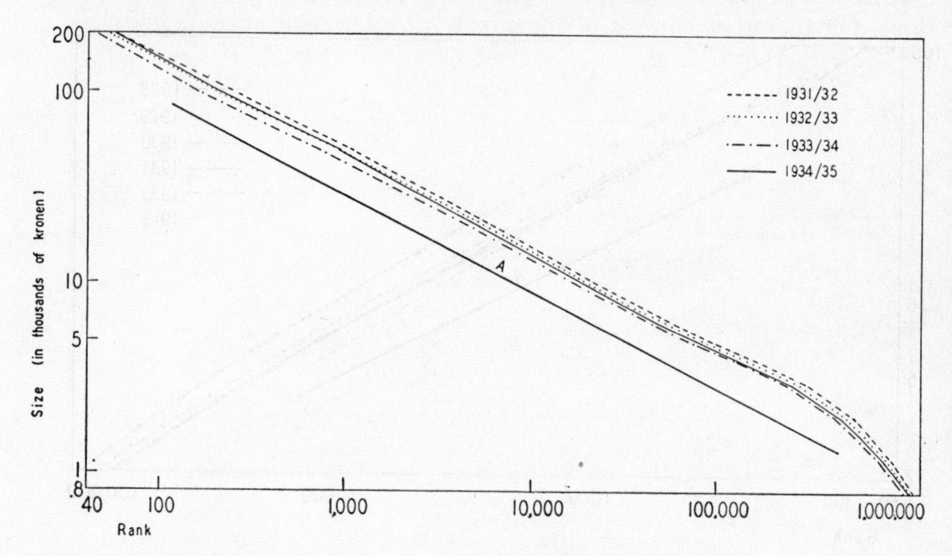

Fig. 11–3. Denmark: incomes for fiscal year, 1931–32 – 1934–35 (line A has an ideal – ½ slope).

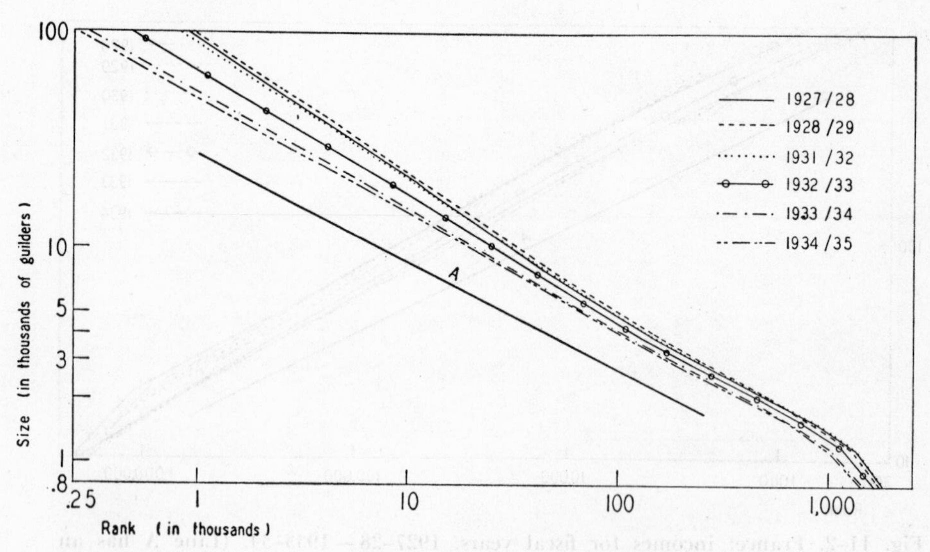

Fig. 11–4. Netherlands: incomes for six fiscal years – Inkomstenbelastung (line A has an ideal – ½ slope).

theoretical distribution of pariah wages. Our discussion at present, let us remember, refers only to the distribution of individual elite incomes that lie above the downward concavity at the bottom; the linearity of this upper portion of the curve is conspicuous in nearly all cases.

It is evident from a more detailed inspection of the charts that many of the individual sets of data approximate quite closely our theoretically expected slope as represented by the *A* line; moreover, no curve has a lesser slope. On the other hand it is undeniable that for some years in the data of the Netherlands (Fig. 11–4) and of Germany (Fig. 11–6), and of the

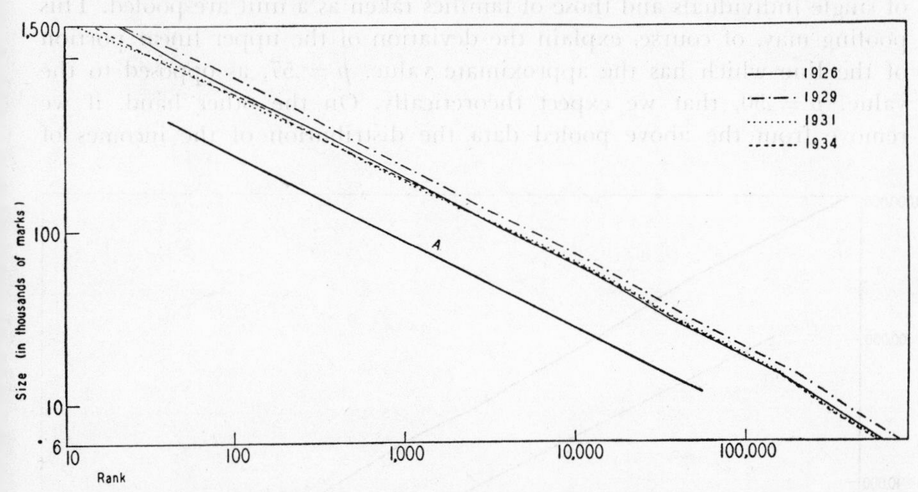

Fig. 11–5. Finland: incomes for four years — Inkomstkatt (line A has an ideal — ½ slope).

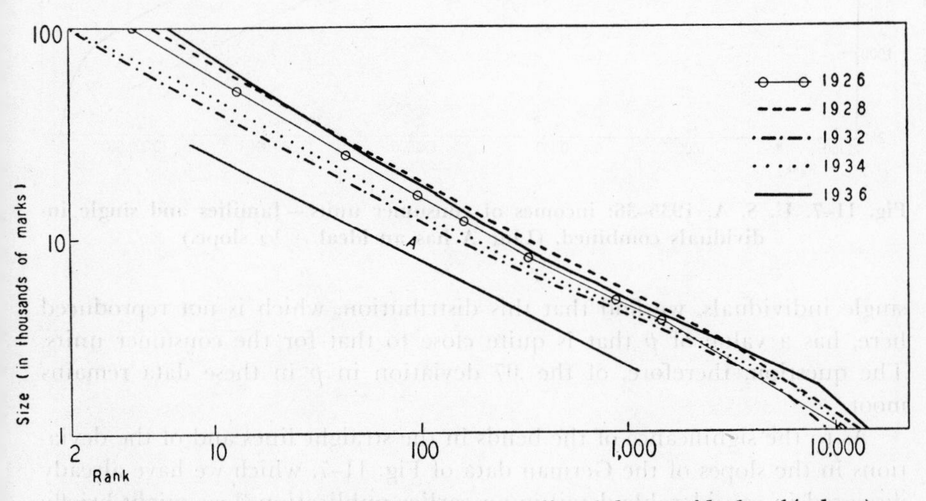

Fig. 11–6. Germany: incomes for five years (line A has an ideal — ½ slope).

data for the U. S. A. (Fig. 11–7), there are steeper slopes, with the result that the value of p will be greater than ½. Although we cannot undertake a detailed analysis of each of these deviations, we shall at least hazard a few remarks about several of them in the belief that they may be fairly typical of the whole.

In Fig. 11–7 for the U. S. A., the data refer to the incomes of *consumer units* in which are combined both the incomes of entire families and the incomes of single individuals, as described and reported in the *Monthly Labor Review* for October 1938, p. 730 ff. Although this distribution is said to be the most complete and reliable that we have for the lower income brackets in the U. S. A. (and perhaps elsewhere), it does nevertheless include more than sheer individual incomes, since, to repeat, the incomes of single individuals and those of families taken as a unit are pooled. This pooling may, of course, explain the deviation of the upper linear portion of the line which has the approximate value, $p = .57$, as opposed to the value, $p = .50$, that we expect theoretically. On the other hand, if we remove from the above pooled data the distribution of the incomes of

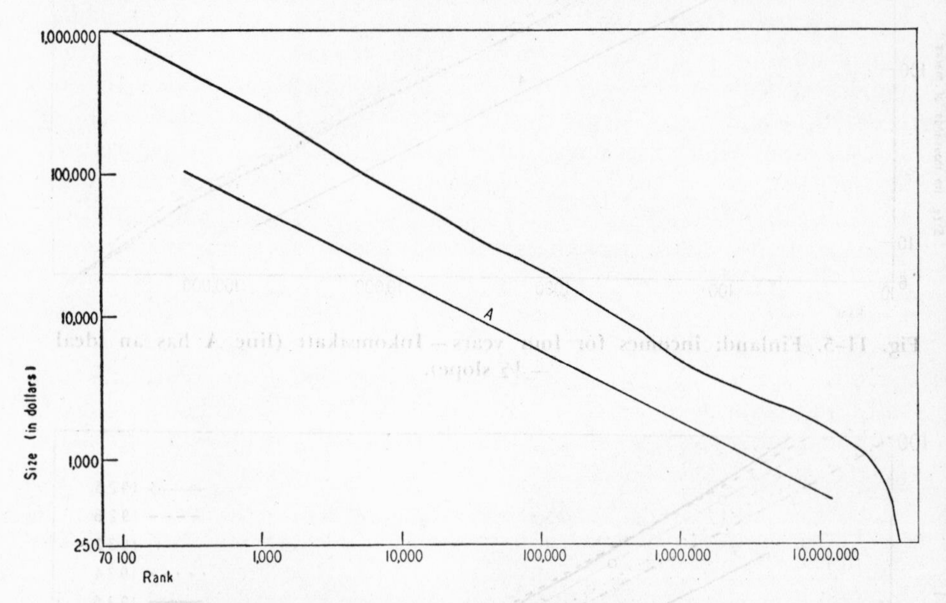

Fig. 11–7. U. S. A. 1935–36: incomes of consumer units — families and single individuals combined. (Line A has an ideal — ½ slope.)

single individuals, we find that this distribution, which is not reproduced here, has a value of p that is quite close to that for the consumer units. The question, therefore, of the .07 deviation in p in these data remains moot.

As to the significance of the bends in the straight lines and of the deviations in the slopes of the German data of Fig. 11–7, which we have already discussed in considerable detail in an earlier publication,[23] we might briefly remark here that the period in question from 1926 through 1936 was one that is usually felt to have been very unstable. Following an extremely severe inflation that virtually annihilated the creditor class, the period in question includes years in which there were enormous borrowings of capital from abroad that were not always used for capital outlays; the period also includes years of extreme depression and unemployment that led to a complete revolution with the rise of Mr. Hitler. This revolutionary movement may be correlated with the bends in the lines and with the differences in slope.* Similar bends can be found for comparable years in the income distributions of the U. S. A. under the Roosevelt Administration which, incidentally, came into power the same year as the Hitlerian one, and as the result of a severe depression. Theoretically, any bend in an income curve above the bottom bend for the pariah wages signifies a prerevolutionary condition in the sense that the "lower part" may be organizing as a class against the "upper part." It is from this populous and well meaning "lower part" in our belief, that revolutions may take their start, even though the "lower part" may soon lose control of the revolutions.[24]

As for the data for the Netherlands, I do not know the reasons for the deviations.† It might be remarked in general, however, that there is an incentive to understate one's income in a tax return, since such an understatement, if successful, will save money for the taxpayer. On the other hand, the taxing bodies are aware of this incentive for making fraudulent income tax returns and therefore investigate returns to find cases of fraud. These investigations, which cost money, are justified only if the sums they recover are sufficient to pay for the investigations. Since the greatest opportunities for sizable frauds in absolute terms are in the upper brackets, it is precisely there where it is to the advantage of the revenue agents to concentrate their efforts if they want a large probable return for a given expense of investigation. (As Aesop wrote centuries ago, the small fish tend to get through the net.) Knowing this, the members of the upper income brackets will tend, theoretically, to be exponentially more honest in their returns. Naturally, the government, in the light of the information which it receives from its fraud investigations, could correct the entire distribution to allow for the effect of fraud (including "bad memory," etc.) ; and in some of the data the governments in question may have done so.

These deviations in slope in excess of the value, $p = 1/2$, bring up the question of the empiric constant of the Pareto school which claims that (in the language of our own co-ordinates and equations) the norm is $p = 2/3$, and, therefore, not our value, $p = 1/2$.‡ The Pareto school, as brilliantly expounded by Dr. Harold T. Davis, the outstanding statistician and econometrist, has admittedly amassed a very large amount of data, including the earlier data that Pareto himself gathered, which, in spite of its often large variations, do indeed approximate the Pareto empiric value.[25] Moreover, the Pareto school has argued (in my opinion correctly) that the value of p tends to increase in "good times" and to fall in "bad times." [26] (In other words the higher brackets tend to feel the effects of good times

* Thus, the bends at the bottom with lesser slope mean that "too many" were receiving "too little" and, therefore, had an incentive in organizing themselves to oppose the entire group above.

† It is worth reflecting, however, that the data are not those of an economic self-sufficient group but of the nucleus of an empire.

‡ The Pareto school reverses our co-ordinates and plots size of income on the X-axis, while the cumulative number of persons who receive at least a given x income is plotted on the Y-ordinate. Hence, the slope of the Pareto manner of plotting the data will be the reciprocal of ours (i.e., the value, $p = 2/3$, represents the -1.50 slope as claimed by the Pareto school).

sooner than others—possibly because of their superior information advantages.)

On the other hand, we have presented quite a few sets of data that approximate the value $p = 1/2$. Moreover, we have presented reasons why deviations above this value may be observed in the cases of income tax data.

The chief drawback to accepting the 2/3 value of the Pareto school is that the value is purely empiric, without any theoretical justification whatsoever. Indeed, if we may quote the words of Dr. Harold T. Davis of the Pareto school,[27] "Our general conclusion would be, then, that the Pareto distribution is a necessary phenomenon of any stable economic state. The reason for the distribution must be sought in the mysterious realm of human psychology which accounts for the existence and distribution of special abilities." * In short, he presents no definite reason.

We, on the other hand, have presented a theoretical reason for expecting the value $p = 1/2$; moreover, we have elaborated upon our theory so that it can be tested from other types of data than those for the entire distribution as derived from income tax returns.

To some of these other kinds of tests let us now turn.

2. Salaries Paid to the Executives of Corporations. In our theory we have argued that the incomes, or salaries, paid to those who direct and supervise a large group, such as is the case with the executive staff of a large corporation, will have the value $p = 1/2$, of the generalized harmonic series, when the salaries are ranked in the order of decreasing size.

To my knowledge the only published extensive data that are available on this subject are the executive salaries of not less than $5,000 per annum that were paid in 1936 by the General Motors Corporation as published in their 28th Annual Report for the year ending December 31, 1936.

In 1941 Dr. Harold T. Davis pointed out [29] that the rank-frequency distribution of these salaries was rectilinear on a doubly logarithmic scale, and calculating the slope, he found (in the language of our co-ordinates) a slope of $-.4833$ against our theoretically expected $-.5000$ slope. Or, in terms of the equation of the generalized harmonic series, the observed value is $p = .4833$ for the General Motors data. A very close approximation to $p = 1/2$.

Dr. Davis noted the possible connection between this set of data and the more general income tax data. We are merely arguing that the value $p = 1/2$ is the correct one and not the value $p = 2/3$.†

* Dr. Davis' statement refers to Dr. A. J. Lotka's pioneer observation [28] known as the "inverse square law of scientific production" which we shall discuss later (Section III) in illustrating the exponential law of incentives. Lotka's data, if ranked, will give the value, $p = 1$, and hence do not support Dr. Davis' conclusion. Moreover, the distribution of pariah wages which is linear arithmetic-logarithmically precludes the easy belief that "special abilities" are doubly logarithmically distributed. Let us reflect: if there are $n + 1$ persons with a given special ability, and only n jobs for the same, then 1 of them may descend into the pariah class. Our argument is based on the assumption that some persons are more capable than others (the distribution of capacities need not be linear!).

† Incidentally, this Pareto value, $p = 2/3$, has no connection with our theoretical *Imperial 2/3 slope* which refers to the negative slope of group incomes and not to that of individual incomes.

To my knowledge the only other detailed information on the salaries of employees receiving more than $5,000 per annum in a large corporation are the data for the year 1941 that were gathered by the treasurer of a large corporation for the specific purposes of this study, with the stipulation, however, that their source be treated as confidential, since the data are not published information. The slope of these data as calculated by least squares is $-.5424 \pm .0056$ (i.e., $p = 54$), or an absolute deviation of .04 from our theoretically expected value (i.e., $p = .50$).[30]

This deviation is perhaps not serious. In this connection it might be remarked that the data refer merely to the employees in the main plant in the home city (say "Chicago"). Since the company has smaller subsidiary establishments elsewhere whose employees are not included in the above, it might be that a complete distribution would have a different slope, and even a smaller slope, since the additions would presumably be mainly to the lower brackets.*

3. Claims against Insurance Companies. In the theoretical discussion of Section I we argued that the settlements of claims for damages against a compulsory automobile liability insurance company would follow the proportions of the generalized harmonic series with $p = 1$, because of what we believe is an exponential law of incentives.

This topic of automobile liability claims has been investigated empirically by V. Myslivec of Prague who, in 1939, published his observations of the claims paid by automobile insurance companies in Austria, where liability insurance was compulsory.[31] His sources of data were taken from an earlier work by W. Lethays, which is unavailable to me.

At this point a word of caution is in order. Although Dr. Myslivec appeals to Pareto's manner of handling income data (i.e., a rank-frequency distribution, with the co-ordinates reversed from our usage), he nevertheless does not make use of Pareto's manner of graphing his data. Instead, Dr. Myslivec used what we have called the number-frequency relationship; that is, he plotted (in our usage) the x number of claims of like y size against the y size, with both axes on logarithmic scale. This method of plotting is quite all right, *provided*—and some members of the Pareto school might note this provision—that one remembers that the resulting slope will be different.

When, as in the present case, we expect that the rank-frequency distribution will be that of the pure harmonic series (i.e., $p = 1$), then, when the data are plotted according to the number-frequency relationship, we must expect that the x number of claims of like y size will be inversely proportional to y^2 (approximate) or, in equation form:

$$x \cdot y^2 = constant$$

* In genuinely thanking the above treasurer, I should like also to thank the treasurers of other large corporations for their co-operation; they either were unable to assemble the data for an earlier year, or else were unable to present it in sufficiently detailed form, or else felt obliged to make it publicly available only in their annual reports. I write with the knowledge of what was made available to me, all in highly confidential form. The problem merits further empiric study.

as we saw in Chapter Two. Theoretically, therefore, we should expect that Dr. Myslivec would observe the exponent, 2.

Dr. Myslivec observed that the 1207 claims he examined, as calculated by least squares, had the exponent 2.1268407 in terms of our co-ordinates; or

$$x \cdot y^{2.1268} = constant.$$

This is an astonishingly close approximation to our theoretically expected value, 2.00; * and Dr. Myslivec is greatly to be congratulated upon the brilliance of his discovery, which seems to go far towards providing an empiric test of our entire theory. Since his data may not be readily avail-

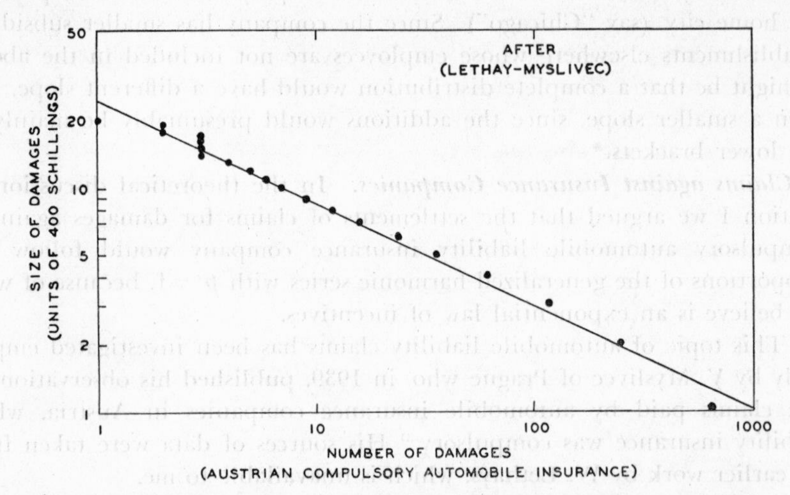

Fig. 11–8. Liability insurance (Austria): the number and sizes of settlements of damage claims.

able to the reader, we shall present them graphically in Fig. 11–8 with the co-ordinates as labelled.

The topic of liability claims whose rank-frequency distribution should have the value $p = 1$ broaches the topic of the claims against *life insurance* companies and *fire insurance* companies, where, however, *the distribution should have the value* $p = 1/2$, for reasons that we set forth in Section I. (We recall that theoretically the claims against life and fire underwriters will be directly related to the distribution of individual incomes, where $p = 1/2$.)

This topic was investigated many years ago by the Norwegian scientist, Professor Birger Meidell, who first published his observation about life insurance companies in 1912.

Dr. Meidell's original publications are unavailable to me; hence I must rely upon an excerpt from one of Dr. Meidell's speeches.†

* In logarithmic form he observed: $\log x + 2.1268 \log y = 2.987628$; theoretically this should be approximately: $\log x + 2 \log y = constant$.

† The excerpt appeared in *Neumanns Zeitschrift für Versicherungswesen,* Vol. 61 (Feb. 9, 1938) pp. 148–149 (a copy of this is in the library of the Harvard Business School). Dr. Meidell's address was delivered before the *Jahrestagung des deutschen Vereins für Versicherungs-Wissenschaft,* Jan. 15, 1938.

Dr. Meidell presented his data in rank-frequency form with the co-ordinates as used in the Pareto school, whose absolute slope will be the reciprocal of p in our equation of the generalized harmonic series in our system of co-ordinates.

In the light of our theory that the amount of a person's life insurance and the value of his dwelling will both vary directly with the size of his income, and that the occurrence of a percentage fire loss is random, we may expect that in both Dr. Meidell's sets of observations the value of p will be ½ (or the reciprocal of his absolute slope, 2.00).

And that is precisely the value, $p = ½$, that Dr. Meidell observed, subject, however, to the addition of a constant, c, in the S sizes of the settlements (i.e., the S size of the settlement becomes $S + c$ in the equation). Dr. Meidell defends the addition of this c constant quite properly, to my mind, on the ground that a dwelling must reach a certain value before it is insured at all. He also observed a preference for round numbers (e.g., 1,000; 5,000; 10,000) in buying insurance. The value of c is much smaller in the case of the settlements of life insurance contracts.

Clearly, Dr. Meidell's observations give cogent empiric support of our theoretical contention that the value $p = ½$ describes the distribution of individual incomes. Dr. Myslivec's observation of the value $p = 1$ (in our language) for the settlement of liability claims seems to support our theoretical contention that persons tend to urge their claims, and to be satisfied for their personal grievances, by amounts that vary with the square of the financial power (or income) of the persons in question.

Further observations are needed.

4. The Bureaucratic Elite: A Possible Case. In our theory in Section I we pointed out how a bureaucratic elite might arise and, for its own advantage, manipulate the productive elite. An example of this *may* be represented by the income distribution of natives and whites in Java and Madura as reported in the official statistical abstracts of the Netherland East Indies.

In Fig. 11–9 are presented the income distributions for (A) combined natives and whites, and for (B) natives, as reported for the years (1) 1924–25, (2) 1928, and (3) 1932, and as generously brought together by my then student, Mr. James M. Conant. The *number* of recipients of incomes of like size are plotted logarithmically on the *abscissa,* with the *size of income* plotted logarithmically on the *ordinate* (with the origin shifted successive cycles as indicated).

This device of plotting *number* (instead of *rank*) against *income size* was adopted to bring out more sharply the differences between the respective A and B *curves.* Naturally the adoption of this *number-size* (instead of *rank-size*) manner of graphing means that the theoretically expected negative slope becomes − ⅓ (instead of − ½, as would be the case with a rank-size distribution).

If we inspect the B sets of data which refer to native incomes, we note that in all cases they approximate fairly closely the theoretically expected − ⅓ slope (i.e., the intercept on the abscissa is between 2½ to 3 times the intercept on the ordinate). Moreover, the B curves are conspicuously rectilinear except towards the bottom. Indeed it is this rectilinearity that chiefly concerns us now, since the slope of the *B* data, dynamically considered, is presumably influenced by the incomes that were paid to the whites and included in the respective *A* curves. The differences between the *A* and *B* curves represent the amounts paid to the whites for the years in question.

Here in Fig. 11–9 we have an example of what *may* represent a *bureaucratic elite* in the form of the white class which largely controlled the gov-

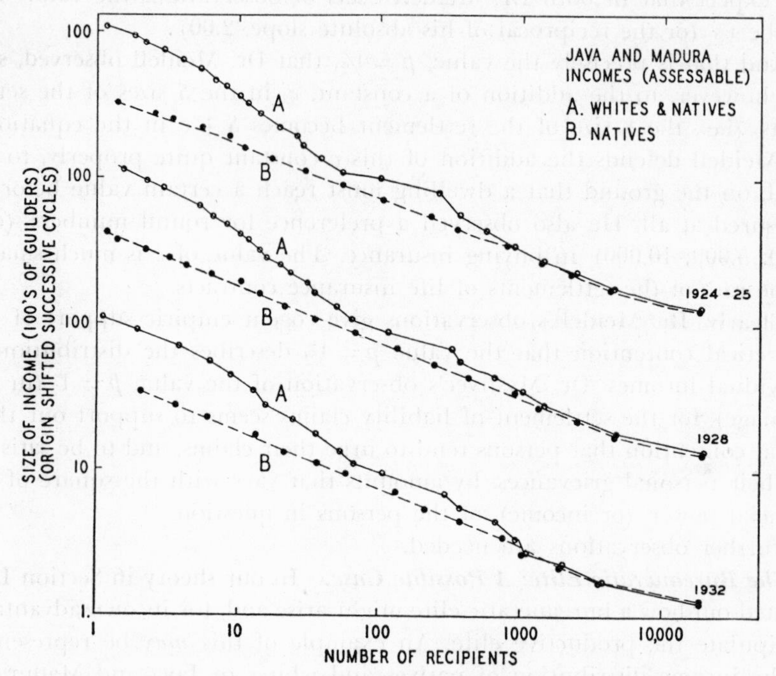

Fig. 11–9. Incomes: Java and Madura (Netherlands East Indies).

ernment, even though some of the whites were also, doubtless, actually performing managerial service in the productive elite.*

Be the connection what it may, in recent years the native populations in these Dutch colonies have revolted against the whites, whose elite roles they have attempted to usurp (as, I think, could almost have been predicted from the nature of these data).

The whites in question constituted not only an economic group, obviously a minority; they also constituted a small cohesive cultural group which, though culturally out of step with the majority, nevertheless represented an organization with police power that attempted to set the rules and to coerce the majority.

It may be that any cohesive cultural minority organized openly or clandestinely in reference to its own cultural objectives, which the majority of the group either *can* not or *will* not share, risks being eliminated from

* The slope of the *A* curve, despite its irregularities, is approximately — 1/2 which, curiously enough, should be the case if the entire distribution follows Eq. (11–2) (i.e., $p = 1$).

the social system—all constitutional guarantees of "minority rights" to the contrary notwithstanding. According to our theory, all economic groupings of any sort can and will tend to be dispersed in the public interest in order to preserve or to restore the distributions of incomes, as described by our equations in Section I.

Before leaving the data of Figs. 11–1 to 11–9 on the distribution of individual incomes of the elite, let us remember that these distributions have sometimes varied in slope and have even revealed important deviations from the theoretical rectilinearity of stable equilibrium. Such variations and deviations may be extremely instructive, as the Pareto school has often shown. Hence, the frequent assertion by some economists that "Pareto's Law is wrong" because of these variations and deviations does little credit to the reputations of the said economists as natural scientists, regardless of how much their assertion may serve to buttress their reputations in other quarters.

Our *only* quarrel with the Pareto school is in the theoretical [32] value of p.

*5. **Pariah Wages.*** We have argued theoretically that towards the bottom of the distribution of individual incomes will be a class of individuals—the

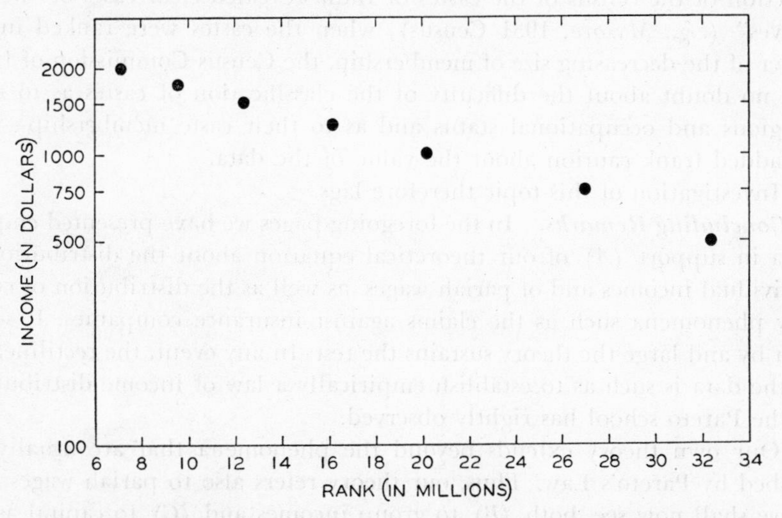

Fig. 11–10. "Pariah incomes": the rank-frequency distribution of U. S. A. incomes (consumer units 1935–36) between $500 and $2,000 inclusive per annum.

pariah class—whose wages, when ranked in the order of decreasing size, will be a linear function, with rank plotted arithmetically against the logarithm of the income.

Since most taxing bodies exempt the very low incomes and, therefore, have no way of ascertaining the precise number and sizes of these very low incomes, it follows that all official *estimates* of the lower incomes are untrustworthy.

Nevertheless, the *actual analysis* of the incomes of Consumer Units in the United States in 1935–36, as presented in Fig. 11–7, was a very careful empiric study of these very low income groups. It has the reputation for a high degree of reliability, which is all the more credible since the purpose of the survey was to determine what our national labor resources were, without any expressed motive of taxation.

In Fig. 11–10 we present arith-logarithmically, as indicated, the rank-income distribution of family units that received from $500 up to $2,000 per annum—nearly 30 million in all—as reported for the fiscal year 1935–36 in the *Monthly Labor Review* (*loc. cit.*). This is the same as the bottom part of the curve presented doubly logarithmically in Fig. 11–7.

The unmistaken rectilinearity of the data of Fig. 11–10, which includes many millions of persons, completely confirms our thesis. Further reliable sets of data are needed.

Above the $2,000 bracket, the distribution becomes doubly logarithmically rectilinear, as we saw in Fig. 11–7. Therefore, any family that received as much as $50 per week in 1935–36 was, theoretically, a member of the elite.

6. Religious Castes. Our theory suggests the possibility of a rectilinearity in the distribution of members of religious castes. Although a sampling inspection of the census of the castes of India revealed clear cases of "hollow curves" (e.g., *Mysore,* 1931 Census), when the castes were ranked in the order of the decreasing size of membership, the Census Commission of India left no doubt about the difficulty of the classification of castes as to their religious and occupational status and as to their caste membership—with an added frank caution about the value of the data.

Investigation of this topic therefore lags.

7. Concluding Remarks. In the foregoing pages we have presented empiric data in support (*A*) of our theoretical equation about the distribution of individual incomes and of pariah wages, as well as the distribution of corollary phenomena such as the claims against insurance companies. It seems that by and large the theory sustains the test. In any event, the rectilinearity of the data is such as to establish empirically a law of income distribution, as the Pareto school has rightly observed.

Our own theory extends beyond the phenomena that are usually described by Pareto's Law. Thus, our theory refers also to pariah wages and, as we shall now see, both (*B*) to group incomes and (*C*) to capital assets.

B. Group Incomes

We have argued, theoretically, in effect that the incomes of social-economic groups with *one or more* members will have the value $p = 1$ of the equation of the generalized harmonic series, when the incomes are ranked in the order of decreasing size.

In Fig. 11–11 we present the rank-frequency distributions of *combined corporation and individual incomes* in the U. S. A. for the ten years, 1927–1936, with the line *A* of the theoretically expected $-$ 1.000 slope added for the convenience of comparison.[33]

This combination of corporation and individual incomes is as close as we can come, with present available data, to a distribution of sheer group incomes. The present data mean that every individual income recipient is to be viewed as a social group of one person that is in many cases also a constituent of a still larger group (or groups) whose income is also included. This view is quite reasonable if we remember that the larger individual incomes almost always reflect the effects of group activity (e.g., a storekeeper with his clerks, or a lawyer with his stenographic help), which is by no means always incorporated or even a partnership. Indeed the data of Fig. 11–11 in representing the "net incomes" both of groups and of groupings of groups become quite instructive; and they become the more readily comprehensible if we bear in mind the analogous view of cities as

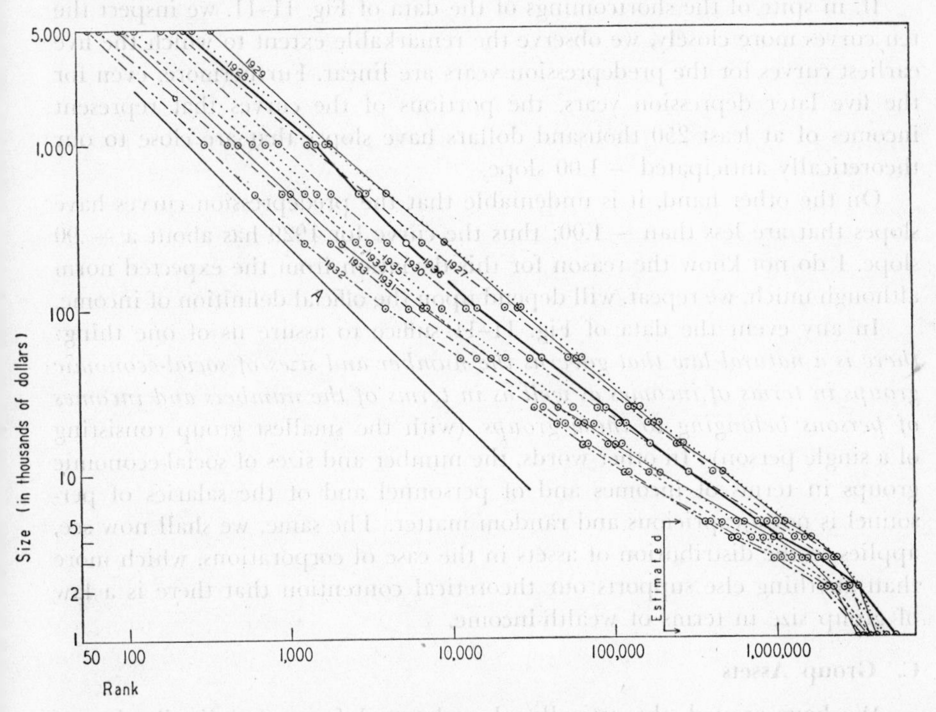

Fig. 11–11. U. S. A. incomes, 1927–36 – combined corporation and individual (line A has an ideal 1.00 slope).

"groupings of trading groups." In terms of incomes there is, therefore, theoretically, an interrelatedness between the entire organization of the social system in the sense that there are a few very large groupings (of groupings) and an increasing number of smaller ones. In this connection we remember our "grand analogue" of this chapter (cf. Section I) which seems to be applicable here.

The ten-year period represented by the data of Fig. 11–11 included a serious depression that shrank all incomes enormously. The five lines at the right are for 1927, 1928, 1929, 1930, and 1936; those for the left are for the depression years, 1931–1935. The bends in these latter five lines may reflect the effect of this depression as the lower middle class presently under the leadership of Mr. F. D. Roosevelt and his coterie of friends set out to help the "forgotten man" by means of an esoteric "planned economy."

Because of the conditions of unstable equilibrium that historically prevailed during much of the period in question, it may be that the above distributions, which regrettably are the only data for combined corporation and individual incomes of which I know, are untrustworthy as a final test of our hypothesis. Moreover there is always the troublesome problem of definition: thus, what is to be considered as a "group income" for tax purposes? Fortunately our theory in regard to the distribution of "group incomes" applies *mutatis mutandis* to the distribution of corporation assets, where some of these problems do not arise (see Section *C* following).

If, in spite of the shortcomings of the data of Fig. 11–11, we inspect the ten curves more closely, we observe the remarkable extent to which the five earliest curves for the predepression years are linear. Furthermore, even for the five later depression years, the portions of the curves that represent incomes of at least 250 thousand dollars have slopes that are close to our theoretically anticipated − 1.00 slope.

On the other hand, it is undeniable that the predepression curves have slopes that are less than − 1.00; thus the curve for 1929 has about a − .90 slope. I do not know the reason for this deviation from the expected norm although much, we repeat, will depend upon the official definition of income.

In any event the data of Fig. 11–11 suffice to assure us of one thing: *there is a natural law that governs the number and sizes of social-economic groups in terms of incomes as well as in terms of the numbers and incomes of persons belonging to those groups* (with the smallest group consisting of a single person). In other words, the number and sizes of social-economic groups in terms of incomes and of personnel and of the salaries of personnel is not a capricious and random matter. The same, we shall now see, applies to the distribution of assets in the case of corporations, which more than anything else supports our theoretical contention that there is a law of group size in terms of wealth-income.

C. Group Assets

We have argued, theoretically, that the rank-frequency distribution of group assets will follow the equation of the generalized harmonic series, with $p = 1$, when ranked in the order of decreasing size, with perhaps a slight increase in p beyond 1 because of the tendency, dynamically considered, for corporations to build up reserves for expansion.

In Fig. 11–12 we present the rank-frequency distribution of U. S. A. corporation assets for the indicated five years as reported by the *Statistics of Income*.[34] These data do not, of course, represent the assets of all social groups, which (as in the analogous case of group incomes) should also include the assets of partnerships and of individual entrepreneurs. Nevertheless the corporations do represent what are doubtless the largest social groups. Therefore the upper portion of the line may be taken as a valid test of our hypothesis, while the concave downward bend towards the bottom—beginning at about ½ million dollars—reflects merely the *deficiency* of the larger noncorporation assets that belong here.

The upper portion of the curve is clearly rectilinear with a slope (about − 1.1) that is consistent with the expected theoretical − 1.00 slope. The shifting of the curve to the right from 1931 through 1936 indicates a tendency during that period for corporations to increase their assets, if we assume that the same measuring scale was used throughout.

Although this is the only set of data that is known to the writer, its striking linearity and constant slope that closely approximates our theoreti-

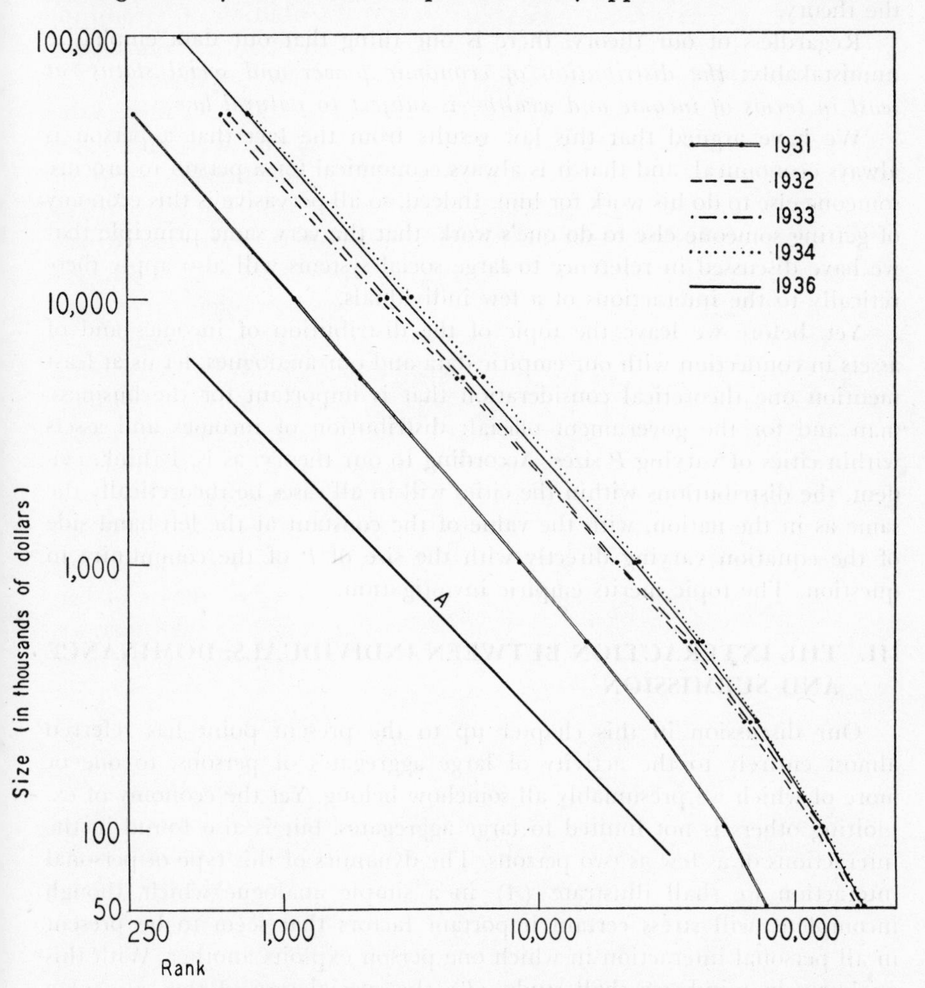

Fig. 11–12. U. S. A. corporation assets for five years.

cally expected value go far towards substantiating our theory. If we assume that the value of an asset is by and large determined by its capacity to produce income, we can see that the present data are closely related to the problem of the distribution of group incomes.

The present data also suffice to show that there is a law that governs the number and sizes (in terms of wealth-income) of social groups. Although the cries against "cartels" and "trusts" remind us of an upper limitation to the size of group organizations, nevertheless let us reflect that there are also lower limitations, below which it may be highly uneconomical for the whole system to reduce its group organizations.

D. Summary

In the foregoing pages we have produced a wide diversity of data as an empiric test of a theory of the distribution of economic power and of social status in all social systems as defined. In all cases the data tend to confirm the theory.

Regardless of our theory, there is one thing that our data emphasize unmistakably: *the distribution of economic power and social status—at least in terms of income and wealth—is subject to natural law.*

We have argued that this law results from the fact that a person is always economical, and that it is always economical for a person to procure someone else to do his work for him. Indeed, so all-pervasive is this economy of getting someone else to do one's work, that the very same principle that we have discussed in reference to large social systems will also apply theoretically to the interactions of a few individuals.

Yet, before we leave the topic of the distribution of incomes and of assets in connection with our empiric data and our analogues, let us at least mention one theoretical consideration that is important for the businessman and for the government official: distribution of incomes and assets within cities of varying *P* sizes. According to our theory, as is, I think, evident, the distributions within the cities will in all cases be theoretically the same as in the nation, with the value of the constant at the left-hand side of the equation varying directly with the size of *P* of the community in question. The topic merits empiric investigation.

III. THE INTERACTION BETWEEN INDIVIDUALS: DOMINANCE AND SUBMISSION

Our discussion in this chapter up to the present point has referred almost entirely to the activity of large aggregates of persons, to one or more of which we presumably all somehow belong. Yet the economy of exploiting others is not limited to large aggregates, but is also found in the interactions of as few as two persons. The dynamics of this type of personal interaction we shall illustrate (*A*) in a simple analogue which, though incomplete, will stress certain important factors that seem to be present in all personal interaction in which one person exploits another. With this analogue in mind, we shall study (*B*) the special case of the ratio of a person's dominance to his submissiveness as revealed in his conversations; this study will serve to connect logically the theoretical argument of Chapter Five with the empiric data of Dr. Eliot D. Chapple, to be presented. Our study of conversations will lead us (*C*) to a consideration of the "conversations," or speeches, of plays and of debates, and so on.

A. The "Ball Analogue"

By way of an introduction to the topics that we are about to explore, let us construct a simple analogue that consists of two persons, Bill and

John, who have a ball with which they are playing a game that is to last, say, an hour.

The rules of the game are simple. Each player will attempt (1) to take the ball from the other player and (2) to keep the ball from the other player as long as he can. The test of the game is clearly one of power and cunning. We are interested in (1) the n number of times that each player gets the ball, and in (2) the l lengths of time that each player keeps it from the other player. For convenience, we shall restrict our attention to the action of one player, Bill.

If we begin with the extreme case in which Bill keeps the ball the entire time while John vainly tries to wrest it from him, then, for Bill, n will be *1*, while l will be the entire time.

Let us now watch the value of Bill's n and l as John begins to take the ball away from Bill, thereby forcing Bill to recapture it. Clearly, every time that John takes the ball from Bill and forces Bill to recapture it, the value of Bill's n increases by 1. Hence a sign of Bill's growing weakness in competition with John is an *increase* in the n number of different times that Bill carries the ball, since n measures the number of times that Bill must recapture the ball from John.

The problem now arises as to the l lengths of time that Bill keeps the ball as his n increases. At first blush it would seem that this problem is similar to that of the n number of different news items of varying S space into which a given news surface is divided, as discussed in Chapter Five, where we saw the applicability of the familiar hyperbolic equation, $r \times S^p = c$. For, after all, Bill, while he has the ball (the quasi Force of Unification), is trying to decrease the n number of times that he carries the ball while increasing their l durations. On the other hand, John, while he has not the ball (the quasi Force of Diversification), is trying to increase Bill's n while decreasing Bill's l. Or, differently expressed, when either one has the ball he tries to decrease n, and while he hasn't the ball he tries to increase n. If no other factor were present, we might expect to find a rectilinear distribution of n and l upon doubly logarithmic co-ordinates for reasons that were presented in Chapter Five and which we shall assume are valid here.

Yet clearly there is another factor present in the ball game that is lacking in the case of the newspaper. Every time that John takes the ball away from Bill, John carries the ball an l length of time himself before Bill recaptures it. And while John is carrying the ball he is decreasing the T total length of time that is left for Bill to carry the ball during the hour. Consequently, as the n number of times increases that Bill loses and recaptures the ball, the total T length of time that Bill carries the ball will decrease.

If this were also the case in the editing of the space of a newspaper, we should be obliged to say that as the n number of different news items increases, the total news space to be edited will shrink. Since we know that such a shrinkage of news space is by no means the case, we can see that the problem of editing the space of a newspaper is not completely similar to that of "editing" the duration of the ball game into the n number of different times that the ball is carried by Bill.

But although the two problems are not completely similar, their difference may be instructive. For, after all, the difference does not lie in the fact that the Force of Diversification increases n, which is also the case with the newspaper; the difference lies solely in the fact that in increasing n, the Force of Diversification *also simultaneously* decreases the size of the total T time that Bill carries the ball.

If we now assume explicitly that the Force of Diversification that increases n is suitably related to the Force of Diversification that decreases T, then our entire argument about the rectilinearity of the n number and S sizes of news items in Chapter Five will apply to the case of the n number and the l durations that Bill carries the ball, *provided* that we plot the *logarithm* of n against the actual *arithmetic* l lengths of the durations. In that case, we must conceive of the relatively increasing Force of Diversification as accomplishing two things. *First* it will be increasing n exponentially as in the case of the news items; *second* it will be whittling down the l length of each duration (or, if one will, it whittles down the total T time) at a rate that increases with the increase in n, thereby altering the inverse exponential rate of decrease of the S length of news items to a simple arithmetic rate of decrease in the case of l.

If we are correct in concluding that in other respects our argument about the Forces of Unification and of Diversification in reference to the n number and S sizes of our news items applies here, then the distribution of the logarithm of the N_1 *number of durations* of like l length, when plotted on the *ordinate* against their arithmetic l *length* in time on the *abscissa,* will yield a rectilinear distribution that is described by the function,

$$\log N_1 = - al + C.$$

For convenience, let us henceforth say that the term d_a, represents the *absolute slope* of the above distribution. Hence as *Bill's* d_a slope *increases,* Bill is *losing* the game to John. Or, as we shall later say, *an increase in* d_a *slope means a decrease in dominance.*

The preceding analogue is recommended rather for its simplicity than for its completeness, since it obviously leaves the distribution of John's n and l completely out of the picture. This incompleteness need not worry us now, since we are at present interested only (1) in showing that the distribution of Bill's n and l will be rectilinear on a semilogarithmic scale, and (2) in defining the absolute slope d_a.

If we wanted to invent a game that included both John and Bill, we might change our ball into a heavy weight of lead suspended from a pole whose respective ends are carried by Bill and John. As long as the weight of lead is in the middle, each person will carry an equal burden. On the other hand, the more the lead is pushed towards John's end, the greater will be John's burden—and the reverse. The game, therefore, would consist of trying to keep the weight near the other fellow's end in this otherwise co-operative venture, which may be typical of any joint enterprise in which "there is a dirty end to the stick."

But instead of elaborating a new game let us turn to the case of a conversation. The only feature of the Ball Analogue that we need to remember is our definition of the d_a slope, which will *decrease* as the person in question becomes *more dominant*.

B. The Case of Conversations

Before turning to the case of a conversation between two persons whom we shall call Bill and John, let us first make a few clarifying assumptions and definitions which will simplify our exposition.

First, we shall assume that while Bill is talking in the conversation, John will remain silent; and while John is talking, Bill will remain silent. This assumption will mean that, at the end of the conversation, Bill and John will have engaged in the same n number of *speech actions* (or at most the difference will be that between n and $n - 1$), and they both will similarly have had the same number of *silences*.

Second, let us assume that each person's *speech actions* will consist of two kinds of verbalizations: (1) *active addresses,* to which the interlocutor responds, and (2) *responses* to the interlocutor's active addresses.

Third, we shall assume explicitly that every *active address* will have a *response* from the other person.

Let us now assume that each person tries to *address* as much as possible and to respond as little as possible, and that a person's *dominance*—or the *ratio* of his *degree of dominance* to his *degree of submissiveness*—is somehow connected with the rate of his addresses and responses. In other words, we shall assume that each person will seek in his addresses to impress, or to command, or to persuade his interlocutor, and that the more that he succeeds in doing so, the more will he *dominate* (or become *dominant* in) the conversation in question. Thus, for example, if the conversation is between a completely dominant king and a completely submissive subject, we may expect that the king will deliver himself of a long *address* to which the subject will meekly respond "Yes!" On the other hand if the interlocutors happen to be "more evenly matched," we may expect to find a "more even" balance of addresses and responses.

It is evident that our foregoing assumptions and definitions apply only to fictitious or hypothetical conversations, since we have by no means shown as yet that they are fundamental in actual conversations (even though we know from experience that persons do try to "dominate" conversations). Nevertheless if (1), on the basis of our above assumptions and definitions, we elaborate our hypothesis of the dynamics of conversational dominance, we shall arrive at a relationship which will admit (2) of an empiric test from Dr. Chapple's set of brilliant observations.

1. Conversations (The Hypothetical Construct). To begin with our hypothetical conversation between Bill and John—and we shall for convenience first concentrate upon the case of Bill—let us remember that Bill will seek to talk as much of the total T time that he can, and will seek to use his speech actions as far as he can in *addresses* that are intended to impress John or to ingratiate himself with John, and so on. In other words, Bill will try to "carry the ball" as long as he can, if we may refer to the language of our previous Ball Analogue, which seems to be roughly applicable here.

That in turn will mean that the d_a slope of Bill's *addresses* will decrease as Bill becomes more dominant in his addresses over John.

Since, however, Bill's share of the conversation will consist of n different speech actions which in turn will consist in part of the n_a number of his active addresses, it follows that as Bill becomes more dominant and, therefore, by definition, makes relatively fewer n_a different addresses of increasing l length, Bill will thereby make a correspondingly *relatively* greater n_r number of responses (i.e., $n - n_a = n_r$).

But although these n_r responses of Bill will become *relatively* more numerous as Bill becomes more dominant, they will nevertheless also have a *decreasing* l length, because the more dominant Bill, who will be devoting relatively ever more of his total time to his addresses, will be devoting relatively ever less of his time to his responses. Moreover, since the more dominant Bill in his *responses* will be doing precisely the reverse of what he is doing in his *addresses,* it seems to follow that the *absolute slope of Bill's responses—let us call this slope* b_a*—will increase, while the* d_a *slope of Bill's addresses will decrease.*

In short, *an increase in the* b_a *slope of Bill's responses with a concomitant decrease in the* d_a *slope of Bill's addresses will betoken an increasing dominance of Bill in the conversation.* At least that is our argument.*

Since the behavior of the above two b_a and d_a slopes is indicative of the degree of Bill's relative dominance, let us objectify the nature of these slopes by viewing them against the total frequency distribution of all Bill's speech actions, in which his responses and addresses are combined. We shall assume that the l lengths of speech actions are measured *arithmetically* with increasing magnitude on the abscissa, whereas the N number of speech actions of like l length will be measured logarithmically on the ordinate.

Now since the speech action curve consists both of (1) *responses* and of (2) *addresses,* and since, as Bill becomes more dominant, (1) his *responses* will become both *relatively* more numerous with an increasing n_r and a decreasing l length, while (2) his *addresses* will become *relatively* less numerous with a decreasing n_a and an increasing *l length,* it is obvious that the entire frequency distribution will cleave into (1) a population of "overshort" responses of increasing b_a slope to the left, and (2) a population of "overlong" addresses of decreasing d_a slope to the right.

Moreover, as Bill becomes ever more dominant, the complete frequency distribution of all of his speech actions—even though the curve will remain continuous—will cleave ever more sharply into these two distinct parts: (1) the "overshort" responses at the left with an increasing b_a slope, and

* Yet in treating a problem with five variables, nothing is gained by being dogmatic. Indeed, the reader may quite understandably prefer to assume explicitly that b_a varies inversely with d_a and b_s, and lirectly with d_s.

(2) the "overlong" addresses at the right with a decreasing d_a slope. We mention this matter again explicitly for the obvious reason that the b_a and d_a slopes of the "overshorts" and of the "overlongs" represent concrete mathematical parameters that can be measured objectively.*

The reverse of the above conditions will be the case when a party to the conversation becomes less dominant and more submissive, as would be the case with submissive John as Bill continues to assert his dominance. Thus if we use the term d_s to define the slope of the more submissive John's addresses, and the term b_s to describe the slope of the more submissive John's responses, we may say that John's values of b_s and d_s will behave in *precisely the opposite manner* from Bill's values of b_a and d_a respectively.

Indeed, upon reflection it is clear that, regardless of the degrees of dominance that are involved, the following equation of adjustment will be valid:

$$\frac{b_a \times d_a}{b_s \times d_s} = K.$$

This equation is valid because as the one person—whether Bill or John—becomes more dominant (or submissive), the four slopes will so alter themselves as to preserve a constant ratio, K. Thus, for example, if b_a increases (or decreases), d_a will do the reverse, while b_s and d_s will alter themselves respectively in the opposite fashion from b_a and d_a; in each case the products will remain the same, and so too the ratio, K.

The slopes (1) b_s, and (2) d_s, are defined as referring (1) to John's "overshort" speech actions, which we assume are his responses and (2) to his "overlong" speech actions, which we assume are his addresses. But since, in the light of our initial assumptions, John's speech actions will correspond to Bill's silences, we may say that b_s will also represent the slope of Bill's "overshort" silences, while d_s will represent the slope of Bill's overlong" silences. By thus redefining the slopes b_s and d_s in terms of Bill's silences, we thereby make our equation refer to Bill's active and silent participation in any conversation he has with anyone. In other words, the foregoing equation will describe Bill's speech actions and silences in his conversation with any arbitrary "John." This equation we shall now state in the following form:

$$\frac{b_a}{b_s} \times \frac{d_a}{d_s} = K. \qquad (11\text{–}14)$$

We have already pointed out that Eq. (11–14) will describe the pattern of Bill's conversational adjustment with *any other person* with whom Bill succeeds in carrying on a conversation, since we have never specified who John is!

Moreover, since we have never specified who Bill is, *we may suspect theoretically that every person will have his own particular value of K in terms of which he will adjust conversationally with his fellow man.* Thus Bill has his own particular value of K, while John in turn has a K value of his own.

* The d_a slope is to be calculated only after the origin has been shifted to the point where the "overlong" addresses begin.

At this point let us interrupt our discussion to ask a few questions. Our first question might be: how does a person assert his dominance in a conversation? The answer to this question, in the light of everyday experience, is that the dominant person interrupts his interlocutor whenever he wants to talk and does not in turn let himself be interrupted by his interlocutor. The second question might be: suppose two very dominant persons find themselves in a conversation? The answer to this question, in the light of everyday experience, seems to be that the conversation will not last long, as each party enrages the other by his interruptions. The third question might be: what happens when two taciturn persons converse? To this we reply: profound and prolonged silences will ensue, as each person eventually seeks some other more "stimulating" conversant.

Our preceding Eq. (11–14), which puts no restriction either upon the total T length of the entire conversation or upon the absolute l lengths of the speech actions and silences, describes essentially the *rate* of conversational interactions between two persons in their speech actions and silences. As such it naturally admits of an adjustment between very different values of K, as will be evident from an inspection of Dr. Chapple's data. On the other hand, it is undeniable that conversations will theoretically be easier among persons whose respective values of K are more nearly reciprocal. Thus, for example, a more talkative person does well to marry a more taciturn spouse; and by and large the reader will find that in successful marriages such is often observably the case.

Implicit in our equation is a definition of *conversational dominance* (and its reciprocal, *conversational submissiveness*) in terms of our slopes. Thus as a person becomes more dominant he addresses relatively less often but at a greater length, while he is silent relatively less often and at shorter length; his responses, though *relatively* more frequent are much shorter; and so on. In terms of the objectives and operations of a conversation as a social system, what does conversational dominance mean? In the light of everyday experience it may be remarked that the degree of a person's dominance represents the degree to which he selects both the topics of the conversation and their treatment. Some persons are by disposition more self-assertive in respect of conversational dominance than others; and that fact should be revealed by the size of their invariant K constant.

Of course, a continual conversational dominance by the "other fellow" may become wearisome to the more submissive. In that case the submissive person has several possible remedial courses of action. Thus, for example, he can simply begin to talk in the middle of his interlocutor's address and continue to talk until after his interlocutor has become silent (i.e., he simply "outalks him").* Second, he can refuse to respond and merely let a silence attend his interlocutor's address; as this silence increases in length the embarrassed interlocutor will have to think up a new address which will be similarly attended by a silence. Third, the submissive person, after managing to deliver an address of his own, can abruptly leave the conver-

* After all, to listen to a person talk is a sign of deference to that person. "Brilliant" conversation is a means of getting deference.

sation without waiting for a response. There are doubtless other devices for combatting the wearisome dominance of others.

Regardless of all the above considerations the question still remains as to whether our Eq. (11–14) can be substantiated empirically. Since we have already suggested how the values b_a and d_a can be disclosed objectively from a frequency distribution of "Bill's" *speech actions,* with the values, b_s and d_s to be similarly disclosed from a corresponding frequency distribution of Bill's conversational *silences,* it follows that the actual values of the four variables can be disclosed for any conversation.

Moreover, if we plot logarithmically on the ordinate the observed ratio, b_a/b_s, for a given conversation of a given "Bill," and if we plot logarithmically on the abscissa the observed ratio, d_a/d_s, of the same conversation, we should have a value, *K,* for that particular conversation of "Bill."

This value of *K* will fall on a straight line descending from left to right at a slope of -1 and intercepting a *K* amount on the abscissa. If our theory is correct, then every conversation that "Bill" has with any other person (e.g., Sue, Mike, or Joe) will have values of b_a/b_s and d_a/d_s respectively that will yield a point that will fall somewhere on the above *K* line of -1 slope.

This value of *K,* as defined by the calculated values of "Bill's" various conversations, will be characteristic of "Bill's" conversational "personality."

To test our theory, we need only to observe the actual l lengths of a person's n speech actions and silences in a set of conversations. From the frequency distribution of his speech actions and his silences, the four variables and the *K* constant can be calculated and graphed as previously described.

2. Empiric Test (The Chapple Data). In 1940 Dr. Eliot D. Chapple published his observations of the speech actions and intervening silences of over fifty different conversations which lasted between thirty-five and forty-five minutes each, as conducted by eight different persons. His method of statistical analysis, which was essentially the one outlined in our previous section, was described in detail in his original publication from which, incidentally, the terms b_a, b_s, d_a, and d_s, were taken.[35]

For each of the conversations, Dr. Chapple plotted the calculated *K* value, with b_a/b_s measured logarithmically on the ordinate and with d_a/d_s measured logarithmically on the abscissa. These *K* values (55 in all) for the eight different persons are presented in Fig. 11–13, which is reproduced with Dr. Chapple's permission from his original publication. Theoretically, we may expect that the calculated *K* values for each person will fall upon a straight line descending from left to right at a -1.00 slope.

An inspection of the data of Fig. 11–13 reveals that the 55 *K* values for the eight different persons (as initialled) are distributed as theoretically expected. Hence our theory is confirmed by what may some day be recognized as one of the most startling sets of observations in the social field. Dr. Chapple's original publications merit a careful study for the additional information that they contain on the matter of interruptions, double silences, and the like, to which our theory does not refer.

Regardless of our own theory, let us not forget that Dr. Chapple's impressive data, which antedate our theory by some years, establish unmistakably in their own right the existence of an empiric law of conversational balance. Moreover, as originally pointed out, the data suggest that a conversation is organized as a unit-whole (to which our own immediate theory does not refer). As far as our own foregoing rationalization is concerned, it is tendered in the attempt to build a bridge of logic from the argument of Part One to that of the present chapter.

Although Dr. Chapple has provided no rationalization of his data, in connection with which he has promised further publications, he has inferred

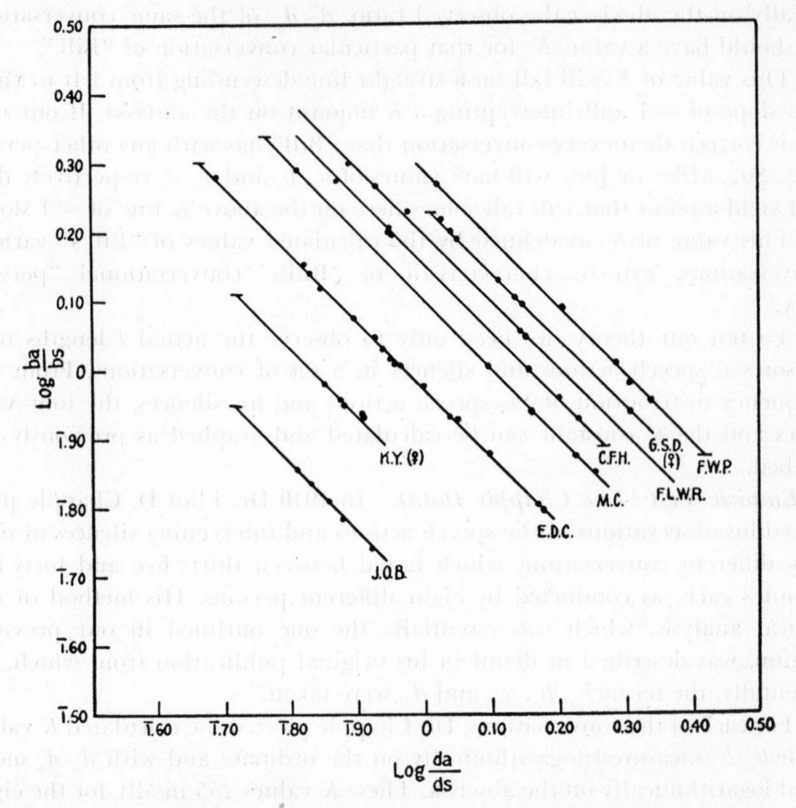

Fig. 11–13. The Eliot D. Chapple observations of conversations (see text).

therefrom (quite correctly in my opinion) that each person has an invariant interaction rate (the *K* constant) in reference to which the person effects his adjustment with others. Working with this inference, Dr. Chapple has turned to the problem of industrial personnel relations, in which he is a practicing consultant. He has observed the practical importance of "synchronized interaction rates" of those who work together, whether in an office or on an assembly line. He has also observed the effect upon a person's family relations of a disturbance to his interaction equilibrium at work, and *vice versa.* Thus an excessively dominant boss, to whom an employee must submit for eight hours, may cause the employee to be excessively dominant at home by way of compensation (and the reverse).[36]

Or, to elaborate the "interaction chain" even further, the boss "beats" the employee, who in turn "beats" his wife, who in turn spanks the children, who in turn beat up the neighboring kids, who in turn throw stones at the dog.

3. Personal Interaction in a Dominance System. Although our initial theory on personal interactions will need further conceptual sharpening, the theory, such as it is, suffices to show that even in co-operative enterprises between as few as two persons there is a tendency to make the "other fellow" do a greater share of the work. Our best illustration of this is perhaps the case of the pole whose ends are carried by two persons, and from which is suspended a heavy leaden weight. Each person, we have argued, will attempt to push the weight nearer to the other person's end of the pole. Although Eq. (11–14) was developed specifically to cover the case of conversations, the same conceptualization seems to be applicable to the case of the pole and weight which, in turn, may be typical of many other co-operative enterprises. The writer first observed this problem of co-operative and competitive balance while acting as a pallbearer.

Since a social system, as we have defined it, is a dominance system that is made up of a population of interrelated "poles" and "weights," whose ends are carried respectively by one or more persons or groups, we can suspect how our 13 equations of Section I of this chapter may have ramifications that extend down into the very small interpersonal interactions whose minutiae may be describable by relationships similar to those to which Eq. (11–14) refers. Intimately connected with this equation are, in turn, the equations for the distribution of words and other speech entities as discussed in Part One. A truly complex total phenomenon which seems nevertheless to be completely orderly!

B. Plays and Debates

In our preceding section we referred to the chain of interactions in which a person in the course of a day interacts with many other persons, each of whom will in turn interact with still further ones. Throughout this chain or network of interactions, each person will theoretically attempt to accomplish compensatorily in his next interaction what he failed to accomplish in his previous ones—with the urge for compensation increasing with the amount of his previous failure—until some sort of balance, or equilibrium, is established throughout the entire social system. Or at least so one could argue theoretically.

But though a theory of interaction equilibrium might be fairly easy to conceptualize, the phenomenon itself, because of its enormously wide ramifications in time and space, is by no means easy to measure. Some light may be cast upon the problem by an empiric study of the structure of a play.

1. The Speeches of a Play. A play upon a stage represents artistically a cross section of at least one integrated part of the total interaction network and, as such, it may be able to shed some light upon the dynamics of the more extended phenomenon. For in a play the actors come and go, each interacting with one or more of the others for greater or shorter lengths of times. Indeed, it is the comparative *n* number and the *l* lengths of an actor's interactions with other actors that often seem to indicate the degree of his dominance in the play.

On the other hand, since a play is structured as a unit-whole, the task of writing a play may also be viewed as one in which the conventional duration of several hours of activity on the stage is "edited" into an *n* number of different speeches of varying *l* lengths which, in turn, are to be distributed among the *A* number of different actors. Hence the problem of writing a play is in many respects similar to that of editing a newspaper (with the possible exception of the additional problem of the "right" *A* number of actors), in which we may again expect to find our familiar theoretical Forces of Unification and of Diversification.

Thus in the case of a play there will be a Force of Unification that operates in the direction of having a single actor who delivers a soliloquy that lasts for the entire play and of whom the audience might understandably become weary. On the other hand, there will be an opposite Force of Diversification that operates in the direction of having a large *A* number of different actors who deliver short speeches which the audience will be expected to take the trouble to patch together into a unified whole. Between these two extremes is theoretically our familiar condition of balance which will refer to the optimal *n* number and *l* lengths of speeches—as well as to the *A* number of actors.

But that is not all. For we may also expect theoretically that the different speeches of varying lengths of each actor will presumably be so distributed over time that they will somehow approximate the interval-frequency relationship of words, as discussed in Chapter Two. For (1) the same Forces that break the play into *n* different speeches of varying *l* length will also operate (2) both (*a*) to prevent an excessive succession of long speeches or of short speeches by one or more actors, and (*b*) to prevent an excessive repetitiveness of speeches of any length by any one actor.

In brief, the problem of distributing the speeches of a play over time seems in many important respects to be theoretically similar to that of the distribution of words in the stream of speech.

There is a further factor present in the organization of a play that has not been discussed in connection with the distribution of words in the stream of speech—that of the relative *"A dominance"* of the different *A* actors in the play. This factor is not new to us in our study, since we have just discussed at least some of its possible aspects in connection with the topic of conversational dominance and submissiveness.

If our argument about conversational dominance and submissiveness should indeed be germane here, then we might perhaps expect that the *absolute slope* of the rank-frequency distribution of *all* the speeches of a given actor will somehow change as his dominance increases, because a sign of his dominance may be that he adds to the lengths of his speeches at a greater rate than to their number. Yet the question is obviously moot, nor are matters helped empirically by the fact that we are dealing with artistic productions which in actual practice may not always succeed in holding the "mirror up to nature." On the other hand, if a play is to be successful it must supposedly at least give the impression of verisimilitude in its conversational structure and dominance dynamics, whatever they may be.

Since the problem of the dynamics of a play is moot, let us simply enumerate a few possible relationships of which, in the light of our entire preceding theory, we may reasonably expect to find at least some evidence. The relationships we are about to mention are familiar to us by now; therefore, we shall not try the reader's patience by developing them theoretically once more.

In the first place, we may expect that shorter speeches will outnumber longer ones throughout a successful play. Second, we may expect that somehow, in the rank-frequency distribution of speeches, there will be an indication of a harmonic seriation. Third, the harmonic seriation may well be found in the distribution of the lengths of time that elapse during the intervals between the recurrences of speeches by the same actor. Fourth, we may expect that the slope of the distribution of an actor's speeches will somehow be correlated with the relative degree of his dominance (the correlation depending upon the manner of graphing employed).

Since the above theoretical expectations, although they are clearly in accord with our earlier arguments, have not been argued in detail, they may be viewed solely as working hypotheses to be used in exploring a new topic which is presumably quite complex.

With the above four points in mind, let us turn to some actual observations, which we owe to the generosity and the expert hands of Messrs. J. P. Boland and W. B. Bryant, neither of whom were at the time aware of the nature of the theoretical problem they were exploring empirically.

Mr. Bryant selected for his analysis Eugene O'Neill's *The Great God Brown* in its entirety except for the prologue and epilogue, with especial attention to the speeches of the main characters, Margaret, Brown, and Dion. Mr. Boland selected for his analysis the first act of Edmond Rostand's *Cyrano de Bergerac,* with especial attention to the n number and l lengths of the speeches of Cyrano. Mr. Bryant used the printed line of text as a unit of measurement of the length of speeches and of intervals between recurrences; Mr. Boland used the printed word as a unit.

In Fig. 11–14 are presented Mr. Bryant's data for *The Great God Brown,* which was treated statistically as if the play were a continuous whole without divisions into acts (a procedure that will introduce minor distortions in the distribution of intervals between recurrences in a character's speeches). At the top of the figure, marked 1*M*, 1*B*, and 1*D* respectively, are the rank-frequency distributions of the *speeches,* by length, of Margaret, Brown, and Dion respectively. These are all essentially rectilinear and thereby confirm our expectations as to a theoretical rectilinearity. Moreover, as we pass from left to right, the slopes seem to become steeper; of course, if we plotted log N on the ordinate and log l (*sic*) on the abscissa, as we did for conversations (where, however, the abscissa was arithmetic), then we should say that our doubly logarithmic d_a slope decreased from left to right. Unfortunately, there are no empiric criteria available for ranking the importance of the three characters.

The middle set of three curves, marked *2D, 2B,* and *2M,* are the rank-frequency distributions of the *lengths of intervals* (in terms of the number

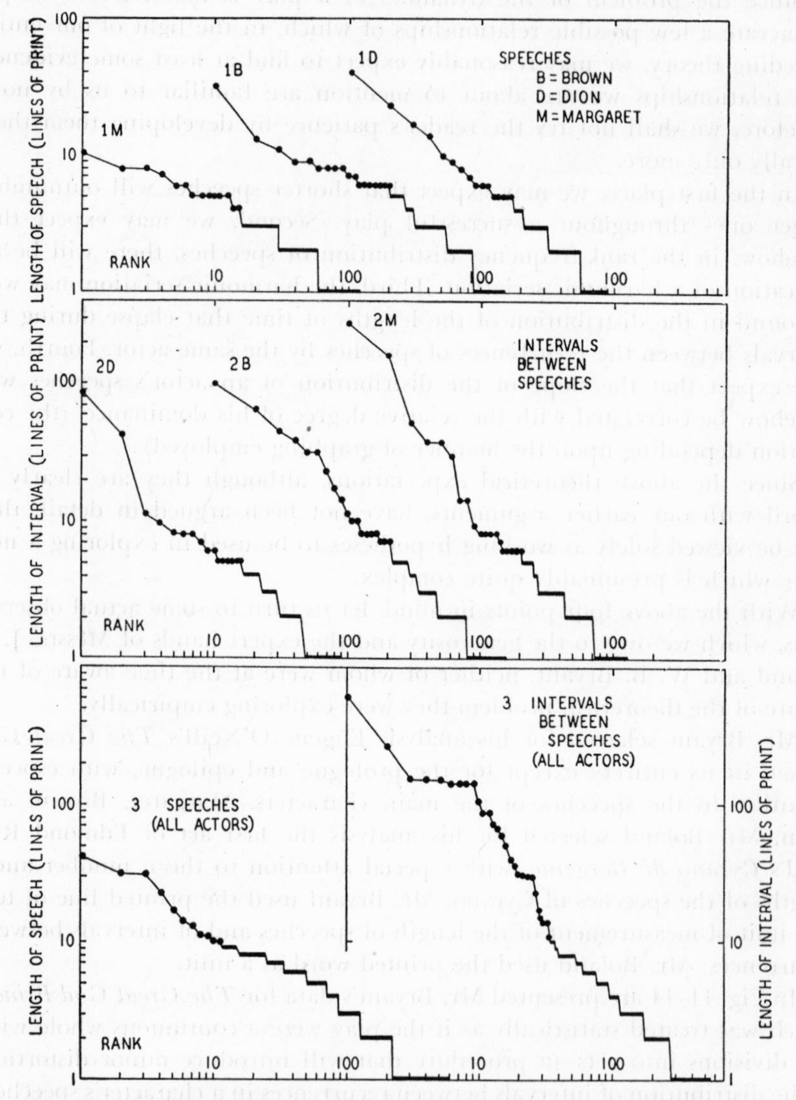

Fig. 11–14. The rank-frequency and interval-frequency distribution of speeches in Eugene O'Neill's Play, *The Great God Brown.*

of intervening printed lines) between the speeches of Dion, Brown, and Margaret respectively. These are clearly rectilinear towards the bottom, with a slope of about − 1; the deviations towards the top may well result from the fact that the intervals were computed without regard for the division of the play into acts. The distributions seem to confirm our theoretical expectations.

At the bottom are two curves. The one at the left (marked, *3, Total Speeches*) represents the rank-frequency distribution of all the speeches of the play when ranked in the order of decreasing length. At the right (marked, *3, Total Intervals*) is the rank-frequency distribution of the lengths of all intervals between the speeches of all characters in the play; the top of the curve should perhaps not be taken too seriously because of the effect of the cleavage of the play into acts. Yet by and large these two distributions have a degree of rectilinearity that is striking when we remember that it refers to *all* the intervals and to *all* the speeches of *all* the characters of the play.

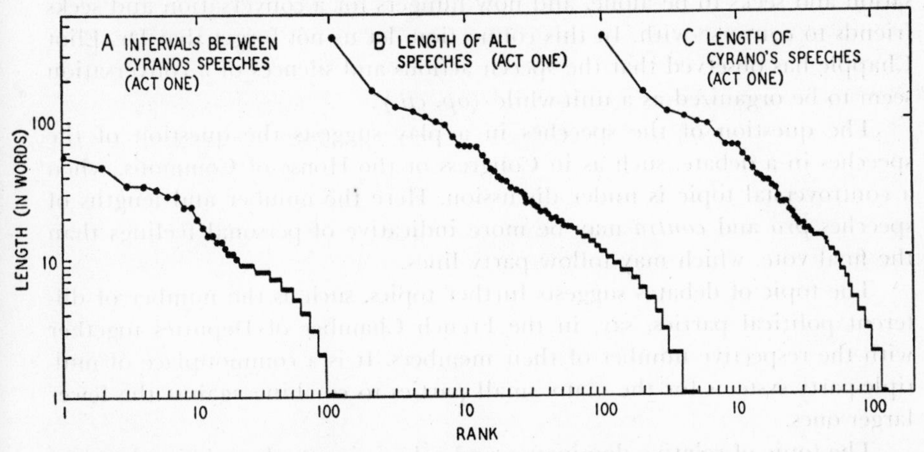

Fig. 11–15. The rank-frequency and interval-frequency distribution of speeches in Rostand's *Cyrano de Bergerac*.

There is, after all, no *a priori* necessity in the light of the null hypothesis for these distributions.

In Fig. 11–15, with appropriate shifts of the origin as indicated, are: (*A*) the rank-frequency distribution of the lengths of intervals between Cyrano's speeches in Act One; (*B*) the rank-frequency distribution of the lengths of all speeches of all characters in Act One; (*C*) the rank-frequency distribution of the lengths of Cyrano's speeches in Act One. The unit of measurement is in all cases the word. This unit, incidentally, is very small.* If a larger unit had been employed, the downward concavity at the bottom might well have disappeared. Nevertheless, at the present early stage of exploration of the problem, the effect of a very small unit is instructive. In any event, the portions of the curves above the very short speeches and intervals at the bottom show an interesting linearity that is quite in line with our limited theoretical expectations.

The foregoing data suggest further questions, such as a possible theoretical law of the *A* number of characters of a play and the total amount of their respective verbalizations. Then there is the related question of the *n* number

* Thus a speech of one, two, or even three words might conceivably not be favored in a poetic composition (e.g., "yes," "yes, sir," "yes, I do").

and l lengths of scenes of a moving picture, which in turn ties up with our theoretical "law of winks" in Chapter Five. By means of such studies we may gain insight into what constitutes a "well-constructed" play.

Although nothing is gained by being dogmatic at this point, nevertheless the above data on the number, lengths, and distribution of speeches in a play suggest clearly that there is an orderliness in the total chain of interaction as far as a play is concerned. This in turn suggests that during the course of a day our "Bill" may seek and leave conversations in such a manner that both his conversations and his intervening periods of silence may be so distributed as to length and frequency that the work of conversation will be evenly distributed over "Bill's" day, as he now wearies of a conversation and seeks to be alone, and now hungers for a conversation and seeks friends to converse with. In this connection, let us not forget that Dr. Eliot Chapple has observed that the speech actions and silences of a conversation seem to be organized as a unit-while (*op. cit.*).

The question of the speeches in a play suggests the question of the speeches in a debate, such as in Congress or the House of Commons, when a controversial topic is under discussion. Here the number and lengths of speeches *pro* and *contra* may be more indicative of personal feelings than the final vote, which may follow party lines.

The topic of debates suggests further topics, such as the number of different political parties, say, in the French Chamber of Deputies together with the respective number of their members. It is a commonplace of multiple-party systems for the many small parties to combine against the fewer larger ones.

The topic of relative dominance and submissiveness has obviously many ramifications.

C. Scholarly Publications (Lotka's Law)

While still on the present topic let us briefly consider Dr. A. J. Lotka's important observation (published 1926) of the scientific productivity of chemists, in terms of their respective n number of different published articles as abstracted in the *Chemical Abstracts,* 1907–1916.[37] Dr. Lotka in his pioneer study restricted his analysis to the letters *A* and *B,* and observed that the f number of persons who published a given n number of articles was inversely proportional to about n^2 (actually $n^{1.888}$). No rationalization, to my knowledge, has ever been given. Incidentally, this "inverse square law of scientific productivity" is obviously another example of the harmonic distribution (i.e., $p = 1$) if the data are ranked according to decreasing n.

This distribution may conceivably reflect the "natural distribution" of specialized abilities," as Dr. Harold T. Davis has concluded (*op. cit.*). Surely such a conclusion, for which I believe there is no further support, would make a very convenient *ad hoc* assumption. We mention this conclusion lest we otherwise seem to ignore it.

Taking a different tack, we can understand how in the limited space of scientific journals and in abstracts, there might be a tendency to favor the selection of articles from scientists who have already established their scientific reputations on the basis of previous articles. For, in a way, an editor tends to select those articles that will strike his readers as "important" and "interesting." Yet what, we may ask, is to be considered as "important" and "interesting"?

Clearly the question of importance and interest is not necessarily decided by the amount of skill or work that goes into a production. Thus it would take a tremendous amount of skill and work to engrave the entire Bible upon the head of a pin, yet it is doubtful that such an achievement would be recognized socially as having a tremendous importance and interest. Nor are the products of work and skill in a chemical laboratory socially assessed otherwise than in accordance with their apparent social importance.

By and large it may conceivably be that scientific productivity is motivated by the desire to be considered "socially important" and "socially interesting." Surely everyday observation does not entirely belie the suspicion that the factor of "bandwagon psychology" is present in the selection of the topics and treatment of intellectual research, even though the history of science does reveal sporadic cases of long hard work against almost insuperable obstacles and with little immediate prospect of a social acceptance in the scientist's lifetime (cf. Chapter Eight for a discussion of this particular dynamic).

Since a desire for "recognition" seems to provide the dynamic for a great deal of research, let us assume as a working hypothesis that scientists by and large desire a personal *prestige,* or a *deference* from others, whether in terms of the number of their students and research associates, or in terms of salary or academic honors, or of engagements to speak before Women's Clubs or in radio panels, or in terms of the pages of reported research that is accepted for publication, or in terms of the n number of different articles or of books that are printed.

Since we have argued in Section I of this chapter that the total *deference* at the disposal of a social system may be viewed as a fixed amount of "goods and services" which, like total income, is to be distributed to the members of the social system, we need not be surprised to learn that Dr. Lotka has observed a case of rectilinearity in the f number of chemical scientists who wrote an n number of articles of sufficient importance and interest to be abstracted in the *Chemical Abstracts.*

The slope $p = 1$, of the Lotka data—when expressed in terms of our equation of the generalized harmonic series—merits especial attention, since this particular slope is associated rather with the activity of social groups than with that of individuals; and that, I feel, is understandable, inasmuch as many chemical findings, though reported by the professor or director in charge of the laboratory, may represent the collective work of many hands and minds of research technicians and students.

The greater the prestige of a person, the *ever greater* will be his power of attraction both for students and for grants of research money for the employment of technicians and for the purchase of expensive apparatus, with the result that his probable opportunities for making and reporting new "important" and "interesting" observations will tend to increase exponentially (i.e., "nothing succeeds like success").

The foregoing argument will apply only to the productions of a recognized *presumable* value for the entire social system, and not to the productions for cultish or esoteric groups which may have a *prestige* of their own to distribute.[38]

If we turn now to the more general case, in which groups are discovering and promulgating "new ideas" throughout a social system, then it is interesting to reflect how a few "new ideas" may meet widespread acceptance, while an increasing number may meet a decreasing acceptance in what might be called the distribution of the effects of Intellectual Forces. A reflection of this sort ties in with our previous discussion of the circulation of information (Chapter Nine) and of the structure of publications (Chapter Five). It suggests that "culturally" or "intellectually," an increasing number of persons will agree about a decreasing number of things in any social system.

This distribution of persons into groups in accordance with the ideas that they share (i.e., in accordance with the particular objectives and modes of procedure that they have) would mean in turn that the members of a population are distributed into one or more general and specialized groups in a manner that is by no means inconsistent with the actual distributions that we have been observing in the present and preceding chapters.

IV. SUMMARY

In the present chapter, which treats the topic of the distribution of economic power and social status, our argument has fallen into three main sections.

In the first section (I) we developed two theoretical analogues that referred to the entire *C* population, and which were then combined into a "grand" analogue that was extended to include the analogue on the economy of geography in Chapter Nine. On the basis of these analogues we arrived at a family of equations whose corollary considerations were then further explored, often in terms of present-day problems.

In the second section (II) we presented a number of sets of empiric data in support of our family of equations.

In the third section (III), just concluded, we turned from the question of the distribution of economic power and social status in the entire *C* population to the question of what might be called the *balance of power* in the personal interactions within groups that were so small as to contain only two persons. The data in support of our theory in this section were of three kinds : (1) Dr. Chapple's data on conversations, (2) the data on the speeches of plays, and (3) Dr. Lotka's data on "scientific productivity."

In this chapter we assumed that it is always economical to have another person do one's work, and that man always behaves economically. Our equations referred, in the final analysis, to a concept of equilibrium in terms of which the economy of individually and collectively imposing upon others is held in check by the individual and collective dyseconomy of being thus imposed upon.

CHAPTER TWELVE

PRESTIGE SYMBOLS AND CULTURAL VOGUES

Our study of a social system in Part Two has up to now consisted of three main steps. The first step was a study of the economy of geography, as set forth in Chapter Nine. Our second step was the application of our argument of Chapter Nine to the general problem of conditions of stable and unstable equilibrium in intranational and international relations in Chapter Ten. Thence in Chapter Eleven we turned to the topic of the distribution of economic power and social status in a social system. Throughout the argument of these three chapters, whether the discussion referred to the economy of the production of goods and services, or to the economy of distributing them to persons of different status, we continually sensed the presence of a body of *rules of procedure* according to which the social activity in question took place.

Now in the final chapter of our book we shall turn our attention briefly to the problem of these rules of procedure—or, in simple terms, *rules*.

This problem of rules is not new to our argument. In our discussion of the structure of the cultural vocabulary in Chapter Seven we studied in detail the dynamics of a code of social correlations, or rules, according to which the social system in question functions. Our argument at the time still applies, nor does it merit a recapitulation here.

All that we propose to do now is to study certain aspects of the rules of a social system that relate to the changing vogues in the particular cultural signals that betoken the relative prestige, or status, of the members of the social system in question. This we shall do first (I) theoretically, before turning (II, III, and IV) to the presentation of empiric data.

There is a risk, of course, that the concept of prestige symbols and cultural vogues may appear somewhat remote and detached from our earlier argument about the general dynamics of the entire cultural vocabulary. For that reason we shall present our empiric data on vogues—which represent on the whole simple exponential and logistic functions—against the familiar background of the equation of the generalized harmonic series. By this procedure, which will also serve to synthesize our argument theoretically, we shall suggest how an exponential development of given cultural manifestations over the years is by no means inconsistent with the observed harmonic distribution of those manifestations at a moment of measurement.

We have just said that the development of prestige symbols and of cultural vogues follows an exponential function (or a closely related logistic curve). This concept of an exponential function we have already encountered in our previous chapter when discussing, for example, the exponential nature of a popular following. We mention this consideration in order to suggest that in the course of our ensuing discussion we shall be for the most part in quite familiar territory. In the course of this argument the reader will become aware of the deepness of our indebtedness to Thorstein Veblen's *Theory of the Leisure Class*,[1] to which we shall refer repeatedly in passing, even though we shall prefer to argue formally on the basis of our own previous discussion and not upon his.

I. THEORETICAL CONSIDERATIONS

In our usage, a person's *prestige* exists only (1) in reference to some actual group of persons, while (2) the *relative degree* of his prestige is indicated by (3) the *comparative extent* to which others in the group will defer to his will and convenience. Thus defined, the concept of *prestige* and its problem of symbolism is seen to fit into our entire earlier argument, and notably into the argument of our preceding chapter.

The most obvious means of compelling others to defer to one's will is the use of superior physical force, as we have already seen. This in turn will mean that the strongest man will tend to have the greatest prestige, as is observably the case in so-called "primitive" societies as well as in groups of present-day small boys, where sheer force is admittedly the final arbiter of all things, and where, if one cannot be strong oneself, one strives to be a friend of those who are strong. From this consideration alone we can see how members of a group will either strive for the positions of top prestige, or else vie for the favor of those who possess the top positions, while the group itself is altered into a dominance system under the leadership of an elite.

Insofar as prestige is based upon the possession of physical power, this physical power must be *repeatedly* exercised in a *conspicuous fashion* so that members of the group will be reminded of the presence of the strong man's power, lest they otherwise lapse with time into an indifference towards his will and convenience. For that reason the person who has (or desires) prestige must repeatedly engage in combat in order to keep his power fresh in the memories of others. Moreover—and this point was apparently overlooked by Veblen—the strong man must express his will in ways that deviate widely from the accepted norms of the group, so that the group's deference to his will can be easily detected. In short, deference must be conspicuous and recognizable.

We may expect, therefore, that (1) a conspicuous display of power, and that (2) conventionally unusual or even unreasonable and whimsical demands upon others will attend the phenomenon of prestige.

Physical combat with others involves the expenditure of work, as well as the assumption of the risk of being defeated by one's adversaries. For that reason, any device of less work and risk that can be substituted with equal effect for an actual physical combat in the struggle for prestige will be recommended for adoption,* yet as soon as we introduce the concept of

* For convenience we shall ignore the obvious case of underhandedly eliminating powerful contenders while conspicuously battling with "men of straw."

substitute devices we introduce, by definition, the concept of symbols (cf. Chapter Seven).

Since these substitute devices in the present case refer to the matter of relative prestige, they may be called *prestige symbols,* which we must conceive of as something conspicuous that will serve to inculcate fear in the observer.

The most obvious prestige symbols are those things like scalps, heads, and teeth that can be removed from the corpses of enemies slain in combat for the purpose of exhibition as signs of one's prowess. In short, one's vanquished enemies, dead or alive, can from their corpses and belongings provide trophies that may be used by the conqueror as *prestige symbols* in evidence of his power.

At this juncture, however, an ugly consideration arises. We refer to the fact that there is no discernible difference between the parts of corpses that have been heroically slain in combat and the parts of corpses that have succumbed to natural causes and which lie available in any fresh grave. Hence, the sheer possession of the bodily parts of others without an *authenticating story* will not necessarily betoken prowess, since people can rob graves. From this consideration there arises the dynamic for authenticating stories which, in turn, will lead to that class of literary products known as *heroic epics.* Minstrels, therefore, are essential to kings, who must always give a mind to history lest the royal trophies of combat be subsequently forgotten or declared spurious.

Once the authenticating story has been produced in support of the trophy, the trophy itself does not need to be displayed as long as the people will believe the story. So arises the cult of paid or unpaid publicity experts that extends historically from the minstrels of old to the society columnists of today.* So, too, arises the cult of antiquarian authenticating experts, which are closely allied to the diffusion of Pied Piper morality, as discussed in our previous chapter.

Trophies need not be restricted to the bodily parts of the heroically slain; the personal property of the slain can also serve as trophies. The plundering of the enemy's estate will always be an inevitable consequence of combat.

Yet, here too, the risk of spurious trophies is present since, after all, who can tell how a particular piece of personal property was acquired by its owner. For that very reason there will arise theoretically a special class of purveyors of spurious *objets de combat* which even a connoisseur can barely distinguish from genuine heroically looted articles; and with the rise of this class of purveyors of spurious *objets de combat,* Veblen's *"pecuniary civilization,"* in which we now live, seems, in my opinion, to take its start.

Against this class of purveyors of spurious heroic loot there is no real permanent defense. There is, however, a makeshift defense; the victors in their heroic looting should try to limit themselves to those objects so costly

* The minstrels of yore, in singing of the virtues of a departed strongman, were wont to digress at length upon his great generosity, particularly towards minstrels.

to manufacture that their spurious imitations will be too expensive for any but the rich and powerful to buy. In this simple fashion the sheer display of wealth becomes a sign of prestige for all persons regardless of how the loot was acquired.

As soon as the display of wealth becomes a sign of prestige, there are certain statements that can be made about the nature of prestige symbols. In the first place, rare and hence costly materials will be used, provided always that the materials are readily conspicuous to view and easily recognizable as to genuineness and value.* In the second place, those goods and services upon which a great deal of labor has been expended—provided that the labor component is conspicuous and easily recognizable as to its value—will also serve as prestige symbols. Thus, an obviously handmade artifact of great labor, and notably if it is stylistically characteristic of an artisan of limited output (preferably dead so that he cannot increase the supply) can be an ideal prestige symbol.

Moreover, and here we are again echoing Thorstein Veblen, the sheer number of a person's servants, provided that they are recognizable both as servants and as the person's servants, are splendid prestige symbols. Not only does their keep betoken the master's wealth; their arms also signify his power. If these servants can be employed conspicuously at trivial tasks, the greater will be the master's prestige.

Nor should we forget, as we pointed out in our previous chapter, that status complacency and the poses of "liberalism" and tolerance (up to a certain point)—*if conspicuous*—can all be excellent prestige symbols. The same applies to a conspicuous sympathy for the poor and unfortunate. Indeed, I doubt that a heretic has ever been burned but that tears of pity for his soul and body have not conspicuously welled down the cheeks of the truly well bred as they watched from their ringside seats while law and justice took their swift course without fear or favor.

Good works, if conspicuous, are always good prestige symbols.

The performance of good works entails the expenditure of some physical work. Nor is this work expenditure a blemish for the elite who, as Veblen pointed out, should conspicuously perform some utilitarian task in spite of the plenitude of their servants. Thus, the conspicuous embroidering of a handkerchief at a meeting of the Altar Guild will go far towards suggesting to the observer the pent-up power that lies behind the prestige symbols. Indeed, at a "benefit performance" in the "Greater Boston-Cambridge Community," I once observed a portly, marvellously clad matron approach with a solid silver tray upon which were two paper cups with chilled flavored water that was being served in a menial fashion as refreshments to us benefactors. The calory content of the refreshment was not enough to supply the energy to move the lady's vastness an inch, nor the coolness therein contained enough to lower her temperature by the tiniest fraction of a degree. And yet when one lifted the drink to one's lip it had a certain

* With the progress of civilization there has arisen the class of purveyors of actually fake prestige symbols (e.g., the skins of rabbits that are dyed to look like mink; the skins of alley cats that are dyed to look like rabbit, etc.).

je ne sais quoi. It is this certain *je ne sais quoi* that is essential to a prestige symbol, as Dr. Veblen made beautifully clear years ago.

There is one point that Dr. Veblen did not treat. We refer to the fact that the continual manufacture of prestige symbols and their imitations (with the exception of servants) may eventually produce such a supply that everyone will be able to have a complete outfit of prestige symbols, with the result that everyone will become as good as everyone else. To avoid this awkward social situation, prestige symbols must be changed from time to time. These changes in prestige symbols are important, since they introduce the factor of *vogues.*

The introduction of a new vogue is a difficult problem. If the new vogue is to be successful it must be sponsored both (1) by the "right" kind of people and (2) by the "right" number of the "right" kind of people.

As to the right kind of people to select for the sponsoring of a new vogue, we see at once that those persons who enjoy the greatest prestige are the ones to select for sponsoring new styles, since theirs is the behavior that is most observed and imitated by others. For that reason the promoters of new fashions do well to give their new fashions to the prominent—or even to pay handsome sums to the prominent—for conspicuously displaying the new styles. Photographs of the socially prominent using the style in question will also aid the vogue; or the written endorsements by the socially prominent of those things which, like tinted toilet paper, are not normally used too conspicuously will also be helpful.

The reason for this concern about the status of the persons who launch a new style in prestige symbols is obvious. For unless the new style is culturally accepted by the entire group, it is likely to appear queer (as defined and discussed in Chapter Seven), or perhaps even be viewed as a nervous tic. Since the powerful are more likely to be imitated than the poor, the powerful should be selected as the sponsors of new vogues. (On the other hand, vogues *can* rise from the lower strata; e.g., the queen can quietly imitate the hairdo of the successful street harlot, who thereby unwittingly sets a fashion.)

The number of persons to be used as sponsors of a new style is a further difficult question, for unless there is a sufficient number of supporting sponsors, the new style is likely to appear bizarre and queer. It was precisely this lack of supporting numbers that frustrated George V, King of England, etc., and Defender of the Faith, in his Gracious Majesty's attempt to introduce the new fashion of pressing men's pants at a 90° angle from the traditional press. For we assume that this was not just a nervous tic on the part of so stable a member of so stable a family as the Hannoverians. Yet for all time His Majesty must now lie in his royal casket with his pants pressed the "wrong" way—unless his loyal subjects, belatedly becoming mindful of their allegiance to the crown, consent for a few months to press what pants they have left at a 90° Georgian angle, thereby posthumously restoring George to the traditional farsighted leadership of British fashion, while simultaneously removing from his illustrious name the ugly suspicion of a nervous tic. Thus, fashions!

Even though an increase in the number of sponsors of a new style will make it more convincing to the total populace, it is obviously not to the advantage of the individual sponsors to be obliged to share the prestige of a leadership in fashion with too many other sponsors. For, as the number of sponsors of a new style is increased, and therewith the probability that the new style will be copied, the actual prestige that attends being a sponsor will be correspondingly *diluted.* So we see that the launching of a new style, or fashion, or vogue, entails the problem of the "right number" of sponsors.

This problem of the "right number" is by now familiar to us, since we have met it in earlier questions. Just as the problem of the "right number" is by now familiar, so too is the general nature of its indicated solution. In brief, the "right number" of sponsors is presumably selected from among those in the uppermost status strata whose behavior will be imitated in turn by those next below. In this manner the new style, and its imitation, will spread down the hierarchy with increasing "crescendo" until it has become a "rage" and a cultural necessity.

Thus conceived, the growth of a vogue is intrinsically exponential, since theoretically it is spreading through classes whose populations are increasing exponentially. Moreover, the same exponential function will appear if we view the growth of a vogue as a spread of knowledge throughout a population, or over a terrain (e.g., as more persons manifest the style, the ever more persons will learn of it).

In stating theoretically that the growth of a vogue is intrinsically exponential, we should not forget that, as an increasing number of persons adopt the style, the prestige of manifesting the style becomes ever more diluted for the leaders of fashion who originally sponsored it. Hence as the new vogue becomes ever more a social necessity for *adoption* by the entire population, it becomes ever more a social necessity for *discard* by the socially prominent. As an extreme case we may imagine a costly new gown of latest style that is worn only once conspicuously with great *eclat* at a gala social event, only to be handed the next morning to the cook.

This theoretical rush on the one hand to adopt a new fashion at the very outset, with a resulting exponential growth of the fashion, only to be followed by a theoretical rush on the other hand to abandon the new style as it becomes ever more popular, may yield a developmental distribution that is quite similar to that of a *logistic curve.*

After a style has reached its peak, it may decline as rapidly as it arose, with an ever decreasing residue of persons who continue to manifest it either from a lack of knowledge of later styles, or from a lack of wealth to adopt them. Cycles, therefore, tend to be inherent in vogues, with a person's prestige measurable to no small extent by his capacity to know when to adopt and when to discard a style.*

It may at times happen that a given style or mode of behavior, because of its utilitarian value for the culture in question, will not decline, but instead will assume a comparatively permanent place in the cultural vocab-

* The ancient paradox in feminine millinery: the hat that is at once worn by everybody else and by nobody else.

ulary. Thus, for example, the ownership of an automobile in the United States was originally a prestige symbol, I believe, that only later assumed a tremendous utilitarian value for our culture. In such a case we may suspect that the increasing rate of ownership of automobiles—if the rate was in fact logistic——would become asymptotic to a more or less stable frequency of usage in the cultural vocabulary of our country. Nevertheless, although the possession of *an* automobile may today be rather a utilitarian necessity than a social must, yet the particular *kind* of an automobile that a person possesses is still to a considerable degree a fashion.

Conversely, a hitherto apparently stable element of the cultural vocabulary may suddenly become unfashionable and decline exponentially (or logistically) in usage. Perhaps the horse and buggy declined in usage in such a manner. Curiously enough, the decline of lynching has been logistic in U. S. A. (*vide infra*), much as if it is becoming increasingly unfashionable to lynch.

But though vogues may in general be cyclical by nature, the duration of the cycles need by no means be the same. An object which, like a house, is costly to produce, may change its style much more slowly than styles in neckties—and for quite obvious reasons. Indeed the cost of production, and therefore the rate of adoption throughout the entire population, is a determinant of the duration of a vogue. For, theoretically, just as a merchandiser who overstays a fashion may be caught with a large inventory of worthless outmoded goods, so too, in his eagerness to be forehanded with new fashions, he can be caught with a large inventory of worthless "newfangled" goods that are never adopted.* Research into the dynamics of vogues, which can be furthered empirically by access to the confidential stock records of large merchandising establishments, can be profitably subvened by those large establishments themselves.

We have previously mentioned the slowness of changes in the styles of houses, thereby suggesting that there is a "sociology" of architectural styles, as well as a "psychology," as intimated in Chapter Eight. Hence, when a solicitor approaches a house he can gain from its appearance an idea of the probable social status of its occupants. As he looks around at the furnishings inside, and hears the occupant speak, he gains further information about the occupant's social status, as well as some insight into the occupant's particular personality. Yet there is still more to the psycho-sociological aspect of the house, as is evident from the often costly materials and expert craftsmanship of a now humble dwelling that obviously was once fashionable. For a house, having lost its fashionableness, is not always immediately razed to make room for a fashionable one. Instead, the occupants often move out into an entirely new district—the "fashionable district"—where they establish themselves in a new fashionable house. Yet as the fashionable persons move into the new "fashionable district," thereby making the district still more fashionable, they are followed by imitators who do not quite

* In America today we may be suffering from an excessive rapidity in changing fashions. Thus unless ample time is allowed for the cook to buy the latest fashion, she might just as well be unfashionable with a ten-year-old hat as with a six-months-old one.

have the same high social status; * and so the chase continues throughout the years, around and around the town, as those of higher status both flee from and are pursued by their social inferiors. Eventually the once costly houses of rare materials and fine workmanship become the domiciles of truly humble people.†

Vogues are not lacking in the other arts, whether in the fine arts or in the more utilitarian artifacts, as we all know from experience. Later we shall analyze the case of music.

Vogues are not lacking in the educational-intellectual process. The A.B. degree is fashionable; hence the increasing number of purveyors of the same (and perhaps a resulting cheapened product?). Higher degrees must, therefore, be sought if they are to be distinguishing. Yet as ever more persons become Masters of Arts and Doctors of Philosophy, still higher degrees must be invented.

Vogues in education are not limited to the matter of degrees. The actual fields of education that attract students come in and out of vogue. Thus, the runs on philosophy, literature, romance philology, psychology, "government," sociology, nuclear physics, and so on. Curiously enough the present type of social research seems to be heading for an "exponential increase."

Political sentiments and social and moral metaphysical beliefs are also subject to vogues, even though we may believe at the time that we are uttering "eternal moral verities." Fealty to such sentiments is socially fashionable, even as a disdain for the same is unfashionable.‡

An excellent example of the dynamics and danger of a political fashion, and one which the present writer is studying in connection with the topic of the social pathology of an educational institution, is found in the political propaganda group of British interventionists that "prepared us for American participation" in World War II. Although the topic is too extensive to merit more than a cursory mention here—and we have already alluded to it in Chapters Seven and Eleven—yet if the reader will recall the manifestations of this political activity, "sponsored" by the socially best that Harvard, Boston, and certain segments of the New York financial dis-

* We must not forget our argument in Chapter Nine about residential propinquity and the probability of marriage.

† These changes in residential fashions will introduce biases, or distortions, in the otherwise rectilinear distribution of the number and distance of residential changes as discussed in Chapter Nine.

‡ The danger of Pied Piper morality we have already discussed in our previous chapter. In this connection, cf. G. B. Chisholm in his William Alanson White Memorial Lecture (reported *Psychiatry*, ix, 1946, No. 1, p. 7): "What basic psychological distortion can be found in every civilization of which we know anything? It must be a force which discourages the ability to see and acknowledge patent facts, which prevents the rational use of intelligence, which teaches or encourages the ability to dissociate and to believe contrary to and in spite of clear evidence . . . which encourages prejudice and the inability to see, understand and sympathize with other people's points of view. Is there any force so potent and so pervasive that it can do all these things in all civilizations? There is—just one. The only lowest common denominator of all civilizations and the only psychological force capable of producing these perversions is morality."

trict could offer, he will remember that more than anything else it was fashionable to send "bundles to Britain," and to have one's children belong to a Junior British Relief Organization. As time passed, it became highly unfashionable not to be identified with these groups, while it was well-nigh treasonable to oppose them. The fact that some of the policymakers of this movement were of doubtful loyalty, while others seemed to represent clear cases of paranoia and exhibitionism, was something that was quietly overlooked, lest one be considered unfashionable. In fact, in Boston–Cambridge, if one were not pro-British, pro-Russian, and pro-Semitic one was un-American. The danger that is inherent in such political fashions is well attested by the outcome of the above fashion: not only did the political fashion finally reduce Western Europe to chaos, but it even involved the United States in the chaos while trifling away our undoubtedly great bargaining position at the time. The educational and other institutions in question whose leaders set this "war style" for America by forcing their particular kind of "international" preconceptions down the throats of others are now, interestingly enough, passing into public contempt, as their underlying motives, and the indirection of their organizations, become recognized (cf. previous discussion of Pied Piper morality, Chapter Eleven, and of paranoia, Chapter Seven).

A study of President F. D. Roosevelt's "fireside chats" reveals the brilliance of the advertising mind that, in composing them, made use of the familiar techniques for promoting any new kind of fashion. Mr. Roosevelt's "chats" generally proceeded as follows: (1) The Union and Human Rights are in grave peril (the *fright technique*—frequently used by advertisers of breath and body deodorants); (2) happily all intelligent and patriotic Americans are already aware of the peril and are rallying to the defense of the Union and Human Rights (the *snob appeal*); (3) there are of course certain misguided persons and groups among us—and you know who I mean, etc. (the *paranoid appeal;* by not specifying the particular persons and groups in question, the President let each auditor believe that his own personal enemies were the ones the President had in mind, and that therefore the President was on his side).

Closely related to political and educational fashions are what may be called "spiritual" fashions, as commonly found in religious organizations whose lore is based upon an original divine revelation. Although we know from history that religious beliefs change—in earlier days they often changed with the fortunes of war—nevertheless, in Western European civilization in recent years, they have changed either too slowly or too covertly to be studied objectively.* We may, therefore, merely suggest as a working hypothesis that one's membership in a religious group may be governed somewhat by the exigencies of politics and fashions.

* Because of "cultural lags" and effectively forcible indoctrination of offspring into parental beliefs, we may not expect to find in religious sects a manifestation of our theoretical Force of Unification (i.e., making for one single all-inclusive religio-brahministic dominance system) and the theoretical Force of Diversification (i.e., each person has his own special god).

Regardless of the question of the rates of change of the metaphysical beliefs of the various religions of the world, the phenomenon of religious rituals is not without interest for our present discussion of vogues and fashions, since the emotional relief that attends the performance of these rituals may not be entirely unrelated to that which attends a manifestation of the current local fashions. Thus, for example, when the customary structure of a small group to which a person belongs is disturbed by changes in its membership, such as might be caused by a death, or a birth, or a marriage, then the persons of the group can mitigate the disturbance by performing the traditional rituals of the more inclusive religious (or other) group to which the members of the small group belong. By performing these rituals, which are nothing more than conventional manifestations of membership in the larger group, one adopts what might be called the "frame of reference" of the older, larger, stronger, and more enduring group. Viewed against this larger "frame," the particular deaths, births, marriages, and the like, which are subjectively of such deep concern to the persons affected, become merely further instances of the statistical cliches of society. With this reassurance of the social ordinariness of what had struck the individual as being highly extraordinary, the individual can more objectively restructure his smaller group. Moreover, the almost invariable rhythmic structure of such rituals helps to induce a quasi-hypnotic state in the performer, with the result that he is more susceptible to the constructive and consoling exhortations of the leader of the ritual. This view of rituals, which follows that of A. L. Van Gennep on the *rites of passage,*[2] has been elaborated qualitatively in terms of "equilibrium," with a vast amount of illustrative material, by Drs. Eliot D. Chapple and Carleton Coon in their brilliant *Principles of Anthropology.*[3]

The manifestation of fashions may be similar to that of performing the *rites of passage* (including, in our usage, the *rites of intensification*). Thus the simple gift of a new hat or dress or compact of latest fashion to the grieving girl may lift her spirits more quickly than if she were presented with a whole library of moral precepts. Conversely, a ban upon the vainglories of the day (together with a taboo upon all "licentious" sexual behavior) would, theoretically, be an excellent device for making the populace regularly attend the public rituals where, in a quasi-hypnotic state, they will listen respectfully to the traditional dogma.*

Our foregoing discussion, which has been largely qualitative, has by no means established the essential exponential or logistic nature of the classes

---

* It is an interesting question as to what will become of public rituals after the authority of revealed religion has departed and given way to the ethics and "metaphysics" of social empiricism. Perhaps the early Christians with their two basic "commandments" (cf. Chapter Eleven) envisaged hopefully just such a time. By the term *the early Christians,* we mean the Christians who antedated that fateful moment when the Christians converted the Emperor Constantine, and with him the worldly wise old Roman elite, who in turn seem to have converted a simple honest way of living into a dominance system along familiar patterns. The Buddhists similarly converted the social elite with similar consequences.

of vogues that we have discussed. Neither have we shown that all other kinds of vogues follow these functions; nor that all cultural changes are vogues.

If we reflect that new words and phrases (e.g., slang) come in and out of vogue, much like the popular tunes of the day, we may possess in the case of speech a useful analogue for the study of other cultural changes. True, the vogues in slang change so rapidly that only the writers of highly ephemeral material (e.g., sports reporters) may safely use slang for its crisp prestige effect. Since there seems, however, to be no dynamic dichotomy between the swift cycles of slang and the slower cycles of "standard" speech, there is no reason to suppose that the elements of standard speech represent anything more than the effects of more slowly changing vogues. Erstwhile standard words like *ween* and *opine* are today a little *"old-fashioned."*

If we recall our discussion in Chapter Three of the cultural-chronological strata of speech, we remember that the new, or *nascent,* words of a vocabulary tend to increase their frequency of usage in a quite orderly exponential manner, whereas the older, or *senescent,* words, in departing from the vocabulary, seem to decrease their frequency exponentially. If we further recall the extent to which we generalized theoretically upon the special case of speech in the total language of culture, we may feel that, behind our present theoretical discussion of prestige symbols and social vogues, we may have at hand in the special case of speech a fairly well systematized theory into which much of our present discussion of vogues may fit. In fact, the student of styles in merchandise would seem to be well advised to study the dynamics of the styles of words and other speech elements.

Yet the didactic value of speech for an understanding of the dynamics of prestige symbols and social vogues extends beyond the structural effects of an imitation of the "King's English" and of the Court's slang. For, after all, vogues in speech, like all other changes in speech habits, spread over distance; the influence of a city's changing speech habits upon the speech habits of surrounding populations is one of the more commonplace observations of dialect geographers. May we therefore suspect that the spread of speech innovations—and perhaps other cultural innovations—is subject to the $(P_1 \cdot P_2)/D$ Hypothesis?

Although this question relates to the highly complex phenomenon of spread of speech changes, nevertheless it is by no means imponderable. Thus, if each of two communities, P_1 and P_2, separated by a least-work D distance, independently develop new and mutually conflicting speech ways, then, if our general argument of Chapter Nine be sound, the line of demarcation between the two fields of influence—provided that their domains touch—will be the arc of a circle of very large radius, except for the special case in which $P_1 = P_2$, where the locus will be a straight line. If we extend the argument to the respective domains of the n different communities of the social system, in each of which speech changes may occur, we can see that theoretically the outer periphery of the domains of historic speech changes will constitute a polygon whose sides (technically called *isoglosses* by dialect geographers) will be essentially arcs of very large radius.* Thanks to the careful research of dialect geographers, the large arc-like nature of *isoglosses,* even to the extent of being almost straight lines as anticipated by our theory, has been established empirically. Whether, from the accumulated crisscrosses of the isoglosses of major linguistic cleavages and of local dialect variations down through the ages, we can reconstruct the ancient values of *P* of the respective competing cultural centers in question remains an inviting question.

The foregoing theoretical argument applies *mutatis mutandis* to all cultural innovations, regardless of whether or not the innovations refer to vogues and prestige symbols.† If such innovations occur at random in a population, then a proportionately greater number and diversity of cultural innovations will occur in communities of larger *P*. The larger communities, therefore, will in general tend to be the ones that set the new styles, whereas the smaller communities will tend rather to follow the styles that are set by others.

The theory of the circulation of information, elaborated in Chapter Nine, can be easily extended to apply to the circulation of vogues. Moreover, if we chose to use our argument of Part One as an underlying analogue, we could arrive at the theoretical conclusion that a few styles will change comparatively slowly, whereas an increasing number will change with increasing rapidity. Furthermore, the general rapidity of change in vogues in a *P* community would tend to be positively correlated with the size of *P,* whereas the rate of "cultural lag" would be negatively correlated.

Curiously enough, if we had available for observation only one single kind of social phenomenon for the disclosure of the principles of human ecology, we could scarcely select a more suitable one than the phenomenon of human speech, which, in our belief, is only a special case of the total language of culture. The vogues and prestige symbols of words and manners of articulation are quite instructive for the more general topic.

* Although dialect geographers have tendered no theoretical explanation of the virtual straightness of isoglosses, their observations have at least disproved Ferdinand de Saussure's famous "wave theory"[4] from which he erroneously predicted that the outer periphery of a phonetic change would be circular and centered on the city in question. Theoretically, they will be circular but not centered on the city. The same applies to W. J. Reilly's pioneer "law of retail gravitation," as well as to subsequent elaborations by J. Q. Stewart and P. D. Converse. It underlies the problem of railway location of trunk lines and branch lines, as brilliantly studied empirically and theoretically by A. M. Wellington.[5]

† Theoretically, the principles that we are discussing in the present and preceding chapters are basic to the dynamics of "public opinion," and for quite obvious reasons. Moreover they should be susceptible of empiric test by means of the suitable application of the technique of public opinion polls. Indeed it is difficult to define "public opinion" except in terms of the objectives and rules of procedure of a group of persons, even as we have sought to do. We mention these considerations to stress the view that the said technique can be used for scientific purposes as well as "practical" ones. Students of public opinion and communication might reflect that prestige symbols (including manners and sentiments) proceed first throughout the elite of the nation and then afterwards locally permeate the lower hierarchy. Thus the prince a thousand miles away may imitate the king sooner than the burgher in the king's capital. Promoters of styles might make note of this.

II. PIONEER EMPIRIC DATA

Our foregoing argument, which was based upon the theoretical considerations and empiric data of earlier chapters, brought us again and again to a consideration of what seemed theoretically to be exponential and logistic functions in the rise and decline of cultural vogues. This type of exponential function has been observed for years in the most diverse kinds of cultural phenomena by outstanding empiricists in the field, who have also often rationalized their data with such ingenuity that the terms *cultural traits* and *cultural patterns* have taken on very precise meanings.

One example of such research is found in Dr. F. Stuart Chapin's "Theory of Synchronous Culture Cycle" (published 1925), in which he observed the cumulative exponential growth of government activities in Detroit from 1840–1925 as an indication of the exponential growth of what he calls a "political culture complex." [6]

Dr. Hornell Hart has observed that a very wide range of cultural phenomena follow the closely related logistic curve that has become familiar in the biological studies of Volterra, Kostitzin, Raymond Pearl and others. His observations include the logistic rise in the divorce rate in the U. S. A. from 1890 through 1940 (is divorce to some extent fashionable?). [7] They include the logistic decline of lynchings in the U. S. A. from 1880 through 1940; [8] the logistic increase in persons graduating from college in the U. S. A., 1875–1942. [9]

Patents granted in the United States and Great Britain from 1852–1930 follow similar logistic trends. [10]

Dr. Margaret J. Hagood has observed that the growth of birth control clinics in the U. S. A. from 1931–1939 has been logistic. [11]

When we remember that the growth of populations and of incomes is logistic, we can see how the more specialized phenomena fit nicely into the more general background. The question is natural, however, as to the extent to which some of these phenomena may be considered as prestige symbols and as cultural vogues.

Thus, for example, Dr. Hart has observed the logistic growth of empire. [12] Is it possible that there is a national vanity—or a national prestige—in the size of one's empire? If we remember that the symbols of cultural vogues theoretically stand for the power of the person or group that exhibits them, then the vying for imperial domains may have been as much a matter of fashion as of business. Understandably, as the size of the domain increases, the cost of administration and of continued subjugation becomes an increasing drain (cf. Chapter Ten).

The chief drawback to using the foregoing data in connection with the topic of prestige symbols and cultural vogues is the difficulty of agreeing that these phenomena were at least at one time vogues. Because of this drawback, the present writer undertook, in association with his students, a study of the particular vogue of musical composers and compositions in the hope that this specialized study might illustrate some aspects of the dynamics of cultural vogues in general.

III. MUSICAL COMPOSERS AND COMPOSITIONS

We know from everyday experience that new songs and other forms of musical compositions become "popular" in the sense that they are performed and heard over a shorter or longer period of time before yielding to the popularity of some other musical composition. Similarly composers—and artists in other media—become "popular." This "popularity" seems to be virtually identical to what we have been calling *cultural vogues.* Moreover, regardless of the genuineness of the enjoyment of the music in question, there is a certain prestige that attaches to the ability to produce and to "appreciate" conspicuously whatever happens at the time to be in musical or other artistic vogue.

Let us assume, therefore, as a working hypothesis, that the phenomenon of the popularity of music is a case of cultural vogues which we shall now examine objectively for the light that it may shed upon the dynamics of vogues in general. This selection of musical vogues for treatment in our final closing chapter happens to be felicitous, since it will serve to synthesize much of our argument in Part One about the harmonic seriation with our present argument about exponential functions. To emphasize this synthesis we shall begin our study of the development of musical vogues by first considering the structure of concert programs, in which we shall find the familiar harmonic distribution.

When the director of a symphony orchestra makes out the programs for a winter series of concerts—say twenty-four concerts in all—he has the limited total amount of time of about 50 hours which he must "edit" into n_1 different *compositions;* or, if one will, he must edit it into the works of n_2 different composers.

Now as the director increases the size of either n_1 or n_2, he adds to the *diversity* of his programs, with the result that his subscription audience will have a wider range of musical experience. On the other hand, if the director decides in favor of the repetition of "popular" works and of "popular" composers—whether new or tried—for the sake of assuring applause, he will decrease the n number of the different items in question. In general, *to increase the frequency of performance of a given item is to decrease either the diversity or frequency* (*or both*) *of the performances of other items: repetition vs. diversity.*

If we consider this matter from the standpoint of the individual subscriber to the concert series, who will presumably desire to hear both the "old and familiar" and the "new and interesting," we note that the subscriber is in essentially the same position as the orchestra director. Thus as the subscriber approvingly applauds a given item, he thereby suggests to the director a desire to hear it repeated—at the expense of some other item. Yet there is a risk in repeating an item, lest the subscriber weary of it, and feel cheated of hearing a wider range of different music.

The director must, therefore, strike a balance between what we shall call the opposing Forces of Repetition (or Unification) and of Diversification. The Force of Repetition will act in the direction of playing only one single popular item during the entire time, as *n* diversity shrinks to one. The Force of Diversification will act in the opposite direction of increasing the *n* in question to such a point that no item is repeated. Naturally, the operation of these theoretical Forces is predicated upon the assumptions (1) that the director knows what his subscribers' past likes and dislikes have been and, therefore, what their probable future likes and dislikes will be; and (2) that the director will respond to his subscribers' likes and dislikes (i.e., he will truckle to the box office).

We know nothing about the relative magnitudes of our two theoretical Forces. Indeed, an audience consists of persons of such diverse tastes that it is questionable whether we can speak strictly of the "relative magnitudes" of the two Forces. Instead, we might better assume that our director will experimentally adopt a safe course in which he finds that the two Forces are equal; thus he will hope that those who complain that he is repeating the "old stuff" too much will cancel out those who complain that he is playing too great a diversity of different things.* As the years elapse, the subscribers of extreme tastes will go elsewhere for their concert music, whereas the subscribers of less extreme tastes will remain with the director. As a result, the director, if successful, will note that although he always receives applause for each of his *n* different items, the applause will not always come from the same groups of persons in the audience.

Moreover, if the director succeeds experimentally in thus treating the two theoretical Forces of Repetition and of Diversification as of equal magnitude, then we can deduce from our argument about the frequency, diversity, and rate of repetition of words (Chapters Two and Three), that the frequency, diversity, and rate of repetition of the different compositions that the director performs will be ordered essentially according to the proportions of the harmonic series.

Or, if we choose for convenience to use the number-frequency relationship that is corollary to the harmonic series (cf. Chapter Two), we may expect theoretically that the N number of different items of like F frequency of performance will be inversely proportional to $(F^2 - 1/4)$ or, in equation form, approximately:

$$N \cdot F^2 = C.$$

The above equation has been tested empirically on the concert programs of Dr. Serge Koussevitsky for the Saturday Evening Concerts of the Boston Symphony Orchestra for the period beginning October, 1924 and ending in April, 1934, as generously undertaken by my then student, Miss Rulan Chao, who was unaware at the time of the nature of the theoretical problem on which she was working.[13] The period in question covered ten seasons of concerts, or a total of 240 Saturday evening concerts in all.

As to the N number of different *compositions* of like F frequency, there was a negative slope (least squares) of .3677 ± .0693; or, in equation form:

$$N \cdot F^{2.7196} = 663.6$$

* Similarly, an editor who receives a large number of letters, one-half accusing him of being too "leftish," the other half of being "too rightish" can infer he is in fact adopting a "middle course" (it is his only way of knowing).

This distribution, however, seemed to consist of the two parts: *first,* the four points for the values of F from 6 through 9, which were below theoretical expectations; and *second,* the lower five points for the values of F from 5 through 1, which represented 97.6 percent of the n_1 different compositions played, and 90.3 percent of all compositions, including repetitions, that were played. These lowest five points, when treated by themselves, had a negative slope of .5072 ± .0155, or, in equation form:

$$N \cdot F^{1.9716} = 355.06$$

From this observed exponent of 1.9716 against a theoretically anticipated 2.0000, we note that over 90 percent of Koussevitsky's selections are a remarkably close approximation to the situation in which our theoretical Forces of Repetition (Unification) and of Diversification are of equal magnitude and of opposite direction.

These pieces, on the whole, were not repeated often enough during the ten-year period to justify an ascertainment of the intervals between their repetitions. Therefore we turned our attention to the number-frequency distribution and the interval-frequency distribution of the n_2 different composers played during the ten-year period. Both of these distributions were strikingly rectilinear.

Thus the N number of composers of like F frequency of occurrence had a negative slope of .6114 ± .2698, or, in equation form:

$$N \cdot F^{1.6356} = 86.34$$

Furthermore the N number of intervals (in units of five intervening concerts) of like s size between the repetitions of composers had a negative slope of .5984 ± .2610, or, in equation form:

$$N \cdot s^{1.6711} = 438.$$

Curiously enough, the slopes for the number-frequency relationship and for the interval-frequency relationship are statistically the same.

If we assume the correctness of our theory, then Dr. Koussevitsky "balances" his programs primarily in terms of *compositions* played, and secondarily in terms of *composers* played. The rectilinearity of the distributions is striking, since one does not normally expect to find an orderliness in an artistic phenomenon of this kind.

Yet the same orderliness is to be found in the case of recorded music, as disclosed by my student, Mr. W. B. Bryant, who generously examined the frequency distribution of the composers listed in *The Music America Loves Best: a selected list of recorded permanent music chosen from the vast Victor Red Seal and Victor Bluebird Popular Record Catalogues* (1943).

Although the criteria that were used for the selection of this list of "permanent music" were not given by the publishers, they presumably included the factor of the relative frequency of sales of the items in question. In any event, it is obvious that the problem of "popular records" is dynamically similar to that of the organization of concert programs which we have just discussed.

Mr. Bryant divided his statistical study into two parts. The first part (*A*) considered the *N* number of different *composers* who had the same *F* number of different compositions in the catalogue. The second part (*B*) considered the *N* number of different composers who had the same total *F* number of different *records* in the list; this *F* total number of *records* was ingeniously estimated by Mr. Bryant on the basis of the cost of the respective entries under each composer (in other words, from the costs and kinds of records, Mr. Bryant estimated the total number of records for sale under each composer).

Both the *A* and *B* analyses yielded exponents (least squares) that were remarkably close to the value, 2.00, that we expect theoretically. Thus, the *A* analysis for the *N* number of composers of like *F* number of *entries* had the exponent, 1.8406 (i.e., slope $= -.5433 \pm .1203$). The *B* analysis for the *N* number of composers with the like *F* number of records had the exponent 2.1336 (i.e., slope $= -.4687 \pm .1175$). In the light of the sizes of the errors, both these calculated exponents may be viewed as nonsignificant variations from our theoretically expected value. The actual sales of the entities in question would be well worth ascertaining.

All the foregoing data and argument about the relative frequency of the playing of the compositions of musical composers can easily be integrated into our entire argument in connection with the "language of sensation" in Chapter Five, which we illustrated with data on the frequency distribution of newspaper items and encyclopaedia articles. Moreover, the data on music are quite similar to those for the speeches of plays, as discussed in the closing section on conversations in our preceding chapter, which in turn were intimately connected with the interval-frequency relationship in the repetition of words (cf. Chapters Two and Three).

In short, our above study of musical compositions reveals a familiar type of phenomenon with which the proportions of the harmonic series are closely associated. We stress this point to make amply clear that our study of the exponential development of a particular kind of music, as we shall shortly show, is by no means inconsistent with an observed harmonic seriation at a particular moment of measurement.*

The next move in the present investigation of music as a vogue was an analysis of Walter Willson Cobbett's *Cyclopedic Survey of Chamber Music* (2 vols. London: Oxford Univ. Press, 1929). Thus, we limited our field to the special case of chamber music, which we assumed to be more or less typical of all music.

This analysis of Cobbett was undertaken in three different steps (*A*, *B*, and *C*), so that this investigation might likewise be kept integrated with our earlier studies in reference to the structure of encyclopaedias and the like.

The *first* step (*A*) was to tabulate the *length* of biographical articles, in terms of running lines, of all the approximately 2100 different composers

* Of course, we may by no means argue in reverse that because we have observed an exponential function in the one case where we have also observed a harmonic distribution, that the two different kinds of functions will *always* be thus associated in all other cases; nevertheless, we may argue that the two functions are by no means mutually inconsistent.

discussed in the cyclopedic survey. For even though the survey also contains some nonbiographical articles, the rank-length distribution of such a large number of biographical articles, when treated alone as a group, might theoretically be expected to follow the proportions of the harmonic series with a − 1.00 slope, as was the case with the articles in the *Encyclopaedia Britannica* (cf. Chapter Five).

The *second* step (*B*) was to ascertain the *m* number of different *named compositions* mentioned in connection with each composer, so that we might disclose any relationship between the length of a composer's biographical account, and the *m* number of his named compositions mentioned therein. This second step was taken in the belief that the relationship between the two factors in question was intrinsically the same as that of the meaning-frequency relationship of words, as discussed in Chapter Two (where *m* varied with the *square root* of frequency), as well as with the exponential effect—or the *"square effect"*—that we discussed in our preceding chapter in connection with the general problem of a person's comparative prestige. Thus, we may ask whether the length of the account of a composer tends to increase with the square of the *m* number of his different compositions that are important enough to be mentioned by name in the article.

The *third* step (*C*) was to ascertain whether the 2100 odd different composers of chamber music, when arranged according to the year of their birth (and in all but a negligible number of cases the year of birth was given), would reveal an exponential increase in the number of composers from the beginning down to the present.

This entire investigation was undertaken by my then students, Messrs. W. B. Bryant, J. P. Boland, D. D. Bourland, Jr., J. M. Conant, and A. Y. Davis, who were at the time unaware of the nature of the theoretical questions involved in the second (*B*) and third (*C*) step, but who presumably were aware of the one that was involved in the first (*A*) step because of its similarity with that of earlier published studies.

The A analysis yielded a rank-length distribution that was on the whole quite linear. Indeed an actual calculation by least squares of the slope of every third rank of the total approximately 2100 ranks of the entire study yielded a − 1.2890 slope with a ± .10615 error; or, $\log y = 3.6999 - 1.289 \log x$, where y is length, and x is rank. This, to be sure, deviates significantly, if only slightly, from our expected − 1.00 slope. Before quarrelling with this deviation, let us reflect that Mr. Cobbett was primarily a musicologist and not a lexicographer, and that we have, after all, excluded all nonbiographical articles. In view of these reflections, the observed slope is a remarkably close approximation.

The next step (*B*) involved the calculation by least squares of the slope of the *m* number of different named compositions of the 702 composers for which the slope was calculated in the preceding *A* analysis, and whose ranks were also used in the present *B* analysis for the values of *m* of the composers in question. Thus, for example, the composer whose rank was 100 in the *A* analysis had also the same rank of 100 assigned to the *m* number of his different named compositions, regardless of the comparative size of his *m*.

The calculated slope, by least squares, of these 702 values of m was $-.5611 \pm .2580$ (i.e., $\log m = 1.6413 - .5611 \log rank$). The error here is, of course, sizable. Nevertheless, when we ranked in the order of decreasing size all the two thousand odd actual values of m, without any regard for the composer's rank in the A analysis, we found a rectilinear distribution on doubly logarithmic co-ordinates with a slope by eye measure that fell between $-.5000$ and $-.6000$, thereby tending to confirm the above calculated value.*

Despite the size of the error in the B analysis, the calculated slope of $-.5611$ is approximately one-half the size of the calculated -1.2890 slope of the A analysis. That fact is well worth noting, since it supports our the-

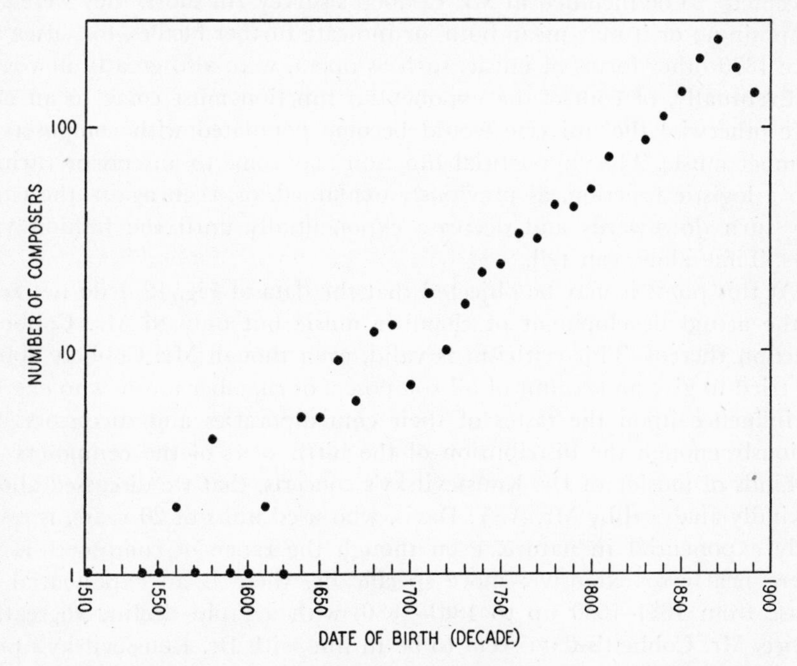

Fig. 12–1. Number of composers of chamber music, according to date of birth (1510–1900).

ory of the "square effect," in the sense that the effect of a person's activities tends to increase with the square of their m number. At least that was the effect of an increasing m upon Mr. Cobbett's editorial judgment.

In summary, the A and B analyses of Cobbett's *Cyclopedic Survey*, which were quite similar in kind to some of our earlier analyses, confirmed our theoretical expectations.

The C analysis, which referred to the rate of birth of the number of composers of chamber music over the years, as listed by Cobbett, did in fact disclose the theoretically expected exponential increase. Thus, the n number of different composers that were born in the same decade showed an exponential increase for the period that began with the earliest decade, 1500–

* Because of the enormous labor involved, this second slope was not calculated.

1510, and ended with the decade 1860–70, after which there is an exponential decrease, as is evident from an inspection of the data in Fig. 12–1.

An inspection of these data reveals a certain amount of variation, notably in the earlier years, which would have largely disappeared if we had used a unit of 20 years instead of a decade. On the other hand, the data for the smaller units of decades are not without some interest in and for themselves; and surely the presence of the exponential function is obvious.

The exponential decline after 1870 may indicate the decline of chamber music as a vogue. It may also mean that a certain amount of time must elapse before a composer's chamber music becomes sufficiently well known and "accepted" to be included in Mr. Cobbett's survey (in short, they were still composing); or it may mean both, or indicate further factors, for, after all, since 1870 other forms of music, such as opera, were also greatly in vogue.

Eventually, of course, the exponential function must come to an end, since otherwise the universe would become populated with composers of chamber music. The exponential function may come to an end by turning into a logistic function, as previously explained, or, then again, the curve may turn downwards and decrease exponentially until the fashion vanishes. Time alone can tell.

At this point it may be objected that the data of Fig. 12–1 do not refer to the actual development of chamber music but only to Mr. Cobbett's selection thereof. This criticism is valid, even though Mr. Cobbett doubtless tried to give an account of all composers of chamber music who exerted an influence upon the tastes of their contemporaries and successors. Yet curiously enough the distribution of the birth years of the composers (of all kinds of music) of Dr. Koussevitsky's concerts, that we discussed above, as kindly analyzed by Mr. A. Y. Davis, who used units of 20 years, is essentially exponential in nature, even though the range of composers is nowhere nearly so extensive; more specifically, there is an exponential increase from 1631–1650 up to 1861–1880, with a rapid decline thereafter. Hence, Mr. Cobbett's data seem to be in line with Dr. Koussevitsky's practice.

Our theory of vogues is not limited to the case of music. For that reason, if it were too difficult to procure a list of all composers whose chamber music (or other music) was played from the "beginning," the investigator can take the case of some other kind of artistic production. The moving picture industry would be an interesting choice, because of its comparative recency, since any observed exponential function in its development could scarcely be ascribed to the observed general logistic growth of the entire population during the period of development in question. The possibility of criticism that one is measuring only the effects of a general logistic growth of population must be borne in mind, even though the charge would appear somewhat strained in reference to the data of Fig. 12–1, as well as to the data of the pioneer empiricists discussed in Section II.

The main thing for us to emphasize now is that our observations about the composers of chamber music are quite in line with our theoretical expectations and with the observations of earlier empiricists who have studied the exponential and logistic curves.

Moreover, the study synthesizes several different theoretical rationalizations of earlier chapters with our present theory of prestige symbols and cultural vogues.

IV. SAMPLES OF CONGRESSIONAL ACTION

A system's vogues at a particular time belong to the rules of the system, since the prestige of the members of the system is judged by the extent to which the members manifest the vogues in question. In other words, vogues are rules of conduct, just like any other social correlations as discussed in Chapter Seven, even though many vogues are highly ephemeral, and even though they may not be formally codified into law, as is the case with the more enduring legal statutes of the land.

Many of the statutes of the land may be the direct result of vogues. By this we do not mean the statutes against "nuisances" and "indecent behavior" that throw upon the policeman and judge the role of arbiters of decency and morals. We refer rather to the enactment of formal statutes that reflect the changing policies of the system. Thus, for example, the current American "policy" of "internationalism" upon whose unarticulated plan, if any, the well-being of millions of American lives and billions of dollars depend, seems to be the result of a vogue which can be traced to a comparatively small group of investment bankers in New York; yet on the basis of this new fashionable policy, innumerable statutes have been enacted. This particular case is also instructive in showing how a rich, small, cohesive minority in a politically critical state can often effectively dominate the entire country by controlling the balance of power in a state whose electoral vote controls the balance of power in the country.

In other less striking matters the enactment of laws may be closely related to the nation's competitive vogues. Political parties are often aligned with group movements to which it is fashionable or unfashionable to belong in particular districts. The sheer fact that a person wears a particular campaign button does not necessarily mean that he even understands what the party he supports is advocating.

The structure of a code of law invites, therefore, to empiric inquiry, since it is an embodiment of some of the more critical changing sentiments of the system. Yet a code of law, like any other cultural code that consists solely of a body of social correlations, can presumably be studied empirically only through its effects upon human action. Thus, for example, we might study a legal code by ascertaining the n number of different laws that are broken *per annum,* and then rank the laws either according to the number of times they have been broken or, say, according to the total (or average) fines paid per breach, or by the total (or average) days of imprisonment. Such studies, for which, to my knowledge, no data are available, would be instructive, since we may suspect *a fortiori* that there are a small number of laws that are broken quite often and for which the punishments are comparatively small, while there is an increasing number of laws that are broken decreasingly often with an increasing amount of penalty. In short, the crimes to which a severe penalty is attached will tend to be few, while those of lighter penalty will tend to be more frequent—in man's collective attempt to "make the penalty fit the crime." We essay this belief because, after all, persons are penalized for their disturbances to a system; the magnitude of their crime is assessed on the basis of the magnitude of the disturbance. Disturbances of great magnitude, if frequent, would destroy the system.

But there are further aspects of the total process of lawmaking that admit of objective study. Thus, there is the question of the enactment of new laws, which in the Congress of the United States involves, for example, the tendering of bills on the part of the legislators, as well as the reporting out of bills by the Committees of Congress.

Turning our attention first to the tendering of bills by individual legislators—and for convenience of immediate discussion we shall include the tendering of amendments and resolutions—we can understand the urge on the part of each legislator to tender specialized bills that are designed to favor the legislator's own constituents without any regard for the well-being of the country as a whole. This urge, which is like our erstwhile theoretical Force of Diversification, will operate in the direction of increasing the n number of proposed bills. On the other hand, there may be a tendency to introduce bills that will favor the entire country without regard for the specialized interests of particular regional or social groupings; this tendency represents our erstwhile theoretical Force of Unification. As we noted in our previous chapter, there will theoretically be a few things about which all will agree, and an increasing number of things about which a decreasing number of persons will agree. For that reason we may expect that all the members of Congress, for example, will tender a few bills (including amendments and resolutions) of special concern for their own constituents, whereas a decreasing number will sponsor bills of wider implications.

As to these legislative proposals of more general implications—as well as to those of specialized interest—we should reflect that in actual practice a member of Congress rarely sponsors a bill on his own initiative without any previous consultation with his colleagues whose support is hoped for. Indeed, the proposals that affect the interests of larger groups of persons will theoretically be sponsored by persons of correspondingly higher status so as to gain added support for the measure. If relative status within a social group tends to be ordered harmonically, as we have argued in Section I of our preceding chapter, then the x number of legislators who introduce a like y number of legislative measures should be inversely proportional to y^2, according to the now familiar number-frequency relationship.

As a test of this theoretical expectation, the x number of Congressional representatives who introduced the same y number of bills (including amendments and resolutions) in the First Session of the 74th Congress, January 3–August 26, 1935, as reported in the *Congressional Record,* was ascertained by a group of my students who were at the time unaware of the nature of the theoretical problem under consideration.* The exponent of y was 2.1313 against our theoretical 2.00, with values of y through 100, though treated in classes of 20; in equation form it was $\log y = -.4792\, x + 1.1559 \pm .1732$, as calculated by least squares. This is a remarkably close approximation for so small a sample of political action that is popularly supposed to be highly disorderly.

Nor is the case different with the reports of Committees of Congress. In order not to dwell tediously upon the theoretical aspect of the question, let us merely point out that there is an economy (the Force of Unification) in having a single committee of Congress cover everything at the risk of a considerable superficiality of committee treatment. So, too, there is an economy (the Force of Diversification) in having a specialized committee for every specialized piece of business. This argument, if continued, would ultimately lead, I believe, to the theoretical expectation that the x number of different Congressional Committees that publish the same y number of reports will be inversely proportional to the square y (i.e., y^2). My then student, Mr. D. L. Duncan-Hall, who was at the time unaware of the nature of the theoretical question, tabulated the x number of Congressional Committees of the House and Senate combined in all sessions of the 74th and 75th Congresses who filed the same y number of reports. With y taking on values up to 200, but grouped in units of 20 (class middles) because of the comparative fewness of the cases, the calculated exponent was 2.2242 against a theoretical 2.00 (or, in equation form, $\log y = -.4496 \log x + 1.0998$, with the error $\pm .0362$).

Even in these evidences of the ultimate mainsprings of political action that enact in formal statement the objectives, rules, and penalties for great portions of the individual and collective behavior of the total system, we observe an orderliness that is completely consistent with the entire argument behind our thesis of the Principle of Least Effort.

These two investigations point to the possibility of further elaborational studies into the *science of politics* (as opposed to the so-called "political science") in which political activity is viewed as a natural phenomenon. Thus, we might inquire into the comparative lengths of statutes in terms of words, paragraphs, sections, etc.—and in terms of amendments offered and adopted. Or we might inquire into the n number of different sums appropriated. And so on and on and on.

In very small groups, such as in a small New England town where all eligible members can take part politically in the Town Meeting, we have a condition that is technically known as *democracy*. In such groups there are the usual subsidiary cliques that vie for power (as everyone knows who, like the present writer, has taken part in a town meeting). Yet as the group

* They were Miss Isobel Bragman, Miss Ramona Nelson, and the Messrs. Wm. R. Chandler, Donald Deixel, Jean Le Corbeiller, Roger F. Perry, John H. Ross, and Frederic W. Rugg II. These persons also studied the x number of headings in the Index to the *Congressional Record* (74th Congress) with the same y number of entries under them; the negative correlation was obvious, with a slope close to $-\frac{1}{2}$ on doubly logarithmic co-ordinates, although the variation was large.

becomes larger, with a resulting unwieldiness in the operation of the *democratic* process, each member of the group delegates his authority to a selected representative under what is known technically as a *republican* form of organization. Hence, as the n number of members of a group increases, the *kind* of organization of the group can change. An understanding of this type of change may be of considerable value for comprehending the general problem of political action in human ecology as well as the action of any other social system in the biosocial continuum, where there is a delegation of one's authority to direct and to control. Therefore let us cursorily inspect certain aspects of the dynamics of the delegation of power. This inspection refers inferentially to the structure and proportion of *any* managerial class (in factory, corporation, labor union, political party) and, as such, serves to tie together the argument of the present and preceding chapters.

If we take the special case of a small town that has a single schoolteacher, we can understand how this single schoolteacher, through her friends and through her favor to the children of influential parents, can become a political factor in the town, and thereby exercise a measure of control over her own treatment by the town.

Yet as the P population of the town increases, and with it, we assume, a *proportional* increase in the n number of schoolteachers employed, the political influence of each individual teacher upon the entire P population will decrease correspondingly. Nevertheless, since the collective n number of teachers continues to stand in the same constant ratio to the entire P population, regardless of the size of P, it follows that the n number of schoolteachers can still exert a considerable political influence if they *"organize"*—that is, if they *agree* upon a course of action, and if they use their individual friends and favor to achieve collectively their ends.

Indeed, as the n number of schoolteachers increases in proportion to an increasing P population, several things will happen. In the first place, the x political influence that any randomly selected schoolteacher can exert upon the entire P population will tend to *decrease* in direct proportion to an increase in n; or,

$$x \cdot n = K. \tag{12–1}$$

In the second place, the individual schoolteacher's need for a y collective action, or *organization,* both to protect and to assert himself politically, will tend to *increase* in direct proportion to n; or,

$$y \propto n \tag{12–2}$$

If, before we attempt to define more precisely the meanings of x and y, we simply substitute y in Eq. (12–2) for n in Eq. (12–1), we obtain the familiar equation of the equilateral hyperbola; or

$$x \cdot y = K. \tag{12–3}$$

From these three equations we see a functional interrelationship between the n size of a group, the y "degree of its organization," and the x extent to which the individual members must "subordinate their own personal interests."

At this point let us inquire more precisely into the meanings of x and y. To this end, let us postulate that the single unorganized schoolteacher in the small town behaves without any reference whatsoever to any other schoolteacher anywhere, and thereby may be said to exhibit a *random behavior in reference to the needs of the group in question;* in this case of the single schoolteacher the value of x "individualism" will be very high, while the value of the y "degree of organization" will be extremely small.

Turning now to the case of the y degree of organization that increases directly with n, let us note that an increase in y will entail two closely related considerations. In the *first* place, it will entail a subordination of the individual's special interests to the special interests of the n group.* In the *second* place, it will entail both a definition of the special interests of the group, and an elaboration of actual procedures whereby those special interests of the group can be realized. If the n group is small, this second step can be accomplished by means of a *democratic process;* but as n becomes larger, the procedure will change into a *republican process* as, say, steering committees and the like are first formed. As n becomes still larger, it may be necessary to elect an m number of delegates to be sent to a convention or a congress, where the best interests and rules of procedure for the entire n group are decided by the m number of delegates.

The ratio of the m number of delegates to the n members of the entire group—or m/n—is a function that seems to be governed by the same considerations that led to our previous three equations. Thus, if we say that a delegate is elected by a *cell* of members of the n group, then we may say that the n group is divided into an m number of different *cells.* Now, as the ratio m/n decreases, it follows that a proportionally larger number of persons are in each cell, with the result that the chosen delegate of the cell will be correspondingly less dependent upon the personal favor of any individual member of his cell. For that reason we may say that a decrease in m/n means, in effect, that the delegate is less subject to the x factor of individualism of his constituents; and the reverse. Clearly, therefore, the size of the m/n ratio is important if the "right amount" of power is to be delegated and the "right amount" of individual control preserved.

This question of the optimal size of the m/n can perhaps be best explored if we inquire more precisely into the Forces that govern the size of m. We know already that the original reason for the m delegates is that n has become so large as to make a democratic process unwieldy. Indeed, as n continues to increase, it exerts a corresponding Force to increase m; in short, there is a Force that acts in the direction of making m increase with n, if we assume that there is some "right size" to the membership of a *cell,* regardless of what the "right size" may be.

* Thus, for example, if the single teacher personally favors a particular group which it is to the advantage of the n teachers to attack, the single teacher must suppress the personal interest and join in the attack.

On the other hand, it is obvious that as m increases, it too becomes unwieldy—just as n has previously become unwieldy—with the result that the increase in m will defeat ever more the original economy of having any m delegation at all. In short, as m increases its economy decreases.

Since, however, (1) m on the one hand tends to vary directly with n; and since (2) on the other hand an increase in m tends to become uneconomical—and, therefore, theoretically to be retarded—at a rate that increases with the size of m; it follows (3) that m tends to increase at an exponential rate that is one-half the rate of increase of n. As a result we may say:

$$m^2 = n \qquad (12\text{–}4)$$

This may be viewed as an equation of our previously discussed "square effect" in the sense that the power of an m group of persons in terms of their n followers is in proportion to the square of m.

In view of Eq. (12–4), we may deduce that as n increases, the assumed "optimal size" of a cell is ever more surpassed, with the result that the individual members of the cell have in practice very little effective control over their delegates and over what they individually consider to be their group interests. Since such a condition is unstable, the m delegates must be prepared to rule with an iron hand, or else to be subject to the effects of rebellion within the cells, or of defection from the cells. It is to the great credit of the Founding Fathers of our country that they carefully made a provision for the effectiveness of said rebellions and defections within the *"cells"* so that there would be no rule by an iron hand (i.e., the provision of regular elections).

There is, however, an alternative to an excessive membership in a cell. Thus, the cells can preserve their "optimal size" and elect delegates to superior cells which in turn elect further delegates, and so on, as seems to be the case, for example, in American political parties whose organization extends all the way down to the local ward groups. In so doing, they construct a dominance system, as discussed in Chapter Eleven. Yet our above four equations, including the one for the "square effect," are still applicable to a dominance system as we saw it in Chapter Eleven. Moreover, our above argument applies to the sizes of steering committees, and executive committees, and nominating committees that provide the "nuclei" of the more modest local groups, or *cells.*

For that reason we need not be surprised to have found a rectilinear distribution in the committee reports, etc., of our own Congressional action as reported a few pages back.

Before taking leave of our n group of schoolteachers, let us point out that their m delegates in convention cannot arrive at common objectives and rules of procedure unless they are able to communicate with one another by means of a vocabulary of n different entities of some form of speech. But instead of inquiring now into the economy of this vocabulary, let us simply turn back to Chapter Two in Part One, where our formal discussion of the economy of speech began.

We mention this consideration of the economy of a speech vocabulary to point out that in the course of the present book we have developed an integrated system of dynamics in terms of the Unifying Principle of Least Effort.

V. SUMMARY

In ancient times one was wont to ask three penetrating questions: What do you think? Why do you think so? What difference does it make? In closing let us ask what we have done; why we have done it; and what difference it all makes.

As to what we have done, we have presented a large number of observations from a truly wide range of living phenomena; this is the empiric aspect of our study, in which we can claim in all modesty to have presented some empiric laws of wide implications. Then each of these different kinds of empiric laws we have attempted to rationalize; this is the analytic aspect of our study. Finally, all these different rationalizations we have attempted to synthesize in terms of a single unifying principle. That is what we have done.

Our reason for so doing was to establish the single unifying principle—the Principle of Least Effort—which is defined as meaning that each individual will adopt a course of action that will involve the expenditure of *the probably least average of his work* (by definition, *least effort*). That is why we have done what we have done.

And now we may ask what difference the disclosure of this unifying principle will make in our lives. As far as I can see it makes a difference in three ways.

First of all, the unifying Principle of Least Effort, if sound, will facilitate a systematization of an exact science of living behavior. Indeed, to a considerable extent, the present study may have inadvertently begun just such a systematization, since it is the nature of a fundamental principle of dynamics to unify in systematic form the phenomena to which it refers. And yet the systematization of social science is only in its early stages. With this systematization we shall be able to make predictions,* as well as to organize our social structures with a view to making life more agreeable for all concerned. In short, a systematic social science will make possible an objective social engineering.

There is a further practical consequence to the establishment of the Principle of Least Effort with its attendant systematization of social science. It will provide an objective *language* in terms of which persons can discuss social problems impersonally, even as physics is a *language* for the discussion of physical problems. The lack of an objective social language

* All of the author's own data in this book are tests of hypotheses that were first worked out theoretically. When students, as part of their course work, undertook the empiric test, they never knew in advance the problem they were testing. The theoretical expectations were explained as the data were laid on the desk. Hence we have already successfully predicted.

is responsible to no small extent for the widespread mental confusion about social problems today. Indeed, an objective social language, more than anything else, will help to protect mankind from the virtual criminal action of persons in strategic political, commercial, social, intellectual and *academic* positions who, in believing that their own personal views are universal absolutes, take the fateful step that leads to the easy descent into paranoia. Nowhere is an objective social language more needed than in the United States, if we remember what chaos our policies have caused.

And yet there is a further use of a systematized social science to which the present writer attaches a considerable value. Today, as the authority of revealed religion and of its attendant ethics declines, something must take its place, not only so that man can continue to live amicably with man, but also so that man can explain God's ways to man. I feel that this type of research may yield results that will fulfill those needs. To many persons this consideration may seem silly. And yet it at least holds out a very real, lasting, and constructive hope for those persons whose walk through the valley of the shadow has been long and desperate without so much as a green leaf to encourage them onwards. For we are finding in the everyday phenomena of life a unity and orderliness and balance that can only give faith in the ultimate reasonableness of the whole whose totality lies beyond our powers of comprehension. Such a faith may conceivably be highly prized by those who have known its lack.

The above considerations are our answer to the healthful and necessary question: So what?

With them we leave in the reader's hands our conception of *The Principle of Least Effort.*

REFERENCES

CHAPTER ONE

1. Discussed L. J. Henderson, "What is social progress?" (in *A Symposium on Social Progress*) *Proceedings of the American Academy of Arts and Sciences,* Vol. 73 (1940), 458–463; cf. particularly p. 460. Henderson cites F. Y. Edgeworth, *Mathematical Physics,* London: Kegan Paul, 1881, p. 117 as an early source.

2. Jeremy Bentham's concept of the "greatest happiness for the greatest number" (the fallacy of which was noticed by Edgeworth, *Mathematical Physics,* op. cit.) is at least as old as the eighteenth century philosopher, Francis Hutcheson (cf. his *Inquiry concerning Moral Good and Evil,* 1725).

3. P. L. M. de Maupertuis, *Essai de cosmologie,* Amsterdam, 1750. For a concise statement of the principle of least action including Hamilton's Principle, cf. J. H. Jeans, *An Elementary Treatise on Theoretical Mechanics,* Boston: Ginn, 323–328. Cf. A. Kneser, *Das Prinzip der kleinsten Wirkung von Leibnitz bis zur Gegenwart,* Leipzig: Teubner, 1928. Also P. E. B. Jourdain, *The Principle of Least Action,* Chicago: Open Court, 1913.

4. Cf. G. K. Zipf, "The unity of nature, least action, and natural social science," *Sociometry,* Vol. 5 (1942), 48–62.

5. N. E. Miller and J. Dollard, *Social Learning and Imitation,* New Haven: Yale Univ. Press, 1941.

6. C. L. Hull, *Principles of Behavior,* New York: Appleton-Century, 1943.

7. J. A. Gengerelli, "The principle of maxima and minima in animal learning," *Journal of Comparative Psychology,* Vol. 11 (1930), 193–236.

8. L. S. Tsai, "The laws of minimum effort and maximum satisfaction in animal behavior," *Monograph of the National Institute of Psychology* (Peiping, China), No. 1, 1932. Abstracted in *Psychological Abstracts,* Vol. 6 (1932), No. 4329. (Original not seen.)

9. R. H. Waters, "The principle of least effort in learning," *Journal of General Psychology,* Vol. 16 (1937), 3–20.

10. R. H. Wheeler, *The Science of Psychology,* New York: Crowell, 1929, 81–85. See also subsequent editions.

11. W. J. Crozier and G. Pincus, "Analysis of the geotropic orientation of young rats, V," *Journal of General Physiology,* Vol. 15 (1932), 421–462, with citations, p. 462, to their previous publications on the subject.

12. *Op. cit.,* p. 294.

13. R. S. Crutchfield, "Psychological distance as a function of psychological need," *Journal of Comparative Psychology,* Vol. 28 (1939), 447–469.

14. M. E. Thompson, "An experimental investigation of the gradient of reinforcement in maze learning," *Journal of Experimental Psychology,* Vol. 34 (1944), 390–403.

15. For general orientation in the field of experimental psychology, cf. E. G. Boring, *A History of Experimental Psychology,* New York: Century, 1929. Also, L. W. Crafts, T. C. Schneirla, E. E. Robinson, R. W. Gilbert, *Recent Experiments in Psychology,* New York: McGraw-Hill, 1938.

16. K. Lewin, *Principles of Topological Psychology,* New York: McGraw-Hill, 1936.

17. J. F. Brown and A. C. Voth, "The path of seen movement as a function of the vector field," *American Journal of Psychology,* Vol. 49 (1937), 543–563.

18. E.g., T. C. Schneirla, "Studies on the army ant behavior pattern. Nomadism in the swarm raider ECITON BURCHELLI," *Proceedings of the American Philosophical Society,* Vol. 87 (1944), 438–457, with excellent bibliography.

19. G. K. Zipf, "Relative frequency as a determinant of phonetic change," *Harvard Studies in Classical Philology,* Vol. 40 (1929), 1–95.

20. O. H. Mowrer and H. M. Jones, "Extinction and behavior variability as function of effortfulness of task," *Journal of Experimental Psychology,* Vol. 33 (1943), 369–386.

21. J. E. DeCamp, "Relative distance as a factor in the white rat's selection of a path," *Psychobiology,* Vol. 2 (1920), 245–253.

CHAPTER TWO

1. G. K. Zipf, *The Psycho-Biology of Language,* Boston: Houghton Mifflin, 1935, Chap. 1. G. K. Zipf, "On the economical arrangement of tools; the harmonic series and the properties of space," *Psychological Record,* Vol. 4 (1940), 147–159.

2. The literature on the topic of *meaning* is enormous. For extensive bibliography primarily from the viewpoint of linguistics, cf. L. Bloomfield, *Language,* New York: Henry Holt, 1933; also, Anton Reichling, *Het Woord,* Nijmegen: J. J. Berkhout, 1935. For bibliography for more general psychological and semantic angles, cf. S. I. Hayakawa, *Language in Action,* New York: Harcourt Brace, 1941; Charles Morris, *Signs, Language and Behavior,* New York: Prentice Hall, 1946 (in this book Dr. Morris himself makes important contributions). For further systematic treatments, cf. Alfred Korzybski, *Science and Sanity* (2 ed.), Lancaster, Pa.: Science Press Printing Co., 1941; also, Rudolf Carnap, *Introduction to Semantics,* Cambridge: Harvard Univ. Press, 1942. For our own systematic treatment of *meaning,* cf. Chaps. 3, 5–8.

3. M. L. Hanley, *Word Index to James Joyce's Ulysses,* Madison, Wis., 1937 (statistical tabulation by M. Joos). Historically considered, Joyce's *Ulysses* was selected for analysis in the attempt to show that the harmonic distribution would not be found in samples of this size [cf. M. Joos, review of Zipf, *Psycho-Biology of Language,* in *Language,* Vol. 12 (1936), 196–210; cf. my reply, with quotations from M. H. Stone, "Statistical methods and dynamic philology," *Language,* Vol. 13 (1937), 60–70]. Dr. Joos's *Ulysses* data provided the most clear-cut example of a harmonic distribution in speech of which I know.

4. The first person (to my knowledge) to note the hyperbolic nature of the frequency of word usage was the French stenographer, J. B. Estoup who made statistical studies of French, cf. his *Gammes Stenographiques,* Paris, 4 ed., 1916 (I have not seen his earlier editions). See also, Godfrey Dewey, *Relative Frequency of English Speech Sounds,* Cambridge: Harvard Univ. Press, 1923; also E. V. Condon, "Statistics of Vocabulary," *Science,* Vol. 67 (1928), p. 300; also Zipf, *Psycho-Biology,* etc., *op. cit.*

5. R. C. Eldridge, *Six Thousand Common English Words,* Buffalo: The Clement Press, 1911; graphed Zipf, *Psycho-Biology, op. cit.,* p. 44.

6. E. L. Thorndike, *A Teacher's Word Book of 20,000 Words,* New York: Teachers College, 1932.

7. The results of the Lorge semantic count for the words in question were taken from E. L. Thorndike, *The Thorndike-Century Senior Dictionary,* New York: Appleton-Century, 1941. For other possible source material, cf. Helen S. Eaton, *Semantic Frequency List for English, French, German,* and *Spanish,* Chicago: Univ. of Chicago Press, 1940.

8. Originally published, G. K. Zipf, "The meaning-frequency relationship of words," *Journal of General Psychology,* Vol. 33 (1945), 251–256. My students who helped with the tabulation were, the Misses E. L. Goucher, L. Hill, R. Hubbard, E. Kleinschmidt, V. T. Spang, E. Yphantis, and the Mssrs. R. L. Borden, L. De Sanctis, T. A. Lehrer, M. Seifert, A. A. Sirna, P. H. Smith, Jr. G. M. Sokol and M. Spotnitz.

9. In the present case, as will be discussed again in detail in our following chapter, we have adopted an operational definition of meaning (i.e., we have counted the different meanings in a dictionary). Cf. P. W. Bridgman, "Operational Analysis," *Philosophy of Science,* Vol. 5 (1938), 114–131; also, his *Logic of Modern Physics,* New York:

Macmillan, 1927. In Chaps. 5 and 7 we shall approach the problem of meanings from a different angle.

10. Argument presented in G. K. Zipf, "Homogeneity and heterogeneity in language," *Psychological Record,* Vol. 2 (1938), 347–367. The argument was essentially as follows: Let N_f equal the number of different words of integral frequency, F. Assume that this includes all words, the $r \times f = C$ distribution, that lie between $F + \frac{1}{2}$ and $F - \frac{1}{2}$. Thence

$$N_f = \frac{C}{F-\frac{1}{2}} - \frac{C}{F+\frac{1}{2}}$$

(i.e., the subtraction of the rank, $R^f{}_{+\frac{1}{2}}$ from the rank, $R_{f-\frac{1}{2}}$. Simplifying we have $N_f = C/F^2 - \frac{1}{4})$. For the more general case in which the rank-frequency distribution has other slopes than -1.00, cf. the ingenious analysis of Mr. Joos, *Language,* Vol. 12 (1936), 196–210, in which Joos shows that the exponent of f of a rank-frequency distribution is approximately larger by 1.00 than the exponent of F of the number-frequency distribution.

11. Cf. G. K. Zipf, *Selected Studies of the Principle of Relative Frequency in Language,* Cambridge. Harvard Univ. Press, 1932, for the frequency lists for Plautus and for Pekingese Chinese.

12. G. L. Prendergast, *A Complete Concordance to the Iliad of Homer,* London: Longmans Green, 1875.

13. Cf. G. K. Zipf, "Repetition of words, time perspective, and semantic balance," *Journal of General Psychology,* Vol. 32 (1945), 127–148.

14. The argument of the bell analogy and its related tool analogy will be found, *ibid.*

15. F. Klaeber, *Beowulf and the Fight at Finnsburg,* Boston: D. C. Heath, 1922.

16. *Op. cit.*

17. Sample from E. Sapir, *Nootka Texts,* Philadelphia (Linguistic Society of America): Univ. of Pennsylvania Press, 1939. *Vide infra.*

CHAPTER THREE

1. G. K. Zipf, "On the economical arrangement of tools; the harmonic series and the properties of space," *Psychological Record,* Vol. 4 (1940), 147–159; "The repetition of words, time perspective, and semantic balance," *Journal of General Psychology,* Vol. 32 (1945), 127–148.

2. This situation, when translated, say, in terms of the principle of least action in physics, suggests an interesting philosophical problem that relates to choice. Thus if a mass, M, must move by least action from a point, p_o, at a time, t_o, to a point, p_1, at a time, t_1, and if two different courses of least action are available, what then governs the "choice?"

3. As we pointed out in Chap. 1, the work of planning, or of designing, is *always* to be reckoned to the total cost in work of performing the job. This prevents a person from endlessly elaborating the details of his problem.

4. Professor J. L. Walsh has pointed out that a typesetter is an excellent example of the tool analogy in practical life, particularly if he is setting Chinese characters (or ideographs) in which one piece of type represents a whole "word" (actually a morpheme, *vide infra*). The most frequently used characters will be located nearest to the typesetter, etc.

5. Presented, Zipf, *Psycho-Biology of Language, op. cit.,* Chap. 2.

6. *Ibid.;* also Zipf, *Selected Studies of The Principle of Relative Frequency in Language, op. cit.*

7. A virtually complete bibliography of the frequency lists of words (up to 1940) can be found in Charles C. Fries and A. Aileen Traver, *English Word Lists,* Washington, D. C.: American Council on Education, 1940.

8. E. L. Thorndike, *Studies in the Psychology of Language (Archives of Psychology, No. 231),* New York, 1938, p. 67.

9. Zipf, *Psycho-Biology of Language, op. cit.,* Chaps. 2, 5 and 6.

10. Essentially an *operational definition* to use P. W. Bridgman's term, *op. cit. supra* Chap. 2, reference 9.

11. An excellent discussion of the problem of classification of speech entities is contained in the article on "Alphabet," *Encyclopaedia Brittanica,* 14th ed. See

also, Leonard Bloomfield, *Language,* New York: Holt, 1933.

12. *Ibid.,* Chaps. 13 and 14 which contain an excellent discussion of the entire problem by one of America's outstanding scholars in the field.

13. E. Sapir, *Nootka Texts,* Philadelphia (Linguistic Society of America): Univ. of Pennsylvania Press, 1939.

14. Leonard Bloomfield, *Plains Cree Texts,* New York: Stechert, 1934.

15. Cf. Chap. 2, reference 10, *supra,* for further discussion of this point with bibliography.

16. Ella Deloria, *Dakota Texts,* New York: Stechert, 1932.

17. F. W. Kaeding, *Häufigkeitswörterbuch der deutschen Sprache,* Berlin, 1898.

18. I am grateful to my friend, Professor R. Y. Chao, for his kindness in calling this book to my attention and in procuring a copy for me.

19. Wilhelm Stritberg, *Die Gotische Bibel,* 2 revised ed., Heidelberg: Carl Winter, 1919.

20. Zipf, *Selected Studies of the Principle of Relative Frequency, op. cit.; Psycho-Biology of Language, op. cit.*

21. For a bibliography of texts and editions of Old and Middle English with a discussion of the history of English, cf. Henry Cecil Wyld, *A Short History of English,* New York: E. P. Dutton, 1937.

22. Cf. Zipf, *Psycho-Biology of Language, op. cit.,* pp. 172–176.

23. For an operational discussion of the *phoneme,* cf. Bloomfield, *Language, op. cit.,* Chap. 5; criticized in part by G. K. Zipf, "The psychology of language," in *The Encyclopaedia of Psychology,* New York: Philosophical Library, 1946; 332 f.; R. H. Stetson, *Bases of Phonology,* Oberlin: Oberlin College, 1945 is the most comprehensive treatment from the philosophical and psychological angles.

24. Zipf, *Selected Studies of the Principle of Relative Frequency in Language, op. cit.*

25. Zipf, *Psycho-Biology of Language, op. cit.,* 68–73.

26. The data of Table 3–3 have been previously published and discussed in one or more of the following publications: G. K. Zipf, "Relative Frequency as a determinant of phonetic change; *Harvard Studies in Classical Philology,* Vol. 40 (1929), 1–95; *Psycho-Biology of Language, op. cit.,* 73–76; G. K. Zipf and F. M. Rogers, "Phonemes and variphones in four present-day Romance languages and Classical Latin from the viewpoint of Dynamic Philology," *Archives Néerlandaises de Phonétique Expérimentale,* Vol. 15 (1939), 111–147. For the frequencies of voiceless dentals in several German dialects not included in Table 3–3, cf. G. K. Zipf, "Phonometry, Phonology, and Dynamic Philology: an attempted synthesis," *American Speech,* Vol. 13 (1938), 283–284.

27. C. V. Hudgins and R. H. Stetson, "Voicing of consonants by depression of larynx," *Archives Néerlandaises de Phonétique Expérimentale,* Vol. 11 (1935), 1–28.

28. The sources of the data of Table 3–4 are the same as those for Table 3–3, as given in reference 26 *supra.*

29. Elaborated in detail, Zipf, *Psycho-Biology of Language, op. cit.,* 81–129.

30. *Ibid.*

31. Cf. Zipf, "Phonometry, Phonology and Dynamic Philology: . . ." *op. cit.,* p. 282, fn. 27.

32. Bloomfield, *Language, op. cit.,* p. 81.

33. E. Zwirner and K. Zwirner, "Phonometrischer Beitrag zur Frage der neuhochdeutschen Quantität," *Archiv für vergleichende Phonetik,* Vol. 1 (1937), 96–113. Further bibliography on the Drs. Zwirners' important work is given in Zipf, "Phonometry, Phonology, and Dynamic Philology: . . ." *op. cit., passim.*

34. W. P. Lehmann and R. M. S. Heffner, "Notes on the lengths of vowels," *American Speech,* Vol. 18 (1943), 208–215. Here also bibliographical material on their earlier publications on the topic.

35. C. V. Hudgins and F. C. Numbers, "An investigation of the intelligibility of the speech of the deaf," *Genetic Psychology Monographs,* Vol. 25 (1942), 289–392; cf. p. 363 f.

36. P. Menzerath and A. de Lacerda, *Koartikulation, Steuerung und Lautabgrenzung,* Berlin and Bonn: Ferd. Dümmlers Verlag, 1933.

37. As the phonemic distinctions are gradually eliminated from a sample of speech, the resulting rank-frequency distributions of words seem to remain linear, with increasing slope, as judged by a preliminary study made by the present author.

38. Taken from D. W. Thompson, *On Growth and Form,* New York: Macmillan, 1943, 338–339.

39. G. K. Zipf, "Cultural chronological strata in speech," *Journal of Abnormal and Social Psychology,* Vol. 41 (1946), 351–355.

40. Sigmund Feist, *Vergleichendes Wörterbuch der gotischen Sprache,* Leiden: Brill, 1939.

41. G. K. Zipf, "Prehistoric 'Cultural Strata' in the evolution of Germanic: the case of Gothic," *Modern Language Notes,* Vol. 62 (1947), 522–530.

42. G. K. Zipf, "Homogeneity and heterogeneity in language," *Psychological Record,* Vol. 2 (1938), 347–367.

43. G. K. Zipf, *Selected Studies of the Principle of Relative Frequency in Language, op. cit.*

44. For the summation of the generalized harmonic series see the approximate formulas published in J. Q. Stewart, "Empirical mathematical rules concerning the distribution and equilibrium of population," *Geographical Review,* Vol. 37 (1947), 464, in which reference is made to J. W. L. Glaisher, "The constants that occur in certain summations of Bernoulli's series," *Pro. London Math. Soc.,* Vol. 4 (1871), 48–56.

CHAPTER FOUR

1. For an excellent up-to-date comprehensive treatise, cf. Leonard Carmichael, Editor, *Manual of Child Psychology,* New York: Wiley, 1946; for the particular interests of the present chapter, cf. Dorothea McCarthy, "Language development of children," *ibid.* Chap. 10 (also contains an extensive bibliography). See also, G. D. Stoddard and B. L. Wellman, *Child Psychology,* New York: Macmillan, 1934.

2. R. S. Uhrbrock, "The vocabulary of a five-year old," *Educational Research Bulletin,* Vol. 14 (1935), 85 f.; also his "Words most frequently used by a five-year old girl," *Journal of Educational Psychology,* Vol. 27 (1936), 155–158. Cf. G. K. Zipf's "Children's Speech," *Science,* Vol. 96 (1942), 344–345.

3. For an equation that describes these differences in slope that result from differences in sample size, under the assumption that the optimum sample is harmonically seriated (and also, I think, that the interval frequency equation of Chapter 2 applies), cf. J. B. Carrol, "Diversity of vocabulary and the harmonic series law of word frequency distribution," *Psychological Record,* Vol. 2 (1938), 379–386.

4. M. S. Fisher, *Language Patterns of Preschool Children* (Child Development Monographs, No. 15), New York: Teachers College, Columbia University, 1934.

5. Cf. G. K. Zipf, "Observations of the possible effect of mental age upon the frequency distribution of words from the viewpoint of dynamic philology," *Journal of Psychology,* Vol. 4 (1937), 239–244, in which is also reported my statistical analysis of the speech-sample contained in L. C. Haggerty, "What a two-and-one-half-year-old child said in one day," *Journal of Genetic Psychology,* Vol. 37 (1930), 75–101.

6. Ernest R. Hilgard, *Theories of Learning,* New York: Appleton-Century-Crofts, 1948.

7. Cf. E. L. Thorndike, "The origin of language," *Science,* Vol. 98 (1943), 1–6. This article contains a discussion of various of the chief theories (or speculations) about the "origin of speech."

8. M. S. Fisher, *Language Patterns of Preschool Children, op. cit.;* also Dorothea McCarthy, "Language development of children," *op. cit.,* reference 1 *supra.*

CHAPTER FIVE

1. This will be an example of our indebtedness to the thinking and terminology of "classical" or "orthodox" economics as acknowledged in Chap. 1, Section V. By the same token the argu-

ment of Chap. 5, Section I, *seq.*, as well as that of Chaps. 9, 10, 11, and 12 may be viewed as an elaboration of economic theory, if one will. We mention these considerations lest we otherwise be accused of "ignoring economics."

2. We described this difference in Chap. 1, Section IV.

3. This *relativism* between tools and jobs was discussed in Chap. 1, Section IV.

4. There is a tendency for interest rates to increase with the length of the term, even with apparently equal security (e.g., U. S. government notes). This tendency is germane to our argument.

5. For an interesting description of the problem of the gibbon ape in wandering through the tree-tops, cf. R. S. Lull, *Organic Evolution,* New York: Macmillan, 1927, p. 649.

6. The entire history of the field of sensation has been brilliantly presented in E. G. Boring, *Sensation and Perception in the History of Experimental Psychology,* New York: Appleton-Century, 1942.

7. For the physiology of homeostasis cf. W. B. Cannon, *Bodily Changes in Pain, Hunger, Fear and Rage,* New York: Appleton, 1929; also his *Wisdom of the Body,* New York: Norton, 1939. See also, R. G. Hoskins, *Endocrinology; the Glands and their Functions,* New York: Norton, 1941.

8. *Op. cit.,* fn. 7 *supra.*

9. The data presented here will be found in G. K. Zipf, "Some psychological determinants of the structure of publications," *American Journal of Psychology,* Vol. 57 (1945), 425–442.

10. Previously presented *ibid.*

11. These standard deviations were kindly calculated by Mr. M. J. Schleifer, *ibid.*

12. Previously presented *ibid.*

13. Previously presented *ibid.*

14. *General Education in a Free Society; Report of the Harvard Committee,* Cambridge: Harvard Univ. Press, 1945.

15. This question of news is again examined from the social angle in Chap. 9.

16. Cf. Chap. 11 for data on speeches of a play with brief discussion of the problem of the scenes of a moving picture.

17. Hence the *n* number of criteria of a class (as well as the *n* number of classes) will always be a positive integral number.

18. For a discussion of the increasing articulation and integration of a person's semantic system with reference to emotion, cf. G. K. Zipf, *Psycho-Biology of Language, op. cit.,* Chaps. 5 and 6.

19. For a discussion of abbreviation as the basic dimension of speech, cf, *ibid.* pp. 283–288.

20. Not to be misunderstood, we are showing the need of living process for a constant clock in an atom. We have not shown that electronic action is the clock, but have merely suggested that it may be.

21. For a discussion of genes of meaning as the smallest units of classificatory action, cf. Zipf, *Psycho-Biology of Language,* p. 287, 299–303.

22. In this connection one is reminded of Henri Le Châtelier's famous principle first established in the field of thermodynamics and subsequently extended in scope (i.e., any system tends to alter itself in order to neutralize the effects of an impingement upon it). The principle also seems to operate in the social field (cf. Part 2).

23. For this view of emotion, and of pleasure and pain, cf. G. K. Zipf, *Selected Studies of the Principle of Relative Frequency in Language,* Cambridge: Harvard Univ. Press, 1932, *passim.;* also, *Psycho-Biology of Language, op. cit.,* p. 191, 207–215.

24. This concept seems to be intrinsic in the *guilt complex* of the Freudian school according to which persons confess to crimes which they never committed for the sake of an official punishment that will satisfy their unconscious feelings of guilt that arise from a desire to commit crimes against society (cf. discussion of a *mother fixation* in Chapter 7 infra). For a comprehensive account of psychoanalytic theories and concepts, cf. J. F. Brown,

The Psychodynamics of Abnormal Behavior, New York: McGraw-Hill, 1940; also, R. R. Sears, "Survey of objective studies of psychoanalytic concepts," (*Bulletin of the Social Science Research Council,* No. 51) New York: 1943. Also, J. M. Hunt (editor), *Personality and the Behavior Disorders,* New York: Ronald, 1944; also, Dr. Hunt's excellent "Experimental Psychoanalysis," in *Encyclopedia of Psychology,* New York: Philosophical Library, 1946, 140–156.

25. For concepts and experimental data of Gestalt psychology, cf. G. W. Hartmann, *Gestalt Psychology,* New York: Ronald, 1935; W. Köhler, *Gestalt Psychology,* New York: Liverright, 1928; K. Koffka, *Principles of Gestalt Psychology,* New York: Harcourt Brace, 1935; K. Lewin, *Principles of Topological Psychology,* New York: McGraw-Hill, 1936; also, K. Lewin, *A Dynamic Theory of Personality,* New York: McGraw-Hill, 1935.

26. Cf. J. G. Miller, *Unconsciousness,* New York: Wiley, 1942, for an excellent critical discussion of the various theories about consciousness and unconsciousness, with important contribution by Dr. Miller himself.

27. For the view of physiological activity as a traffic system, cf. C. M. Child, *Physiological Foundations of Behavior,* New York: Holt, 1924, Chap. 17. Cf. Chaps. 9–10 *infra* for the dynamics of a social traffic system, and Chap. 11 for a discussion of a hierarchy of controls.

28. The effect of the "cumulative force of chance in speech" discussed in Zipf, *Psycho-Biology, op. cit.,* 200 f.

29. A great deal of aging may be governed by cultural conventions. Thus we tell a child (generally incorrectly) "that is not the way an 8-year-old boy behaves." People tend to behave at a given age as they are supposed to: at forty, we behave and feel forty; at fifty, fifty; at three score years and ten we tend to act as respectable persons are supposed to act in anticipation of death. For a discussion of cultural roles cf. Chaps. 7 and 8.

30. On the other hand, the persons of greater intelligence tend to be more successful in the sense of receiving greater incomes and positions of higher status, and therefore can buy themselves more favorable environments (cf. Chap. 11 *infra*).

31. If a portion of the brain is removed, the functions of the removed part are frequently taken over by what is left of the brain.

CHAPTER SIX

1. For a discussion of this transformation of energy, cf. A. J. Lotka, *Elements of Physical Biology,* Baltimore: Williams and Wilkins, 1925, Chaps. 24–28; also, D. W. Thompson, *On Growth and Form,* New York: Macmillan, 1943, Chaps. 1–6, and *passim.*

2. For a discussion of "the ego as a coordinate reference frame," cf. A. J. Lotka, *Elements of Physical Biology, op. cit.,* 372–374.

3. The problem of the length of an organism's life is discussed, D. W. Thompson, *On Growth and Form, op. cit., passim.*

4. It is by no means true that all physicists ignore the problem of life. In this connection see the brilliant study of E. Schrödinger, *What Is Life?,* New York: Macmillan, 1945. This study is particularly interesting for our purpose, not only because an eminent physicist brings his great knowledge to bear on the topic, but more particularly because he points out (p. 21) that chromosome structures are both "law code (*sic*) and executive power—or, to use another simile, they are architect's plan (*sic*) and builder's craft—in one." This concept of "code" and "plan" ties in with our own belief that the artisan of our tool analogy (Chaps. 3 and 5) is present in the tiniest minutiae of living behavior and that *all* living action is classificatory throughout in terms of a plan of the whole organism in question (cf. G. K. Zipf, *The Psycho-Biology of Language, op. cit.,* Chap. 6, and 299–303). Dr. Schrödinger views the organism in the light of known physical laws and finds the known physical laws inadequate (e.g., "For it is in relation to the statistical point of view that the structure of the vital parts of living organisms differs so entirely from that of

any piece of matter that we physicists and chemists have ever handled physically in our laboratories or mentally at our writing desks," p. 3). We for our part view organic action against the background of the speech process and postulate an identity point in order to keep an organism from collapsing. Is this identity point somehow a supervisory control? If existent, does it imply a further property of matter and if so, what? (cf. Schrödinger's Chaps. 6 and 7). Is there some sort of "vital" factor in all matter that manifests itself organically on the surfaces of very large masses? If so, the so-called "vitalists" (a school of psychologists) have scarcely shown it. There is little doubt that organic process, in its capacity as sheer organic process, is itself orderly, and, for all we know, quite as orderly as inanimate physical processes. It may be that the principles of organization of human speech are the laws of organization of the organism. Perhaps the hypothesis that the entire universe is alive may be helpful in studying the dynamics of animate phenomena within the framework of presumably inanimate phenomena. For discussion of consciousness, cf. A. J. Lotka, *Elements of Physical Biology, op. cit.*, Chaps. 29–32, in which there are extensive references to earlier literature.

5. T. R. Malthus, *An Essay on the Principle of Population, as it affects the Future Improvement of Society*, London: J. Johnson, 1798; the final revision, *An Essay on the Principle of Population, or, A View of its Past and Present Effects*, London: J. Murray, 1817.

6. The growth rate slackens long before the hunger line is reached. For bibliography on the studies of Raymond Pearl and others, as well as for critical discussion, cf. D. W. Thompson, *On Growth and Form, op. cit.*, 155 f.

7. The absurdity and the danger of the dichotomy between self and environment, as well as the topic of mind as a scientific fiction, are interestingly discussed in A. J. Lotka, *Elements of Physical Biology, op. cit.*, 374–375. In Chap. 7 we shall assume that mind is a scientific fiction. In order to emphasize the viewpoint that living process is a manner of organizing the earth's surface, and that a person is merely a part of the entire universe, there may be a certain didactic value in suggesting speculatively that the *N* number of organisms that are alive on the surface of a large mass varies directly with the mass. This speculation may fit in with certain observations of astronomy (cf. G. K. Zipf, "On the economical arrangement of tools; the harmonic series and the properties of space," *The Psychological Record*, Vol. 4 [1940], p. 159), as will be elaborated subsequently in greater detail in connection with the generalized harmonic series.

8. For a discussion of food chains and cycles cf. A. J. Lotka, *Elements of Physical Biology, op. cit.*, p. 136 f., 176–184.

9. Cf. V. Volterra, *Fluctuations dans la lutte pour la vie*, Paris: Gauthier-Villars, 1938; V. A. Kostitsin, *Biologie Mathématique*, Paris: Librairie Armand Colin, 1937; A. J. Lotka, *Elements of Physical Biology, op. cit.*

10. If we substitute the term, *frequency of occurrence*, for *area* in this sentence we have a statement that applies *mutatis mutandis* to words in the stream of speech.

11. For his most recent statement, with data, cf. J. C. Willis, *The Course of Evolution*, Cambridge, England: The University Press, 1940. See also his *Age and Area*, Cambridge, England: The University Press, 1922.

12. *Ibid.*

13. It may be that the first explanation of the dynamics of any phylogenetic mutation was that of human phonetic change (in 1929). According to the important and original observations of Herbert Friedmann, different species of birds in similar environmental situations seem to develop similar modes of behavior, e.g., colorings, nesting habits, etc. Cf. H. Friedmann, "Ecological counterparts in birds," *The Scientific Monthly*, Vol. 63 (1946), 395–398. ["The number of possible permutations and combinations of the different colors and patterns (spots, bars, stripes, etc.) found in birds is far greater than the number of kinds of birds. It is, therefore, interesting, and

probably significant, that there should be as many instances of convergence among unrelated groups as there are. It is all the more intriguing when we find that these similarities in appearance are so often correlated with equally marked similarities in habit," *ibid.*, p. 398.]

14. Discussed with literature in D. W. Thompson, *On Growth and Form, op. cit.*, p. 155 f.

15. There is no single official Freudian Theory but rather a more or less well-recognized body of doctrine that includes conflicting views. These are critically discussed in J. F. Brown, *The Psychodynamics of Abnormal Behavior, op. cit., passim.* In our discussion of Freudian Theory (as we understand it) we shall refer to the general theories without specific reference.

16. The topic of rate of growth is exhaustively treated by D. W. Thompson, *On Growth and Form, op, cit.*, Chap. 3, 78–285.

17. The view of phonemes as norms may be of general applicability to biosocial process, cf. G. K. Zipf, *The Psycho-Biology of Language, op. cit.*, Chap. 3. There are abundant observations of the "normal curve" that attest to the frequency of this type of distribution and yet which, for the most part, remain unrationalized.

18. Enunciated by Ernst Haeckel in his *Generelle Morphologie,* Vol. 2, 1866. It is in sum "ontogeny repeats phylogeny." Copious illustrations in R. S. Lull, *Organic Evolution, op. cit.*, Chap. 14 and *passim.*

CHAPTER SEVEN

1. Cf. E. D. Chapple and C. S. Coon, *Principles of Anthropology,* New York: Holt, 1942, Chap. 12, 13, and biblography. See also relevant articles in *The Encyclopaedia of the Social Sciences,* New York: Macmillan, 1931.

2. For brief bibliography on Freudian and general psychoanalytic concepts cf. reference number 24 in Chap. 5.

3. Cf. B. Malinowski, *Sex and Repression in Savage Society,* New York: Harcourt Brace, 1927; *The Father in Primitive Society,* New York: Norton, 1927; *The Sexual Life of Savages in Northwestern Melanasia,* 3d. ed., 2 Vols., London: Routledge, 1932. F. Boas, *The Mind of Primitive Man,* Revised ed., New York: Macmillan, 1938.

4. The terms, *fixation, mother fixation, mother's image,* are borrowed from current psychiatric terminology.

5. For an excellent discussion with a very complete bibliography, cf. G. H. Seward, *Sex and the Social Order,* New York: McGraw-Hill, 1936. For empiric data on human male sexual behavior, with extensive bibliography, cf. A. C. Kinsey, W. B. Pomeroy, and C. E. Martin, *Sexual Behavior in the Human Male,* Philadelphia: Saunders, 1948; see particularly Chap. 21 ("Homosexual Outlet") and Fig. 161, p. 638, for a theoretical diagram of heterosexual-homosexual frequency distribution. These three scientists, on the basis of their extensive observations, arrived inductively at their concept of heterosexual-homosexual balance at which we arrived on the whole deductively from our Principle of Least Effort, as tested by the male-female birth ratios; hence, the studies complement each other, with ours confirming theirs and attempting to rationalize the balance in question. We mention this in this note because the manuscript of our text was essentially complete before the publication of the book by Dr. Kinsey and associates. The speculative concept of a universal sexual bipolarity is quite old.

6. Reported in G. W. Henry, *Sex Variants,* 2 Vols., New York: Hoeber, 1941. This study contains a wide selection of case histories with physical measurements.

7. For the very considerable literature on sexual hormones cf. bibliography in G. H. Seward, *Sex and the Social Order, op. cit.*

8. Cf. H. Ellis, *Studies in the Psychology of Sex,* 4 vols., New York: Random House, 1936.

9. For the general Freudian views on oral and anal eroticism, cf. J. F. Brown, *The Psychodynamics of Abnormal Behavior,* New York: McGraw-Hill, 1940, 186–193. For the general clinical background, cf. A. P. Noyes, *Modern Clinical Psychiatry,* Philadelphia: Saunders, 1935.

10. For his earliest statement of his theory, cf. A. Meillet, "Le genre féminin dans les langues indoeuropéennes," *Journal de psychologie normale et pathologique,* Vol. 20 (1923), 943–944. Equally important is the ensuing discussion by M. Mauss, *ibid.,* 944–947, with references to J. G. Frazer. Dr. Meillet elaborated his theory further in a lecture delivered at Harvard University in 1930.

11. Cf. Karl Brugmann, *Kurze vergleichende Grammatik der Indogermanischen Sprachen,* Strassburg: Trübner, 1902–04. For a different view, cf. H. Hirt, *Handbuch des Urgermanischen,* Teil II (Stammbildungs und Flexionslehre), Heidelberg: Winter, 1932, p. 15 ff.

12. Sir J. G. Frazer, *The Golden Bough,* 12 Vols., 3d ed., New York: Macmillan, 1935; also abridged ed., *ibid.,* 1922.

13. For mathematics cf. article, "Groups, theory of," in *Encyclopaedia Britannica,* 11 ed., Vol. 12, 626–636.

14. M. Wertheimer, *Drei Abhandlungen zur Gestalt Theorie,* Erlangen: Philosoph. Akademie, 1924 (new ed. 1925).

15. The term, *superego,* is borrowed from Freudian theory, for a discussion of which cf. J. F. Brown, *The Psychodynamics of Abnormal Behavior, op. cit.,* pp. 162–167 (p. 167 ". . . all behavior is economical . . . conflict situations are resolved in accordance with the least expenditure of energy possible in one existing total situation. This proposition cannot at the present time be proved but it is an invaluable working hypothesis for psychology. Through accepting it we are able to see order in behaviors which were previously thought of as accidental and chaotic").

16. The structure of a code of social correlations will be discussed in considerable detail with empiric data in Part 2, Chaps. 9, 11, and 12. For an excellent discussion of culture, cf. B. Malinowski's article on "Culture" in *The Encyclopaedia of the Social Sciences, op. cit.,* Vol. 4, p. 621 f., also, his *A Scientific Theory of Culture, and other Essays,* Chapel Hill: Univ. of No. Carolina Press, 1944.

17. For a penetrating discussion of the sympathetic nervous system, cf. W. B. Cannon, *The Wisdom of the Body,* New York: Norton, 1932. Also J. Y. Dent, *The Human Machine,* New York: Knopf, 1937; L. Clendenning, *The Human Body,* New York: Knopf, 1927. See also John C. Whitehorn, "Physiological changes in emotional states," *Research Publications of the Association for Research in Nervous and Mental Disease,* Vol. 19 (1939), 256–270.

18. See reference no. 15 above.

19. Closely associated with this belief in the capacity of a word to create is the adage, "Speak of the devil and he is bound to appear." As philologists long ago pointed out, in olden days the people who lived in a land where there were bears tended not to use the name, *bear,* lest one appear; instead they referred to him, say, as "the brown one." The Greeks had a highly flattering (and hence placating) name for the dreaded Furies. Closely related is the phenomenon of inverse semanticism, e.g., "the hog is well named since he looks and acts like a hog."

20. I am indebted to Dr. J. C. Whitehorn for this concept. For an actual case history, cf. J. C. Whitehorn, "The material in the hands of the biochemist," *American Journal of Psychiatry,* Vol. 92, (1935), pp. 318–319. For a discussion of the relationship between psychiatry and culture and sentiments, cf. J. C. Whitehorn, "Psychiatry as a basic medical science," *The Connecticut State Medical Journal,* Vol. 6, No. 9 (1942), 693 f.

21. In this connection, cf. Henry Sturt's article on "Induction," *The Encyclopaedia Britannica,* 11th ed.

22. Cf. G. K. Zipf, *The Psycho-Biology of Language, op. cit.,* 304–309 for concept of social reality in speech.

23. Cf. E. A. Strecker and F. G. Ebaugh, "Dementia Praecox (Schizophrenic reaction types)" in Gardner Murphy, ed., *An Outline of Abnormal Psychology,* New York: Modern Library, 1929, 71–101 (graph on age of admissions of 200 schizophrenic patients in Phila. Gen'l Hospital on p. 72). Reprinted from their *Practical Clinical Psychiatry,* 2nd ed., Philadelphia: Blakiston (3rd ed.), 1931.

24. J. C. Whitehorn and G. K. Zipf, "Schizophrenic language," *Archives of Neurology and Psychiatry,* Vol. 49 (1943), 831–851. For his views on autism and schizophrenia, the writer is deeply indebted to the thinking of Dr. Whitehorn.

25. N. Cameron, "Schizophrenic thinking in a problem-solving situation," *Journal of Mental Science,* Vol. 85 (1939), 1012–1035. Subsequently, Dr. Cameron has elaborated his theory in his *The Psychology of Behavior Disorder,* Boston: Houghton Mifflin, 1947.

26. Cf. G. K. Zipf, *The Psycho-Biology of Language, op. cit.,* 267 f. for a discussion of a word as a name of a frequently used category of experience.

27. Cf. E. Kretschmer, *Physique and Character* (translated by W. J. Sprott from the 2nd revised German edition), New York: Harcourt Brace, 1925.

28. In this connection, cf. G. Birkhoff and S. MacLane, *A Survey of Modern Algebra,* New York: Macmillan, 1941.

29. The constructs of Chaps. 9 and 11 may conceivably serve as useful analogues of the organization of a person's mind.

CHAPTER EIGHT

1. Barrett Wendell introduced these terms, also *charm, force, elegance* in his Lowell Institute lectures on "English Composition" (cf. B. Wendell, *English Composition; Eight Lectures given at the Lowell Institute,* New York: Scribner's, 1891, and subsequent printings). In the opinion of a friend, many successful plays seem to have none of Wendell's desired characteristics.

2. For extensive statistical studies of music, cf. J. Schillinger, *The Schillinger System of Musical Composition,* 2 Vols., New York: C. Fischer, Inc., 1946.

3. S. de Grazia, "Shostakovich's Seventh Symphony; reactivity-speed and adaptiveness in musical symbols," *Psychiatry: Journal of the Biology and Pathology of Interpersonal Relations,* Vol. 6 (1943), 117–122.

4. L. V. Furlan, *Das Harmoniegesetz der Statistik,* Basel: Verlag für Recht und Gesellschaft, 1946. Cf. W. Kull, "Das Harmoniegesetz der Statistik: eine Buchbesprechung," *Zeitschrift für Volkswirtschaft und Statistik,* Vol. 82 (1946), 414–433.

5. F. Benford, "The law of anomalous numbers," *Proceedings of the American Philosophical Society,* Vol. 78 (1938), 551–572.

CHAPTER NINE

1. This lemma is presented in somewhat greater detail in G. K. Zipf, *National Unity and Disunity,* Bloomington, Ind.: Principia Press, 1941, 100–135; also "The generalized harmonic series as a fundamental principle of social organization," *Psychological Record,* Vol. 4 (1940), 43.

2. Argument presented in G. K. Zipf, "The unity of nature, least-action, and natural social science," *Sociometry,* Vol. 5 (1942), 48–62.

3. From this it follows that an inventor can be "ahead of his time."

4. Cf. G. K. Zipf, "On the economical arrangement of tools; the harmonic series and the properties of space," *Psychological Record,* Vol. 4 (1940), 147–159.

5. Cf. G. K. Zipf, "The hypothesis of the 'Minimum Equation' as a unifying social principle: with attempted synthesis," *American Sociological Review,* Vol. 12 (1947), p. 627–650.

6. This concept will apply to the locations of persons of tabooed variations in human sexual behavior whose sexual demands and services are of an unusual nature. Theoretically, the percentage of such persons in a *P* city will tend to increase with *P,* and so, too, the *m* diversity of their variant behavior.

7. Later, in this chapter, and in subsequent chapters, we shall note repeatedly how these "difficulties" tend to increase according to the square of the *n* items. In general a population of *C* size, with each member interacting with every other member, will have C^2 interactions (treated in G. K. Zipf, "On Dr. Miller's Contribution, etc.," *op. cit., infra,* no. 9.

8. Cf. Felix Auerbach, "Das Gesetz der Bevölkerungskonzentration," *Petermanns Mitteilungen,* 1913, p. 74 f.; A. J. Lotka, *Elements of Physical Biology,* Baltimore: Williams and Wilkins, 1925, 306 f.; E. P.

Goodrich, "The statistical relationship between population and the city plan," *American Journal of Sociology,* Vol. 20 (1926), 123–128; R. Gibrat, *Les Inégalités Économiques,* Paris: Recueil Sirey, 1931, Fig. XI, p. 280; G. K. Zipf, *National Unity and Disunity,* Bloomington, Ind.: Principia Press, 1941, Chaps. 1–4.

9. Reported in G. K. Zipf, "On Dr. Miller's contribution to the $P_1 P_2 /D$ hypothesis," *American Journal of Psychology,* Vol. 60 (April, 1947), 286, fn.; also his "The hypothesis of the 'Minimum Equation' as a unifying social principle: with attempted synthesis," *American Sociological Review,* Vol. 12 (1947), 627–650. My student, Mr. Robert M. Ritter, helped materially in the tabulation of the data of Fig. 9–2.

10. *Ibid.*

11. In our hypothesis as developed in Sections I and II *supra* on the boundaries of cities we deduced theoretically that the actual densities at the boundaries of all cities would be about the same and that, therefore, there was a natural limit to a city's area. Dr. J. Q. Stewart in his "Suggested Principles of 'Social Physics'," *Science,* Vol. 106 (Aug. 29, 1947), 179–180, reports on the basis of his important studies of population densities (p. 180): "There is strong evidence for the following standard internal pattern, as a first approximation: The normal city, regardless of size, has roughly the same density of population at its edges, averaging there about 3 people per acre or 2,000 per square mile." This confirms our deduction empirically.

12. Reported in G. K. Zipf, "The frequency and diversity of business establishments and personal occupations: a study of social stereotypes and cultural rôles," *Journal of Psychology,* Vol. 24 (1947), 139–148; also Zipf, "The hypothesis of the 'Minimum Equation' as a unifying social principle," etc., *op. cit.* My students, as listed below, helped materially in the tabulation of the data: Messrs. J. P. Boland, D. D. Bourland, Jr., A. Fellows, R. V. Johnson, M. I. Liebmann, T. Macklin, D. G. Outerbridge, R. L. Perry, R. M. Ritter, J. A. Sevin, and J. D. Stanley.

13. Presented *ibid.*

14. Reported *ibid.*

15. The deduction that the constant C_P will vary directly with the P sizes of individual communities, cf. *supra* (also G. K. Zipf, "The frequency and diversity of business establishments and personal occupations . . . . " *op. cit.,* p. 144), has been confirmed empirically by my student, Mr. D. D. Bourland, Jr., on the basis of the rank frequency distribution of professions listed in the classified telephone directories of cities of varying P sizes.

16. For earlier publication see references in note no 12 *supra.*

17. *Ibid.*

18. In our discussion of occupations in Chap. 6 (*q.v.*) as an introduction to the J. C. Willis data we argued that different occupations would be distributed as the genera species data of Willis which, as we note in Fig. 9–7, is the case. Since, however, there is no degradation of energy in the case of human occupations as is theoretically the case with the "food chains" of species, the distribution of "Specific" and "Generic" classes of occupations should have a slope (number-frequency relationship) that is $-\frac{1}{2}$, as is approximately the case.

19. Since this was written, my student, Mr. D. D. Bourland, Jr., has confirmed this theoretical expectation; see note 15 above. This same concept of the C_p constant for a city of P size will apply to the distribution of incomes and social status within cities of varying P size, as is clear in Chap. 11.

20. Cf. G. K. Zipf, "The frequency and diversity of business establishments and personal occupations," etc., *op. cit.*

21. E. G. Ravenstein, "The laws of migration," *Journal Royal Statistical Association,* Vol. 48 (1885), 167–235 [continued, Vol. 52 (1889), 241–305].

22. See W. J. Reilly, Methods for the study of retail relationships, *University of Texas Bulletin* No. 2944, 1929. See also F. Strohkarck and K. Phelps, "The mechanics of constructing a market area map," *The Journal of Marketing,* Vol. 12 (1948), 493–496.

23. See J. Q. Stewart, "An inverse dis-

tance variation for certain social influences," *Science,* n. s. Vol. 93 (1941), p. 89; also his "The 'Gravitation,' or geographical drawing power, of a college," *Bulletin American Association University Professors,* Vol. 27 (1941), 70; also his "A measure of the influence of a population at a distance," *Sociometry,* Vol. 5 (1942), 63–71; also his "Empirical mathematical rules concerning the distribution and equilibrium of population," *The Geographical Review,* Vol. 37 (1947), 461–485. Very important: his "Demographic gravitation: evidence and applications," *Sociometry,* Vol. 11 (1948) Nos. 1 and 2, 31–57.

24. Not to be overlooked is the pioneer study by A. M. Wellington, *The Economic Theory of the Location of Railways,* 6 ed., London: Chapman Hall, New York: J. Wiley, 1906; his final law of the increment of traffic (p. 713): "The productive traffic varies as the square of the number of tributary sources of traffic." This is elaborated with tables pp. 707–718; also elaborated in reference to the individual with the result that the traffic density varies directly with the square of the population (as is to be expected theoretically from our Sections I and II above, if every person is both the point of origin and a point of destination of a $1/C$ share of all m kinds of goods). Wellington argued that the density of traffic between two cities is more than inversely proportional to their intervening D distances though he did not work out the relationship more precisely as did Stewart.

25. The cities in question are virtually the same as those mentioned below in connection with Figs. 9–15 and 9–16, though they are listed specifically with a detailed discussion of the analysis in G. K. Zipf, "Some determinants of the circulation of information," *The American Journal of Psychology,* Vol. 59 (1946), 401–421. The students in question: the Misses Isabelle Abrahams, Sally Doyle, Frances M. Eaton, Mary Johnstone, and Mrs. Jeanne H. Gwinn of Radcliffe College, and Messrs. M. E. Bovarnick, Henry D. Burnham, Hubert A. Doris, Robert D. Kemble, John Francis Keogh, Marc P. Moldawer, Frederick E. Penn, Arthur W. Perkins, Marshall G. Pratt, Paul C. Richter, John D. Stanley, John L. Turner, and Peter D. Watson.

26. *Ibid.*

27. *Ibid.*

28. *Ibid.*

29. J. Q. Stewart, "A measure of the influence of a population at a distance," *op. cit.,* p. 70.

30. Cf. G. K. Zipf, "The hypothesis of the 'Minimum Equation' . . ." *op. cit.,* p. 642. Also W. J. Reilly, *Methods for the Study of Retail Relationships, op. cit.,* in which is a "law of retail gravitation" for trade areas between cities (the point of equilibrium is the population divided by the square of the distance). Subsequently studied by P. D. Converse, *A Study of Retail Trade Areas in East Central Illinois,* University of Illinois Bulletin, Vol. 41, No. 7 (Business Studies No. 2), 1943; also his *Retail Trade Areas in Illinois, ibid.,* Vol. 43 (Business Studies No. 4), 1946. Also F. Strohkarck and K. Phelps, "The mechanics of constructing a market area map," *op. cit.*

31. G. K. Zipf, "The $\frac{P_1 P_2}{D}$ Hypothesis: the case of Railway Express," *Journal of Psychology,* Vol. 22 (1946), 3–8. Also, his "The $\frac{P_1 P_2}{D}$ Hypothesis: on the intercity movement of persons," *American Sociological Review,* Vol. 11 (1946), 677–686.

32. These data with additional data on passenger fares paid by travellers on railways and buses are presented *ibid.*

33. Cf. G. K. Zipf, "Some determinants of the circulation of information," *op. cit.*

34. Dr. George A. Miller has made an ingenious theoretical construct on the assumption of a random sending of messages in his "Population, distance and the circulation of information," *American Journal of Psychology,* Vol. 60 (1947), 276–284; cf. G. K. Zipf, "On Dr. Miller's Contribution," *ibid,* 284–287.

35. Cf. G. K. Zipf, "Some determinants of the circulation of information," *op. cit.*

36. From R. H. Paddock and R. P. Rodgers, "Preliminary results of road-use studies," *Public Roads,* Vol. 20 (1939), 33–45, Tables 8 and 9. The states were Florida, Kansas, Louisiana, Minnesota, New Hampshire, Pennsylvania, South Dakota, Utah, Vermont, Washington, and Wisconsin. I am grateful to Mr. R. E. Royall, Chief of the Division of Research Reports, Public Roads Administration, Federal Works Agency for his kindness in helping me locate this material.

37. Cf. W. Christaller, *Die Zentralen Orte in Süddeutschland,* Jena: Fischer, 1933, Karten 1–3.

38. Cf. E. Ullman, "A theory of location for cities," *American Journal of Sociology,* Vol. 46 (1940–41), 853–864. Also E. M. Hoover, *Location Theory of the Shoe and Leather Industries,* Cambridge: Harvard Univ. Press, 1937.

39. Cf. J. Q. Stewart, "Empirical mathematical rules concerning the distribution and equilibrium of population," *op. cit.*

40. J. Q. Stewart, *Coasts, Waves, and Weather,* Boston: Ginn, 1945, 164 f.

41. Cf. *Report of Commission of Housing and Regional Planning,* State of New York, Jan. 11, 1926. I am grateful to Professor Arthur Coleman Comey for information on this subject. There is an excellent collection of material on traffic surveys in the Harvard Library of Regional Planning (Robinson Hall) under the far-sighted direction of Miss K. McNamara to whose kindness in locating the origin-destination studies mentioned in the text I am deeply indebted.

42. The only information I can find on the subject of traffic density on elevators is in F. A. Aust and H. F. Janda, *A Method of Making Short Traffic Counts and Estimating Traffic Circulation in Urban Areas,* University of Wisconsin, 1931, where I find the statement (p. 50) without data, "Street car traffic acts like traffic in an elevator which is heaviest on the ground floor, while decreasing proportionally the higher up it goes."

43. My students, at that time Messrs. R. C. Bernard, Jr., W. B. Bryant, A. Y. Davis, and S. L. Washburn, measured the traffic distributions on the above survey maps. Mr. Bernard prepared the chart of Fig. 9–21 from the *Milwaukee and Metropolitan Area Origin-Destination Traffic Survey,* 1946, Figs. 17, 18, and 19.

44. Extremely important in this connection is the observation by J. Q. Stewart, "Suggested principles of 'Social Physics'," *op. cit.,* p. 180, that the rural nonfarm rent in 28 states east of Colorado and north of the Deep South was on the average proportional to the "potential of population" as defined by Dr. Stewart (closely related to the $P_1 P_2 /D$ relationship). In this article Dr. Stewart reports measurements of densities from city limits to city centers.

45. Cf. J. H. S. Bossard, "Residential propinquity as a factor in marriage selection," *American Journal of Sociology,* Vol. 38 (1932), 219–224.

46. Cf. M. R. Davie and R. J. Reeves, "Propinquity of residence before marriage," *American Journal of Sociology,* Vol. 44 (1939), 510–517.

47. R. H. Abrams, "Residential propinquity as a factor in marriage selection: fifty year trends in Philadelphia," *American Sociological Review,* Vol. 8 (1943), 288–294.

48. The literature on this subject is very large. Reference is made to the specialized journals. Particularly penetrating into the semantics of the problem is the excellent article by G. A. Lundberg and V. Beazley, "Consciousness of kind in a college population," *Sociometry,* Vol. 11 (1948), Nos. 1–2, pp. 59–74.

49. Cf. S. A. Stouffer, "Intervening opportunities: a theory relating mobility and distance," *American Sociological Review,* Vol. 5 (1940), 845–867. See also D. S. Thomas, "Interstate migration and intervening opportunities," *ibid.,* Vol. 6 (1941), 773–783, E. Isbell, "Internal migration in Sweden and intervening opportunities," *ibid.,* Vol. 9 (1944), 627–639.

50. This hypothesis about radio stations that was first published in G. K. Zipf, "On Dr. Miller's contribution," *op. cit.,* has been confirmed empirically by my student, Mr. J. P. Boland, whose important paper, "On the number and sizes of

radio stations in relation to the populations of their cities," appears in *Sociometry,* Vol. 11 (1948), 111–116.

51. Cf. A. J. Lotka, "The frequency distribution of scientific productivity," *Journal of the Washington Academy of Sciences,* Vol. 16 (1926), 320. The percentage should be less than 60% for our equation which contains the *b* constant.

52. N. W. Ayer and Son's *Directory of Newspapers and Periodicals,* Philadelphia: N. W. Ayer and Sons, Inc., 1941, 1139–1160.

53. Previously reported, G. K. Zipf, "The hypothesis of the 'Minimum Equation' . . .," *op. cit.,* p. 648 f., and also in his "On the number, circulation sizes, and the probable purchasers of newspapers," *American Journal of Psychology,* Vol. 41 (1948), 83–92. For all the extensive measurements and calculations that underlie Table 9–1 I am grateful to the following students of mine: the Misses A. R. Boyle, R. Cunningham, G. Peterson, and the Messrs. R. C. Bernard, Jr., J. P. Boland, D. D. Bourland, Jr., C. Bridge, Jr., W. B. Bryant, J. M. Conant, A. Y. Davis, A. Fellows, J. M. Gillespie, R. V. Johnson, M. I. Liebmann, T. Macklin, D. G. Outerbridge, R. L. Perry, D. D. Scarlett, J. A. Sevin, J. D. Stanley, S. L. Washburn and W. S. Wheeling.

54. *Ibid.* My students, Messrs. J. M. Conant and A. Y. Davis have observed that the *N* number of different periodicals that issue (editorial office) from a city of *P* population size varies directly with *P*. "A measurement of the number and diversity of periodicals in ninety-two American cities," *Sociometry,* Vol. 11 (1948), 117–120; William R. Chandler, "Relationship of distance to the occurrence of pedestrian accidents," *ibid.,* 108–110.

55. In this connection, cf. D. W. Thompson, *On Growth and Form,* New York: Macmillan, 1943.

CHAPTER TEN

1. Presented in greater detail in G. K. Zipf, *National Unity and Disunity,* Bloomington, Ind.: Principia Press, 1941, pp. 21–24.

2. For a further discussion of conditions of *surfeit* and of *deficiency* with graphical representation cf. *ibid.,* 27–40.

3. Discussed in greater detail *ibid.,* 40–46. The topic has been treated by one of America's outstanding experts in the regionalism of the South, cf. H. W. Odum, *An American Epoch,* New York: Holt, 1930; also (with H. E. Moore), *American Regionalism,* New York: Holt, 1938. His recent treatise *Understanding Society,* New York: Macmillan, 1947, merits careful study.

4. The concept of the saturation point of community organization within a nation has been discussed in detail in G. K. Zipf, *National Unity and Disunity, op. cit.,* Chap. 2.

5. Cf. J. Q. Stewart, "Empirical mathematical rules concerning the distribution and equilibrium of population," *The Geographical Review,* Vol. 37 (1947), 468–469.

6. The case of Germany has been treated in greater detail in G. K. Zipf, *National Unity and Disunity, op. cit.,* 135 f., 140 f.

7. The case of Austria is discussed in greater detail *ibid.,* 191–197.

8. *Ibid.*

9. For an interesting discussion of the Harvard "intelligentsia," cf. Porter Sargent, *Mad or Muddled?,* Boston: 11 Beacon St., 1947. Also his *The Continuing Battle for the Control of the Mind of Youth,* Boston: 11 Beacon St., 1945; also his *Getting Us into War;* and his *Education in Wartime* which are published from the same address. Let us hope that Mr. Sargent probes a little more deeply.

10. E.g., Svend Riemer's review of *National Unity and Disunity* in the September, 1942, issue of the *American Journal of Sociology* (pp. 285–287). This review, which apparently represents the view of one European school of sociologists, is particularly interesting to read today. For my reply, cf. *ibid.,* Vol. 48 (January, 1943), 503–504 in which are presented evaluations of scholars of the American tradition.

11. We hope to return to this topic in a future treatment of the societal pathology of an educational institution

which will be presented in a more popular style.

12. Presented in greater detail in G. K. Zipf, *National Unity and Disunity, op. cit.*, Chap. 4.

13. For the data on French communities, cf. *ibid.*

14. Discussed in detail *ibid.*, Chap. 5.

15. *Ibid.*

16. The case of the British Empire is discussed in greater detail *ibid.*

17. The case of Europe is discussed in greater detail *ibid.*

CHAPTER ELEVEN

1. Equation 11–2*b* is discussed in reference to historical consideration in G. K. Zipf, *National Unity and Disunity*, Bloomington, Ind.: Principia Press, 1941, Chap. 5.

2. An excellent account of the empirical aspects of the Pareto school in reference to the distribution of individual incomes can be found in H. T. Davis, *The Theory of Econometrics*, Bloomington, Ind.: Principia Press, 1941, 17–53 and *passim*. Later in this chapter we shall discuss the above in greater detail.

3. This statement that is so frequently imputed to J. J. Rousseau seems to evade specific reference although its sense is apparent in his *Contrat Social.* I am grateful to my colleague, Professor M. Françon, for his generous help in this matter.

4. These terms are borrowed from the current political language of an academic hierarchy with which the present writer happens to be familiar.

5. This concept of the economic value of prestige symbols was developed by the late Edward Sapir in his brilliant Tercentenary Lectures at the Harvard Summer School in 1936 which I heard. For a complete bibliography of Edward Sapir's publications, cf. Ruth Benedict's obituary of Edward Sapir, *American Anthropologist*, Vol. 41 (1939), 469–477. Perhaps the best general view of Professor E. Sapir's school of thinking is to be found in L. Spier, A. I. Hallowell, and S. S. Newman, Editors, *Language, Culture, and Personality; Essays in Memory of Edward Sapir*, Menasha, Wisc.: Sapir Memorial Publication Fund, 1941.

6. One is reminded of the famous concept of D. Bernoulli of the increment of wealth in the utility of money, cf. Daniel Bernoulli "Specimen Theoriae Novae de Mensura Sortis," *Commentari Acad. Petropol.*, Vol. 5, 1730–1731, published 1738, pp. 175–192 (reference from H. T. Davis, *The Theory of Econometrics, op. cit.*, p. 82, original not seen). Dr. H. T. Davis, *op. cit.*, Chap. 3, and notably p. 74 f., discusses Bernoulli's concept in connection with what is called the *Weber-Fechner Law* in psychology: "In order that the intensity of a sensation may increase in arithmetical progression, the stimulus must increase in geometrical progression" (before accepting the above formulation of the Weber-Fechner Law as a description of fact *in sensation*, one may profitably read the able discussion of the Law in E. G. Boring, *Sensation and Perception in the History of Experimental Psychology*, New York: Appleton-Century, 1942, *passim.*; one may also profitably inspect some of the actual measurements of eminent physiologists like Dr. W. J. Crozier, for references to whose work, cf., index under Crozier, *ibid.* and also in *Biological Abstracts and Psychological Abstracts.* We remember, in general, that the manifestation of a principle in the operation of a machine is subject to the limitations of the machine which may have been designed to discharge additional tasks according to other principles under the general theoretical Principle of the Economical Versatility of Tools). For a statement of Bernoulli's famous postulate relative to the satisfaction that a man receives in adding an increment of wealth to his fortune as well as a statement of alternative postulated equations by C. Jordan and by R. Frisch, cf. H. T. Davis, *The Theory of Econometrics, op. cit.*, Chap. 3. Although our (theoretical) Exponential Law of Incentives is not based upon any of the foregoing postulates, but upon our own argument, nevertheless the phenomenon under consideration is the same; and if our argument be sound it may support one of the postulates, etc.,

with the result that a synthesis of several viewpoints may be possible with a common mathematical description.

7. The argument expressed in this footnote would seem to provide a rationalization of not a few of the numerous observations (reference must be made to the specialized literature) in which, superficially stated, socio-economic likes show a preference for an interaction with socio-economic likes, even in reference to the *minutiae* of social conduct. As examples of the studies in question which, for the most part, contain important bibliographies, cf. E. W. Burgess and P. Wallin, "Homogamy in social characteristics," *American Journal of Sociology,* Vol. 49 (1943), 109–124; L. Nelson, "Intermarriage among nationality groups in a rural area of Minnesota," *ibid.,* 585–592; C. Tietze, P. Lemkau, M. Cooper, "Personality disorder and spatial mobility," *ibid.,* Vol. 48 (1942), 29–39; C. W. Schroeder, "Mental disorders in cities," *ibid.,* 40–47; H. Binder-Johnson, "Distribution of the German pioneer population in Minnesota," *Rural Sociology,* Vol. 6 (1941), 16–34; George A. Lundberg and Virginia Beazley, "Consciousness of kind in a college population," *Sociometry,* Vol. 11 (1948), 59–74.

8. Ernst Engel, the nineteenth century German economist, whose studies of family budgets led to the following formulation ("Engel's Law" and "Engel Curves"): with increasing family income the percentage spent on necessities like food decreased, whereas the percentage spent on luxuries increased, while that spent on intermediate classes like clothing and shelter remained constant. Cf. M. C. Elmer, *The Sociology of the Family,* Boston: Ginn, 1945; H. Davis, *The Theory of Econometrics, op. cit.,* Chap. 8 with extensive bibliography. Cf. also J. M. Conant, *Statistical Treatment of Spending Behavior,* Honors Thesis for the Bachelor's Degree at Harvard University June Commencement, 1948, in which there are extensive measurements of budgets and classes of expenditures including governmental expenditures. Mr. Conant has reported to me privately his observation that the estimated length of time covered by different courses in history (and in English literary history) at Harvard University, when ranked in the order of decreasing length, reveals an approximation of the proportions of the harmonic series which, incidentally, would seem to tie in with our theoretical argument in Chaps. 4 and 5 in reference to the economies of Generic and of Specific correlations, and the economies of Versatility and of Specialization.

9. Let us not forget that according to "Engel's Law" (cf. preceding footnote), the percentage amount spent for shelter observably tends to be a constant of the family income. Hence, Ernst Engel and his followers have observed empirically what we derived theoretically from our above *second analogue* (*supra*).

10. Historically considered, "Engel's Law," despite the fact that its linearity fails to hold for large incomes and for expenditures on luxuries, was, I believe, instrumental in introducing the graduated income taxes of today.

11. For a nontechnical discussion cf. K. Sax, "Population problems of a new world order," *Scientific Monthly,* Vol. 58 (1944), 66–71. See also R. Pearl, *Natural History of Population,* New York: Oxford Univ. Press, 1939.

12. For the case of the distance of motor vehicle accidents to pedestrians in relation to their *D* distance from home, cf. W. R. Chandler, "The relationship of *D* distance to the occurrence of pedestrian accidents," *Sociometry,* Vol. 11 (1948), 108–110.

13. Cf. C. Snyder, *Capitalism the Creator,* New York: Macmillan, 1940.

14. This consideration is elaborated in very considerable detail in G. K. Zipf, *National Unity and Disunity,* Bloomington, Ind.: 1941, Chap. 5.

15. Cf. V. Pareto, *The Mind and Society: a Treatise on General Sociology* (English translation), New York: Harcourt Brace, 1935. For an excellent treatment of Pareto, cf. G. C. Homans and C. P. Curtis, *An Introduction to Pareto,* New York: Knopf, 1934. Also analyzed critically in T. Parsons, *The Structure of Social Action,* New York: McGraw-Hill, 1937.

16. The writings of most of the above social scientists can be found cited for the most part in any standard treatise on sociology (for their books, cf. Library of Congress cards). Their articles, except for Wesley C. Mitchell, the economist, and A. Korzybski, have been published mostly in the standard journals of sociology (e.g., *The American Sociological Review, Social Forces, The American Journal of Sociology*). Cf. W. C. Mitchell, "The public relations of science," *Science,* Vol. 90 (1939), 599–607. Cf. A. Korzybski, *Science and Sanity, op. cit.* The mathematical studies of Professor N. Rashevsky, though by no means devoted exclusively to human social relations, nevertheless make a significant contribution to the growing literature of social theory. In particular see his "Outline of a mathematical theory of human relations," *Philosophy of Science,* Vol. 2 (1935), 413–429; "Further studies on the mathematical theory of human relations," *Psychometrika,* Vol. 1 (1936), 21–36; "Studies in mathematical theory of human relations," *ibid.,* Vol. 4 (1939), 221–239; continued *ibid.,* 283–299. See also his recent book, *Mathematical Theory of Human Relations,* Bloomington, Ind.: Principia Press, 1947. For the most recent statement of the Dodd theory of Dimensional Analysis, cf. S. C. Dodd, "A systematics for sociometry and for all science," *Sociometry,* Vol. 11 (1948), 11–30. See also V. Cervinka, "A dimensional theory of groups," *ibid.,* 100–107.

17. E. B. Wilson, "What is social science?," *Science,* Vol. 92 (1940), 157–162. I refer to his statement beginning, "Indeed, unless I am much mistaken, so great is the prestige of this sort of thinking and writing on the part of those who are in a position to award recognition for work in social lines. . . ." See also his "Methodology in the natural and the social sciences," *American Journal of Sociology,* Vol. 45 (1940), 655–668.

18. G. A. Lundberg, *Can Science Save Us?,* New York: Longmans, Green, 1947; *Foundations of Sociology,* New York: Macmillan, 1939. See also presidential address at the 38th Annual Meeting of the American Sociological Society, New York, Dec., 1943, "Sociologists and the peace," published in the *American Sociological Review,* Vol. 9 (1944), 1–13.

19. Cf. F. S. Chapin, "Social obstacles to the acceptance of existing social science knowledge," *Social Forces,* Vol. 26 (1947), 7–12.

20. In addition to A. Korzybski's own writings, see also the publications of the Institute of General Semantics, Chicago, Ill., including the papers of the Second American Congress on General Semantics (held at Denver University, 1941); also the *General Semantics Monographs,* Iowa City: Institute of General Semantics, 1939 and following. For complete bibliography on general semantics and for the program for the coming Congress of General Semantics in Denver, 1949, contact Miss M. Kendig, Institute of General Semantics, Lakeville, Conn.

21. Cf. W. Johnson, *People in Quandaries,* New York: Harpers, 1946.

22. The income tax data presented herewith have been presented previously and discussed in detail along with further income tax data in G. K. Zipf, *National Unity and Disunity, op. cit.,* Chap. 5. For a virtually complete bibliography of income data and of significant studies of the same through 1940 cf. H. T. Davis, *The Theory of Econometrics, op. cit.,* 51–53 and *passim.*

23. *Ibid.*

24. For a discussion of a theory of revolution, cf. H. T. Davis, *The Theory of Econometrics, op. cit.,* 200–205 and also Chap. 2, *passim.* For a discussion of the revolutionary implications of bends and changes of slope in income curves, cf. G. K. Zipf, *National Unity and Disunity, op. cit.,* Chap. 5.

25. For a summary of Pareto's own observations which refer to data from 1471 to 1894, cf. H. T. Davis, *The Theory of Econometrics, op. cit.,* p. 30; with many further sets of observations *ibid.,* Chap. 2.

26. *Ibid.*

27. *Ibid.,* p. 51.

28. A. J. Lotka, "The frequency distribution of scientific productivity," *Jour-*

nal of the Washington Academy of Sciences, Vol. 16 (1926), 317–323.

29. Cf. H. T. Davis, *The Theory of Econometrics, op. cit.,* p. 49.

30. Since this text was written a further set of data has been made available in the 146th Annual Report of E. I. du Pont de Nemours and Company for the year 1947, which is particularly interesting because the range of annual salary or wage is given both *gross before* federal taxes and *net after* federal taxes. These data farsightedly raise the knotty question of whether we should view a wage or salary as the gross amount paid by the employer, or as the net amount received by the employee. With the very heavy taxation of individual incomes, employers may have to bargain ever more in terms of *"take-home pay."* In this connection one might profitably read the theory of revolution of H. T. Davis, *loc cit.,* p. 200 f.

31. Cf. V. Myslivec, "Paretos Funktion und ihre Anwendung zur rationellen Berechnung der Versicherungstarife in der Automobilversicherung," *Archiv für mathematische Wirtschafts-und Sozialforschung,* Vol. 5 (1939), 51–68; data pp. 57 and 59.

32. Before leaving the topic of individual incomes we call attention to the observation of W. J. Reilly, *Methods for the Study of Retail Relationships,* University of Texas Bulletin, No. 2944 (Nov. 22, 1929), Fig. 1, p. 20, which shows (8 points plotted) how large the x size of a typical city must become before it controls the style goods trade of the various y income classes. According to my eye, for income classes above $4,500 the function is

$$y = \frac{x}{3}.$$

This function as disclosed by W. J. Reilly, who also first formulated the "law of retail gravitation" and first observed precisely the P/D function in the circulation of a newspaper, *ibid* (cf. our Chap. 9 *supra*). The above function suggests that the higher priced styles are in the larger cities. If we now assume that persons live near their sources of supplies, then the richer persons will tend to live in the larger cities, as is to be inferred theoretically from our "grand analogue" in Section I of this chapter. Reilly's observation seems to be susceptible of theoretical synthesis with the deduction [G. K. Zipf, "On the frequency and diversity of business establishments and personal occupations," etc., *Journal of Psychology,* Vol. 24 (1947), 139–148] that the rank frequency distribution of occupations and of establishments *within* cities will follow the equation of the harmonic series ($p = 1$) with the value of the constant, $F \cdot Sn$, varying directly with the city's P size—a deduction that has subsequently been confirmed by my student, Mr. D. David Bourland, Jr., in the case of "professions" as disclosed from the data of Classified Telephone Directories (to be published in his article entitled, "On the distribution of professions within cities in the United States").

May we perhaps not argue that the distribution of incomes *within* cities is distributed according to our equations, and that the constant in the income equations varies directly with the city's P size? Surely Reilly's observations in his Fig. 1 (*loc. cit.*) are consistent with such a theoretical expectation. (According to our argument, the N number of cities of P size varies inversely with the square of P size, while the N number of incomes of like size varies inversely with the cube of income size.)

The problem seems to merit further empiric study and theoretical elaboration.

33. Discussed more fully in G. K. Zipf, *National Unity and Disunity, op. cit.,* Chap. 5. The relationship between group incomes and individual incomes seems to be an example of the "square effect."

34. Presented and discussed more fully *ibid.*

35. Cf. E. D. Chapple, "'Personality' differences as described by invariant properties of individuals in interaction," *Proceedings of the National Academy of Sciences,* Vol. 26 (1940), 10–16. See also A. C. Norwine and O. J. Murphy, "Characteristic time intervals in telephonic conversation," *The Bell System Technical Journal,* Vol. 17 (1938), 281–

291 (also published separately in *Bell Telephone System Technical Publications, Monograph* B–1074).

36. Cf. for example, E. D. Chapple, "The analysis of industrial morale," *The Journal of Industrial Hygiene and Toxicology,* Vol. 24 (1942), 163–172. This contains reference to further important publications by Dr. Chapple. In collaboration with the distinguished ethnologist, C. S. Coon, Dr. Chapple enunciated his principles of anthropology, cf. C. D. Chapple and C. S. Coon, *Principles of Anthropology,* New York: Holt, 1942.

37. Cf. A. J. Lotka, "The frequency distribution of scientific productivity," *Journal of the Washington Academy of Sciences,* Vol. 16 (1926), 317–323. For the productivity of 278 authors of mathematical papers as ascertained by Dr. Arnold Dresden, cf. A. Dresden, "A report on the scientific work of the Chicago Section, 1897–1922," *Bulletin of the American Mathematical Society,* Vol. 28 (1922), 303–307, discussed by H. T. Davis, *The Theory of Econometrics, op. cit.,* p. 48.

38. This vying for attention by those who have goods and services for sale has been studied quite interestingly by my three students, Messrs. W. Baird Bryant, Stephen L. Washburn, and Donald G. Outerbridge in connection with the advertisements of a classified telephone directory (to be published shortly by them in an article entitled "Some psychological determinants of the structure of advertising in a classified telephone directory," *American Journal of Psychology,* in press.

CHAPTER TWELVE

1. Cf. T. Veblen, *The Theory of the Leisure Class,* new Ed. New York: Macmillan, 1919. The edition of the *Modern Library* has a valuable preface by Mr. Stuart Chase.

2. Cf. A. L. Van Gennep, *Les Rites de Passage,* Paris, 1909, cited in E. D. Chapple and C. S. Coon, *Principles of Anthropology,* New York: Holt, 1942 (original not seen).

3. Cf. E. D. Chapple and C. S. Coon, *Principles of Anthropology, op. cit.,* Chap. 20.

4. Cf. F. de Saussure, *Cours de Linguistique Générale,* 2nd Ed., Paris: Payot et Cie., 1922.

5. The same argument applies to W. J. Reilly's "law of retail gravitation," as well as to the subsequent related formulations by P. D. Converse, and J. Q. Stewart (*loc. cit.* Chap. 9 *supra*). It is also basic to the pioneer traffic study of A. M. Wellington (*loc. cit.* Chap. 9 *supra*).

6. Cf. F. S. Chapin, "A theory of synchronous culture cycle," *Social Forces,* Vol. 3 (1925), 596–604. Cf. William F. Ogburn's important hypotheses in W. F. Ogburn, *Social Change,* 5th Ed., New York: Viking, 1928, 103–111.

7. Cf. H. Hart, "Logistic social trends," *American Journal of Sociology,* Vol. 50 (1945), 337–352.

8. *Ibid.*

9. H. Hart, "Depression, war, and logistic trends," *American Journal of Sociology,* Vol. 52 (1946). See also H. Hart and H. Hertz, "Expectation of life as an index of progress," *American Sociological Review,* Vol. 9 (1944), 609–621.

10. President's Research Committee, *Recent Social Trends,* New York: McGraw-Hill (1 Vol.), 1933, p. 306.

11. M. J. Hagood, *Statistics for Sociologists,* New York: Reynal and Hitchcock, 1941, p. 288, Fig. 31.

12. Cf. H. Hart, "Logistic social trends," *op. cit.,* 342.

13. Reported in G. K. Zipf, "On the dynamic structure of concert programs," *The Journal of Abnormal and Social Psychology,* Vol. 41 (1946), 25–36.

INDEX

T